Trinity College.
Cambridge
Jan 25 1896.

My darling May

I think in my last letter I gave
you a somewhat detailed description of
the little social affair or Mother's meeting
at which I assisted Mrs J.J. in trying
to amuse the poor of Barnwell: this letter
will also deal more or less with description
of — a dinner which I attended to night but
which seems so unreal to me at present
that I had better put my impressions
down before they fade: I know you will be
interested in these somewhat trivial descriptions
as you consider of social intercourse a thing
that I sadly lack but — really. I have been
plunging deeply lately — But to lead up
gradually to my discourse — there is nothing
much of importance to relate that has
happened to me since my last letter: my
friend Townsend knows Sir Robert Ball & has
lunched there several times for as two Trinity
College Dublin men they are very thick.
Well Sir Robert developed a tremendous
interest in my experiments in the detection
of electric waves for long distances & must
needs make an appointment to come down
to the Lab & see the effect & apparatus
in general. He turned up one morning
& I showed him how easily I could
detect a man through half a dozen walls

Peter

The loved and dear friend of Margaret and the late Bruce. (The New Zealand connection).

Although we have lived so far apart our lives have crossed in many ways. Thank you for a happy stay, and I did enjoy all those "weak" gins

Margaret

14 September 2003

Rutherford

Scientist Supreme

Rutherford

Scientist Supreme

John Campbell

1999
AAS Publications
PO Box 31-035
Christchurch, New Zealand
aas@its.canterbury.ac.nz

ISBN 0-473-05700-X

ISBN 0-473-05700-X

AAS Publications
PO Box 31-035
Christchurch, New Zealand
aas@its.canterbury.ac.nz

First published   Nov 1999
2nd printing   Mar 2000

Typeset in Berkeley Book 12 on 15 point

Design by John Campbell and Jo Dickson
Typesetting by Jo Dickson, Christchurch
Lithography by Precision Lithographic, Christchurch
Graphics by Tim Nolan, Jo Dickson
Printed by The Caxton Press, Christchurch

CONTENTS

PATRONS OF THIS WORK

This book has been printed, and the information it contains
made widely available at reasonable cost, because of the generosity of

Stout Trust
Bayer New Zealand Ltd
Network Tasman
Nelson Pine Industries Ltd
Brian Mason Scientific and Technical Trust

I am extremely grateful to the following patrons whose financial support
facilitated the extensive travel, archival research and interviews on
which this work is based.

Nelson College Old Boys' Association
New Zealand Institute of Chemistry
The Rutherford Birthplace Project
New Zealand Institute of Physics
The Commonwealth Foundation
Cray Communications (NZ) Ltd
Frederick W G White KBE FRS
Baigent Forest Industries Ltd
The Royal Society (London)
Nelson Pine Industries Ltd
The New Zealand Physicist
New Zealand Literary Fund
Rutherford Den Committee
Sir Jack Newman CBE JP
Canterbury Savings Bank
Quality Hotel Rutherford
Monier Brickmakers Ltd

Stout Trust
Pub Charity
McKee Trust
L B Kain Trust
British Council
A J Park & Son
Southpower Ltd
Oenone Whitley
Dianne Campbell
McGill University
Massey University
P J Skellerup CBE
Quentin Rutherford
KPMG Peat Marwick
JEMBCA Enterprises
Lindsay Missen Design
Honda New Zealand Ltd

The New Zealand Returned Services' Association (Inc)
Canterbury Branch, Royal Society of New Zealand
Electricorp Production - Southern Thermal Group
Department of Scientific and Industrial Research
Scientific Research Distribution Committee

AUTHOR'S NOTES

Direct Quotations

All verbatim quotations from original archival sources are in *italics*.

Scope of this book

Because this book is the result of the first ever careful investigation from the New Zealand point of view it is longer and more detailed than future books need be. Some sections may be skipped during a first reading, depending on the particular interests of the reader.

May Newton

Rutherford's wife, née Mary Georgina Newton, was known in both families as May to distinguish her from her mother, Mary Kate De Renzy Newton.

Monetary system

New Zealand metricated its currency in 1967. In the times being written about we used the then British system of twelve pence (d) per shilling (s) and twenty shillings per pound (£). Professional people often used the guinea (21 shillings) as their unit of currency. Sums of money should be compared with the typical weekly wage or cost of a staple of diet at that time. Consult a local newspaper of the appropriate period.

Measurements

During the times covered by this book everyday measurements were in the old British Imperial units. Verbatim quotations in the book retain these units. The following conversions may help.

one mile   = 1.6 kilometres
one acre   = 0.405 hectares, or roughly 4 hectares per 10 acres
one ton   = one tonne approximately
one pound = 0.454 kilograms
one ounce = $\frac{1}{16}$th of a pound or roughly 28 grams
one quart = 1.136 litres
one pint   = ½ of one quart = 568 ml

Acknowledgements

Over 200 people have given me assistance with this research and book, rather too many to list personally. I, and I hope New Zealand, thank them all for their help.

FOREWORD

by

Professor Sir Mark Oliphant A.C., K.B.E., F.R.S., F.A.A., F.T.S.E.

Ernest Rutherford was my inspiring teacher, colleague and friend. Almost all who knew Rutherford say he was the greatest experimental scientist since Faraday. Max Born, whose own contributions to theoretical physics were formidable, told me that Rutherford was the greatest scientist he had ever known, including even Einstein.

In 1925 Rutherford toured Australia and New Zealand. I heard him lecture in Adelaide and was so impressed with his great enthusiasm for science and his own pioneering researches that I resolved to go to England to work with him. I arrived in 1927 as the holder of an Exhibition of 1851 Scholarship, the same one that took Rutherford to Britain as a young man. I worked with him, and spent time with him at his holiday cottages, until just before his untimely death in 1937. I will never forget Niels Bohr's impromptu valediction to the members of the conference celebrating the 200th anniversary of the birth of Luigi Galvani, where many of us were when Rutherford's death was announced.

Because of Rutherford the Cavendish laboratory had a continuous throughput of distinguished scientists as visitors. I have recounted many of my own reminiscences in the book *Rutherford, Recollections of the Cambridge Days*. Rutherford just bubbled with enthusiasm for research. That is what made him so influential. He had only to write to the Americans and they would send him all the heavy water that we wanted. Rutherford was so productive of ideas and opinions and feelings about his work that you couldn't help but absorb some of that enthusiasm. He was full of ideas but they were always simple ideas. He liked to use words to describe what was going on. He drove us by inspiration and was Papa to all of us. He jollied me along and sometimes metaphorically kicked me in the behind. He drove us mercilessly but we loved him for it.

John Campbell has researched and written an exhaustive account of Rutherford's origins, life and work, in particular from the New Zealand point-of-view. This task involved many years of research into documentary records all over the world. He has interviewed every person he could trace who had known Rutherford well and has had the full co-operation of the Rutherford family. His personality is such that no one could refuse to co-operate fully.

I am also impressed with his efforts to mark the birthplace of Rutherford. Worried that there was no tangible memorial to Rutherford in New Zealand, though there were several in England, Canada and elsewhere, he set to and raised the money needed. Again his obvious devotion to the task, his persuasive personality, and his determination, has resulted in the erection of a magnificent memorial on the site of the house in which Rutherford was born. A bronze figure of a child presides over a series of panels recording the highlights of his life and achievements, all in a garden setting.

Rutherford was an exceptional scientist and human being who inspired me and many others of my generation. This book is a fitting memorial to him. It is to be hoped that through it Rutherford inspires future generations of young antipodeans.

Mark Oliphant

PREFACE

I have always been very proud of the fact that I am a New Zealander.
Ernest Rutherford,
Auckland 1925

I have in mind one who by his brain-power, grit and perseverance has forced his way to the top rung of the ladder, until he now ranks amongst the highest, if he is not the highest, in the scientific world. ··· He is a New Zealander bred and born, and we should be so proud to claim him; but owing to our neglect he is drifting away from us.
Letter to the Editor,
Pelorus Guardian 30 June 1911

Ernest Rutherford is one of the most illustrious scientists the world has ever seen. He is to the atom what Darwin is to evolution, Newton to mechanics, Faraday to electricity and Einstein to relativity.

He achieved enduring international fame because of his incredibly productive life during which he altered our view of nature on three separate occasions. Combining brilliantly conceived experiments with much hard work and special insight, he explained the perplexing problem of naturally occurring radioactivity (atoms are not necessarily stable entities as had been assumed since the time of the ancient Greeks), he determined the structure of an atom (an object so small that it would take five million atoms in a line to cross a fullstop on this page) and he was the world's first successful alchemist (he changed nitrogen into oxygen).

The New York Times, in a eulogy accompanying the announcement of his unexpected and unnecessary death in 1937, stated

⋯ It is given to but few men to achieve immortality, still less to achieve Olympian rank, during their own lifetime. Lord Rutherford achieved both. In a generation that witnessed one of the greatest revolutions in the entire history of science he was universally acknowledged as the leading explorer of the vast infinitely complex universe within the atom, a universe that he was first to penetrate.

Any one of his secondary achievements, many of which are nigh forgotten, would have been sufficient to bring fame to a lesser scientist. He dated the age of the Earth, he invented an electrical method of counting individual ionizing radiations, he briefly held the world record for the distance over which wireless waves were detected, he predicted the existence of the neutron, he oversaw the development of large scale particle accelerators, and during the First World War he led the Allied research into the detection of submarines.

His work ensures his immortality. He is highly honoured world-wide: he has appeared on the stamps of four countries (Sweden, Russia, Canada and New Zealand), been granted three civil honours (Knighthood, Order of Merit and Peerage), given his name to a train, been interred in Westminster Abbey, been awarded over 32 university degrees and had more than 40 books written about him.

Sir Oliver Lodge, the grand old man of British science, stated

Lord Rutherford's death was a terrible calamity and a terrible loss for New Zealand and the whole world.

Lord Rutherford O.M., F.R.S. belongs to the world but Ernest Rutherford B.A., M.A.(Hons), B.Sc. belongs to New Zealand.

People from overseas usually forget, or were never told, that he was born, raised, moulded and educated here in New Zealand. After failing on several occasions to obtain a job, he left in 1895 as a highly trained young man of 23 with three degrees from the University of New Zealand and having had two years of independent research working at the forefront of the advanced electrical technology of the day. His forte, his brilliance at experimental science, was quite evident before he left.

He was always proud of being a New Zealander and always referred to himself as such. When raised to a peerage he chose the territorial designation of Lord Rutherford of Nelson in honour of ⋯ *my birthplace and home of my grandfather.* His dying words were to remind his wife that he wished to leave a bequest to Nelson College.

During the past few decades New Zealand has curiously, and to its shame, chosen to neglect Ernest Rutherford. Every house he lived in has been demolished. In 1987, on the 50th anniversary of the death of Ernest Rutherford, the state of the place of his birth remained a national disgrace. I went there at dawn and gazed despairingly at the untidy piles of river boulders which had been dumped on the site many years previously. In the field beyond, a cow raised its tail and spoke for me.

New Zealand has done a tremendous disservice to Ern in continually presenting him as a god-like figure: a portly, 65-year-old Lord who wore a truss and had a brilliant childhood. No New Zealand child can identify with such an image.

We incorrectly project his adult fame back to bias the events of his youth. In actual fact every major scholarship he gained in New Zealand he obtained only on his second attempt. In 1938, a reporter for a Wellington newspaper wrote to the headmistress of Foxhill school for details of Ernest's life in the district. She replied ⋯ *I have been trying to get some more details from the district but it is very hard going as he seems to have been just an ordinary child* ⋯ . And so he was.

We must in future use him to stimulate the children of New Zealand. We must tell them "Look at Ern. He had no better start in life than you did yet look at the fame he achieved. There is no reason why, with hard work and perseverance, you cannot achieve in any field in which you have a passionate interest."

In times past this country could not give the world an accurate account of his formative years here. We have him giving a talk at Canterbury College which was actually given by another student. A government press release married him off to his mother-in-law. A plaque at Canterbury College recorded the dates of his enrolment incorrectly. We have him addressing the Canterbury Philosophical Institute when at the time he was on a ship in the Red Sea. A recent Prime-Minister incorrectly gave him the Nobel Prize for splitting the atom, an endemic error. And for many years one of New Zealand's foremost public companies, which built Rutherford House as its head office, worshipped a portrait of the curator of the Otago Museum, mistakenly believing it to be Lord Rutherford's.

In all of the archival work and interviews which form the basis of this book I tried to abide by one golden rule. A story would be used only if it met one or more of three criteria; it was written down in a reliable contemporary record; it was a first hand reminiscence; or it came from at least two separate informants via independent routes which could be traced back to the original contemporary source. This rule is essential if fact is to be separated from fiction. There are many patently false stories lurking as time bombs in newspapers, biographies and interviews, waiting to be trotted out in fifty years time as gospel or overlooked 'fact'. There has been a tendency for Rutherford Lecturers touring New Zealand in the 1970s and 1980s to tell stories in lectures and interviews which reporters treat as first hand. However, the initiated know from which book the lecturer took the sometimes doubtful story. And in the past some authors have received the University of Canterbury's seal of approval on false information, not knowing that the response to their query had been obtained not from original archives, but from an early paperback biography whose author used anecdotal, and not archival, material.

Of the books written about him several are in Russian and one in Chinese. As late as a decade ago not one of those 40 books was written by a New Zealander. It is an amazing fact that no Kiwi had systematically studied this country's most famous son. Incredibly nobody had interviewed the people who worked with him in that dank cellar at Canterbury College. Nobody had systematically interviewed his family in New Zealand. Nobody had searched the archives in New Zealand to uncover the forces which moulded him.

I, a solid state physicist, became involved purely by chance. In 1977 I was invited to help develop the Rutherford Den at the old Canterbury College site as a tourist attraction. This invitation was on the strength of my interest in marine archaeology: I had just completed a survey of the shipwrecks of the Chatham Islands for the New Zealand Historic Places Trust. Such were the credentials of the local person who was perceived to possess the nearest thing to an interest in the history of physical science at that time.

While re-creating the electrical experiments which Ernest Rutherford conducted at Canterbury College I gradually became aware of how flawed were our recollections of him, his background and his work. So I delved into archives and interviewed his friends, colleagues, the locals from the areas where he had lived and all thirty-two of his then living nephews and nieces, to whom he was just 'Uncle Ern'. This evolved into a world-wide search which was to dominate my life for the past two decades. I loved every minute of it. It has been a great privilege to re-live historical and everyday events through people who were there: from the young girl hidden under Rutherford's desk in Manchester through to Mark Oliphant who was close to, and deeply loved, Ernest Rutherford.

Nevertheless, the motivation for this research and this book was, quite simply, to remedy a nation's neglect.

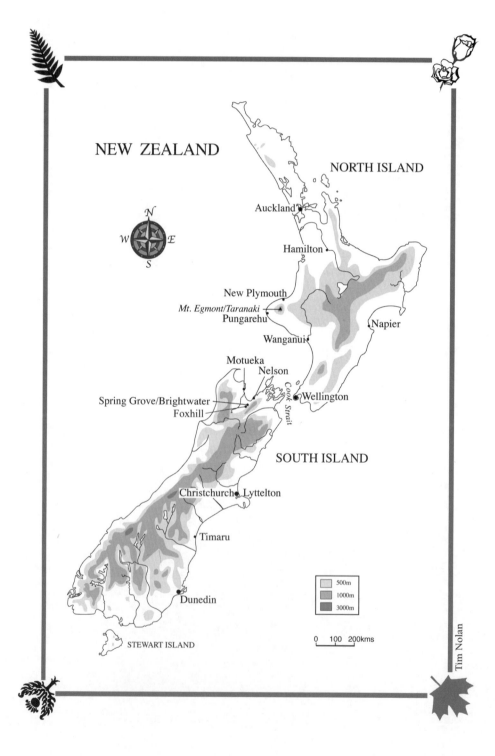

NEW ZEALAND

NORTH ISLAND

Auckland

Hamilton

New Plymouth
Mt. Egmont/Taranaki
Pungarehu

Napier

Wanganui

Motueka
Nelson

Cook Strait

Wellington

Spring Grove/Brightwater
Foxhill

SOUTH ISLAND

Christchurch Lyttelton

Timaru

500m
1000m
3000m

Dunedin

STEWART ISLAND

0 100 200kms

Tim Nolan

Chapter 1

LUCKY INFANT – CAREFREE CHILD

Spring Grove and Foxhill 1871-1883

··· the thing to be aimed at is not so much to give information, as to endeavour to discipline the mind ··· by bringing it into immediate contact with Nature herself. For this purpose a series of simple experiments has been devised ··· .

Preface to Ern's first science book
Foxhill 1882

Rutherford's Ancestors

Earnest Rutherford was born lucky.
Lucky he was born neither female nor the eldest son.
Lucky to be born amongst hard-working, practical people.
Lucky to get each of the three scholarships he was awarded.
But once he got into scientific research he made his own luck.

Family background often has a strong influence in moulding children. The full story of his parents, and that of their forebearers, prior to the fates allowing their meeting, has been told in the little book *Rutherford's Ancestors*. Ern's Rutherford grandparents (George and Barbara) were amongst the earliest formal colonists, arriving in New Zealand in March of 1843. George was an assisted emigrant brought from Scotland to help establish a saw-mill at Motueka, near the top of the South Island.

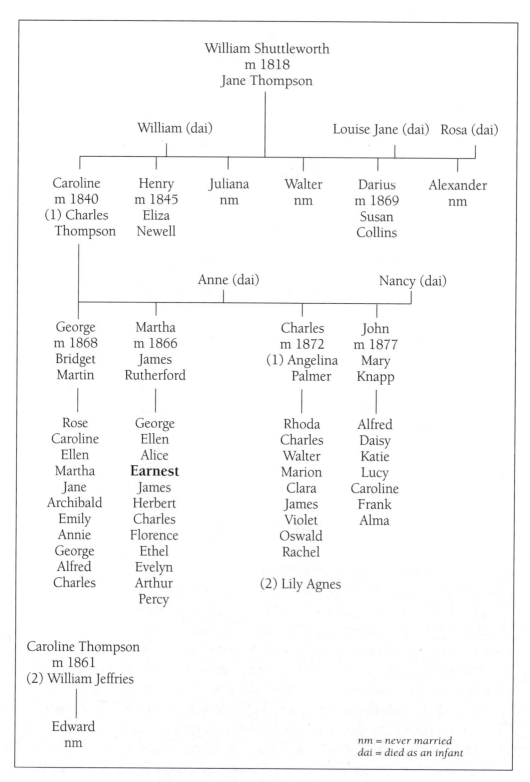

William Shuttleworth
m 1818
Jane Thompson

William (dai)   Louise Jane (dai)   Rosa (dai)

Caroline   Henry   Juliana   Walter   Darius   Alexander
m 1840   m 1845   nm   nm   m 1869   nm
(1) Charles   Eliza   Susan
Thompson   Newell   Collins

Anne (dai)   Nancy (dai)

George   Martha   Charles   John
m 1868   m 1866   m 1872   m 1877
Bridget   James   (1) Angelina   Mary
Martin   Rutherford   Palmer   Knapp

Rose   George   Rhoda   Alfred
Caroline   Ellen   Charles   Daisy
Ellen   Alice   Walter   Katie
Martha   **Earnest**   Marion   Lucy
Jane   James   Clara   Caroline
Archibald   Herbert   James   Frank
Emily   Charles   Violet   Alma
Annie   Florence   Oswald
George   Ethel   Rachel
Alfred   Evelyn
Charles   Arthur   (2) Lily Agnes
                  Percy

Caroline Thompson
   m 1861
(2) William Jeffries

Edward
   nm

nm = never married
dai = died as an infant

Shuttleworth/Thompson Family Tree

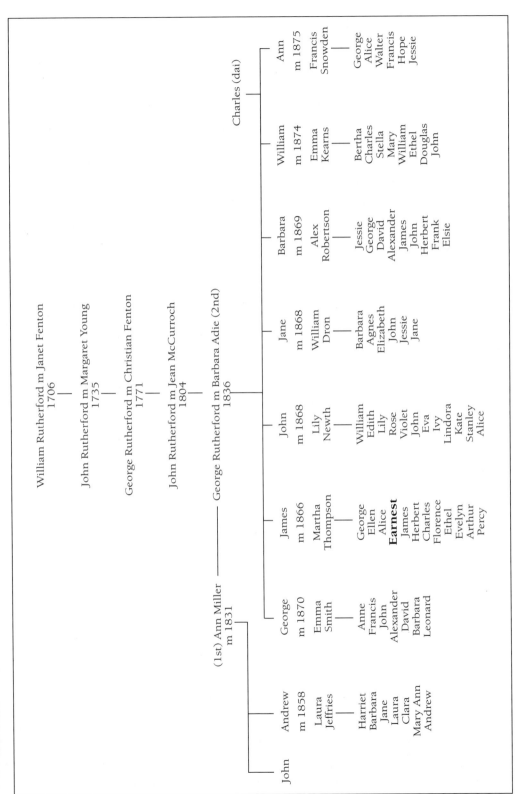

Rutherford Family Tree

Ern's father, James Rutherford, was four years old when they arrived. He shared his family's set-backs and hardships – the madness of the mill-owner, the fears following the Wairau massacre and the hard life while turning virgin bush into farmland. Education was not a top priority.

George and Barbara Rutherford finally settled the family at Spring Grove some 21 kilometres south of Nelson. Their children were prolific in populating New Zealand. The eight who lived to adulthood produced 67 grandchildren. Ern's four Rutherford uncles were all skilled rural-artisans. The older two (Andrew and George) were wheelwrights with their father, John was a prosperous flour-miller and flax-miller, and William a waggoner/butcher/farmer. Of Ern's three Rutherford aunts, Jane and Ann married local farmers and Barbara married the Wakefield blacksmith. His uncles on his mother's side were all farmers. As a child Ern was surrounded by practical people and this certainly influenced his life and outlook.

Just one branch of the enormous Rutherford family thistle and Thompson family rose bush nestles educational achievement. The common denominator is Ern's English, ex-schoolteacher, mother. Martha Thompson's background was English – solid, country, and reasonably well-to-do. In 1855 her mother and grandmother, both widows, had emigrated to New Zealand where her uncles had set up as Shuttleworth Brothers, merchants, in New Plymouth. In 1860, during the Taranaki war, their farmhouse was burnt and she and other women and children were evacuated to Nelson as war refugees. Her mother remarried, to a Spring Grove farmer, and became the teacher of the girls at the two-teacher school at Spring Grove. Twenty-year-old Martha, on the basis of having been highly educated in England to age twelve, took over the position when her mother became pregnant.

A sound basis anchored education in the Nelson Province. In 1861 the Nelson Inspector of Schools stated

> ··· *I think it matters comparatively little how much a child knows, if he has not learnt how to learn more. The desire for more knowledge and the conscious power of getting it for himself; these to my mind are the most valuable products of primary education, and the surest guarantees that its effect will last.* ···

Martha was an excellent teacher. In 1864 the school inspector said of the girls' side of the Spring Grove school

> ··· *Few of our schools reflect more credit on their teacher than this. Though numerously attended, 35 being the daily average, the girls are thoroughly well taught in every branch, the reading and writing being*

particularly good. The arithmetic also goes much beyond what is usually expected from a school taught by a female teacher. The scholars are quiet and well behaved. ···

On the death of the male head-teacher Martha took over the whole school (seventy pupils) until her own pregnancy necessitated the end of her promising career as a head-teacher. From then on she had the education of her own children to look after.

The James Rutherfords of Spring Grove

James Rutherford (27) and Martha Thompson (23) were married on Saturday the 28th of April 1866. When the first of the Rutherford boys, Andrew, married in 1858 he had a house built on his father's land, alongside the main road from Nelson to the West Coast. Similarly, James had a house built next to Andrew's in time for his own marriage.

The James Rutherford house was a standard colonial weatherboard cottage with a steeply pitched roof and a dormer window in front. The ceiling cavity housed the bedrooms. James reckoned the house to be one of the best built in the district but it lasted only fifty-four years. [By 1920 the house was in an advanced state of deterioration so it was demolished.]

The babies arrived at regular intervals – George, Ellen, Alice. In rural society their future was preordained. The eldest son helped father (becoming Rutherford and Son) and the eldest daughters helped mother raise the subsequent large family of twelve children. Lucky was he who was destined to be merely second son.

On the 30th of August 1871 the fourth child and second son was born. Two months later James registered the child. 'Earnest' was recorded in the 'name, if any' column of the Waimea South Birth Register. The same Registrar recorded three Ernests and four Earnests over a four year period centred on this time. Presumably the Registrar wrote the name down as it sounded and fathers, who mostly were of limited education, failed to notice the mistake when signing the Register.

When the Civil War in America led to a shortage of manila for rope-making, men once again turned towards preparing New Zealand flax. No longer did the industry rely on the skill of the Maoris at dressing flax by hand, or on the crude hand-driven machinery of the 1840s. Powered machinery had become available and several patents were taken out for improvements.

No. -	When Born and Where.	Name, if any.	Sex.	Name and Surname of Father.	Name and Maiden Surname of Mother.
115 116	Aug 30th Spring Grove	Earnest	Boy	James Rutherford	Martha Rutherford Formerly Thompson

John and James Rutherford constructed a water-powered flax mill somewhere in Waimea West by 1872. The mechanized flax-dressing processes go under the delightful names of stripping (the fibre is separated from the fleshy part of the leaf), washing, bleaching (drying in the sun) and scutching (the dried fibre is mechanically scraped to remove surplus vegetable matter). The water wheel and gear train drove the stripping and scutching drums at very high speed (about 2000 rpm), emitting an ear shattering scream. The starting of the mill caused consternation in the district as it is said the piercing scream coincided with the visit of an evangelist who was preaching that the end of the world was at hand. James dressed flax at the mill for a year or two, until the bottom dropped out of the market in 1874. Highly regarded for his engineering ability, he had surprised the locals by riding around on a wooden bicycle he had himself built.

James and Martha continued to produce children at the rate of nearly one per year – James, Herbert, Charles, Florence. As each child was born to Martha, her stepfather, William Jeffries, used to say to his wife, "Well Caroline, which of the children are we going to take home this time?" (Jeffries Rd at Spring Grove points to his land.)

The younger Rutherford children wore clothes that had served several previous owners in the family but new ones were also fed into the system. Martha had a local girl make a dress of Scottish plaid for Ernest the toddler. [The custom of young boys wearing dresses persisted in British based societies until the 1920's at least.]

Waimea South *Nelson*   NEW ZEALAND.

Rank or Profession of Father.	Signature, Description, and Residence of Informant	When Registered.	Signature of Registrar.	Name, if added after Registration of Birth.
Mechanic	*James Rutherford Spring Grove*	*Oct. 30th*	*Alfred Sargent*	

In 1875 the family patriarch George Rutherford, ill with heart disease and dropsy, tidied up his affairs and wrote a will leaving to Andrew and James the tiny plots of land on which their houses stood. George died the next year, and was followed to the cemetery by his wife, Barbara, less than two years later. James and Martha Rutherford's younger children never knew their Rutherford grandparents.

Nelson had great hopes for a railway line which would link it to the gold-rich West Coast and on to Canterbury and Dunedin. The first section joining Nelson and Foxhill opened on the 29th of January 1876. This line crossed the road diagonally and cut through a corner of Andrew Rutherford's small section. [The railway was dismantled in 1955. Until recently, a keen eye could still see the line of the rails registered in the tarmac of the road. Less keen eyes can follow the embankment flanked by scruffy apple trees grown from apple cores thrown by generations of schoolboys. The section of the line near the Rutherford birthplace is now the line of the road bypassing Brightwater.]

The railway had several effects on the district, one undoubtedly being that it soiled Martha's washing. The Rutherfords were between stations, one to the south at Spring Grove and the other to the north near the Wairoa river. The latter station had initially been called Wairoa but there were too many large rivers of that name in New Zealand. Eventually it took its name from Alfred Saunders' nearby flour-mill 'Brightwater'. He was an enthusiastic temperance man. When fighting to get his cranky steam engine to run reliably he was know to sing the temperance song, 'Bright water, bright water, bright water for me.' When a post office opened at the station the district assumed this name. With the Brightwater/Spring Grove parish boundary later being fixed at Jeffries Road, the birth-site of Ernest Rutherford is no longer in Spring Grove but is today in Brightwater.

The opening of the Nelson-Foxhill railway had another effect. James, being the youngest of the three members of the Rutherford Brothers, Wheelwrights, had to look for other work whenever business became slack. During the early 1870's he is variously listed as Mechanic, Flax Dresser and Wheelwright. With his little house bursting at the seams with children, no land to help support them, and, as third son, no chance of inheriting his father's land, his position looked insecure. However, plans were in hand to extend the railway a few more kilometres towards the West Coast so work opportunities existed at the railhead, Foxhill, some ten kilometres from James Rutherford's house. The Foxhill district could also supply that other badly needed commodity – land.

The James Rutherfords left Spring Grove for Foxhill with young Ernest just five and a half years old. He retained no memory of life at Spring Grove.

Foxhill

Foxhill received its name during a campfire discussion between some early settlers. The wooded area reminded one of Foxhill, a small farm outside Bristol (England) where he had lived as a boy. Foxhill comprised the narrow valley of the Wai-iti river sandwiched between hills. The district had no definable focus except perhaps Gaukrodger's hotel.

On a fine day in March of 1877, the Rutherford family loaded a four-horse waggon with furniture, bedding, eight children and even the grandfather-clock, and lumbered their way to Foxhill. Jim Rutherford, then four years old, later recalled that as they crossed the Wai-iti bridge the clock struck twelve.

Martha's brother John Thompson, in his last year of bachelorhood, farmed and had a carting business at Foxhill so the Rutherfords were not going to a strange district. James purchased the thirtyfive-acre farm next to John Thompson's.

The farm ran from the main Nelson-West Coast road down to the Wai-iti River. Beyond the river rose bush-covered hills. The twelve-roomed house stood not far from the road, and opposite the school. It was a large, solid, house, having been a stopping place for the stage coach service between Nelson and the West Coast. A veritable treasure trove of discarded bottles awaited discovery under the house. A good orchard of over a hundred trees flourished

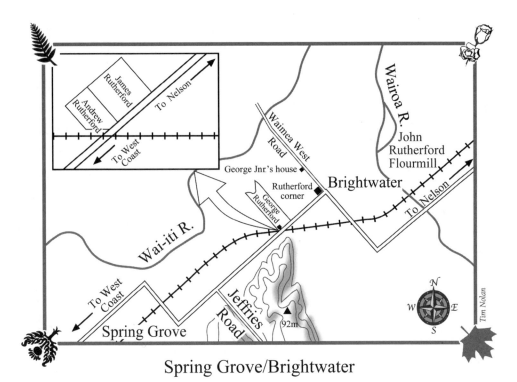

Spring Grove/Brightwater

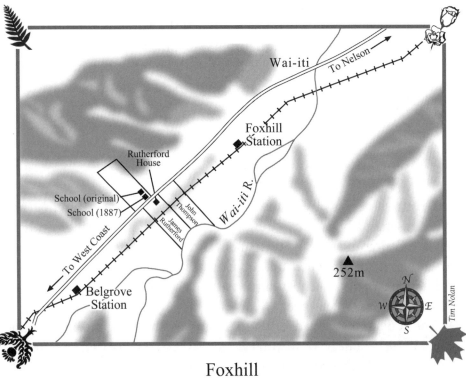

Foxhill

on the river-terrace below the house, with peaches lying deep on the ground when the family arrived. The farm was largely unimproved, in scrub, with a hectare or so still in virgin bush, mainly pine and matai.

Foxhill was an excellent environment for moulding the Rutherford children, with the river for swimming, the bush for bird-nesting and the orchard for raiding. The farm fed the growing family and the children fed the fowls and pigs and milked the cows. A dozen hives of bees completed the live-stock. Sweetbriar on a large area of the river flat was eradicated to make way for potatoes, onions (for the Nelson market) and five acres of wheat. As the wheat ripened the whole family acted as scarecrows to keep the plague of sparrows from the crop. [Years later, the council paid children to collect birds' eggs for destruction.] James built a large brick oven in which George baked thirty-five loaves of bread a week. But the farm had not been meant to support the family completely. James often worked away from home and the children saw little of their father during the week.

James' initial occupation at Foxhill is uncertain as he had signed for his land as a flax-miller, but within a few months went back to calling himself a wheelwright, the trade he probably worked at most while there. [A three metre by half metre sign 'J Rutherford, Wheelwright' formed part of the workbench in the old Foxhill store when I saw it in 1981.] Early in 1880 the Railways purchased a strip of land through his orchard for the Foxhill to Belgrove extension, and it is said that he was bridge-building and contracting for the railway during the summer and wheelwrighting at home on wet days. He built (or helped build) the railway bridge over the Wai-iti river.

Foxhill School

On arrival at Foxhill the older children were enrolled at the school, where Ernest disgraced himself by being punished for a misdemeanor on his very first day. George did not sign on that day: even though he was not quite ten his role as eldest son ordained that he help his father. James and George made several more trips between Spring Grove and Foxhill before George too enrolled at the school two weeks later.

The community elected James to the first Foxhill School Committee at the start of 1879. Because he was a worker in wood the committee paid him to construct desks and book cupboards at various times; because he was a mechanic they asked him to repair the pump in the school well; and as he lived over the road he supervised various jobs such as bailing-out and deepening the well. The following year John Thompson was also elected, starting his run of twenty-five years on this committee. He fulfilled the carting contracts for spreading shingle around the school and supplying red-pine roots for firewood.

As usual the committee oversaw the teacher and in young Harry Ladley they had a good one. He had been born at Spring Grove, attended school there and after two years at Nelson College took up school teaching at Foxhill. Aged twenty-two when the Rutherford family enrolled, Harry Ladley was more or less a self-taught teacher. He had built up the school to an average daily attendance of forty, ranging in age from five to fourteen, the age to which education was free. There were lesser numbers at the top end as few people stayed on at school after the age of twelve, the age to which education was compulsory. Such large mixed classes were very difficult to control. The Nelson Education Board had abolished corporal punishment, a decree deplored and ignored by the teachers and the school inspector alike. The committee had to request that Mr Ladley be less severe in his mode of punishment of the children in extreme cases of correction – that a strap be used instead of a stick.

A teacher's conditions of service were very arduous by today's standards. The committee, mostly local parents, even decided when the teacher could take his holidays. These were two weeks at Christmas/New Year (sometimes starting Christmas Eve), two or three weeks in March for the hop-picking season (when there would be no children at school) and one week in midwinter (June or July). At the end of 1880 Mr Ladley's load eased with the appointment of a local girl as assistant, but after serving for two years she became eligible for a large rise in salary, so the Nelson Education Board abolished the position.

The school building was a tiny one; cramped, unsafe and in ill repair. The committee pressured the Board to build a new one, and this they did early in 1879. One fireplace barely heated the new, much larger, building. It was closer to the road and had a belfry. [The building was later extended and today serves the Foxhill district as the Rutherford Memorial Hall.] The old building remained behind the new school as a second classroom and library. The grounds were almost spartan – just the school, a well, toilets at the end of the one-acre section, a gravelled yard and the schoolmaster's house. One ball game culminated in a broken window which resulted in a severe caution to the children not to play near the school.

Most certainly Ern was lucky to be born to parents who valued education. James appreciated education because he never really had any. At the age of 11 he could read but not write. Martha on the other hand appreciated it because she had had a relatively good education as a child, and both she and her mother had been schoolteachers.

The Rutherford children owed their education mostly to their mother. Before each reached school-age Martha taught the child the alphabet, to read and spell one syllable words and to know their multiplication tables up to twelve times. Lessons, family spelling bees and quizzes around the fireside at night helped achieve this standard. Jim in later years told his own children how Martha was a martinet as far as her children's education went. She made sure they did their homework, often saying *"All knowledge is power"*. The children's background showed up in their first year at Foxhill. With about ten children in each of their age groups at school Ern was first in his group, Jim second, Ellen third and George fourth. The next year Ellen was first, Jim second, Ern third and George gained a special prize for marks attained.

During the year the school inspector visited each school and conducted the school examinations. Foxhill's turn came each July or August. Pupils were examined in Arithmetic, Grammar, Geography, and History. A Standard IV student (age 11 ± 2) would be asked six questions in arithmetic, mainly involving multiplication and long division (*e.g. How many drams are there in 35 tons 17 cwt 1 qr 23 lbs 7 oz 13 drams?*). Three or more correctly answered questions ensured a pass. For Grammar they would be asked to name the parts of speech in a given sentence and to write a short letter. For Geography there were typically four questions (*e.g. Explain the causes of rain. Name 5 groups of Islands in the South Pacific*). As New Zealand was not regarded as having a history, schools taught English history (*e.g. Name in the order of their succession, the English Sovereigns from 1216 to 1485*). In such ways was New Zealand just a distant splinter of olde England.

Following the annual exams the children who passed were promoted to the next standard. At Foxhill they moved up with an average age several months younger than the average for the Nelson district. This caused the school inspector to worry that the younger scholars, many of whom had barely escaped failure, would not do well the following year. The relative achievements of the older Rutherford children can be inferred from the ages at which they passed their Standard IV exam. George, Ellen and Alice passed at age twelve, while Ernest and Jim did so just before their tenth birthdays. With the average passing age throughout Nelson being just under twelve, this represented a remarkable family achievement bearing in mind that George as the eldest boy, and Ellen and Alice as the oldest girls, had numerous household duties. Herbert and Charles were also showing the same potential at schoolwork as Ernest and Jim.

Science was first taught at Foxhill in 1880. In 1882, just prior to his eleventh birthday, Ernest Rutherford received a science primer 'Physics' by Balfour Stewart, the Professor of Natural Philosophy at Manchester. The preface states

> ⋯ *the thing to be aimed at is not so much to give information, as to endeavour to discipline the mind in a way which has not hitherto been customary, by bringing it into immediate contact with Nature herself. For this purpose a series of simple experiments has been devised, leading up to the chief truths of each science. These experiments must be performed by the teacher in regular order before the class. The power of observation in the pupils will thus be awakened and strengthened; and the amount and accuracy of the knowledge gained must be tested and increased by a thorough system of questioning.*

Stirring words. One experiment combined the measurement of the time interval between flash and boom of a distant cannon, and the known speed of sound in air (about one kilometre every three seconds), to determine the distance the observer was from the cannon. During a spectacular electrical storm one evening Ern impressed his family by using this method to estimate the distance to each lightning flash.

Ern's first recorded illicit experiment concerned the making of a cannon out of the brass tube of a hat-peg. A touch-hole was filed into the tube which was clamped to a wooden frame. With a target fixed twenty metres away, a generous charge of black powder was inserted in the lethal device and a marble rammed home to serve as a cannon ball. The cannon exploded, demolishing the frame, but luckily hurting no one.

Ern and Jim shared a four-poster bed and were inseparable (as were Charles and Herbert). Until he was eight-years-old, Ern was inclined to be delicate. Jim, though a year younger, matched him physically so they regularly wrestled each other. Ern at Foxhill is described as a quiet, solitary lad. He dribbled a bit. [One reminiscence stated he went home at lunchtimes to change his shirt.] Not surprisingly he suffered under the nickname of 'Dopey'. He was partly shunned by the other school children, did not join in sports and often sat under a tree reading while the others played games during breaks. As a boy he made no impact at Foxhill and neighbours, later in life, had trouble recalling him.

The Rutherford name first came to local prominence in the field of education at the start of 1881. Following a special examination at the end of the previous year, one of the two scholarships to Nelson College which were available to boys in country districts, was awarded to 13-year-old George. The scholarship gave George two years free board and tuition at Nelson College. He did well at school. In his last year there, in the upper-fifth-form, he obtained a prize for bookkeeping and passed the Junior Civil Service Examination, coming fifth in New Zealand out of 100 candidates, a most noteworthy achievement for the eldest son of a large family.

Life on the Farm

At weekends George would return home to Foxhill and there were many pleasant interludes. He would take Ern and Jim frolicking in the Wai-iti river but only on the understanding that both would be ducked. One day he had a brain-wave to dip the dog also and jumped off a high bank with the dog in his arms. As they descended deep into the pool, the dog went up him like a threshing machine, a very painful experience for the completely naked George. Jim and Ern sniggered behind his back at what they considered righteous retribution vented by the dog.

On spring Saturdays, after their chores were done, the boys would take their lunch (usually a large meat pie) and head for an afternoon's bird-nesting down by the river. They collected birds' eggs, mainly goldfinch, kingfisher and red and yellow parakeets, but never disturbing a bird or taking a warm egg, Jim later reminisced. This activity had its dangers. On one occasion George, when faced with a long climb down a tree, placed the eggs in his mouth for safe keeping. Falling from the last branch he learned the hard way that the eggs were old and rotten. George sold blown eggs to the town boys so that he and his brothers could buy the little necessities of boyhood such as rubber for catapults and string for kites.

They played a typically boisterous game called 'Indians'. Ern and Jim would pick sides and defend their respective forts behind briar bushes, with bows and arrows and stones. Jim once laid Ern out with a well-thrown stone, the bleeding wound being treated at the riverside with a wet sock. On another occasion Ern, while learning to throw the bolas, sent it vigorously over the roof of the house to yield screams from the other side. It had hit one of the younger boys, who contemplated going to tell their mother. He saw reason after Ern had sat on his head for half an hour. Ern's favourite amusement was singlestick, which is fencing with a basket-hilted stick of sword length. Ern would do Jim's chores for the day in return for a bout. [Years later the skill became of great value to Ern, who, while Librarian at Nelson College, kept order using a cricket wicket].

It wasn't all play for the boys. Ern and Jim looked after George's vegetable garden during the school term and held competitions using brands of liquid manure to promote the growth of their respective pumpkins, the day's growth being measured each day after school. Ern figured that by using a powerful microscope one could see a plant actually grow.

They also had the standard chores of feeding the calves and pigs, milking the family's seven cows (after George went to Nelson College, Ern milked five, Jim two), and gathering firewood from the stumps of fallen matai trees. They combined the latter task with fetching the cows from the bottom paddock by the Wai-iti river. The return journey, during which they dragged a small sledge loaded with wood while also driving the cows, traversed some three hundred metres culminating in the track traversing a steep bank with a sharp right-angled bend at the top. [The track and bend can still be seen today.] One day Ern had the bright idea of tying the loaded sledge to a cow's tail and letting the cow do the work of sledging the load up the bank. This worked fine until the bundle jammed on a gate-post at the sharp bend at the top. It was 'goodbye end of cow's tail'. The boys waited in fear and trembling for their father's return home on Saturday night. There are several versions of the sequel, with Ern adjusting the account according to audience. In old age Jim recalled that they were so penitent they escaped punishment ⋯ *the only time they didn't get the birch when probably we deserved it,* ⋯ while on one occasion Ern recalled that ⋯ *the cow's tail was pretty sore, but it wasn't half as sore as mine when my father had finished with me.*

When he was nine, Ern earned twenty-five shillings, possibly from hop picking or helping his uncle John Thompson. [This sum lay forgotten in his savings book account for fifty-five years by which time interest had increased its value nearly five times.]

Family outings included visiting Belgrove to see the charcoal production industry; Wakefield to see a troupe of Negro singers and Brannigan's Circus. Jim long recalled both the thrill of seeing lions and tigers in their cages behind the circus and the all-pervading, horrible animal smell. The next day he and Ern improvised a tightrope to emulate the tightrope walker.

At Foxhill the babies continued arriving – Ethel, Evelyn, Arthur, Percy – taking the total to twelve, and family life consolidated. Saturday night was bath night with water drawn from the ten-metre deep well and heated outside. George and Nell gave the younger children their weekly bath, two at a time. On Sunday evenings the family gathered round Martha's polished Broadwood piano which she had purchased with money she had saved while teaching at Spring Grove, and, with James playing the violin, they would all sing songs and hymns. The oldest girls, Alice and Ellen, served supper. The children had the upbringing of a typical, close-knit, large, educated, religious, hard-working, country family.

They were becoming well settled when 1883 brought them another shift. Apparently initiated by the reduction of public works on completion of the Foxhill-Belgrove railway line in July of 1881, and by a slight upturn in flax prices, it seems to have been viewed initially as a temporary move. The children left Foxhill school on the 5th of April 1883, after the hop picking season, and the family proceeded indirectly to the Marlborough Sounds.

Ern was eleven years old and life was about to get serious.

The James Rutherford house at Spring Grove/Brightwater c. 1920. The line of the railway is now the Brightwater by-pass at the intersection of Lord Rutherford Road. Andrew's old house at left.

(*Davis, Cawthron Institute, Neg 698*)

Close-up of the Rutherford house at Spring Grove/Brightwater. The only known photographs of this house were taken as it was being demolished.
(Rita Snowden, Rutherford Family)

Rutherford house at Foxhill, photographed later when owned by the Palmers.
(pu, Private Collection)

*James and Martha Rutherford with
Florence and Nell.*
(Tyree, Rutherford Family)

*Martha Rutherford with Eva and
(l to r) Charles, Ern, Jim and
Herbert, 1885.*
(Tyree, Rutherford Family)

Rutherford family at Havelock before 1886, l to r, Alice, cousin Mary Thompson, Arthur, Ern, Eve, James, Nell, Ethel, George, Herbert, Flo, Martha, Charles and Jim.
(Wm Collie, Rutherford Family)

Chapter 2

TRAGEDIES AND TRIUMPHS

Havelock 1881–1887

Mr and Mrs Rutherford are much respected and this sad affair has cast quite a gloom over the whole district, and the two deceased lads were very much liked by their schoolfellows.

Havelock correspondent to the Marlborough Express,

on the drowning of Herbert and Charles Rutherford.

The Pelorus Valley Flax Mill

After some years of depression, 1881 heralded a slight upturn in the demand for flax. John and James Rutherford looked for an area ripe for cutting. They found this in the swamps at the mouth of the Pelorus River where it flows into the Marlborough Sounds. James took out a ten-year lease of a flax-covered Maori reserve at Ruapaka, seven kilometres west of Havelock. He erected there a steam-driven flax mill on the site of an earlier water-driven mill. The site took advantage of the ease of transport to the port of Havelock, via either the Pelorus river or the cart track, and the reliable flow of water in the Ruapaka stream for soaking the stripped flax. [James diverted the Ruapaka stream in December of 1882. The soaking-pond was still visible in a paddock at Ruapaka until the mid-1980s when flood control works obliterated it.]

By April of 1882 the Pelorus Valley Flax Mill employed twenty men and processed six tons of green flax a day. The steamdriven Rutherford mill was one of six or so mills in the whole of the Marlborough Province, the others all being earlier water driven mills. A *Marlborough Daily Times* reporter, on business in Havelock in November of 1883, wished to visit the Wakamarina gold fields before returning to Blenheim. On leaving Havelock his report stated

> ⋯ *After a pleasant drive of about half an hour we pulled up at Mr Rutherford's flaxmill. Mr Rutherford, who kindly showed us over the mill, informed us that he turns out from eight to ten tons of flax per week, and the article seemed to be of a very superior description. His flax brings the second highest price in the Home market, and he can always command a ready sale for it in Melbourne. The raw flax around the neighborhood grow very long, some of the blades measuring no less than 12 to 14 feet.*

The Township of Havelock

Havelock was a small country town which fringed the hills at the head of the Pelorus Sound, where the Pelorus and Kaituna rivers join. The name honoured Sir Henry Havelock who, in 1857, relieved Lucknow during the Indian Mutiny. On the main overland route between Nelson and Blenheim, it consisted of but one house in the early 1860s. The discovery of gold at the Wakamarina in 1864 saw it grow as the port servicing the diggings. By the 1880s the gold had fallen off and the easily accessible timber had been cut from the hills leaving them scrub-covered monstrosities. Detractors referred to the town as dying, but timber milling, flax processing and farming throughout the district kept it from expiring. With a town population of only 350 and declining, it serviced nearly a thousand more people in the surrounding area.

The township of Havelock boasted a Post and Telegraph Office, three hotels, several stores, a town hall, a public library, a school, two churches (Roman Catholic and Church of England), a lawn-tennis court, a doctor, stables, assorted tradesmen and a dilapidated wharf. The port of Havelock, though small, was the heart of the district. Regular coastal sailing ships carried away the produce, particularly timber. The little steam tug S.S. *Pelorus* towed the ships within the sounds as there was little room for manoeuvring under sail.

Although Havelock may have been regarded by some as dying it had its livelier moments. One man ordered his coffin in advance from the local joiner and tested it for comfort by being carried round the pubs by four mates, the

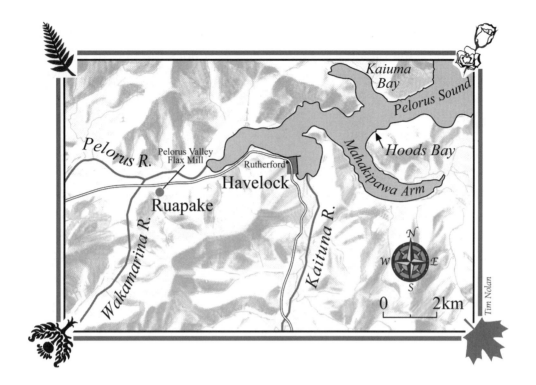

Tim Nolan

FOR SALE.

STEAM FLAX MILLS in Pelorus Valley, with good supply of Flax, all in good working order, with THREE YEARS' LEASE.
    For particulars apply to
JAMES RUTHERFORD, on the premises;
    or JOHN RUTHERFORD, Brightwater.
—6

Ern's education survived the vagaries of the flax market

'body' sitting up to receive its refreshment. But it was the famous croton oil case of 1883 which made Havelock's name headlines throughout the land. Reporters flocked there. The local solicitor, doctor, publican and barman were charged with lacing a local builder's egg flip with croton oil which is a powerful purgative. Ten drops will clean out a man and the dose they gave him was about right for an elephant. As a practical joke it backfired in a big way. The builder spent all night on the toilet and subsequently took the other four to Court where they were given the benefit of the doubt and acquitted.

Havelock was fairly isolated. Towards the north the Sounds puncturing the rugged hills provided the only roadway to the open sea. Long pulls by rowing boat were often the only means of communication. Two men and a boy in a whale boat took about a month to deliver and collect the census papers out to Cook Strait and through French Pass to Croisilles Harbour. On another occasion seven children rowed fifty kilometres to present themselves to the School Inspector for examination.

A similar feat was achieved by a bridegroom who, with the vicar, left Havelock at 5 am and travelled forty kilometres by whaleboat to the isolated bay where his bride resided. After the ceremony and wedding breakfast they returned to Havelock arriving at 11.30 pm and the happy couple left immediately for their honeymoon in Blenheim, a six-hour waggon ride away. One would assume they slept-in next morning.

Telegraphic communication with the outside world was available except when a tree had fallen on the wire. Then the postmaster/telegraph-operator/linesman would have to close shop and spend a day or two locating and fixing the fault, much to the annoyance of people who had come into town to pick up their mail. Twice a week a steam launch ran east from Havelock to Mahakipawa whence passengers and goods travelled by coach to the Grove, to connect with another steam launch to Picton, where a safe deep harbour served Marlborough province. The one-way fare of ten shillings swallowed more than a day's wage for a good man.

The road south from Havelock to Blenheim was of sufficient standard to allow a twice-weekly coach service. The road which wound westward through rugged mountains to Nelson was much more rudimentary. Though described as new and in excellent condition it was in fact no more than a track. The first wheeled vehicle to cross the Pelorus Bridge and penetrate a kilometre or two towards Nelson did so only in November of 1882. During winter the road was regarded as unusable. William Pickering, the Havelock coachman, extended the Blenheim – Havelock coach service through to Nelson in 1885. The route was not easy. On one trip from Nelson to Havelock he had to cut through thirteen trees which had fallen across the road. On another he had to cut through a large tree, ford a creek with sixty centimetres of water in the coach and then travel some distance with the road more than a metre under water. Until the new Pelorus bridge was completed the passengers would help wheel the coach over. [In later years Pickering's grandson, William Pickering, attended Havelock School. After a year at Canterbury College he went to America where he rose to become the head of the National Aeronautical and Space Agency's Jet Propulsion Laboratory. He was deeply involved with many scientific rockets sent to the planets. He appeared twice on the cover of *Time* magazine, was given an honorary Knighthood in 1976, and retired in 1979.]

It was along such rough tracks that James Rutherford travelled every three months or so on his brief visits home to his family at Foxhill. The demand for flax continued and so therefore did the separation. James would write love letters to Martha and got loving replies in return. Occasionally he would go to a hill and look towards his wife and family. This was not the same as having them with him so he decided to transport them temporarily to Havelock, the town closest to the flax mill.

The Rutherford Family Arrive – 1883

James arranged for the S.S. *Lady Barkly*, a little coastal steamer from Nelson which had just been converted from paddle wheel to screw propulsion, to call at Havelock for a load of flax. It arrived at 10 am on Saturday the 12th of May 1883 carrying, amongst others, the Rutherford family and their household goods. George, who was a boarder at Nelson College, was left behind. James did not sell the Foxhill property but merely rented a house at Havelock since flax prices would determine the length of stay.

The family lived on the Terrace at the north end of the town, on the main road to Nelson and opposite the road down to the wharf. From their front porch they had a good view of the head of Pelorus Sound. To their right was the township and the swamp formed by the Kaituna River, to their left the swamp and flax country of the Pelorus River. The house had an excellent orchard full of blossom in spring. Behind, the land rose steeply into bush clad hills.

The family had hardly settled in when a winter epidemic of whooping cough swept Havelock. Percy, the baby of the family, caught the insidious disease. His coughing disturbed the family's sleep for two months. Two days after his first birthday he died. The distraught family sent out funeral notices and buried him in an unmarked grave in the Havelock cemetery.

Child deaths were quite common due to epidemics, poor hygiene and relatively poor living standards. Medical diagnosis and treatment left a lot to be desired. One lady in Westport reportedly died *of a surfeit of joy*. Her brother left her a small legacy and she was on the way to the solicitors to collect it when she dropped dead.

Perhaps typical of the minor health problems of the time was when Frank Matthews, a local apprentice carpenter, developed toothache. His boss's wife tried collodion which made it worse and the doctor gave a painkiller. Ten days later the day was cold so he stayed at home with his jaws tied up with flannel. No wonder that quack medicines and cure-alls flourished. Even Havelock had its own wonder water from a local spring which reportedly had curative properties for eye diseases. Free samples were sent around the country to those wishing to test the locals' claims.

Accidents were a major cause of death. The carnage on the roads was appalling with people being thrown from horses, kicked by horses and run over by wagons. However, most people had the usual objectives of hoping to die in bed or to die with their boots on. A miner at Deep Creek achieved both these laudable aims. He was sitting on his bunk pulling on his boots when a tree fell on him.

The Rutherford family quickly settled into life in an isolated country town. James lived at the mill, working the normal six-day week, and came into Havelock on Saturday night, partly for any Saturday night entertainment but certainly for Church on Sunday. The Rutherfords were a religious family who strictly observed the Sabbath. Bans on Sunday activities included the reading of newspapers. For the children, Sundays meant morning church, afternoon Sunday school, evening church and then hymns around their mother's piano. *Altogether a too strenuous sabbath*, recalled Jim, who received his last dose of the birch for whistling and attempting to dance on a Sunday. James served as a vestryman at the Anglican church but the family attended Presbyterian and Wesleyan services as well, depending on which minister happened to be in town. The family even supported the Catholic Church Bazaar, so there appeared to be no strong rivalry between denominations in this small community.

With their musical background, the Rutherford children were involved with regular practices in the Town Board Office for the November 1883 Sunday School Anniversary Tea Party. After a morning of various sports and an afternoon feast for the children, the adults attended a Tea Party which was followed in the evening by the children's entertainment in the Town Hall. Thirty items graced the programme. Ernest and Ellen Rutherford performed 'Rosabell',

Charles helped recite 'Army and Navy', Ellen sang a solo, 'Home is Home' and Jim gave the final recitation, 'The Last Hymn'.

Havelock's most important influence on the Rutherford children though was their weekday education.

Jacob Reynolds, Country Schoolteacher

In 1881 Havelock's 70-year-old schoolteacher was forced to retire. He was replaced by a youthful teacher from Wellington's Willis Street (Te Aro) school, 25-year-old Jacob Reynolds. When he had left, the pupils of the fifth standard presented him with a handsome ink stand and writing tablet as a mark of their esteem for him.

From a line of English lawyers, (his brother was a Cambridge B.A. and barrister), Jacob had come to New Zealand as a young man, shortly before his marriage. That Havelock suited him is shown by the given names of the eleventh of his twelve children, Henry Havelock, whilst his classical education is celebrated in the names given to his seventh child, Cyril Septimus. Reynolds settled in to become a notable member of the small Havelock community – an initiator of the debating society, singer, handy member of the sporadic cricket team, chairman of a committee which tried unsuccessfully to form a local volunteer corps after the Russian invasion scare of 1885, comic actor, church vestryman, foreman of a Coroner's court jury, spokesman for the goldfield industry, committee member for the hoped-for Nelson-Havelock-Blenheim railway line and Marlborough representative to the New Zealand Educational Institute.

Jim Rutherford recalled him as a broad-minded man with vision, physically a fairly stout man but not at all lethargic. He had sound ideas on physical development, teaching the boys to hold high their heads, to throw out their chests and to look the world in the eye. Never a highly qualified teacher in the academic sense, he appeared quite happy to rise no higher than E1 grade which placed him in the fifth rank. Teachers were graded on two counts. The letter grade (from highest to lowest, A to E) recorded their academic achievements. Holders of Masters degrees were graded A, holders of bachelor degrees B, people part way through a degree C and those who had passed teachers' examinations D or E. The number grades (from highest to lowest, 1 to 5) were assigned on the basis of the teacher's experience, practical skill in the art of teaching and school management. The rank, of which there were 9, combined both gradings.

Within six months at Havelock school, in absurdly overcrowded conditions,

Jacob Reynolds had impressed the school inspector as an energetic teacher who had brought into perfect discipline a school previously noted for unruly children. Throughout his teaching career at Havelock, Mr Reynolds was renowned for his discipline and the academic success of his pupils. Parents regarded him highly.

The Havelock School

Mr Reynolds arrived to 100 pupils with another 50 of school age awaiting places (or so their parents said). He taught the 50 older pupils in the upper school while a female taught the 50 younger children in the lower school. The schools were some 500 metres apart. Both were grossly overcrowded.

After some months of discussion, the Marlborough Education Board decided to construct a new building to house both schools on the same site, so that the Headmaster could maintain supervision of the assistant teacher as well as all the pupils. During the planning and construction phase they avoided overcrowding in the upper school by temporarily using the Town Hall. Two men using a horse and block and tackle put the now vacant 'upper' school on wheels and shifted it to behind the Town Hall where it served as an annex and also as the office of the Havelock Board of Works.

When the Rutherford children arrived in Havelock in May of 1883, the younger children went to the lower school and the older children to Mr Reynolds in his temporary quarters. Thus the first school building Ernest Rutherford attended in Havelock was the old Town Hall.

After the midwinter holiday the school reunited in the new building on the south side of the town. The Prime Minister himself later described it as one of the best he had seen in the Colony. It was a spacious and functional structure twenty-seven metres long, divided into two equal size classrooms of ten by eight metres, each with a porch at the end. At the back a veranda, three metres wide, ran the full length of the building. This could be used as another classroom if necessary. The rooms were high and airy but without the defect of having too much draught in winter. A fireplace in each room supplied winter heating. The partition between the classrooms reached only as high as the eaves leaving a triangular gap up to the ceiling which proved ideal for boys to toss things over into the junior classroom whenever teachers were absent. Twelve large windows facing west on to the main road and the hills behind gave excellent illumination, with venetian blinds to shield the afternoon sun. [To take maximum effect of the sunshine, the building was rotated through ninety degrees in 1928 so that the class-room windows faced north. Today the building serves as the Havelock Youth Hostel.]

The earlier schools had no water supply of their own, leaving the children to seek a drink of water from the neighbouring houses. For the new school two men dug a thirteen metre deep well in a day and a half. Trees and shrubs were planted in the grounds during spring and, when necessary, the entrance was gravelled. The committee added playground equipment a year later but the school had been up for three years before the playground was levelled. The girls dissipated their surplus energy in the enclosed portion of the playground while the boys had the rest of the educational reserve to play in.

However the real moulding of the children took place inside the schoolhouse.

School Work 1883

The lower school was in the middle of a period of turmoil. The School Committee fired Mrs Erskine from her temporary position for uninspiring teaching. With up to sixty children crammed into her classroom she did not have an easy task and she had inherited some poorly prepared children. Several of age ten or eleven hardly knew their alphabet. The teacher replacing her lasted but a few months before resigning. By contrast, in the upper school stability reigned under the reinsmanship of Jacob Reynolds. This period of tight discipline and excellent examination results was to last for more than a decade.

In class Jacob Reynolds was assisted by a senior girl, Jessie Matthews; with her official title Pupil Teacher, she looked after standard two. Jessie was the first of a chain of Matthews children who excelled academically during and after their education at Havelock school. Of her brothers and sisters, Laura matriculated to the University of New Zealand and became a school headmistress, Walter entered the building trade and became Town Clerk for Havelock, Charles passed the Junior Civil Service examination and rose to be Under-Secretary for Justice, Frederick won a Marlborough Scholarship to Nelson College and became private secretary to the Prime Minister. Outside the classroom Jacob Reynolds was assisted by the Truant Officer, the local constable. This position was most necessary as on any given day some twenty to thirty children would be absent out of a roll of over 100.

Ernest Rutherford, approaching his twelfth birthday (the age when most children left school), went into standard six so was immediately under the direct control of Mr Reynolds. Contemporaries later remembered Ernest at Havelock as a quiet, rather dreamy boy who did not care for games. At playtime he would be found standing at the porch door in the sun. Often the most his classmates could extract from him would be an "*It's a nice day isn't it*" in a slow drawl. The slim, somewhat untidy, youngster acquired the nickname of 'Windy'. Whether this arose from his lack of verbosity, a reflection on his courage or a liking for baked beans is not known. The logic involved in schoolboy nicknames is often convoluted.

Such a boy would benefit from the well-disciplined atmosphere engendered by a teacher who aimed to produce results.

Each year the Inspector came to examine the school, assessing both pupils and teachers. The pupils sat an examination, success in which would permit them to proceed to the next standard. Previously the Inspector had visited Havelock before October but sought, and was granted, permission to change this to February or March. This left little time for preparation between the end of the summer vacation and the examinations. Mr Reynolds attempted to reduce the school summer holidays to a week over Christmas – New Year, postponing the balance until after the school examinations. Foiled, he tried another tack, recorded in a letter from a parent to the Editor of the *Marlborough Daily Times*.

To The Editor

Sir, —— The Havelock schools were closed for the usual Christmas holidays on Friday last, 14th inst., and as usual with children on such occasions, their hearts were light and joyous at the prospect – a spell from work. Imagine, then, their disgust when told by their master, Mr Reynolds, that during their holidays each and every one of the upper school pupils would have to do, during the vacation, ten sums and learn eleven pages of geography, or in default they would receive a good thrashing.

Now, Sir, we have been boys, and therefore feel for the youngsters. Is it not monstrous? Is Mr Reynolds, in addition to being schoolmaster, to be Committee and Board rolled into one? If so, Heaven protect the youthful pates of the Havelock children!

Perhaps Mr Reynolds does not know, so let me tell him one or two facts which may be useful to him hereafter. First – Legally he has no right to give these lessons to the children during the vacation; secondly – As to thrashing those who do not comply with his illegal order, perhaps it will be wise for him to think over that point, as the R.M. Court might settle it in a manner not altogether agreeable to him.

Mr Reynolds, when asked why he gave these unjust lessons, coolly replied – "Ah you see the Inspector examines the children in February, and if I don't give them something to do during the holidays it will be a nice old mess." What does this prove? One simple fact – that the children are not <u>grounded</u> at all but simply <u>crammed to pass a certain standard</u>. Mr Reynolds' system of teaching must be poor indeed if the children cannot retain in their heads for one month that which has taken six to put in.

In conclusion, I ask every parent having children attending the Havelock School not to allow their children to do one single atom of the unjust work allotted to them, and if Mr Reynolds does as he says, gives them a thrashing, I say teach him a wrinkle he is at present ignorant of.
– Yours, &c.,

A Parent.

Havelock, December 17th, 1883.

Thrashing children had its hazards. The teacher at Fairhall School had resigned after the mother of one of the children so punished had, in front of the class, punched him. Academically though, Mr Reynolds' tactics worked. The results impressed the school inspector ⋯ Havelock is now fairly abreast of the best schools in Marlborough ⋯ The organisation and discipline are all that could be desired. ⋯

1884

This year started on a bright note due to the magnificent sunrises and sunsets caused by the fine dust thrown into the upper atmosphere from the enormous volcanic explosion of Krakatoa in Indonesia.

However 1884 was more sombre for some of the local community. Mr Pickering was run over by his own coach (he was only bruised); the Havelock doctor died and was not replaced for several months; a nor'west gale blew down both chimneys at the school and an employee at the Rutherford flax mill, while loading tow for shipment by schooner to Nelson, went over the end of the wharf – horse, dray, tow and all – when the horse took fright during a heavy gust of wind.

Brownlees' large sawmill at Kaituna cut out but a lawsuit prevented them from constructing a tramway up the Pelorus Valley to unharvested forest. [Scientific American, 22 March 1884, published a letter from Brownlee & Co., concerning the reason for the loss of power in their steam locomotive.] Havelock was gradually losing its inhabitants. Were the Brownlee mill to be removed from the Havelock area the town might indeed become the Deserted Village it was half jokingly referred to as.

For the Rutherfords the omens were sombre indeed. As the flax prices were down once again, James arranged to stop the flax mill. It was hoped the stoppage would only prove temporary but rumours or facts spread.

> ··· Mr Rutherford will leave here with the good wishes of all for better luck in any place he may choose to start again. The removal of his family will make a serious alteration in the school roll, and they will be missed by their many play fellows and friends.

Perhaps the Havelock correspondent to the *Marlborough Express* had been overly pessimistic in this report of the 24th of January 1884 for the family stayed on in Havelock. However the family fortunes were probably at a low ebb as around this period James contributed only five shillings to the Shirriff family fund when all other contributors gave one to ten pounds.

By August John and James Rutherford's Pelorus Flax Mill, together with a good supply of flax, was up for sale. There were no takers. All branches of trade were in the doldrums and there seemed no prospect of revival. One saw-miller at Kaituna went bankrupt and another, W E Dive, a prominent member of the Havelock community, shifted his family to the North Island. [W E Dive owned the house in which traditionally the Rutherfords are said to have lived – section 113 overlooking the road to the wharf. Maybe the Rutherfords did not move in until this date.]

Young George Rutherford would have been aware that times were tough. His scholarship at Nelson College had ceased at the end of 1883 but his academic ambitions had not. He had hoped to become a doctor. Presumably the family could not afford to support him for another year at secondary boarding school so instead, after studying at home, he sat the Senior Civil Service Examination at Havelock in April of 1884. The younger children may not have been as aware of the family circumstances. They swotted on.

The Sunday school had an average attendance of forty-one. Ernest Rutherford received the highest marks over all for the year. He pipped Charles Matthews, who was a year younger, with Laura Matthews and Jim Rutherford next with fewer than half of Ern's marks. Obviously there was a large tail end of no triers. Charles Matthews and Ern were both nearly perfect on remembering the Catechism (a printed list of questions and answers on the Anglican religious doctrine) but Charles pipped Ern for the number of biblical verses memorised (678 vs 644).

Three years after he had taken over the Havelock School, Jacob Reynolds produced the district's first notable academic success when one of his pupils won the prestigious Marlborough Scholarship to the Nelson Colleges. It was a just reward for the scholar, the bright, hard working Laura Matthews who obtained marks not only higher than those of the ten Marlborough candidates but also higher than those of the thirty-five candidates in Nelson town, Nelson districts and the West Coast who sat the same examination for similar scholarships. But even with the scholarship, Laura's parents were not rich enough to send her to Nelson Girls' College. As a consolation, Mr Reynolds offered her the position of Pupil Teacher at Havelock.

Ernest Rutherford had passed his standard six examinations, the highest examinations in the New Zealand state school system. He was promoted into what was unofficially called standard seven, the link between primary and secondary school. Had he lived in a large town, he could have transferred to a secondary school provided his parents were willing to pay the fees. At Havelock this was not an option. Because he was two years younger than the average age for passing the standard six exams (thanks to Martha Rutherford's tuition at home and Mr Ladley's good work at Foxhill), Ernest still had two more years free schooling in hand.

1885

Just before school resumed after the summer holidays, the Havelock School Committee held its annual meeting. James Rutherford's name went forward for a position on the Committee but he received the lowest number of votes and was not elected. Some Marlborough schools were closed because of a diphtheria epidemic, yet Mr Reynolds and his two pupil teachers (Jessie and Laura Matthews) had again worked wonders with their 110 pupils when school inspection rolled around. The inspector reported

> ··· I have not seen, either in this or any other district, a better taught and better disciplined school than Havelock. The work was good all round, the Arithmetic and letter-writing being excellent. The arrangements for examinations so complete, and the scholars knew so thoroughly what they were about, that the work was got through in an unusually short time ··· .

After the school examinations and near the end of the fruit season, Martha, four of the boys (Ern, Jim, Herbert and Charles) and six-year-old Eva went back to their house at Foxhill for the month of March during the hop-picking season. Martha had travelled by ship while James took the boys over the Maungatapu track. As they walked, James related the story of some infamous murders on the track two decades earlier so it was no wonder the boys received a scare near Murderer's Rock when they met a horseman with a gun on his shoulder.

An uncle, with a pack-horse, met them at the top of the track and escorted the boys down to his waggon. The boys were soon busy in their large orchard at Foxhill, gathering fruit which their mother turned into jams and jellies. Jim recalled 'countless' large stone jars being filled. Ern and Jim put in several weeks hop-picking. Although they earned £13, Jim did not regard the venture as very lucrative. The boys had to be content with the poorer vines and with waiting until last each evening to have their harvest measured. Jim swore they never received a fair spin. Though first to work and last to leave, their bin never measured up to their neighbours.

To cool off one warm lunch hour at the hop-field, Ern and Jim went as usual for a frolic in a deep pool in the Wai-iti River. Neither could swim and Ern got into difficulties with Jim just managing to grasp his fingers as he went under for the second time. Both boys were badly frightened and kept this episode a close secret for otherwise all bathing would have been banned.

After family photographs in Nelson, James fetched the boys back to Havelock where they re-entered their routine of Sundays – church, weekdays – school, and Saturdays free. Often Ern and Jim would go up to the flax mill at Ruapaka, either to work all day or just for a social visit. It was a fun place for boys, a place where George let Ern fire his shotgun at a kingfisher. He missed. [Diaries are valuable sources of accurate information. Consider another entry George made.

March 31 Shot duck.

April 1 Duck season came in today.]

The mill had recommenced work the previous September. George lived and worked at the mill, putting in ten-hour days cutting and processing flax. Aged seventeen going on eighteen, plus tall and handsome, he had a favourite pastime of eyeing the local girls. The rest of his spare time passed with making ginger beer, tending his garden, cooking, jumping his horse, shooting ducks and pigeons, and reading books from the Canvastown library. Occasionally he would ride into Havelock for entertainment such as Professor Rice's lecture on 'Spiritualism, Clairvoyancy and Physiology' or the talk 'From Pekin to St Petersburg'. He volunteered for the militia, as had his father and uncles in their day, but a local corps never eventuated. Come Sundays he did not have to follow the rigid regime of his brothers and sisters. He would ride to Havelock and attend just one church service, the rest of the time being spent in socialising or on the water in canoe or boat.

Jim long remembered with affection the undated day he, Ernest, Herbert and Charles spent with kind old Mrs Reader.

> ⋯ *Ostensibly it was to find turkey eggs, but actually, it was to give us boys a good go at the fruit. The black heart cherries were just ripe and on our arrival we were invited to the orchard to sample them. We were then told where the turkeys were nesting and like sleuth hounds on the trail we scoured the fallen bush and had soon collected baskets of eggs. When we got back to her home we were invited to sample her elderberry wine, plum wine, blackberry wine and we had our first taste of mead. After lunch we paid another visit to the cherries, then returned to our home, laden with turkey eggs and cherries. ⋯ Another memorable day was an outing to Port Ligar in the tug 'Pelorus'. The cherry orchard there belonged to a Mrs Chrichton and the cherries were a wild variety. There were unlimited cherries and some thirty or more of us who were guests of the Brownlee family had a royal time. On the evening of our arrival several settlers arrived with boats to take us ashore to their homes and have a social evening. They also brought fishing lines and were towing behind the boat a piece of wood painted red with a hook in it. We were shown how to catch barracoota. We had a fish supper before returning to the tug. The ladies of the party retired below, while the boys and men slept on deck.*

The flax industry had settled down again to the extent that James Rutherford put the Foxhill property up for sale. [It was rented out and was not finally sold until September of 1888.] But within three weeks word came from John Rutherford that the merchants had stopped buying flax for three months and he had thirty tons of dressed flax unsold at the Brightwater Mill. James had five tons at the Ruapaka mill and the same amount on a ship en route to Nelson. This marked the end of flax milling at Pelorus for the Rutherfords.

James immediately looked for stands of timber suitable for milling.

Sawmilling 1885

The South Island trunk railway was being extended to Hurunui and Bluff, with the Government buying railway sleepers cut from native woods. Australian hardwoods were much more satisfactory but much more expensive so totara, matai (black pine), silver pine and birch were the main timbers used. This sparked a revival of saw-milling in the Marlborough Sounds and came just at the right time for the Rutherfords. At two shillings and sixpence a sleeper (minus a royalty of three pence for those cut on crown land) the rewards were not high but adequate.

James and George quickly searched the Pelorus Sound for an area of bush overlooked by the big sawmills which had been working the area since the mid-1860s. All the good, easy wood had been cut long ago but patches suitable for a small mill remained.

James applied to the Marlborough Land Board for a licence to cut sleepers on 200 acres of the Wakamarina gold field. In the meantime George scutched the last of the flax at the mill and then shifted the steam engine a short distance to Wilson's bush, where on the 18th of July, James, George and their few workmen cut their first five sleepers.

James built a hut at the sawmill for George to live in. On a good day the engine and saw could cut fifty sleepers. By November around 1500 brown and black birch sleepers cut at the Rutherford mill had been accepted on the Havelock wharf by the Government Inspector. More were ready to be transported to the wharf but that stand of bush had been cut out. The sawmill was therefore shifted to the Kaituna Valley at the back of Reader's farm where Ernest is remembered as cutting logs for this mill during his school holidays.

George built a new hut by this mill. Many men in many little mills and some large mills were engaged locally in the railway sleeper industry. As James had obtained a licence for a block at the Wakamarina he was presumably saving it for a rainy day but maybe he was just waiting for the Brownlee tram line to reach the area to ease transport problems.

Marlborough Scholarship Examinations 1885

Marlborough children of less-than-wealthy parents could afford to attend secondary school only by winning an Education Board Scholarship which gave free board and tuition at Nelson College. For the December 1885 Scholarship examinations there were sixty-two candidates spread over the seven different categories; town (i.e. Nelson) boys and girls, Waimea boys and girls, Distant Scholars (included the West Coast) boys and girls, and Marlborough candidates. In 1885 the seven candidates seeking the one scholarship for the latter category included three sitting at Havelock – Ern and Jim Rutherford and Charles Matthews.

They were lucky to still have their guiding hand, Jacob Reynolds, to tutor them. In July he had made inquiries about teaching positions in the Wellington district and was quickly notified of two becoming vacant at small schools the following month. The Secretary of the Wellington Education Board was to telegraph him which one to apply for. With the salary offered being considerably less than what he already received at Havelock, Mr Reynolds seems to have pursued this no further. Hence the education of his pupils at Havelock continued uninterrupted at a time most critical to several of them.   .

The scholarship examinations were held in morning and afternoon sessions over two days, the four subjects being English (including composition and dictation), Arithmetic, English History and Geography. After the examinations George Rutherford looked over the papers. With the exception of arithmetic he declared they were hard. Then came the waiting.

When the results were announced Ern had dipped out as he had come only second, with Charles Matthews sixth and Jim, the youngest candidate, seventh (or last). For Ern it was a big disappointment. There would be no secondary school for him next year. However he had put up a very good performance. With 452 marks out of 600 he finished only 15 marks behind the winner. He had scored higher than all of the candidates in the Nelson Districts (only six of whom were within a hundred marks of his total), obtaining full marks in the arithmetic paper (as had four other candidates).

Mr Lambert, a local farmer and member of the Marlborough Education Board, had invigilated the examination at Havelock. He urged the Board to apply to the Governors of Nelson College for a special scholarship for Ern. John Tinline, one of the pioneer settlers of Nelson, had recently given the College a large sum of money to establish two more scholarships but the details of the Tinline Scholarships had yet to be finalized. Nothing came of Mr Lambert's efforts so Ern stayed on at Havelock School because at age fourteen he was eligible for a few more months of free education at the state school.

1886

1886 passed as a notable year. In the middle of one June night distant but loud explosions awakened people at Havelock. To some this signalled ships at war, to others the distress signals of a ship in trouble. More than a few assumed that the Russian corvette *Vestnik*, which had departed from Wellington five days earlier, was bombarding some luckless port. In reality Mt Tarawera had blown its top. The devastating volcanic explosion created a ten kilometre line of craters in the Mt Tarawera-Lake Rotomahana region of the central North Island.

In 1886 Jacob Reynolds gave extra lessons, for a fee, for an hour before school. Martha Rutherford recalled many years later that Ellen, Alice, Ern and Jim Rutherford, and Laura and Charles Matthews received extra tuition. Ern remembered the subjects as Latin and Algebra, while George and Jim mentioned only Latin. Other subjects may have been offered. Certainly Latin was taught: ⋯ *the basis of the English language* emphasised Mr Reynolds. As neither Latin nor Algebra was needed for Nelson College Scholarship Examinations, the objectives of these extra lessons is not totally clear. Perhaps they were initiated to prepare one or two senior pupils for secondary school, to further educate the pupil teachers, to prepare adults for the Senior Civil Service Examination (possibly for George Rutherford in 1884) or perhaps just to provide a little 'higher' education in an isolated community. [I do not know when these paid, out-of-school-time classes were first offered. In 1890 Jacob Reynolds advertised night classes in the *Pelorus Guardian* ⋯ *Should a significant number signify their intention of joining, I propose holding classes on Tuesday and Friday evenings* ⋯ *6.30 to 8.30 pm* ⋯ *Latin and higher mathematics extra.* Within five weeks the classes ceased for lack of support.]

Herbert and Charles Rutherford

1886 would never be forgotten by the Rutherford family. On the 8th of January the Rutherford girls held a party. The boys' activities were described three days later in a letter which 16-year-old Nell wrote to her aunt Mary Thompson back at Foxhill.

morning and Herbert said he had come for water, when Mother went out, he said he was going to pull down to Hoods Bay 4 miles down to fish & he wanted Ernest, James & Herbert, to come. Ernest had to go to the Mill so he could not go. The boys cut 8 slices of bread & butter. Mother came in and said it was a lot for two, and Charlie said I am going too.

There were three of our boys two of Matthews one five, other 13 or 14 year and Price.

They started from the wharf about ten, and pulled to the point about half a mile, directly out of sight he put up a sail, did not go straight down but sailed about, think they got their about 2 oclock, started from Hoods Bay between three & four, put up a sail coming round Shag point & the wind blowing in an opposite direction caught the sail. Price let it go, the water was coming in the boat & he jumped on the side, the boat capsized & threw them in the water. George Price got on the one end of the boat, and Matthews with his brother on his back other end, our three dear boys in the middle, the boat kept turning over, those at the end could keep on our boys had to swim every time because of the sail. They were hanging on for about two hours when Herbert & Charlie were both on the boat. Price was on the high part and when the water got to his neck he jumped up & Charlie was knocked off and the boat touched him. Jim tried to get him on but he had no strength and he sank, Herbert went a little farther and they saw him sink. Dear Charlie was telling them all to pray a great many times. Herbert they do not think spoke once. When the boat came along with some women an hour after they disappeared when they got the rest in the boat they fell to the bottom like logs & were taken to a vessel & put to bed for half an hour & then brought them to Havelock. It was about eight & Mother was wondering what had become of them and she asked Lily who was here with some girls to tea if he had a sail, she did not know, some were singing at the piano, some writing their names in the birthday book, when Ern rushed and said Herbert & Charlie were drowned.

Mother was like one out of her mind, it took Rose & I & Mr Pope to hold her, is better now. Price had been told never to take a sail & mother never thought to ask him about it.

Mother says they were murdered by Price, and when you come to think it was so as the only thing he did was to kick Matthews for calling for help, and to push his little brother off the boat & was rescued by Jim.

Jim did his best to try & save them, search parties have been out but nothing has been seen or heard of them, 14 boat were out & 50 men with drags were out yesterday. Left before 5 this morning with John & George Rutherford & others.

Price never said an encouraging word to them. Cannot write more, so must say Goodbye.

Nellie Rutherford.

Martha had been playing her Broadwood piano when Ern burst into the room blurting out that the boys had drowned. She never played that piano again.

Herbert at twelve years old was a quiet, retiring lad with fair hair and full blue eyes. The *best apple dumpling in the school* according to the school inspector. By contrast ten-year-old Charles was impulsive and joyous, a good singer, a dear little fellow with dark eyes and hair, devoted to his younger sisters and brother. While the accident was overwhelming them, little Charlie had said *"Let us all pray to God to help us. He is sure to send a boat to save us."* Instant swimming lessons would have been more to the point. Only George Price could swim and he would not leave the upturned hull.

Luckily Jim and the other four survivors, all in the last stages of exhaustion, had been saved by three ladies who happened to be rowing past on their way home. The bodies of Herbert and Charles were never found.

Poor Charles and Herbert, Gentleman Charlie and Herbert the girls called them for they were well mannered and would lay out their handkerchiefs for the girls to sit on. Their potential, like the infant Percy's, would never be realised. The local regard for the family and the boys showed in the closing comments of the Havelock correspondent to the *Marlborough Express* ··· *Mr and Mrs Rutherford are much respected and this sad affair has cast quite a gloom over the whole district, and the two deceased lads were very much liked by their schoolfellows.*

There were various aftermaths to this tragedy. Ern and Jim learnt to swim using a small bundle of dry flax-sticks until they could swim a mile, Ern developed an athletic prowess and Arthur became the spoilt baby of the family. Martha's nature changed. For a long time she was on the verge of a nervous breakdown. She lost weight and her cheery nature. Even her letters became cold and matter-of-fact. She never got over this tragedy. Any aspirations Nell may have had for further education were shattered. As the eldest daughter it was now her place to look after Martha and the family.

Two years later Charles Matthews was presented with a certificate of merit

In Loving Memory of
PERCY RUTHERFORD,
YOUNGEST AND BELOVED SON OF
JAMES AND MARTHA RUTHERFORD,
BORN AT FOXHILL, NELSON,
19th August, 1882,
DIED AT HAVELOCK MARLBOROUGH.
21st August, 1883,
AGED 12 MONTHS.

Blessed are the pure in heart; for they shall see God
MATT. v. 8.

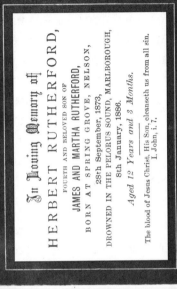

In Loving Memory of
HERBERT RUTHERFORD,
FOURTH AND BELOVED SON OF
JAMES AND MARTHA RUTHERFORD,
BORN AT SPRING GROVE, NELSON,
28th September, 1873,
DROWNED IN THE PELORUS SOUND, MARLBOROUGH,
8th January, 1886.

Aged 12 Years and 3 Months.

The blood of Jesus Christ, His Son, cleanseth us from all sin.
I. John, i. 7.

In Memoriam

In Loving Memory of
CHARLES WILLIAM RUTHERFORD,
FIFTH AND BELOVED SON OF
JAMES AND MARTHA RUTHERFORD,
BORN AT SPRING GROVE, NELSON,
14th January, 1875,
DROWNED IN THE PELORUS SOUND, MARLBOROUGH,
8th January, 1886.

Aged 10 Years and 11 Months.

Call upon Me in the day of trouble; and I will deliver thee,
and thou shalt glorify Me.—PSALM l. 15.

from the Royal Australasian Humane Society for having saved the life of his younger brother Fred by carrying him on his back throughout the ordeal.

George Price was of course shunned by the locals. Martha forbade the Rutherford children to play with the Price children. He stayed indoors a lot and all this preyed on his mind. He suffered periods of acute depression and started complaining to his parents that he was going out of his mind. On the 6th of April 1894, some eight years after the event, he solved his problems by taking a teaspoon of Rough-on-Rats, which is also rough on humans, and died the slow agonising death of arsenical poisoning. He is buried in the family plot in the Havelock town cemetery.

Suicide was a fairly common occurrence in those pre-social security times. Another suicide created more impact. A young master at Wellington College put the muzzle of his rifle in his mouth and painted the ceiling of his study with his brains.

> ⋯ *he is the latest victim to over-study, the latest sacrifice offered up to the Moloch of cram and over-work, whose chief embodiment in New Zealand is the system of Secondary Education* ⋯

thundered the subsequent editorial in the *Marlborough Express*. Meanwhile, back in Havelock, students were cramming for the examination which might yield for them a scholarship that would allow them a secondary education.

Civil Service Examinations

Following his failure to win a scholarship to Nelson College, Ernest had reviewed his options. He indicated an interest in a career in the Civil Service for which the Government held two National examinations. Anyone wishing to enter government service had first to pass the Junior Civil Service Examination. These examinations filled a real need as New Zealand's only national examinations, apart from the matriculation examination for those very few going on to university.

The Junior Examination had a minimum age limit of fifteen and consisted of four compulsory subjects, English (including dictation, reading, spelling, grammar and composition), Arithmetic (including vulgar and decimal fractions), History and Geography. Shorthand and Maori were optional subjects and seldom taken. The Senior Examination had three compulsory subjects – English, Arithmetic and Geography – and thirteen optional subjects – Latin, Greek, French, German, Italian, Maori, Plane Trigonometry, Algebra,

Geometry, Physical Science, History, Book-keeping and Shorthand. Candidates had to take at least three of the optional subjects, one of which had to be a language.

In the April 1884 examinations George Rutherford had passed the Senior Civil Service Examination, coming 8th of the twenty-one candidates. The optional subjects he took were Latin, Geography, History and Algebra. (The latter he failed). As only eight candidates throughout the country passed he was in by the skin of his teeth but it was still an impressive result for someone who not only was the eldest son of a large family but also held a full-time manual job. In 1886, still while working full-time and without the benefit of teachers, George sat and passed the University of New Zealand Matriculation Examination. Times were hard, the family finances not great and he was needed in the family business so there was no chance of George going to University to become a doctor. [George's bad luck didn't stop there. He proposed to Jessie Brownlee the day after she had promised her ill father she would never leave him. Her father held her to that promise and she remained single for life. She was highly regarded by the Rutherfords and remained a close friend of the family, especially Nell, with whom she corresponded in later life. She regularly inquired after George who was by then married to another. Nell's daughters called her Aunty Jessie.]

Two months after his fifteenth birthday, Ern followed in his brother's footsteps and sat the two-day Junior Civil Service Examination, signifying to the examiners that he wished to enter the Civil Service. Ern was the only candidate in Havelock and the local Postmaster supervised his examination.

When the results came out Ern had not done quite as well as George had before him, coming 15th of the 202 candidates who sat throughout New Zealand. [Five years later Jim Rutherford, then aged eighteen, took the same examination coming 25th of the seventy-eight people who passed.] Each paper was marked out of 600. Ern obtained 321 in English, 586 in arithmetic, 350 in history and 490 in geography. Arithmetic was his strong point but it should be borne in mind that six candidates received full marks in this paper. All but one of the candidates above him were at secondary schools and therefore taught by specialist teachers, a considerable advantage over the one teacher, good though he was, available to Ern. As cadetships arose, they were offered to the top candidates, though not necessarily in strict order of placing. A year after the examination the New Zealand Government invited Ernest Rutherford to join the Civil Service. The delay proved to be a blessing.

Marlborough Scholarship 1886

An accident of geography prevented 15-year-old Ernest from being limited to a career in the Civil Service. Candidates for the Education Board Scholarships to Nelson College had to be under the age of fifteen, except for the province of Marlborough where the limit was sixteen years. To gain this concession, Marlborough officials had argued that country children developed more slowly than children from large towns.

Of the sixteen Marlborough children who applied to sit the Marlborough Education Board Scholarship Examination in 1886, three were from Havelock; Ernest and Jim Rutherford and Charles Matthews, all of whom were sitting for the second time. With only one scholarship for all of Marlborough, Ernest had this one last chance. He was getting long in the tooth at fifteen years and three months – the second oldest of all seventy-six candidates sitting the various Nelson College Scholarships. Ern and Jim studied hard, rising each morning at 5 am.

The Havelock candidates sat the two-day examination, again supervised by Mr Lambert. At the end of the first day Mr Lambert wrote up his diary ··· *got there about 10 – found all prepared at new school room. Boys did fairly well especially Ernest Rutherford* ··· . During the examination Mr Lambert filled in time trying out the papers himself and checking his work against that of the candidates. When Mr Reynolds inquired how the examination was going Mr Lambert prophesied to him that *not only would Ernest Rutherford win the scholarship but would go on until he reached the top of the tree, for he could see difficulties were only made for Ernest to overcome* (or so he, 38 years later, recalled saying).

Now began the two week wait until results were announced and futures decided. A week after the examination the Postmaster (and telegraphist, etc.) walked past the Rutherfords' front gate and told Martha that Mr Reynolds had sent Ernest a telegram from Nelson, *Final results of scholarship examinations known next week. You are safe.* Indeed he was. Ern topped the Marlborough list, with Charles Matthews sixth and Jim ninth. (Jim beat Ern in Geography). Scoring 580 marks out of a possible 600, Ern had headed off the next candidate by only seven marks. Both obtained the full 200 marks for the arithmetic paper, 30 more than the next highest candidate. Ern topped English overall (130 marks out of 140), ranked 4th equal in geography (125 marks out of 130) and 8th in history (125 marks out of 130).

The second candidate, Edward Pasley, eight months younger than Ern, beat Ern in geography and history and they tied in maths. If Pasley had not crashed in English, Ern may have missed out yet again and may have ended up a civil servant, a flax miller or a primary schoolteacher. Pasley went on to three years at Nelson College and became a manufacturer's representative in Palmerston North.

The maximum marks allocated to each paper emphasised the importance of arithmetic. The examiner conceded the paper had difficulties

> ⋯ *such as could not be overcome by mere deftness of manipulation of figures, but which demanded for their solution considerable exercise of thought. ⋯ The general neatness and good arrangement of the figures, together with the clearness with which the several steps of each process were shown, deserved special commendation. ⋯*

This was no surprise at Havelock School where Ernest had a reputation for inventing methods and shortcuts for himself when solving mathematical problems, whereas his contemporaries followed stereotyped paths.

Marlborough had once more triumphed over Nelson, supplying the top seven of all seventy-six candidates. Even Jim was beaten by only three Nelson pupils, so once again the cry went up that Nelson children could get scholarships with marks vastly inferior to those of Marlborough children who missed out. [The Marlborough critics consistently and conveniently overlooked the difference in age limits. In 1888 members of the Nelson Education Board accused the Marlborough supervisor of cheating by opening the packet of exam papers ahead of time. This led to a court case with the Blenheim supervisor claiming he had to break the seals in order to extract the papers for those candidates sitting at Havelock. Nelson-Marlborough feuds continue to this day.]

However, there were the two Tinline Scholarships available for the first time. Mr Reynolds had entered Ern and Jim for these but Ern was not eligible, being over the age limit of fifteen. Therefore the Tinline Scholarships were awarded to the next highest Marlborough boy and girl, while Ern was awarded the Marlborough Scholarship.

There is no justice in this world. The Tinline Scholarship gave three years free board and tuition at Nelson College but the Marlborough Education Board Scholarship gave only two.

The Havelock School Committee praised both pupil and teacher.

> ⋯ *Mr J. H. Reynolds deserves great credit for his tuition and they congratulate him for having acquired the most enviable distinction through one of his pupils* [Laura Matthews] *winning the Marlborough*

Scholarship two years ago and another pupil winning the Marlborough Scholarship and passing the Junior Civil Service examinations so high on the list this year.

The Blenheim newspaper commented enviously, ··· *While we should be sorry to rob Havelock of a good teacher, it seems a pity that Mr Reynolds' services cannot be secured for a larger town.*

When school recommenced in January of 1887 the Havelock School Committee held a special ceremony to honour Ernest's achievements. They presented him with five volumes of 'The Peoples of the World' as a token of their appreciation of the industry and ability he displayed in his Civil Service and Marlborough Scholarship examinations. Ernest replied with a speech in which he thanked them for their kind gift, and especially thanked Mr Reynolds for his tuition and hoped one of his schoolmates would be successful and follow him next year. The school gave him three cheers and he was their hero for they were given the rest of the day off.

Ern was poised to join the rich and the elite. James Rutherford got out the sulky and he and Martha drove 15-year-old Ernest to Nelson College.

WINNER OF THE MARLBOROUGH SCHOLAR-SHIP.— Ernest Rutherford, the winner of the Marlborough Scholarship who so creditably passed the Junior Civil Service Examination, and who is at present at the Nelson College, has been offered a cadet-ship in the Government Service. As he has yet fifteen months to remain at College, and purposes going in for the Senior Examination next year, and also the Matriculation Examination, he has declined the offer. It is to be hoped that some better appreciation of his abilities will be possible at the end of his College career, as he is proving himself a credit to his late instructor, Mr Reynolds, the master of the Havelock School.

Chapter 3

EARNEST SCHOOLBOY

Nelson College 1887–1889

··· The student who ··· on any given subject can give one creation, one idea of his own, is and ought to be the crowing student of examinations, and moreover is the one who will help to fashion the age or the society he moves in. The most voluminous and accurate repeater of the knowledge of others, is like the fly, merely a thing to live and die.

Colonist 6 Jan 1880

Secondary School Education

In principle, the Education Act of 1877 ensured that all New Zealand children received a free education from age five to fifteen years, and compulsory education from seven to thirteen. In practice nearly half had left school by the age of thirteen. Fewer than one child in three remained until the sixth standard (average age fourteen years one month), and a mere one in fifty went on to secondary school.

Each large town had a secondary school. Most had been set up as centres of higher learning in the early days of the town and several had been planned in England when New Zealand cities were designed by land settlement companies before the actual site of the antipodean city was known. All were private, fee-paying, schools. Only relatively well-to-do families could afford to buy their children education after the age of fifteen. Scholarships were available but even these were often not enough. When Laura Matthews had to decline her Marlborough Scholarship to Nelson Girls' College the Blenheim newspapers sympathized with her and

> ··· *the difficulties that stand in the way of poor children taking advantage of the Nelson Scholarship which they have won by their intelligence and industry, At present the value of the scholarship is so small* [The scholarship paid full board plus tuition fees] *that only the children of parents who are well enough off to send them to college can avail themselves of it. But this is the case, more or less, all over the Colony, and furnishes the strongest argument against a penny of the public money being voted for such a purpose* ··· *as things are, the Nelson Scholarships are no benefit to the public at large, and ought to be abolished. The money thus saved is greatly wanted for elementary schools in Marlborough.* ···

[It should not be forgotten that Ernest Rutherford received a secondary school education because the Government of New Zealand gave, through the Marlborough Education Board, a £40 scholarship which covered board at Nelson College and the College contributed free tuition (£12 and 10 shillings).]

Times were tight for the Government as well as individuals. Parliament contemplated raising the school starting age from five to seven as one money-saving scheme. This move prompted an outcry over the expenditure for the education of the rich (secondary schools) at the expense of the poor (state schools). Though secondary schools were fee-paying the Government spent £37,000 on them in 1884, a sum of which the *Marlborough Express* said

> ··· *would have been far better applied to relieving the taxpayer of a portion of the heavy cost of primary education* ··· *the secondary schools are at present the happy hunting grounds of people who can well afford to pay for the education of their own children,* ··· .

Many, if not most, of the pupils at secondary schools were aged from ten to fifteen years and thus paying for much the same education as was available free at the state schools.

> ··· *We are aware of the desire that some people have to keep their children from mixing with the little ones of the 'lower orders'. It is a piece of snobbishness not peculiar to New Zealand, but it must not be any longer gratified at the public expense* ··· .

Secondary schools were however the only establishments offering advanced education below university level.

Nelson College before 1887

Nelson College serviced the northern half of the South Island, the nearest other secondary schools being Wellington College at the bottom of the North Island; and the Girls' High School, the Boys' High School and Christ's College in Christchurch to the south. (Rangiora High School, just north of Christchurch, was very small with just two teachers and twenty-two pupils of whom only nine were 15 to 18-year-olds.) Nelson College, like all colleges, mirrored the strong educational and religious principles of the early settlers. The

> *"… College is hereby founded for the advancement of religion and morality, and for the promotion of useful knowledge, creed not being admitted as a disqualification, either as regards teacher or pupils … ."*

The Deed of Foundation had been written a year before the Nelson College Act of 1858 formalized the College. Its roots were much earlier when the New Zealand Company had set aside money for this purpose but the collapse of the Company in 1845 had tied up these funds for a decade. They had finally been released after action by Dr Greenwood. (This was the same Dr Greenwood who had been Surgeon-Superintendent on the *Phoebe*, the ship the Rutherford family arrived on.)

In mid-1886 a new headmaster arrived. W J Ford M.A. (Cambridge) had been teaching for nine years at Marlborough College, a public school in England. [In New Zealand, schools which charge fees are called private schools. In England, schools which charge fees but are open to all are called public schools. The term 'state schools' was used for the Government-funded primary schools in New Zealand.] Every bit an English public-school master and classical scholar, he was also a very tall man with a black beard, a heavy smoker with a deep voice, an excellent teacher of English and the Classics, a singer of a lively song, a popular figure and an outstanding cricketer. He and two of his brothers had played for Cambridge. A terrific hitter, he once smashed three bats in as many overs, causing some spectators to shout, "Fetch him a tree!". He was a very safe fielder, usually at point, and a slow break (googlie) bowler. Mr Ford formed the backbone of the Nelson College cricket teams.

There always has been, and always will be, heated discussion over what children should be taught and how they should be taught. The primary school history syllabus had been attacked by *The Colonist*.

> *… What matters it to the mere child of the present, whether a certain pig-headed king lost his head, or his profligate buffoon of a son succeeded*

him? ⋯ If this baneful system of cramming is to be continued, it is to be hoped that some compassionating Babbage, [Charles Babbage invented the mechanical computer in the 1830s] *seizing the brilliant idea, will invent some machine that will grind out the answers ⋯ The student who ⋯ on any given subject can give one creation, one idea of his own, is and ought to be the crowing student of examinations, and moreover is the one who will help to fashion the age or the society he moves in. The most voluminous and accurate repeater of the knowledge of others, is like the fly, merely a thing to live and die.*

Mechanics Institutes had quickly spawned throughout the young colony to broaden the education of artisans but even by the 1880s technical education had barely penetrated the public education system.

⋯ the large majority of people are destined to toil with their hands, and for these the knowledge of some of the subjects now taught in the schools might well be bartered for a more thorough acquaintance with the particular branch of industry intended to be adopted for a means of livelihood. We are not advocating ignorance by any means. An elementary education is absolutely necessary, and with this and the broad knowledge gained by a course of general reading a man can take a stand far above those who merely filled their brains brimming full of the subjects taught in schools and colleges, and considering their education complete, have stopped there.

As a new headmaster of a few months standing, Mr Ford wished to change certain aspects of the school that were not in accord with the principles of the English 'public' school system. Henceforth, all boys were to wear school colours. Several cases of wilful dishonesty showed, he hoped, not a want of all sense of honour but the schoolboy notion that it is no breach of truthfulness and straightforwardness to deceive a master. With time, the establishment of a higher tone throughout the school would, he postulated, eradicate this attitude.

Nor was he happy with the teaching, except of mathematics. History, geography and English grammar consisted solely of facts force-fed to the pupils by him and his staff (⋯ *we are, at present, little more than crammers*). In Mr Ford's view, anything more uninteresting could hardly be conceived. The problem, he decided, was the strong link between class work and the Civil Service Examinations. In order to be free to teach English literature, classical history and more classical languages he severed the link and discouraged Nelson College boys from sitting the Civil Service Examinations. His views were expounded at the 1886 College prize-giving by the Mayor of Nelson who lambasted the Civil Service Examination system ⋯ *as encouraging a system of useless cram that was strangling real education throughout the colony*. Mr Ford hoped the Civil Service would adopt the University Matriculation Examination as its standard.

Mr Ford's brand of 'real' education now made Latin compulsory for all pupils whereas in the past only those going in for the Senior Civil Service Examination or on to university bothered to take it. Greek was to be introduced half way up the school at the fifth-form level. To encourage Latin he had used the big stick. For Greek he used a carrot: the Senior Classics Scholarship to be awarded only to a student studying Greek as well as Latin.

Now he needed pupils for the Greek class.

Ernest at Nelson College 1887

When James and Martha Rutherford arrived at Nelson they met Mr Ford who had a request to make to them.

"As your son Ernest has aired his Latin very freely in his examination will you allow him to learn Greek?"

"No" said James *"as he is not going in for theology."* Mr Ford persisted, asking them to treat it as a personal favour to himself. He explained that the Bishop of Nelson's son, who had been at the College since 1882, was down to learn Greek and if there is no competition there is no emulation. Finally James agreed. Ernest entered Nelson College as a boarder in the fifth form, as was appropriate for his age and qualifications, taking the subjects English, Latin, Greek, arithmetic and history (possibly also German or French).

James and Martha left Ernest to investigate his new companions, surrounds and mode of life. Nelson College had 80 pupils ranging in age from ten to twenty-one years. The younger boys were preparing for the same standard examinations as all children under fourteen or fifteen at state schools. The older boys were there for a variety of reasons. The six Wither boys, at their father's request, stayed ten years or so until each reached his 21st birthday. Others were studying for B.A. degrees for the University of New Zealand. (The University disaffiliated the College early in the year but it was quickly reinstated after the intervention of the local member of the House of Representatives.) Some of these young men were studying to sit for a scholarship to take them to University. One of these, Fred Gibbs, also landed a job as assistant master at the local state school so he quickly saw life from the other side. He confided to his diary, ⋯ *Slight row with Spencer in porch. Boxed his ears and had him caned.*

The day boys arrived by all manner of transport. They parked their pennyfarthing bicycles, horses, ponies and traps of all descriptions in the field behind the College. The train boys, those arriving from the Waimea area by the one daily train, had no stop near the College but the driver conveniently slowed down so they could jump off. At the top of the pecking order were the twenty-five boarders who lived in the College.

In contrast to the two-room school at Havelock, Nelson College was palatial. Designed as a mini-Eton by an ex-Etonian architect, it was a wooden two-storied building overlooking the city. The front and side wings formed the main block. Behind the loggia along the front were two class rooms separated by an entrance hall, itself used as a class room for the junior (primary) class. The north-east wing contained the sixth-formers' room, staircase, library and large classroom where the school also assembled for morning prayers and for prize-givings. The north-west wing comprised the Headmaster's study, staircase, boarders' dining room and Matron's study. The upper floor comprised mainly boarders' dormitories with the masters' sitting room above the sixth-form room below.

Service buildings at the rear almost enclosed a quadrangle; kitchen, storeroom, dairy, flour and bread room, wood and coal shed, laundry, washhouse and the boarders' bathroom. In the courtyard a lean-to against the front two classrooms housed the gymnasium. The loggia looked out on to the terrace down to the playing field, a rough area sloping away to the hedge on Hampden Street. A level area thirty metres square provided the cricket pitch. When the boys were given the choice of arithmetic or stone picking on the field, arithmetic never won.

Four masters looked after the boys. The headmaster, Mr Ford, lived in the College to oversee the boarders. He taught classics, English and how to be a chap.

The backbone of the school for many years was its second master, William Still Littlejohn, M.A. (Aberdeen). Though slim, he was affectionately known to the boys as 'Porky', the lazy schoolboy's version of the French translation of Littlejohn's persistent query, why? why? why? (pourquoi). William Littlejohn had arrived in New Zealand, as a newly qualified teacher following his family, who had established the business of Littlejohn, Watchmakers, in Wellington. Though a classics graduate, having originally intended to go into the church, he taught mathematics and some elementary science. The boys had a great respect for the slim, ruddy-whiskered young Scot, both academically and socially. A tremendously hard worker, he did not confine his interest in the boys to school hours. He coached cricket and rugby, playing for the College

Havelock 1909. Until 1888 the Rutherfords lived behind the tree marked R and facing the road to the wharf.
(Akersten, 1035 Havelock Museum)

Nelson College 1888. Mr Ford (headmaster) at right. Ern is standing in the third row 9th from left.
(Tyree T 8x10 24, Nelson Provincial Museum)

Nelson College 1889. Mr Joynt (headmaster) at left. Any rugby team chosen from this group would include as a forward Ern, the head boy, standing 5th from left. This photograph illustrates how few boys in the provinces of Nelson, Marlborough and the West Coast received a secondary education. (Tyree 1278, 10x8 123 ATL)

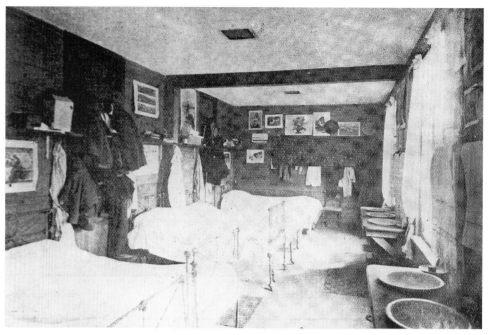

Nelson College, boarders' accommodation 1895.
(Brusewitz in NZ Graphic 2/11/95 p541 C10,344 Auckland Institute and Museum)

Nelson College rugby team 1890, with 'Porky' Littlejohn at back right and Jim Rutherford standing 2nd left. (Tyree, T57 Nelson Provincial Museum)

in both. In the latter sport he had played for Aberdeen University and may have been under consideration for the Scotland team. With a quizzical glance or a humorous remark, this strict disciplinarian would reduce any unruly boy to instant order. The Nelson College Cadet Force under Captain Littlejohn had a reputation as one of the best drilled volunteer units in the country.

The third master was A P Bennett B.A., the tall, athletic, modern languages teacher, late of Blackheath College, London. Like Ford and Littlejohn he entered fully into the academic and sporting life of the school. As a fast and accurate bowler he was a valuable member of the college cricket team. He also played rugby.

The fourth master, a German national, Carl Harling, taught modern languages and the junior (primary) class. His hobby was gardening. A very fine gymnast, he had responsibility for all gymnastic work. He was a lovable character but not a very strict disciplinarian.

Miss Bell, the lady Matron, looked after the boarders and Sergeant Major Nixon drilled the cadets. Part-time tutors in dancing and drawing, and sundry cooks and servants completed the establishment.

Ernest Rutherford settled in to the life of a boarder along with twenty-four others. Sparse bedrooms became home. Each long dormitory held four beds with no facilities apart from washing bowls. The outside washhouse served equally well for the ceremonial ducking of the new boarders and the venue of the odd well-advertised knuckle fight, one of these affrays reputedly running between school hours for three days with neither boy yielding. The boarders were not allowed upstairs during the day nor to leave the school grounds without permission. But boys will be men. One lad the previous year had obtained permission to visit his uncle for a few hours one evening. He spent the time boozing and playing billiards in a hotel at the port, returning to give a loud description of his adventures in very unseemly language.

The daily routine started with the ringing bell at 6.30 on summer mornings. Half an hour to dress, breakfast at 8. The school bell again called the whole school to assembly and morning prayers in the large classroom, the bell-ringer carefully keeping it going until Mr Littlejohn arrived on the trot from his house five minutes away. School hours were 9 to noon and 2 to 4 p.m. divided into one hour periods, with half-holidays on Wednesdays and Saturdays. Lunch was at one. After school, impromptu cricket games would often be played. Occasionally swimming expeditions to a hole in the Maitai River were arranged. Following tea at six, the boarders settled down to prep (homework). For the younger boys, evening prayers were read at 9 p.m. after which they had ten minutes to undress before the candles were removed for the night.

Ern, following the earlier example of his brother George, volunteered for the Nelson College Cadet Corps. With their blue frock-coats, Glengarry caps, Snider artillery carbines and brown leather belts, the Corps was a fine body of boys whose bearing and training put many volunteer units to shame. When the senior cadets travelled to New Plymouth for the Easter encampment of volunteer units, they won the bayonet exercise tournament, and were described in the report to the Minister of Defence as a unit as nearly perfect as it is possible to conceive. No small praise indeed and a tribute to the efficient, hard-working Mr Littlejohn, his lieutenants and the local instructor. For the new recruits, cadet life consisted of regular drill sessions with long courses of aiming and position drill preceding the few rifle-firing practices. At the final monthly "Battalion Parade", bayonet and sword competitions were held.

Academically, Ern mapped out his course. He declined the eventual offer of a cadetship in the Civil Service as he still had fifteen months of scholarship support at College. The *Marlborough Express* endorsed his decision ⋯ *It is to be hoped that some better appreciation of his ability will be possible at the end of his College career.* There were no Civil Service Examinations in 1887. Changes were underway, from the previous twice-yearly examination in April and October to once a year in January. Ernest aimed to sit both the Senior Civil Service Examination and the Matriculation examination for entrance to the University of New Zealand at the end of his second year at Nelson College. He could not have been aware that the college now discouraged boys from sitting the Civil Service Examinations. In the previous two years six Nelson College boys had passed the Senior Examination, but in the following two years none appeared on the lists.

Of more immediate interest were the end-of-year school examinations. Ernest's Marlborough Scholarship covered board and fees but not the other expenses of attending secondary school. Tied in with the school examinations were various scholarships and monetary prizes designed to help the best scholars stay on. At the College prize giving at the end of the year a hush descended in the large classroom as the first examiner rose to read his report. He

> ⋯ *recommended Rutherford for the first classical scholarship* [available to boys under seventeen] *whose answering distanced competition, except in Greek in which Broad was slightly superior. Preponderance was given to Latin, in which the examination embraced three Latin authors (Cicero, Horace and Virgil), as well as Roman History.*

In mathematics the prize went to Neve who easily led the whole mathematical course though he had been beaten in trigonometry and arithmetic by Rutherford. In the senior English scholarship Ern came fourth. The Principal had offered special prizes for boys who would read authors such as Dickens, Thackeray and Scott ⋯ *in the hope that by nibbling around so very tasty a cake they might acquire a healthy appetite for such kind of reading.* The first of these three prizes went to Ern. So too did one of the College's most prestigious scholarships, the Stafford History Scholarship, open to all boys over fifteen years, and worth £20 a year for three years.

With this and the Senior Classical Scholarship of £20 for one year added to his Marlborough Scholarship, and which had one more year to run, Ern was elated. He telegraphed home *Won Stafford and Senior Classical Scholarships. Short of funds coming home tomorrow.* The telegram arrived too late. James and Martha were already driving through the Rai Valley to fetch him home to Havelock.

Havelock 1887

The year had started bleakly for the railway-sleeper sawmilling industry in the Pelorus Sounds because the Railways Department could get cheaper sleepers from other areas. The Marlborough Land Board reduced its tax on each sleeper cut to one penny per sleeper but this did not compensate for the reduction in price offered by the Railways Department for sawn sleepers. The sawyers had to accept the lower prices as preferable to complete cessation of activity. Close on the heels of this blow, the mill owners were informed that the Government would take only 100 sleepers a week from any one sawmill. Even the small Rutherford mill could produce this amount in two good days.

The site of James' mill at this time is not known for certain as the Government had stopped the small mills in the Kaituna Valley. Presumably it was now at the Wakamarina as the Brownlee tramway had reached there and James was using this tramway. James and George had an old wharf on the Pelorus river from which they loaded their sleepers onto punts. James, while unloading chaff from Havelock, stepped on the end of a loose decking plank. He fell forward across one of the stringers of the wharf tramway breaking five ribs, three on one side and two on the other.

James had just recovered from this calamity when the Government sprang another on him. Overnight, they stopped purchasing sleepers from the Pelorus Sounds. The results were catastrophic for the area. A great many people were thrown out of work. The small mill-owners had two or three weeks worth of sleepers on hand but the Government would not take even these.

For James and George Rutherford, sawmilling ended.

The only bright spot for the Rutherford family at the end of the year were the academic successes of the boys, Ern's at Nelson College and Jim's at Havelock School. Once more Jim had entered for the Marlborough Scholarship, this time with better results. He came second equal of the 70 candidates for all categories of Scholarships to Nelson College. Unfortunately the candidate above him was also a Marlborough boy and Jim was too old to be eligible for a Tinline Scholarship. The lack of a scholarship, the poor state of the family finances and the pending family uprooting, prevented Jim from moving on to Nelson College. (Jim worked for his father for two years, saving £38. In 1890 he went to Nelson College for one year, passing the Junior Civil Service Examination at 25th place and the University of New Zealand matriculation examination.)

Ironically, the demise of the Pelorus sleeper industry coincided with the decision of American farmers to use string instead of wire for wrapping hay bales produced by their harvesters. Furthermore, sisal and manila were in short supply because of epidemics amongst the workers in the tropical countries where these crops grew. With New Zealand flax being suitable for binder twine, prices and production started rising.

The Pelorus Valley had little flax left. Besides, Havelock had cost the Rutherfords three sons. James' brother, John Rutherford, had opened up a new flax-mill amongst the extensive flax areas of the lower North Island so James went exploring. He crossed to Wellington to search for an extensive area of flax for himself. John Rutherford's new mill, run by a manager, was at Foxton and Martha Rutherford's relatives, the Shuttleworths, were general merchants and flax buyers in New Plymouth. By coach and saddle horse James explored the coast between. His saddle caused an abscess at the base of his spine, which put him in hospital at New Plymouth. But he had chosen a site.

James quickly returned to Havelock and packed up. On the 30th of January 1888 the little coastal steamer S.S. *Murray* left the wharf at Havelock. James had chartered her but it was George who drew the £80 from his Post Office account to pay the captain. On board were the flax mill, engine, waggons, household furniture, three Havelock boys, three horses, 800 black birch sleepers (for fence posts) and the family, – everything the Rutherfords had in the world. Both George and Jim reminisced that Ern was not on board yet the shipping notices list a Master Rutherford on her upon arrival back in Nelson (via Wanganui and Wellington), the day after Nelson College reopened.

Nelson College 1888

Ern returned to College in the sixth form to prepare for the end of year University (Matriculation) examinations. The College year comprised four quarters separated by the summer holidays, two short (one week) breaks and a longer (one month) break in mid-winter. At the end of the first quarter school reports were issued. Ern topped all his subjects: classics and English (fourteen boys), mathematics (six) and French (fifteen). *Satisfactory in every way* ⋯ the Headmaster summed up. For mathematics Mr Littlejohn was more expansive, ⋯ *Has been most conscientious. Shows very good ability* ⋯ .

The short holidays from Nelson College were spent with the many relatives close to Nelson: uncle John Rutherford, the miller at Hope; uncle George Rutherford, the wheelwright at Brightwater; grandmother Jeffries at Spring Grove and uncle John Thompson, the farmer and contractor, at Foxhill. All were just a short train ride away. The Thompsons were special favourites, partly because this took Ern back to the area where he and Jim had such fun as young boys. Besides, his aunt Mary made bread the way he liked it, with plenty of holes in it for butter and honey. Ernest is remembered as a tall, fair-headed boy who took after his mother's people in looks. The mechanical ability obtained from his father showed in the wooden potato masher he made for his grandmother. [Ted Jeffries gave it to Ernest Marsden who gave it to the Royal Society of London].

On holidays at the John Rutherfords', Ernest was recalled as a studious lad. He was also recalled with gratitude as talking uncle John out of taking cousin John's horse to make up a team.

During the second quarter of the year there were severe upheavals amongst the staff of Nelson College. The third Master, Mr Bennett, had resigned at the end of 1887 to go to Cambridge University and then to the British Diplomatic Service in which he served with distinction, being awarded the C.M.G. The Board of Governors declined to appoint the person whom the Headmaster recommended as a replacement. Instead they asked Mr Ford if the school could be run with just three masters, bearing in mind the small number of pupils. Times were tough. Fewer people were sending their children to secondary school and the College roll had dropped by 20 or 30 pupils since the early 1880s to around 80.

To reduce the teaching staff to a balanced threesome, the fourth Master, Mr Harling, was given notice (he went to Christ's College, Christchurch); and Mr E F W Cooke was engaged as third Master. He became much liked by his pupils. Although not of the highest academic standard, he taught in a friendly and helpful fashion and thereby extracted the most from his boys. They respected him for his integrity of character and kindness of heart. As third Master, he lived in, being responsible for the boarders.

Further economies were introduced. The Board recommended disconnecting the telephone unless Mr Ford paid half. They cut his £600 salary by £100 but offered a bonus of £2 for each boy on the roll over and above 80. (Mr Littlejohn's lesser salary was also reduced by £75 with a £1 per head bonus added.) Mr Ford had recently married and insisted on his right to live now outside the College. The Board of Governors thought otherwise and insisted the Headmaster must reside in College where he was charged for board, lodging and use of the College servants.

Mr Ford resigned. As six months notice was necessary he would be Headmaster until the end of the year. (Actually he stayed on into the following year.) The boys were never told details of these events, just that Mr Ford was leaving for 'financial reasons'. Luckily for the senior boys he was there to help with their preparations for the end of the year school examinations and higher examinations.

Mr Littlejohn gave extra instruction out of school hours to the senior boys sitting special examinations. He extended the offer to Ernest Rutherford, who, with others, was studying for the University Matriculation (Entrance) and University Junior Scholarship examinations. From then on Ern regularly went to Mr Littlejohn's house after dinner for this extra tuition in mathematics and science. Often he would arrive to find Porky still playing with his young children on the sitting-room floor. The children would be ushered out and the session would begin with Mr coaching Ernest and Mrs sewing by the fire or taking care of some of her husband's school administration.

Ernest thoroughly enjoyed Mr Littlejohn's teaching in mathematics but was not so attracted by science since Mr Littlejohn himself was learning as he went. [In 1890 Mr Littlejohn was appointed science teacher to both the Boys' and Girls' Colleges. Dressed in frock coat and semi-dress bell-topper, he would walk from one to the other, hanging up his hat as he arrived. Many a love-note was transported between the colleges hidden in the lining of that hat.] The small chemical laboratory, a converted boot shed and bathhouse, could hold a few boys at a pinch. Ern attended this laboratory, later recalling an example of the habit of instant obedience in the boys under Mr Littlejohn. A boy had taken a chemical reagent bottle, which he did not need to use, from the shelf. At the casual request "Drop it", meaning replace it, the boy at once let the bottle fall from his hand to the floor. Ern, aware that Porky did not have the same knowledge of science that he had of mathematics, never studied chemistry

[PRIVATE.]

Nelson College.

Name _Rutherford_

Report for Quarter ending _Dec. 17. 1888_

SUBJECTS.	NO. OF FORM OR DIVISION.	NUMBER OF BOYS.	PLACE IN CLASS.	REMARKS.
CLASSICS	VI	14	1	Has worked, as usual well: I am a little afraid that he has got "stale", & may not do himself full justice in the J.S. examination
ENGLISH SUBJECTS	VI	14		
MATHEMATICS ...	A₁	9	1	He has overhauled the work in shorter time than any boy I ever had. The only fear is that he may not have quite assimilated all of it.
MODERN LANGUAGES	B⁺ / Iᵃ⁺	14	1	Has the making of a good French scholar: his foundation in grammar is capital, & his composition is very promising.
SCIENCE				

GENERAL REMARKS—

E. I can say nothing new about him: he is top in every form. His conduct is irreproachable.

The next Quarter will begin on _Feb. 2_ , when a punctual attendance is requested.

seriously at Nelson College, particularly as it was merely an alternative to French. With Mr Harling's departure German had been replaced by chemistry and this was the first year it had been taught as part of the curriculum rather than as an extra. However some boys learned sufficient chemistry to prompt the boarders among them to carry out experiments in the dormitories, thereby terrorizing the uninitiated.

Mr Littlejohn taught some physics (mechanics, light and sound) as part of the mathematics course. The school also had physical apparatus for studying electricity and magnetism.

At the end of the year prize-giving the boys' efforts, or lack thereof, were rewarded. For the first time the staff were the examiners. Each stepped forward in turn to read his report. Mr Ford ⋯ *For the Senior Literature Scholarship I recommend Rutherford.* Mr Littlejohn ⋯ *Papers were set in Arithmetic, Algebra, Euclid, Trigonometry, Mechanics and Light and Sound. In division A the work done includes what is required by the University of New Zealand for the B.A. degree, for Junior Scholarships and for Matriculation. The following are the best:– Rutherford, Neve, Mules.* ⋯ Mr Cooke, the modern language teacher stepped forward. *As deserving of special notice for his excellent work, I make mention of Rutherford, whom I recommend for the French Scholarship. Neve, too, deserves honorable mention.*

Ernest's school reports carried qualifications. Mr Ford wrote *Has worked as usual well : I am a little afraid that he has got 'stale' and may not do himself full justice in the Junior Scholarship examination.* For Mathematics Mr Littlejohn stated *He has overhauled the work in shorter time than any boy I ever had. The only fear is that he may not have quite assimilated all of it.* Mr Cooke contributed *Has the making of a good French scholar: his foundation in grammar is capital and his composition is very promising.* Mr Ford, as Headmaster, summed up *I can say nothing new about him: he is top in every form and his conduct is irreproachable.*

Book prizes presented to Ern included Kingsley's *Hereward the Wake* for Mathematics and *Fifteen Decisive Battles of the World* for Classics.

Financially Ern was well set up to return to Nelson College the next year but hoped it would not be necessary. Were he to be successful in the Junior National Scholarship Examination he could afford to go on to University. With these thoughts in his mind he sat the University of New Zealand Scholarship examinations then boarded the steamer for New Plymouth and his new home.

Taranaki

When James Rutherford had ridden along the coastland towards Taranaki he ignored advice not to go beyond Opunake as ⋯ *the land was no good and there was no flax*. This advice was given either ignorantly but well-intentioned or un-ignorantly and mal-intentioned. James found what he had been looking for further north, at Cape Egmont where the tail of the large dormant volcano flowed into the sea. Between the rounded volcanic lahars (hillocks) the coastal swamps were seas of flax. Mountain streams draining the bush clad slopes of Mount Egmont (Taranaki to Maori) would provide the large quantities of water required by the flax industry. Flax was by no means a new industry in Taranaki. Martha's relatives (the Shuttleworth Bros.) for example had been shipping flax since before New Plymouth had wharves. In 1869 seven flax-mills were at work including two at Opunake. The Cape Egmont area however had only recently been opened up to settlers. The reason was tied up with the noteworthy Maori settlement at Parihaka.

The Taranaki wars of the 1860s saw armies of up to twenty-five hundred men marching and sometimes fighting on Taranaki soil. The cause had been the perennial problem of land, the settlers wanting more but most Maori refusing to sell. In 1863 the Government unjustly confiscated from the Maori all of Taranaki except the uninhabited hinterland. Again the Maori resisted the land surveys and again the militia attacked.

One of those who sought to stop the slaughter without surrendering the land was Edward Te Whiti of Warea. The prosperous Maori flour-mill and settlement at Warea had been on the receiving end of a naval bombardment in the first days of the war and then destroyed by an army from New Plymouth. In a clearing in the bush on the banks of the Waitotoroa river, in view of mountain and sea, Te Whiti built a village of peace. This village, Parihaka, became one of New Zealand's most remarkable settlements in the 1870s.

Te Whiti-o-Rongomai was a prophet preaching passive resistance; not conceding the land confiscation but appreciating that armed resistance would lead to their annihilation. He always distinguished between individual Europeans, and the Government and its agents. Most were welcomed with dignity, courtesy and generous hospitality unless they refused to agree that the Maori had a legitimate grievance. In 1879 teams of Parihaka Maori started ploughing land in the confiscated area. This land, some less than ten kilometres from New Plymouth, had been farmed by settlers since the war. As one team of Maori ploughmen was arrested another took its place. Two hundred Maori were in jail before a truce was declared so that the legality of the land confiscation could be tested in the Supreme Court. To avoid this taking place the Government set up a Royal Commission and introduced the West Coast Settlement Act of 1880 which, amongst other things, made it an offence for anyone to disturb surveying, farming, road building, etc., taking place on the confiscated lands. The road and telegraph were being pushed through the Cape area just below the bush line. Te Whiti's response was for Parihaka men to replace fences across the road to keep animals away from crops. The armed constabulary based at the Pungarehu blockhouse broke down the fences: the stoic Maoris rebuilt them. As men were arrested others took their place, then old men and boys, then young children. This resulted in the men receiving two years hard-labour while the constabulary were ordered to provide slip rails wherever a fence crossed a road.

In June of 1881 the Government sold 753 acres of the Parihaka block for a little over £2 10 shillings an acre. The Maori continued farming the sold land as well as the part of the block the Government had 'generously' awarded them. For many settlers only a war would solve the problem once and for all. Te Whiti's strong influence however prevented any Maori retaliation that would have sparked such a war. But he could not stop the scaremongering which raised the fear of war.

The Government called up thirty-three Volunteer companies from Nelson in the south to Thames in the north for special service in Taranaki. (The Nelson College Cadets were not called out but many cadets unsuccessfully volunteered to go.) At the end of October 1881 an army of volunteers, armed constabulary and militia, some 2,500 men strong, assembled on the plains at Rahotu. There they drilled, as some hardly knew how to load their rifle. On the 5th of November 1881 the troops mustered and advanced through Parihaka's first line of defence, two hundred small children who were singing and playing tops. Te Whiti and two others were arrested. His followers were dispersed. As the Courts questioned the legality of the Parihaka expedition the Government introduced the West Coast Peace Preservation Bill which allowed it to keep Te Whiti and the others in exile in the South Island.

Te Whiti afterwards returned to Parihaka. One ready source of income for his people involved the gathering of fungi to sell to a Chinese merchant who sent it to China, where it fetched a high price as a food fashionable among epicures. By the end of 1884 several dairy farms were in operation between Parihaka and the Cape. Farmer and McReynold's store and bakery at Pungarehu turned out 400 loaves a day, with more being brought in from Opunake to satisfy the demand from Maori. In July of 1886 Te Whiti was once again arrested and imprisoned for some months before returning once

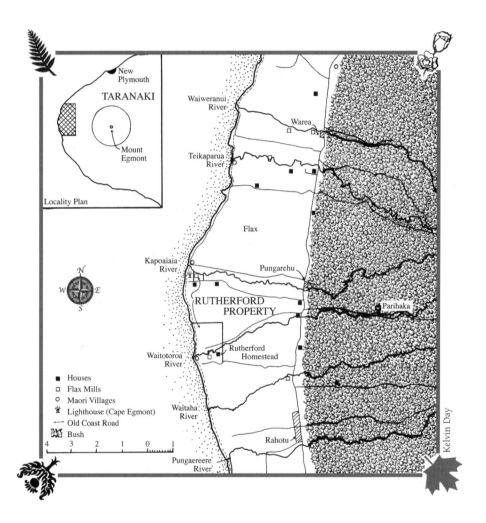

more to Parihaka. By 1887 the land was firmly in Pakeha hands. Increasing numbers of settlers were starting to alter the face of the lower slope of the Parihaka block.

Pungarehu

James Rutherford, his family, flax mill and chattels arrived at New Plymouth on the 1st of February 1888 after a rough passage. George was never so sick in his life. James, after two days of organising his affairs in town, left with George and Jim for Tipoka on the coast near Pungarehu and Parihaka. There they built a hut of two small rooms and a cookhouse and quickly set up the steam-driven flax mill. Within two months it was working day and night producing six tons of dressed flax a week with a profit margin of £10 per ton. The factory employed twenty hands with others on contract: cutting flax, supplying rata firewood and carting the flax to New Plymouth. The cartage contract was for two years, emphasising James' optimism in the industry even though several other mills were opening in the general area. Four months after James Rutherford's arrival, the *Taranaki Herald* could report ⋯ *There is a great boom in the flax industry on the Coast since Mr Rutherford came over from Blenheim and started a factory down near Rahotu.*

Flax milling became a main source of employment in the district and a major source of income for local Maori. Similarly it provided ready cash for settlers who were converting swampland into dairying land.

Ernest's longer vacations, midwinter 1888 and the following summer, were spent working at the mill where his mathematical ability was put to good use by helping his father take the levels when constructing a large pond for soaking the stripped flax. A small diversion channel upstream fed the pond. The outlet water falling back to the stream now drove a turbine which powered the mill. No longer need James pay out fifteen shillings a cord for firewood nor run the steam engine. Ernest also worked around the mill, paddocking the soaked hanks of stripped flax.

George Rutherford was a keen shooter. In their spare time Ern and Jim also tried their hands at it. Their shotguns were poor specimens and their home-loaded ammunition seemed weak. One morning they went after pheasants but after they had fired off a packet of ammunition without scoring a feather, the spaniel with them gave up in disgust and made a beeline for home. What they needed, Ern and Jim decided, were sitting targets. Native pigeons. Some eight kilometres up a track into the bush were three miro trees to which the pigeons flocked in winter to feed on the berries. After a cold dawn start Ern and Jim rode their horses, ploughing through mud up to the horses' girths, to arrive at the trees as the sun rose. The pigeons flew in from all directions but their guns and ammunition still could not kill the birds who were all feeding high in the trees. Ern then suggested firing as they landed with their wings outstretched. This made all the difference, the wings no longer acting as a suit of armour. Twenty-three birds were taken.

Ern had learned boxing at Nelson College. He coaxed the younger Jim to put on gloves and then, before a crowd of mill hands, pasted him. (Before the next Nelson College vacation Jim took lessons from a mill hand but Ern got wind of this and did not challenge Jim again.)

On one outing Ernest went with his father to the Cape Egmont Lighthouse where James aimed to tender for the local flax and set up another mill. Martha, the girls and young Arthur remained in New Plymouth for some twenty months until a New Plymouth builder had constructed a substantial house for them near the Tipoka mill. In the meantime the girls had the advantages of town living, attending Miss Rose's school.

University Entrance Examinations 1888

Early in December the University of New Zealand held its entrance exams. At least five Nelson College boys sat the Matriculation examination. (Two went on to become surgeons.) Three others (Rutherford, Mules and Neve) opted for the more difficult Junior National Scholarship Examination which would help pay expenses as well as admitting a successful candidate to the University.

Late in the summer holidays the results were announced. The top ten candidates on the list received Junior Scholarships. A further thirty-one who obtained more than three-quarters of the total marks of the lowest successful candidate were deemed to have passed with credit. Ern was the only Nelson College boy on the list. However at number 26 he had missed out on a University Scholarship.

Ernest and his family now faced a decision. Though he had qualified to go on to University, finance loomed as a major problem. Without a scholarship his father would have to pay all expenses, but the family fortunes, though rising, were not good. The flax-mill made a useful profit but had been running for less than a year. Offset against this were the large expenses involved in purchasing the land and erecting the mill buildings. The Foxhill property had been sold but a fine new house was under construction near the mill. No, just now the family could not afford to support a son at University.

Ern did however have scholarship money available to attend Nelson College. The Marlborough Scholarship had run out but the Stafford Scholarship was good for two more years. The Modern Languages and the Senior Literature Scholarships were each worth twelve pounds ten shillings for one year. All in all they would pay his tuition fees and thirty-two pounds ten shillings of the fifty pounds needed for board. If he went back to Nelson College he had two options open. He could choose to matriculate (sign on, promising to obey the rules and regulations) to the University of New Zealand. In doing so he would nominate the College of the University with which he wished to be associated in order to study for, and sit, that particular College's first year examinations. This would give him one cheap year towards a three year B.A. degree. [Mules and Neve took this option. They were not on the passed-with-credit list but both did well enough to be awarded a pass in the Matriculation examination. Both matriculated to the Auckland University College but stayed on at Nelson College for another two and one year respectively. In the Auckland University College term's examination of 1889 both passed, with Mules obtaining first-class honours in pure mathematics. Nelson College was given a half holiday in their honour. Mules became a schoolmaster in England, gaining a B.A. and M.A. from Cambridge University. Neve went to Auckland gaining B.A., M.A., LL.B., and B.Sc. Initially a science teacher, he later practised law.] On the other hand, as Ern had not yet reached the age limit of nineteen, he could choose not to matriculate but to have another go for a Junior National Scholarship which guaranteed three years' financial support.

The latter option was chosen. Ern went back to Nelson College as a schoolboy.

Nelson College 1889

Ernest Rutherford returned to be head boy. The school roll had dropped to sixty-eight, of whom fifteen were boarders. More importantly the number of boys over the age of fifteen had halved to twenty-nine. The ranks were thin and not the least of Mr Littlejohn's worries now centred on how to field a passable rugby team. Only two forwards and two backs remained from the previous year's team, so most of the new squad were raw beginners. Being a tall lanky lad, Ern played in the forwards. [In later life Jim Rutherford reminisced that a game between two Taranaki teams containing barefoot Maoris had inspired him and Ern to take up football but as a Nelson College boy Ern would have seen many matches previously. After all, had not New Zealand rugby started in Nelson?]

The team was fitted out in a motley collection of banded jerseys; some new, some worn; some long sleeve, some sleeveless and some in-between. Long tight shorts reached below the knee; banded socks above the knee and ordinary street boots completed the uniform. All games were played in the Botanic Gardens or the Park.

The first match of the season brought a loss to the weak, inexperienced College team. Few of the forwards could control their feet and still fewer kept on the ball. Ern gained a mention as one of the five College forwards who played well enough, according to the reporter who wrote under the pseudonym of 'Pass'. (Actually Mr Littlejohn.) The team played once a fortnight against the three other teams of their standard. The second match saw an improvement and a further loss. ··· *What with a better knowledge of the rules, a decrease of adipose tissue, and an increase of experience and skill, the combatants fought a good fight,* ···· Once more Ern was one of four College forwards named. He was to be cited in six of the eight games that season. ··· *Rutherford by his fine following up and good tackling, being the best* (of the college forwards). ··· *Rutherford especially doing some good dribbling.* Unfortunately the team achieved a poor record of one win, one draw and six losses. None the less, under Mr Littlejohn's dictum of persistence, most, if not all, would have played their hearts out, for Porky taught by example.

They would have recalled his performance on the cricket field at the time when the then headmaster and well-known batsman Mr Ford, was visited by a friend from England who was obviously another first-class cricketer. A friendly match with these two opening degenerated into a competition to see who could score the most runs. When the boy bowlers were spent, it was Porky Littlejohn who left his wicket-keeping to take up the battle. For over an hour he tried every kind of bowling but to no avail. Ernest Rutherford, a spectator at the game, recalled in later life for Porky's biography

> ... *I never saw a better example of grit and persistence in an unequal contest. He refused to give in, and attacked with the light of battle in his eye ... The whole episode left on my mind an enduring impression of courage and resource under difficulties, and, though technically defeated, I thought he was the true hero of the occasion, notwithstanding the brilliant display of pyrotechnics by the batsman.*

Nelson College had a great influence on Ernest Rutherford's development. Later in life he still recalled many of his experiences, both pleasant and unpleasant. He had vivid memories of his life in the dormitories for on occasions he literally had to fight his way through them. Joining the school at the late age of fifteen probably shielded him from many of the unsavoury episodes usually inflicted on young new chums. [With the passage of time the memories of the unpleasant events fade while those of pleasant occasions grow. As he lay on his death bed he turned to his widow-to-be and emphasised *"I want to leave a hundred pounds to Nelson College. You can see to it. Remember, a hundred to Nelson College!"*] Much of that influence rested with Porky Littlejohn. His sincerity, his persistence, his hard work, his standard of values, his discipline, all had a marked effect on the lanky schoolboy. Ern did not shine at athletics or games. Many an afternoon after school, while most boys were playing cricket, master and boy would be seen strolling up and down the streets at the foot of the playing fields, Littlejohn, with stick in hand, obviously drawing diagrams in the roadway.

Porky also continued giving Ern individual tuition at night after dinner. Ern was lucky to receive this tuition in 1889. In appointing a new Headmaster to replace Mr Ford, the Governors had passed over young Mr Littlejohn (because he was a good Presbyterian in an Anglican College and town, said the Presbyterian minister with candour, if not bias). In February of 1889 Mr Littlejohn had applied for the position of Headmaster of Timaru Boys' High, but missed out there too.

The new Headmaster of Nelson College had been appointed from the beginning of 1889, but had applied for leave to return to England for the first few months of the year, during which time Mr Ford filled in for him. John William Joynt, a classical scholar with an excellent M.A. from Trinity College, Dublin, and an orator of note, had had no experience of school teaching. He had come to New Zealand in 1886 because his health had broken down. At Nelson College he encouraged every form of sport, playing in the College cricket team for over ten years. [J W Joynt became the Registrar of the University of New Zealand and later served as the University's representative in England.] Twenty years on, Mr Joynt described Rutherford the schoolboy as one who ··· *displayed some capacity for mathematics and physics but not to an abnormal degree. He was a keen footballer and a popular boy.*

At the start of 1889 the school year had been altered to three terms rather than the four quarters of previous years. The first term reports showed that Ern was not slacking even though basically repeating his previous year's work. *85 per cent. Working steadily and making progress. Has undoubted ability,* wrote Mr Littlejohn covering the advanced mathematics class. The new Headmaster had only been at the school a few days so he summed up in general terms *A very good boy from whom one may look for good results in the future.* [An appropriate political statement which has since been elevated to prophesy.] Ern topped each subject group but it should be borne in mind that each group consisted of nine or fewer boys. The same result followed in the second term reports. *An excellent boy in every way.*

During the longer August holiday Ern took the steamer to New Plymouth. At last the family was reunited at the new house at Pungarehu. There Ernest would report to them on the year to date; his term reports; how he had been promoted to Sergeant in the Cadet Corps and had done much drill, tent pitching, distance judging, lots more drill and some ambulance lectures.

Being the top pupil at Nelson College brought an irritating problem for Ern. As Dux, schoolboy logic dictated that his nickname would be 'Quacks'. He had no liking for this being used at home. Young Arthur, however, thought the nickname a huge joke. He would follow Ern at a safe distance making a proper nuisance of himself by quacking all the time. Ern could never catch him before Arthur reached the safety of his sisters, so Ern and Jim laid a trap. Ern led the quacking Arthur past Jim's hiding place. The ambush was sprung and retribution meted out by Ern before the girls could intervene. James Rutherford was annoyed that Ern and Jim had taken the law into their own hands but they escaped with just a talking to and the action had cured the problem.

Ern had a keen sense of humour and a hearty, infectious laugh. However his outstanding feature was his really extraordinary powers of concentration even under the most trying conditions. When immersed in the solution of some mathematical problem, no uproar in the prefects' room could disturb him. Some class-mates would take full advantage of his abstraction in various boyish ways such as banging him on the head with a book and then bolting for their lives.

The third term held the highlight of the year for the school, the visit of the Governor-General of New Zealand, Lord Onslow. Ernest Rutherford, as head boy, delivered a short address of welcome which had been written by Mr Joynt.

At the end-of-year school prize-giving, Ern picked up the prizes for sixth-form Latin and advanced mathematics as well as the Simmons Prize of £6. He received an honourable mention as top of sixth-form classics but the teacher cited the whole class in French. Optics had been studied as part of mathematics. *Rutherford was first, having proved himself as good a Mathematician as they had ever had.*

Ernest Rutherford left his mark at Nelson College, his name being inscribed in the record books as well as (reputedly) on a desk and a piece of scientific apparatus.

University Scholarship Examinations 1889

The spring term brought final preparation then, once again for Ernest, the University of New Zealand Junior Scholarship Examinations. Candidates sat five subjects from a list of eight. The relative worth of each subject in the eyes of the University is shown by the maximum marks allocated for each: Latin, mathematics (1500 marks); Greek, English, science (1000); history and geography, French, German (750).

Ernest sat in Latin, English, French, mathematics and science. The first three subjects consisted of the matriculation paper plus an additional paper on paraphrasing or translation as the case may be. Mathematics consisted of two papers; arithmetic and algebra, then Euclid and trigonometry. For science, two papers were to be chosen from six offered; inorganic chemistry, electricity, sound and light, heat, elementary mechanics of solids and fluids, botany. Ern once again chose sound and light and mechanics, the only science topics taught at Nelson College apart from chemistry.

On the 11th of January Ern had recorded his ownership on the fly leaf of Professor Everett's book *Sound and Light*, part four of Deschanel's series on *Natural Philosophy*. This was a university level book full of standard lecture demonstrations and illustrations of scientific apparatus, including Becquerel's phosphoroscope.

The standard required in the sound and light paper is illustrated by question 3.

> Show that the velocity of sound in air is not affected by variations of pressure, but that it is affected by variations of temperature.
>
> If the velocity in air be 360 metres per second, find the velocity at the same temperature in hydrogen gas, which is $14\frac{1}{2}$ times lighter than air.

The mechanics paper consisted mainly of problems involving static forces. Example:

> 7. The movable weight of a common steelyard is 4 ounces. A tradesman diminishes its weight by half an ounce; of how much is a person defrauded who buys what appears to weigh 8 lbs by this machine?

The paper consisted predominantly of applied mathematics, the examiner being the Professor of Mathematics at Canterbury College.

Now came the time of waiting for the results to be announced in the following January. Ern could not look forward to the outcome with confidence. No longer was he just competing against three or four good boys at Nelson College. Now he was up against the best New Zealand had to offer that year and only ten Junior Scholarships were available for the whole of the country.

Just as he was sitting for the second time, so were many who had done better than him in the previous year's examination. Obviously a Junior Scholarship could not be relied upon and other plans should be laid.

The control of the New Plymouth High School had just been transferred from the Taranaki Education Board to a Board of Governors. The school had an average attendance of just over forty, with slightly more girls than boys, but only eighteen pupils were over the age of fifteen. They were taught by a head teacher and a female assistant. Early in December the Board of Governors advertised for a second master capable of teaching physical science and practical drawing. Ern applied for the position and awaited the outcome.

By now James and George Rutherford were in partnership as Rutherford and Son, with three mills producing fourteen tons of dressed flax per week. (Within a thirty-two kilometre stretch along this coast nine mills employed around 500 men.) Flax prices were falling slightly but increased production aided the family fortunes. So much so that 18-year-old Jim could look forward to a year of secondary schooling at Nelson College.

In mid-January 1890 the Board of Governors of the New Plymouth High School selected their new master after much deliberation. The job went to Henry Kitchingman, a C2 classification teacher from the Wood End School near Christchurch. Mr Kitchingman was an undergraduate of the University of New Zealand who had passed part one of mathematics and physical science some years earlier in 1883. For the physical sciences he had failed one of the two papers but been awarded the topic as a whole. In the Canterbury College examinations the same year he had failed in mathematics. However, though academically not as good as Ern he was older and had teaching experience. [During a visit to the school in 1925 Sir Ernest Rutherford said he had applied for the position but later withdrew his application and went on to University. This version may or may not be correct.]

A week after this appointment the results of the Junior National Scholarship examinations were published with the top candidates to receive scholarships. Ern's percentage marks in each subject were Latin 54%, English 55%, French 72%, mathematics 78%, sound and light 66% and mechanics 76%. His marks were enough to place him a very creditable fourth on the scholarship list, his total being 3792 marks out of a possible 5750. The highest score was 4426 obtained by Willie Marris of Wanganui Collegiate. He sat in Greek, which was worth 250 more marks than the number allocated to French. Of the ten scholarship winners at least seven had sat and missed the previous year.

The details were incidental. Ern had his scholarship to University and the family fortunes were rising. Academia beckoned.

JUNIOR SCHOLARSHIPS

Year.	Name of Scholar.	Tuition.	Subjects.
1889	Marris, W. S. ..	Collegiate School, Wanganui	Latin, Greek, English, Mathematics, Electricity, Mechanics
,,	Pearce, E. H. ..	Girls' High School, Dunedin	Latin, English, French, Mathematics, Botany, Chemistry
,,	Buchanan, E. S.	Boys' High School, Ashburton; and Boys' High School, Christchurch	Latin, English, French, Mathematics, Heat, Chemistry
,,	Rutherford, E...	Public School, Havelock; and Nelson College	Latin, English, French, Mathematics, Sound and Light, Mechanics
,,	Macdonald, W. M.	Boys' High School, Dunedin	Latin, English, French, German, Mathematics
,,	Rainforth, E. ..	Girls' High School, Dunedin	Latin, English, French, Mathematics, Botany, Chemistry
,,	Sheard, Flo. ..	Girls' High School, Christchurch	Latin, English, French, Mathematics, Heat, Botany
,,	Connon, M. G.	Girls' High School, Christchurch	Latin, English, French, Mathematics, Heat, Botany
,,	Boyle, J. ..	Tuakau District School; Auckland College and Grammar School	Latin, English, French, Mathematics, Electricity, Botany
,,	Tebbs, B. N. ..	Auckland College and Grammar School	Latin, English, French, Mathematics, Electricity, Chemistry

Chapter 4

ACADEMIA

Canterbury College 1890

Rutherford is a student at Canterbury College, is working very hard, and is likely to win distinction.

Headmaster of Nelson College,

Recommending that Ern's Stafford Scholarship continue.

Christchurch

Christchurch was tail-end charlie of the planned settlements in New Zealand. Founded in 1850, it followed Wellington by a decade. The Canterbury Association in England envisaged a Church of England based settlement incorporating all the 'better' things of English life. The Association named its town-to-be from the suggestion of a member whose college at Oxford University had been Christ Church. It then proceeded to sell sections of land. In late 1848 surveyors were dispatched to find and survey a suitable site to be ready for settlers by 1850.

The surveyors inspected and rejected the Wairarapa Valley at the south end of the North Island. Too small, it lacked a harbour and held more Maori than could be ignored. As storms prevented a planned investigation of the south of the South Island the surveyors recommended a place that had already been rejected for the site of Nelson and also by the Free Church of

Scotland settlers – Port Cooper (now Lyttelton Harbour) on Banks Peninsula in the middle of the east coast of the South Island.

Over youthful geological time, shingle eroding from the uplifting alpine spine of this island fanned eastward out to sea until the land joined an off-shore volcanic cone. Christchurch owes its siting to several causes: the sea's breaching of the extinct volcanic cone thus forming a safe harbour; the forest fires, during the halcyon days of the Moa hunter period of Polynesian settlement, which turned forested plains into pastoral land; Te Pehi's contemptuous description of Moi Moi's facial tattoo that was a tiny link in the chain leading to Te Rauparaha's massacres of the local Ngai Tahu people in the 1830s. The overall result was a safe anchorage, extensive lands to sell to the wealthy and no native population worth worrying about. What more could a planned settlement wish for?

As befitting a Church of England clone, many streets were named after Bishoprics. Before the immigrants arrived, the surveyors first laid out the streets of the port, then of Christchurch. This explains why Lyttelton received high-class street names such as Canterbury, London, Oxford, Winchester etc. while Christchurch has the likes of Colombo, Armagh, Montreal, Antigua, Hereford and Worcester.

For the site of the town itself the mud-flats at the head of the harbour were ruled out as not having enough level land for the necessary number of suburban sections. Hence Christchurch was established on the plain north of the volcanic cone near where some early Scottish settlers had a farm. Here the river Orotare (Avon) wound through the swamp giving small boat access almost to the centre of the town. As a Student Review of the 1960s put it, depicting the first Canterbury Association settlers arriving dressed in the school uniforms of the posher schools, and carrying cricket bats or hockey sticks according to sex:

> "We shall found the city of Christchurch here!"
> "Why here?"
> "Because it's the only swamp for miles."

The low-lying nature of the land produced health problems but eventually with the laying of sewers and drilling of artesian wells, the town became one of the healthiest in the colony according to its biased city engineer.

By 1890 the population of Christchurch approached 50,000 people and 10,000 houses. The water supply was pure, the footpaths asphalted and the houses and streets lit by coal gas. Naturally a grand Anglican cathedral graced the centre of the city, its first tall spire surviving an earthquake or two. The weft and warp pattern of the streets deviated from a straight line grid only by

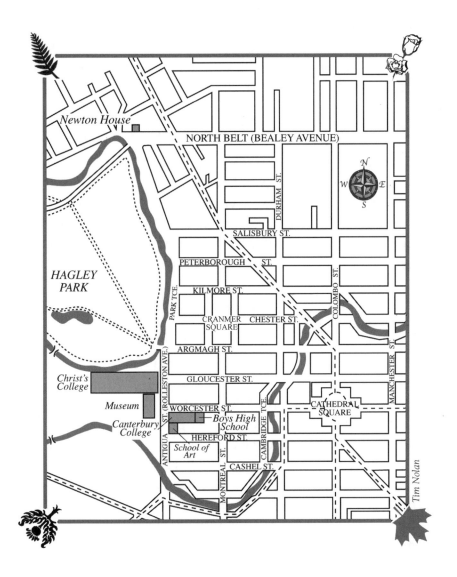

Tim Nolan

the meandering Avon river and a couple of roads going to places now extinct. A railway line (with tunnel) linked town to port whence fast steamers connected Christchurch to the world.

With two morning, two evening and two weekly newspapers, Christchurch seemed a veritable metropolis compared to Nelson. It also boasted a college on a higher plane than a secondary school.

Canterbury College

Canterbury College had been vaguely conceived by the Canterbury Association, in its formative days in England, to be the Oxford or Cambridge University of the south. There were visions of attracting students from India and Australia. In reality, higher education was initially taken care of by the private (fee-paying) high school, Christ's College, higher education naturally being reserved for boys only. As New Zealand boomed in the early seventies, so did advanced education. Otago, the Scottish-settled and gold-bearing province, founded the University of Otago in 1869. In the following year the University of New Zealand came into being as merely an examining body overseeing the work of the affiliated colleges. The University of Otago affiliated, as did the Collegiate Union in Christchurch, the latter being the forerunner of Canterbury College which came into existence, in name only, in 1873. Canterbury College started formal classes in the Trinity (2nd) term of 1874 before it had any professors. It is to the young town's credit that women were admitted with equal status from the start.

As appropriate for a new colony and an agricultural province with gold fields nearby, the academic staff members sought for Canterbury College were to be firstly a chemist followed by a geologist, a biologist, a mathematician and then one person to look after classics, history and English literature. The chemist arrived in 1874 to no students and no buildings. But the place quickly grew.

The Staff

By 1890 some 150 students aiming to sit University of New Zealand exams, and the same number of part-timers (teachers, skilled mechanics, educated citizenry etc.), were looked after, principally by the five professors.

Alexander Bickerton, professor of chemistry, was an unconventional academic. The son of a builder's clerk, he retained for life the lessons from his schooldays – an abhorrence of learning by rote, a dislike for classical education and a fair inability to spell correctly. At school he had been a failure, one teacher praising him as *not a complete idiot*. Professor Bickerton later attributed this failure to his lack of verbal memory, no other faculty being used at school. After various employments connected with engineering he established a factory in the English Cotswolds, working wood with machinery of his own invention. When twenty-one-years old he attended night classes in science and took to the subject like a flea to a warm dog. So successful was he that his teacher encouraged him to start up his own classes in Birmingham. In 1867 he won a Royal Exhibition Scholarship, (funded from the profits of the 1851 Exhibition), to the Royal School of Mines in London (now Imperial College), winning one National Silver Medal, two Bronzes, six first class Queen's Prizes, seven second class and four third class Prizes. The subjects ranged widely, including applied mechanics, economic botany, electricity and magnetism, animal physiology and geology showing the breadth of his interests. Leaving his Birmingham classes in the hands of his most able artisan students he shifted to London.

During his three years at the Royal School of Mines he studied many scientific subjects. More importantly he overcame opposition to start up night classes in science, all previous attempts in London having failed. His first, well-advertised, lecture drew an audience of one. Undeterred, Alexander Bickerton attended services by noted preachers to learn their techniques for attracting large audiences. He discovered that to instruct a Londoner the lecture must be made as entertaining as a music hall and as sensational as a circus, a maxim he embraced for life.

Several of his lectures at the Royal School of Mines used spectacular demonstrations to illustrate points in class. He realised that explosions and loud bangs were most effective in keeping students awake, in retaining their interest, and in increasing attendance. To this end he studied every available explosive reaction and in the process gained himself the nick-name of 'Fireworks' in the College of Chemistry. The tactics worked. The audiences outstripped space in the Chelsea schoolroom so he took over a disused factory. Night after night the tradesmen in the class laboured at no charge to convert the factory into a modern science lecture room and laboratory.

By 1869–70, his final year at the Royal School of Mines, Alexander Bickerton had found his niche in life. Academically very successful in science and a noted organizer, he had developed into a superb public lecturer bringing science to the populace. Five schools scattered about London were under his wing. One or two of his College fellows tried to help him in his classes but they looked on science as a serious matter and could not stand the heckling of the witty artisan students. In contrast Bickerton thrived on the banter, regarding it as a mental boxing match with himself as instructor. Unfortunately government inspectors also regarded education as a serious business. The virulent official opposition to his methods caused him to give up his large London classes as soon as he completed his studies at the Royal School of Mines. Once more his classes were handed over to his most able students.

From several offers Bickerton chose to accept that of teaching chemistry and physics at the Hartley Institution, Southampton. Again he excelled as a highly successful teacher of day and night classes and also at the Winchester Training College where over 96% of his students passed in 1873. While at the Hartley Institution he also served as County Analyst and furthermore carried out original research in electricity. After three years there he lost faith in its future, the Institution having failed by procrastination to become the Technical Training College for the whole of the Indian Services. Writing to his old professors at the Royal School of Mines, he inquired about other jobs. Offered, but turned down, were several professorships in Japan, Canada and England before one approaching his ideal was accepted. This involved a new college in a new country where he would have a chance of moulding scientific education as he saw fit. In 1874, after holding out for more money for apparatus and for an assistant to accompany him, Alexander Bickerton accepted the Chair of Chemistry at Canterbury College, New Zealand.

Alexander Bickerton was the first professor appointed. He arrived in Christchurch in June of 1874, some six months before the college's second overseas appointment. Thus he was a novelty, drawing an audience of 400 people to his first public lecture on the 12th of August 1874. That evening established him as an entertaining lecturer and a scientist who promised to be of great service to the province. The college prospectus of 1876 stressed the value of Professor Bickerton's public lectures in making the college known to the public.

Bicky started teaching formal classes in 1875. By popular demand his work from the start involved physics and technology as well as chemistry. No formal motion seems to have been involved: becoming the Professor of both chemistry and physics just developed through necessity. His department was known under various names, the Laboratory Department being that which he used on his letterhead.

Professor Bickerton became a notable member of the Christchurch community. Initially there were no science students so he therefore had to change the education system by writing a book for primary school teachers, *Materials for Lessons in Elementary Science*, by manufacturing and selling Technical teaching apparatus, by lecturing at the Girls' High School and by introducing science into high schools. He defined science as organized commonsense and, in the preface to his book, he encouraged primary school teachers to let the pupils assist in experiments and to encourage them in private.

As an educational reformer he was outspoken and enemies were made. As Government Analyst his name came to the fore in cases of food adulteration, mineral assaying and murder-by-poison inquests. As a public lecturer in Applied Sciences he brought the latest technologies to the skilled artisans of the city. As an inventor he patented some of his developments. A noted free-thinker, he proposed many social schemes. He was the only university professor to be president of the Tailoresses' and Pressers' Union. Bicky was a socialist – the champion and darling of 'the common man.' During his brief spell as a Christchurch City Councillor during the slump of the late seventies he moved many motions, including one to recommend to Government that the unemployed be paid a benefit, but his only success was a by-law restricting horse traffic to no more than walking pace when turning at the Colombo and Hereford street intersection.

His public popularity was due in no small way to his acclaimed public lectures. No other professor brought the University to the ordinary citizen, to whom it remained a distant place, an ivory tower for the highly educated only.

> "Why", asked the little professor, "do Chinese gentry affect long fingernails, except to emphasise that they scorn to do anything useful ? What signify the immaculate white cuffs of his western brethren except the same lofty scorn of soiling the hand?"

Bicky would regularly draw 100 people to his evening talks, all of which were well illustrated with demonstrations. They were informative, they were entertaining. Inside Bicky lurked a showman. When the new museum wing was opened in 1877, he had seized the chance to display new technologies to the public. Using a small searchlight, driven by a forty-cell battery, he illuminated the approach to the museum, Worcester Street, the Clarendon Hotel and the Cathedral. A large room at the museum allowed the public to interact with displays of the physical sciences and modern technology. [Professor Bickerton was even then over a hundred years ahead of his time. The interactive displays he built up are now the basis of a modern development in museology called Science Centres.] That night too, many people had their first contact with electricity, quite literally. As the *Lyttelton Times* reported

⋯ It was, by the way, exceedingly thoughtful of the Professor to place that huge basin of cool looking water so temptingly behind the door, but those who chanced to dip their fingers therein, scarcely thanked him for his shocking results.

His behaviour often shocked the clergy too. While basically religious, he refused to accept dogma that stifled inquiry. *The Bulletin* (Sydney, 15 April 1893) recalled one scientific meeting at which Bicky

⋯ seemed disinclined to refer to the Bible as an authority. This angered a clergyman, who wanted to know if the professor had ever read St. Matthew. "Yes, some time ago," replied Mr. Bickerton. "Then", said the reverend "read it again and tell us what you think of it at the next meeting". When the time came, the parson fished diligently for the Professor's opinion. "It is full of a beautiful morality – I never read anything which so delighted me" said the enthusiastic Professor – "indeed, so impressed am I that when the census is next taken I shall enter myself as a Christian." "Good Heavens! What did you call yourself before?" cried the alarmed pastor. "Oh, a member of the Church of England."

Alexander Bickerton was not the sort of person some clerics wished to see influencing young minds.

In 1890 Professor Bickerton was forty-eight years old – short, carelessly dressed, flashing blue eyes and a flowing beard – and a College institution with an amazing personality that simply declined to be overlooked. Still active, still inspiring, exuding tremendous energy and overwhelming enthusiasm, he guided physical science well at Canterbury College.

John Macmillan Brown, the Professor of English, hailed from Ayrshire in Scotland. At Glasgow University he had won many distinctions in mental philosophy, English and mathematics. His arts degree included a course in physics. A scholarship took him to Oxford, and classical languages, literature and philosophy. Thoughts of taking double honours in mathematics and English came to naught when he dropped maths because he felt it injured his essay style and made his imagination move in rigid lines. Even so, success took its toll. Recommended to seek outdoor employment because of insomnia and headaches, he completed the necessary mathematics and geology exams required to join the Geological Survey. Expeditions surveying the lava dykes east of Loch Lomond followed for several months until his ill-health passed. So much so he felt fit enough to seek a new post, preferably a professorship in some other part of the British Empire. But not just any old part.

The loan of a book written by a 'Pakeha Maori' interested him in New Zealand, and in anthropology, a lifelong love. He turned down positions in India and Canada prior to the creation of the Chair of Classics, History and English Literature at Canterbury College. An hour's tough questioning by one of the three selectors for that post culminated in an approving slap on the back as the selector shouted "You'll do, you'll do." John Brown was their unanimous choice. Called to London to talk to Lord Lyttelton, the university's agent, he was dumbfounded by the agent's opening exclamation.

"If I had the choice for this appointment, you would not have got it."
Then in quieter tone added "You cannot write Greek verse."

"God help me," ejaculated the new professor, "What would be the good
of Greek verse for pioneers in a new colony?"

After that they got on fine.

John Brown arrived in Christchurch on Christmas Day of 1874. By dint of hard work and enthusiasm, he built up his classes to the extent that the Board of Governors created a new chair in classics to lighten his load. As a bachelor he lived at the Christchurch Club. Recreation consisted of Saturday evenings at the theatre, walks over the hills to Lyttelton coming back via Sumner, and Sunday afternoons at the Bickertons' house. No longer religious, after turning away in his youth from a planned career as a preacher, he did utilize the skills of the second career he considered but never took up, when the local newspapers actively sought his journalistic contributions.

His eligible bachelor days ended in 1886 when he married Helen Connon, the young headmistress of the Girls' High School. A scholar in her own right, she had been one of the earliest women to enrol at Canterbury College. Helen Connon has gone down in history as the third equal lady graduate, and the first female honours (M.A.) graduate, in the British Empire.

In 1890 John Brown approached his 44th birthday. A little man was he, dapperly dressed with a poorly trimmed beard. Extra classes, private tuition and a good salary made him well off. Canny investment already had him on his way to making and holding a reasonable fortune, the only one of Canterbury's founding professors to do so. A tremendously hard-worker, he spared neither himself nor his students. Shirkers were savaged but for the earnest student he had nothing but encouragement and help. Because he was over-enthusiastic his classes sometimes ran an hour over time, a most irritating habit for the football players in his Saturday lectures, who had a hired carriage waiting outside and kick-off imminent at a distant field.

Charles Cook, the Professor of Mathematics and Natural Philosophy (i.e. theoretical and mathematical physics), had a distinguished record in mathematics and in law at the University of Melbourne and at Cambridge University. He had returned to England to enter the legal profession and was within a year of being called to the English Bar when he applied for the Chair at Canterbury College. Conventional, dignified, solid, serious, friendly, helpful, esteemed; perhaps the finest of all the Professors. He was a big man with a beard and a rather fierce face which hid a very friendly character. Certainly he cared for his students. When one ran out of money, Professor and Mrs Cook took her in as a non-paying lodger. The clarity, thoroughness and standard of his teaching showed in the number of senior scholarships in mathematics won by Canterbury men, twice as many as Otago and Auckland combined.

Professor Cook championed women's education; a medical school at Canterbury which never eventuated; and an engineering school which did. He superintended the latter for three years until a permanent lecturer in charge was appointed in 1890. His service to the community included being on the finance committee of Christ's College for many years.

In 1890, at the age of 56, Professor Cook already had the look of a patriarch. For recreation he avidly supported athletics and cricket. Though keenly interested in the Canterbury Society of Arts his real love was music, being a member of the Christchurch Cathedral choir as he had been at St John's in Cambridge. He encouraged music at the college and in the town.

Francis Haslam M.A. was appointed to the new chair of Classics in 1880 when it splintered off from Professor Brown's chair. Educated at Rugby and Cambridge University, he had been head of the Classics department at the United Services College, Westward Ho. Rudyard Kipling was a pupil under him. Haslam often recounted with pride that Kipling, in his 1899 book *Stalky and Co*, had based his ginger-whiskered, classics-master King, on Haslam himself. Yet from the boys' point of view 'King' was not a particularly nice type. Kipling always remembered the time Haslam acidly criticised one of his compositions in front of the whole class, winding up with general remarks about how Kipling would die a scurrilous journalist.

Professor Haslam was very highly regarded as a teacher of classics and a master craftsman at translation. In 1888 he had translated from the Greek, and updated, Aristophanes' comedy 'The Clouds' for the Diploma Day celebrations. Skillfully worked in were Gilbertian songs and a latter day foible, Professor Bickerton's theory of astrophysics. (Curtain fall triggered calls of

"Author". The stage manager's apology for the author's inability to take the call as he had died several thousand years ago brought forth from an undergraduate in the gallery "Trot out his mummy, then.")

Though Professor Haslam cut a picturesque figure each morning as he drove his yellow dog cart to College from his home in Riccarton, he was not a worldly man and lived modestly. [When he returned to England on leave in 1898, he left his teaching and affairs in the hands of a Boys' High teacher, a brilliant ex-student with a triple honours M.A. degree, J P Grossmann. Grossmann, in debt, forged Haslam's signature on two promissory notes. Haslam narrowly averted bankruptcy while Grossmann was sentenced to two years in jail, and later became the Professor of Economics at Auckland University College.]

In 1890 Professor Haslam was a fairly youthful forty-one and still fond of all forms of outdoor sport. President of the Canterbury College Rugby Club from its inception until he left the College, Haslam in his early days played halfback in the team before rheumatism caught up with him. He also golfed, fished, encouraged rifle shooting and presided over the students' smoke concerts whereat he was wont to warble that classic 'Little Billee'. Slim, red-haired with a neatly trimmed beard just starting to go grey, Haslam, though married, was a lady's man. Perhaps over-sexed is the word. At the College dances he glided around with the lady students and with some, it is reliably reputed, tried to go further. [In 1912 Haslam was forced to resign after unsuccessfully putting the hard word on a lady student.]

Captain F W Hutton, who succeeded Julius von Haast to the chair of geology and biology, had an unusual background which included active service in the Crimean war, and in the Indian Mutiny, a Fellowship of the Geological Society of London, Provincial Geologist for Otago, curator of the Otago Museum and Professor of Natural Science at Otago University. In 1861 he had reviewed Charles Darwin's book *The Origin of the Species*, recognizing at once the fundamental ideas of the theory of evolution. This drew in response an appreciative letter from Darwin himself. Being an 'evolution man' had not endeared Hutton to the powers-that-be in Otago. In that bastion of dour Scottish religion he had been criticised from the pulpit by the University Vice-Chancellor for opening the museum on Sundays. Hutton left for a more congenial atmosphere when the Canterbury post became vacant in 1880. He was a shy, quiet man wrapped up in his subject.

All in all, the Canterbury College Professors were reasonably well liked by the students. To a man they were regarded as most helpful, particularly by students specializing in their fields. They were, as would be expected, all different. A student, Willie Marris, set their physical differences to song, (Tune: 'D'ye ken John Peel').

> D'ye ken our professorial clique
> Stout, slim, untidy, grim, and sleek
> Cook, Haslam, Bickerton, Hutton, and eke
> Our friend on the job this morning.

(the 'friend' being Brown). Their personal differences counted more. They did not mix socially with one another and no two seem to have got on together. Brown hated Haslam (partly, it is thought, a Scottish vs English feud). All the others ostracized Bickerton for his socialist views and envied him for the popularity of his public lectures (or possibly more accurately, the fees brought in). Cook certainly did not number Bickerton as amongst his most favourite people. Hutton and Bickerton were both evolutionists, Cook probably not. Only occasionally did feuds erupt, and in the main the Professors behaved civilly to each other but had little to do with one another outside of the College.

The Professors' long vacations (so called) were taken up with university administration and marking matriculation, college, teachers and school exams. They were adequately remunerated. With salary and fees, each earned about three times as much as did an American Professor. The latter were expected to marry rich women.

One of the most important influences of the College on the community concerned its training of teachers. On Saturdays they flocked to the college for lectures in all subjects. Country teachers came by train thus giving up most of their day. Through these lectures, ranging between 9 a.m. and 4 p.m. on Saturday, the skills and enthusiasm of the Professors were distributed throughout the province. Midweek evening lectures catered for working people and teachers in town. All English and Physics lectures were given between 4 and 7 p.m.

The University of New Zealand had just three colleges (Auckland University College was established in 1882) so each professor, through his students, influenced education in New Zealand for decades to come. The other main influence of the college on the community concerned the technical education it offered to skilled workers in industry. All of the engineering lectures took place between 7 p.m. and 9 p.m. each weekday. The academic staff of the College was completed by four lecturers in mechanical engineering, civil engineering, law and modern languages (French and German). The last three were part time. 1890 marked the first year of a full-time lectureship in engineering, and the transfer of control of the embryonic school of engineering from Professor Cook to an engineer. A Registrar, clerks, caretaker, chemical

Jacob Reynolds,
Havelock schoolmaster.
(Tyree, Nelson Provincial Museum
T ¹/₂ 286)

Ern (at right) with his
surviving brothers Jim,
Arthur and George at New
Plymouth.
(W. Collis, du, Rutherford Family)

G. H. WHITE   NEW PLYMOUTH, N.Z.

Rutherford house and flaxmill near Pungarehu, looking towards the sea. (*Rutherford Family*)

Ernest Rutherford, possibly taken for his 21st birthday 1892.
(Rutherford Family)

Canterbury College buildings (right) c.1891, looking down Worcester Street (now The Boulevard) to Cathedral Square, German Church at left, Boys' High School at mid-right. The Museum is at the photographer's back.
(pu, Hocken Library, L1148 neg E1566/2)

laboratory assistant, lab 'boys' and messengers saw to the day-to-day running of the college.

In overall power at Canterbury College reigned the Board of Governors. Even the students had reservations about this group. As Willie Marris put it in a song about earlier times

> _And a Board was a thing to be sat upon then_
> _Not a thing that sat upon you._

Through its subcommittees the Board ran the College and other institutions under its care – the museum, public library, School of Agriculture, School of Art, Girls' High School and Boys' High School. The Girls' High School had been started in 1877, to provide for girls a bridge between the state primary schools and the University. Boys had always had Christ's College for advanced education but as they had a tendency to stay on there rather than attend Canterbury College the Board started the Boys' High School under its own auspices.

The public of Canterbury had no real say in the running of these 'public' organizations as initially the Governors were elected for life by the Board until the college had produced thirty graduates of the University of New Zealand. Thereafter (1884) as a vacancy fell due, the local graduates elected the Board member. By 1890 the Board consisted of fifteen 'life' members and eight elected by the graduates. As only fifty or so graduates lived locally, the community was still not well represented.

The students themselves were not representative of society. Canterbury's population of 20-year-olds hovered around 2,500 yet only fifty or so of that age group attended Canterbury College full time. Furthermore, these few were drawn from the bottom half of the North Island as well as the top half of the South Island. In the main the city looked on the College as something outside, a rather faddy though harmless sort of thing.

In 1890 the working man was more concerned with the long, ever deepening depression. Christchurch had its unemployed, its destitute and a three-times-a-week soup kitchen. When the wharf labourers went on strike volunteer 'free labourers' took over. These were a different class from the usual workers. In Auckland they had to be escorted home past the unionists. In Christchurch a society gossip columnist reporting a society music and dancing afternoon penned ⋯ _not many men. I suppose they were all free labourers that day._

To the undergraduates the college was many things, some summed up in a capping day song, a take-off of 'When a Man's Single'.

You'll 'ave 'eard of the Democrat Varsity
Wi' the govenin' Board at its 'ead,
Its speeches all foam – its Professors from 'ome
Wat shows us the way to earn bread,
  (Poor beggars! its crusty that bread)

It was to this background that the Taranaki flax-manufacturer's son came.

Arrival

Eighteen-year old Ernest Rutherford had commenced his studies at home in Taranaki prior to the start of term, as the following reply from his old headmaster, Mr Joynt, shows.

Nelson College
11 Feb 1890

My Dear Rutherford
 I doubt if it will be possible to procure Bradley's "Airs to Latin Prose" in New Zealand; but I shall try, and shall have it sent to you if it can be found. You are right to try to do some work while waiting for Term to open. I was very glad indeed of your success primarily for your own sake, and next for the sake of the College; and I hope it is only the beginning of a distinguished career. ⋯

Ern arrived in Christchurch by steamer on the day lectures commenced. Of the ten Junior Scholarship winners throughout New Zealand, five entered Canterbury College. The two lasses in this group immediately signed the book promising to obey the rules and regulations of the College. For some reason the three youths did not. [The three of them signed at the start of the following year. This explains why, when Canterbury College erected a brass plate to Ernest Rutherford on the wall of the Great Hall, it erred by ascribing the year which he started to 1891. The plaque has since been corrected but the error lingers.]

The new student found the college buildings in a very pleasant district, the educational quarter. A mere five minutes walk from the centre of the city, the college was bounded over the road to westward by the tranquillity of the Public Gardens and Hagley Park, the Museum and Christ's College. The north side faced mainly empty sections. On the same block were the School of Art and the Boys' High School. The Girls' High School had outgrown its original buildings (the School of Art) and now thrived in newer premises two blocks away at Cranmer Square.

The clock tower on Worcester Street signalled the College's main entrance. Here were the administration offices where students enrolled, paid their fees and collected their scholarship monies. Two-storied wings contained the four large lecture rooms; Mathematics under English to the West, Classics and Modern Languages under Botany and Geology to the east. The Great Hall joined the west wing to the western boundary. Recently added to the south end of the Hall were various rooms including Professor Haslam's study, the library and a small lecture room upstairs. Passing through the portal neath the clock tower, the new students were greeted by a small grassed quadrangle, the opposite side of which merged into that ugly monstrosity known to the students variously as the tin shed, the realm of stinks or the Physical Sciences building. This two-storey, corrugated-iron building encompassed the domain of Professor Bickerton. It contained the chemical lecture room, chemical laboratory and preparation rooms. Hidden behind were the ladies' asphalt tennis court, the caretaker's cottage and, facing Hereford Street, the ladies' cottage where the ladies ate lunch, studied and discussed. The mens' tennis court, within months to vanish under the new School of Engineering, and the newly built male students' rooms completed the students' facilities. Stables, toilets and sundry storage sheds supported the college buildings.

If they transgressed, the new students quickly had the college rules spelled out to them by the Registrar. Both whistling and smoking were banned in college grounds and buildings. Mortar-boards and gowns had to be worn at all times on the premises. The lecture rooms were steeply tiered away from the portal end leaving an odd shaped space set into the ground under the end of each ground floor lecture room. In these 'dens' students stored their caps and gowns when going off the premises. The dens also contained basins where the students could wash their hands. These rooms served no other function for the low, sloping rafters made them uncomfortable spaces in which to loiter. Besides, any chatter, surreptitious smoking or horseplay brought down wrath from on high in the form of the professor in the lecture room above who would storm down to put an end to the problem.

First Term 1890

The academic year was divided into two terms; the students enrolling for courses at the start of each term. Ernest Rutherford enrolled in the usual three year B.A. course, which covered arts and sciences. Latin and pure mathematics were compulsory, each scheduled for five hours of lectures per week. He selected other courses for his first year from his strongest subjects: French (four hours) and applied mathematics (mechanics and statistics) (two hours). He also tacked on the one hour Saturday morning Physics-for-school-teachers class. Perhaps he still contemplated a career in school teaching? It appears that he attended this course only towards the end of term. He did not re-enrol for it in the second term; the class numbers then dropping from seventeen to six. (Most likely it was only a half-year course).

The part-time lecturer in French, the Reverend Mr Turrell (an excellent chess player), was over sixty and about to be retired after public complaints about the standard of the French honours paper in the 1889 College examinations. The questions looked as if they had been obtained straight from a dictionary (e.g., give the French for a custard, the badger, horseradish.) Hence in his first year at Canterbury College Ernest Rutherford came principally under the influence of the stern Professor Cook and the genial Professor Haslam.

As a Junior Scholarship holder he went straight into the upper mathematics class which contained but five students, for few students took more mathematics than necessary. In that class Professor Cook methodically drilled them. They were encouraged to write out their bookwork 19 times.

The Latin classes comprised some thirty-five students. Here good humour reigned. Professor Haslam greeted his classes with a smile and dismissed them the same way. Contrary to the character of King in *Stalky and Co.*, one student recalled that the only classroom rebuke he saw Haslam administer was accompanied by a smile. In keeping with King, another recalled Haslam using caustic satire to deal with a blunderer.

As usual, the front rows were occupied by the ladies. From their steeply tiered seats, the students looked down on the Professor who occupied a sort of pulpit in one corner, his foot subconsciously tapping the boards rapidly whenever class work was not going well. A bust of Clytie, a daughter of Oceanus, ruled from the mantelpiece over the fireplace. Professor Haslam was a true scholar with a deep love of his subject. In this lecture room, perhaps more than anywhere else in the stone part of the college, the student was given the impression that what counted in the long run was not the examination result but the spirit of the student's studies.

Quiet, shy, serious Ernest Rutherford settled into the life of a first-year undergraduate.

The students had little interaction with their fellows as they usually returned home immediately after lectures. The college library existed in a little room behind Professor Haslam's rooms. Small, and open only during office hours, it offered no place to loiter. Nor did the male students' room with its two little 'boxes' of studies behind. Chances were that an impromptu indoor football match would be in progress there, played by less-than-serious students. Occasionally it housed someone indulging in the spectacular pastime of turning on the gas to the ceiling light some time before throwing a match up to the ceiling.

The junior students' only social interaction took place at the debating club (Dialectic Society) which met every second Saturday night, the tennis courts, the football field, and the occasional dance. The dances were organized by groups such as the Dialectic Society, the Lady Students' Tennis Club, the Diploma Day Committee, the Ladies Boating Club and the Students' Committee. (The last was formed to administer the men's student-rooms.) Two nights a week some students frequented a rough boxing class, others studied collision of particle problems at a fashionable billiard room. One group studied together at the most central of their lodgings, taking a team-walk every night before midnight.

Because its predecessor, the Collegiate Union, had accepted women, so too did Canterbury College right from its foundation. In its first teaching term of 1874, 11 of the 50 enrolled students were female. Professor Bickerton's first chemistry classes of 1875 contained his wife and three other females. [The acceptance of females by Canterbury College was later attributed to Professor Brown by Professor Brown. However it was a fact before he was offered a position there.]

All took segregation of the sexes for granted. The lady members of the Canterbury College Lawn Tennis Club had to apply to the Board of Governors for permission to *invite the gentlemen members to play on our court on Saturday afternoons*. The segregation in lectures had earlier been carried to ridiculous extremes when in one class of two people, the youth sat in the row behind the lass.

The junior students had many seniors to look up to, the older ones keeping a fatherly eye on the newcomers. Several newcomers were to be respected too: Willie Marris from Wanganui, who had topped the Junior Scholarship exam. Edgar Buchanan from Ashburton, third on the list and to become a B.A., M.A. (Hons.), B.Sc., before being ordained as a priest, Florence Sheard, also destined to attain B.A., M.A.(Hons.), B.Sc. status.

Ern, Marris and another ex-Wanganui Collegiate student, John Bannister, shared rooms somewhere on Montreal Street. Lectures and study filled Ern's time. Some of the work should initially have been relatively easy for a Junior Scholarship holder, so not all lectures may have been attended. The lecturer called the roll in each class but in the larger classes a good mimic could always respond for friends engaged elsewhere.

Ernest reviewed his finances. At Nelson College he had held the three year Stafford Scholarship for just two years prior to his departure. Thinking it worth a try, he applied through his old headmaster to be allowed the third year while at Canterbury College. Mr Joynt placed the matter before the Nelson College Governors recommending in Ernest's favour.

> ⋯ Rutherford is a student at Canterbury College, is working very hard, and is likely to win distinction. I shall leave the matter in your hands.

The Board had to decline the request because no precedent existed.

Ernest was not athletic. For sport he played some tennis but rugby came closest to his heart. The College Rugby Club held practice matches and entered three teams in the town competitions. After a few weeks, the list for the third team included 'Rutherford'. Of the sixteen names listed, he and another were bracketed as the reserve. On the following Saturday afternoon this team trotted onto the Cranmer Square ground to play Merivale Thirds. A noteworthy game ensued in which College scored a converted try in the first spell. A quarter of an hour later the referee disallowed the try when he discovered that College had sixteen men on the field. This seems to have been Ern's only appearance of the season.

1890 Second Term

The midwinter break separating the two terms lasted a month which Ernest spent at home in Taranaki. The second term brought changes at Canterbury College. A new porter in his new uniform served from his new office in the entrance hall. The School of Engineering buildings took shape as an extension to the East Wing. Endowments for such a School had been set up with the establishment of Canterbury College in 1873. Disregarding Professor Bickerton's earlier public lectures, practical education in technical subjects had started, at the School of Art, in 1885. The course on building construction attracted thirty-two students while the popular Professor Bickerton's course on applied science gathered in ninety-two. In 1887 Bicky had proposed to the Board that he use his facilities also as a School for the Study of the First Principles of

Technology which would prepare boys for technical careers. The Board however entrusted the early academic supervision of the School of Engineering to the mathematician, Professor Cook, until Robert Scott, the former manager of the Addington Railways Workshop, took over in 1890. Scott had been a part-time lecturer in mechanical engineering since 1888. Forty engineering students attended the College. Only four had matriculated, the rest being employed mainly in the engineering trade.

General rugby skills became one casualty of the new buildings: no area of the College's cramped grounds now being large enough for impromptu practices.

Lectures finished in mid-October and end-of-year examinations loomed. As the University B.A. exams were not taken until after the second and third year of study, first year students had only the College exams to worry about. These were duly sat and quickly marked. Willie Marris and Ernest Rutherford took first-class honours in mathematics thereby sharing the Mathematics Exhibition, a prize worth £20. Each year six Exhibitions were awarded by Canterbury College in Latin, English, Mathematics, Political Science or French, Geology or Natural Science and Chemistry or Physical Science. Willie Marris shone as an outstanding classical scholar and also shared the Latin Exhibition. The friendly rivalry between them, particularly in mathematics, proved a great stimulus to Ernest Rutherford. Marris always maintained that Rutherford was the better mathematician, but was more nervous and did not do so well in examinations.

With a satisfactory academic year completed, Ern departed for Taranaki and home.

Taranaki 1890-1891

Taranaki boomed as the dairy industry took over the cleared lands. Further fortunes lay beneath the feet. Experts for the Taranaki Oil Company declared that oil indications on the New Plymouth foreshore were very good and that the people who drilled twenty-five years previously had stopped too soon.

For the Rutherfords, Taranaki consisted mainly of their isolated house, farm and flax-mill. A mere five kilometres ride away from the Pungarehu Post Office, their land bordered the coast and the track from Parihaka down to the fishing settlement of Tipoka where the Maoris used a canoe run to draw their craft from the water. The house and the Tipoka mill nestled amongst the volcanic hillocks forming the foot of the volcano. The mill cook captured the scene in a watercolour painting. From the house the family could look over the mill buildings and out to sea, signalling each time the Manukau Harbour – New Plymouth – Wellington – Lyttelton steamer went past with Ern or one of the other family members on board.

The mill facilities had increased during Ern's absence. James and George had established a library and reading room for the men at the mill. Magazines, the latest newspapers and a good stock of books bearing the bookplate 'The Rutherford Library' were available. James was regarded as a good employer. This did not stop him closing ranks with other employers when the men at Bayly and Weiram's flax-mill went on strike for more pay (date unknown). Striking men tried to work for James during the strike but he refused to employ them. (Bayly took them back at their original pay but with the hours of work now increased by one hour to twelve hours per day.)

For Ern the summer vacation passed with a balance between work and pleasure. Accounts of some of his activities at Pungarehu have passed down through the family without being specific in time (nor, often, even in place). He painted the house, he and Jim laid down a tennis court, he managed the rope walk where fibre was twisted into rope, he carted grass, he made a box to hold batteries, he and Jim pinched pears from a neighbour, he electrified a door knob giving a neighbour a shock, he paddocked flax, he went on a well-provisioned expedition on Mt Egmont. The little details, the personal details, appear to have been lost forever.

The younger children had a governess/tutor. Occasionally Martha would prevail on George or Ern to give them a lesson. Ern would oblige provided his mother mustered them, while George did so with more sympathy. Even then Ern was known to tie the girls' pigtails together to hold their attention or to keep them quiet. He appears to have played havoc with their long hair for when it got caught in the rope being twisted in the rope walk, he would merely snip off the trapped bits.

Jim, too, was home from Nelson College. He had passed the University Entrance examinations obtaining full marks in arithmetic. In January he sat and passed the Junior Civil Service Examination at 25th place. Although Jim was qualified to go to University he had no scholarship. Ern regarded Jim as a mathematically clever person who preferred the outdoor life. Maybe the deepening recession had an influence but for whatever reason Jim did not go on to University. Instead he worked briefly for a bank. (This indoor period of his life did not last long. He worked mainly as a flax-miller and farmer).

With the start of the new academic year in mid-March Ern took the steamer south, back to Canterbury College.

I do solemnly promise that I will faithfully obey the Regulations of the Canterbury College so far as they apply to me.

NUMBER.	DATE.	NAME OF UNDERGRADUATE IN FULL.
337	March 23	Willie Sinclair Morris.
338	" "	Ernest Rutherford
339	" "	Edgar Simmons Buchanan.
340	" "	Edgar Bromley Cocks.
341	" 25	John Angus Erskine
342	" 26	William Balch
343	April 1	Thomas Walter Cane.
344	"	George Gerald Stuart Robson
345	"	Emma Amelia Orr.
346	"	Elizabeth Matilda Rowley.
347	"	Apirana Turupa Ngata.
348	April 1	Kate Isherwood
349	Apr. 2	James Hight
350	Apr. 2	Alfred Johnson Buchanan
351	Apr. 2nd	Jessie Winifred Inglis.
352	Apr 2nd	John Stevenson
353	Apr 6th	Delena Sarah Berry
354	Apl 6th	May Sira Patten
355	April 6th	Edith Marion Stringer.
356.	April 8th	Eva Veronica von Haast
357	April 8th	Mary Jane Morrison
358	April 9th	Edith Mary Harvey.
~~359~~	~~April 10th~~	~~Edward Neville Blakiston~~ (see no 919)
~~359~~	~~April 13.~~	~~Henry Williams~~ (see no 329.)
360	April 17th	John James Lang
361	" 21st	Leah Martha Chrystal.
362	" 30th	Esther Ward
363	May 20th	Peter Menzies
364	June 1st	Alice Mary Fordham.
365	July 2nd	Emily Rose Broome.
366	July 20th	Harriet Davy

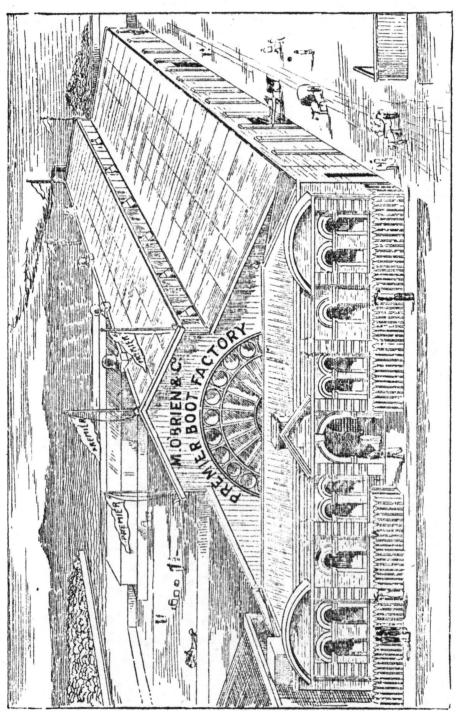

O'Brien's boot factory in Gloucester Street used electrical lighting during winter evenings. (NZ Graphic 7Feb 1891)

Chapter 5

SENIOR UNDERGRADUATE

Canterbury College 1891–1892

The remedy is obvious. ⋯ Science must be banished from the College curriculum.

Letter to the Editor,
The Press 23rd Sept 1891

1891

The discovery of the Sutherland Falls embellished the continuing exploration of the more remote parts of New Zealand. In Auckland a former-premier, Sir George Grey, spoke into a phonograph to preserve his voice for posterity on New Zealand's first recording. The slump worsened. Flax prices were low. Sheep owners advertised for men to shear their sheep and keep the wool in lieu of wages. Overseas, experts discussed the options for the next great war predicting that either France would invade Germany via Switzerland or Germany would invade France via Belgium. (They were a war or two early.)

A ladies' football team toured New Zealand causing a lady society gossip columnist to remark that *No ladies should play and I fancy the 'appreciative crowd' would not be composed of the gentle sex.* The tight restraints on women were further loosened following a British Medical Journal report that several female monkeys, encased in plaster of paris jackets to imitate stays, died of suffocation.

The pressures on women were not all of their own doing. The start of the year almost hatched a scandal with the potential to shatter Canterbury College. Two lady students complained to a vicar of certain improper familiarities to which they had been subjected at the College. No names were mentioned and as the ladies' families would not allow them to give evidence to the Board the incident never became public knowledge. It was not the first, nor the last, complaint of sexual harassment.

1891 marked the end of the roller skating fad. The massive Palace Skating Rink, over 2000 covered square metres in the centre of town, became a boot factory in which the proprietors planned to use electric lighting during the long winter evenings. The only person in Christchurch attempting to educate the population in this newest of technologies was Professor Bickerton.

Whilst not new in New Zealand, (the streets of Reefton were lit by electricity in 1888), electricity was finding ever wider use and capturing the public's imagination. A miniature electric house planned for the Chicago World's Fair aimed to show the future when a house could be run without servants by utilizing appliances powered by electricity:– burglar alarms, heaters, fans, cooking range, dish washer, clothes washer, dumb waiter, clothes iron, floor scrubber, incinerator and window cleaner.

Citizens speculated on the hazards in such a house. Could electricity be safe? Their fears were justified. Four years later in Wellington a helpful passer-by picked up a loose electrical wire in the street and tied it to an iron rail so that no one would trip over it. The next two people who touched the rail were burnt.

Canterbury College 1891

At the start of the new academic year Ernest Rutherford finally signed the College Declaration Book pledging *I do solemnly promise that I will faithfully obey the Regulations of the Canterbury College as far as they apply to me.*

Among the new intake of matriculating students were Jack Erskine from Invercargill who, third on the scholarship list, was to become Ernest Rutherford's co-worker in research at Canterbury; Alfred Buchanan, fifth on the list, later becoming B.A., M.A.(Hons.) and a journalist in Australia; Kate Isherwood afterwards to be B.A., M.A.(Hons.) before entering a teaching career; George Robinson, a future registrar of Victoria University College in Wellington; James Hight, subsequently to have a twelve-storey library named after him following a distinguished academic career at Canterbury; Christopher Craig from Nelson College, who was to board with Ernest and to specialise in mathematics, gaining

B.A., M.A.(Hons.) before dying young; Louisa Bing, soon to be an excellent French linguist; and William Dawson, who would specialise in Chemistry and medicine becoming B.A., M.A.(Hons.), M.B., C.M., F.R.C.S., Ph.D.

Of the new students, one stood out in any crowd. Apirana Ngata, a Ngati Porou from the East Coast North Island, was the first Maori to enrol at Canterbury College. A distinguished scholar, orator, dancer, linguist, essayist, debater and lawn tennis player, he was to specialise in law. *The Press* devoted an article to this noteworthy enrolment.

> *In the past the Maoris in their land transactions have too often been the victims of unscrupulous Pakeha agents. If there were in the colony a few Native Lawyers, who would add to their knowledge of the Statutes an intimate acquaintance with Native custom, and a regard not for their own pockets merely but for the best interests of the race, Native matters might be placed on a much more satisfactory footing ····.*

Knowledgeable in several languages, Ngata enrolled for Latin, English and law courses. As a deeply religious man, he would travel out to Tuahiwi Pa on Sundays to take the service, preaching eloquent sermons in Maori and leading the singing with a fine voice. [By 1900 *NZ Illustrated Magazine* could contrast portraits of the new Maori, Ngata (by then a Member of Parliament), with the old Maori, a fine old warrior of 76-years-old who had seen *the cannibal days of old* and who had *fought against the ever encroaching white man with all the dispairing valour of his race*.]

Ernest Rutherford enrolled for the same two Latin classes as the previous year, five classes in English, advanced mathematics, pass physics and honours physics.

In English classes, the dogmatic Professor Brown had the manner of a schoolmaster. Though claiming to protect the purity of the English language, he would not hesitate to use a long word of his own invention. Essays were set regularly. The best excerpts were, with the writer's permission, read to the class as good examples. The worst bits were also read out but anonymously. To assist with the marking the Professor paid an assistant. Professor Brown's English classes were always very popular and therefore crowded: for his composition class 164 students crammed into his lecture room which had been designed to seat seventy-two comfortably. The students described the overcrowding as inhuman and many felt the class should be split into two: one for people taking University exams, the other for the itinerants. Always the Professor, never the Prof, John Brown worked his students hard. They were expected to take prodigious quantities of notes. Jack Erskine wrote home to Invercargill that in a one hour lecture, which overran to an hour and a quarter, he had filled twenty-two pages of an exercise book ··· *3 minutes to a page – pretty quick work. He reads now faster than he used to* ··· Jack purchased a fountain pen to help keep up. A thriving industry existed in copying notes obtained during Professor Brown's lectures for sale to out-of-town students. In this way two senior students, Oscar Alpers and William Ward, had regularly made £600 a year (two thirds of a Professor's salary) between them.

With such large classes, Professor Brown could not get to know all his students well. After his marriage, he initiated at Canterbury a custom, of which he had fond memories, from his own student days at Oxford. On Sunday mornings he and his wife entertained small groups of students to breakfast at their home. *"Who's the black man?"* asked their daughter with the innocence of youth when Apirana Ngata first attended. He soon became a regular visitor.

The advanced maths class consisted of merely four students: Willie Marris, Ernest Rutherford and two senior students, Charles Adams and Edward Hardcastle, both of whom had already passed mathematics towards their B.Sc. and B.A. degrees respectively. Four lectures a week were scheduled under Professor Cook.

In contrast, Professor Bickerton allocated only one hour per week for the honours physics course and two hours per week for the pass physics course. Complaints were surfacing at Professorial Council and Board of Governors level that he should be giving more lectures to the honours students.

The junior English and mathematics classes had large tail ends which provided much employment for senior students as coaches. Thus began Ernest Rutherford's professional coaching career (presumably in mathematics). Two students were taken at a time for a fee of two shillings and sixpence each for the hour.

The approach of autumn turned many a young man's fancy to rugby football. With the season lasting only the first term (apart from representative matches), the College club's A.G.M. had been held promptly on the first day of lectures. Sixty men attended, enabling the club to enter three teams in the local competitions. Ernest had a permanent but undistinguished place in the undistinguished third team which was undistinguishedly thrashed most weeks, even by the Lyttelton juniors second-fifteen. Amongst his team mates two new students made brief appearances: Jack Erskine and Apirana Ngata, the latter in probably the only rugby game he played for the college.

The artistic side of the college increased with the appointment of the first lecturer in music, a move vigorously opposed by Professor Haslam (Classics) on the grounds that there were more important priorities. Such opposition could not have endeared Professor Haslam to the musical Professor Cook.

Late in the year student drama reached a pinnacle – then rocketed down the precipice on the other side. The Theatre Royal was hired to stage various scenes from Shakespeare. Although a packed house greeted the production with appreciation, the scenery and accessories had cost much more than the money taken at the door. The loss, being born by the two student organizers, ensured that drama lay dormant at the College for six long years.

Canterbury College Science Society

The debating club (Dialectic Society) met on alternate Saturday nights, to provoke discussions on literary, social and political problems amongst the students. A magazine club, housed in the male students rooms, existed primarily to help the debaters. The Philosophical Institute of Canterbury held monthly meetings where scientific talks were given (usually read from notes), by respected people in the community. The Institute was not connected with the College as it had its own rooms in the Public Library, and, lacking the interest and sparkle required by undergraduates, typically drew attendances of only nine people. Two weeks into the first term of 1891 moves were set in train to fill the gap. A notice was posted on the College Notice Boards.

Notice

A meeting will be held on Saturday April 11th

at 7.30 p.m. in the Chemical Lecture Theatre.

Object *The formation of a Society for the*

discussion of **Scientific Questions**

All students are requested to attend.

Canterbury College,	*B.S. Bull*
Christchurch.	*W.G. Pye*
7th April, 1891	*C.E. Adams*

Forty people turned out. The Science Master at the Boys' High School, Mr Laing, took the chair. Mr Bull moved the formation of the Society and, following general remarks by Professor Bickerton and others on the necessity for a Science Society, the meeting voted the Society into existence. Bull, Pye and Adams had drawn up a proposed constitution which the meeting considered and voted on clause by clause. Ernest Rutherford had little to do with the formation of the society, merely seconding three of the sixteen clauses.

The leading lights were an interesting group. Ben Bull, already a B.A. and M.A. with first class honours in chemistry, was studying for a B.Sc. in geology and mathematics. To pursue his chemical studies he later went to England, where he died young. Walter Pye was in his final B.A. year taking physical science, chemistry and political science. He later took an M.A. with Honours in Latin and English followed by a B.Sc. in geology, becoming a journalist in Sydney and also dying young. Charles Adams, an engineering student in his third year, had been the first student to win an Engineering Entrance Scholarship. As such he was taking geology and English to complete a B.Sc. as well as taking second year courses for a Certificate of Engineering. Years later he obtained an M.Sc. and D.Sc. After many years as a lecturer at the Lincoln Agricultural College, and some years in private practice as a civil engineer, he became Government Astronomer (Government Astrologer according to the official history of Canterbury College), and had a distinguished career in this field.

A person attending the meeting was as likely to be specializing in arts subjects as in science subjects. The Professors of Classics and French for instance joined as life members, but Cook, the Professor of Mathematics and Natural Philosophy (theoretical physics) did not join.

The Science Society launched itself in grand style. Its Saturday night meetings, alternating with those of the Dialectic Society, drew attendances of around a hundred. Generally two talks were given each night, often illustrated with lantern slides projected by the chemistry assistant, Sammy Page. Following discussion and supper, Professor Bickerton would often demonstrate an experiment, or microscope slides would be made available for viewing.

The science students were a particularly active group breathing plenty of life into their controversies. They were a radical section at heart, full of theories and reputedly quite militant. Some were socialists and one or two, in their more extravagant moods, even declared themselves to be anarchists. Any organization with Professor Bickerton as Honorary President was sure to be at least slightly radical. This radicalism showed up in the year's programme drawn up by Walter Pye. Of the twelve talks to be given, four had the word 'evolution' in their titles.

Bull.   The Evolution of the Elements
Laing. Evolution in Biology
Pye.   Evolution in Psychology
Watt.   Evolution in Morality and Religion.

Other talks were more conventional: Methods of Book Illustration, Paleolithic Man, The Pyramids of Egypt.

The Society was predominantly a student group but its radicalism sent shudders through some people. Possibly it was the Society's programme that finally induced the Bishop of Christchurch to state from the pulpit, in a manner that must have reminded Professor Hutton of his experiences in Dunedin, that the students were saturated with agnosticism. A letter writer to *The Press* suggested that since the Bishop was on the College Board of Governors he should move for a select committee to investigate the matter. Another made no bones of it

> ···*The remedy is obvious and there need be no difficulty in tracing the cause to its origin. Science must be banished from the College curriculum.*

Bicky replied with a long letter to *The Press* which drew an editorial in *The New Zealand Church News* and there the matter lay dormant, festering, ready to erupt when required in the future.

An extravagant conversazione, an open night to which the public were invited, featured as the highlight of the Society's year. For this, members festooned the Hall with shrubbery and objects of interest. Tables held apparatus, much of it operating or able to be operated by the public: a piercing siren, microscopes and slides, an electric railway, motors, magnesium lamp, lecture demonstration apparatus invented by Prof Bickerton, differential thermometers, visual illusions, working mechanical models from the engineering school and multitudes of electrical appliances.

The military took part. The Canterbury Engineers exhibited their signalling equipment and *various appliances pertaining to the wholesale destruction of human life in a scientific manner.* Towards the end of the evening a couple of electric fuses were detonated, startling the audience.

The Tin Shed was also a hive of industry. Bicky, in his element in the lecture room, conducted a number of electrical experiments and Mr Seager showed lantern slides. Students displayed chemical experiments, such as dropping sodium into water, in the students' laboratory. This room also contained the electrically-ignited gas engine and other working engines. The chemical preparation room held more engines. The physical preparation room metamorphosed into a dark-room where Ernest Rutherford displayed fluorescent tubes, phosphorescent paint and spectroscopes. The following day Ern wrote home.

Christchurch Sunday

Dear Mother,

So far I have received a letter from Alice and George and it seems a long time since I left NP. I have been pretty busy since I came down here and expect to be pretty well occupied the whole of this term. Saturday week was the Dialectic Concert. It was held in the College Hall and all the musical celebrities of Chch performed before a crowded audience. The students were supposed to turn out in Academic costume so of course we all did. The concert was fairly slow considering all things. Some of the singing was first class. Mr Wallace performed on the violin. I believe he is supposed to be the best violin player south of the line. I liked some of his playing very much but some of it was uncommonly tame. I was very busy all last week preparing physical apparatus for the science conversazione which came off last night. The Conversazione was given in honour of the formation of the Science Society which was started at the beginning of the year and of which I am a member.

The college hall was fixed with tables on which all sorts of scientific apparatus was exhibited – mirrors, electric trains, motors, batteries and every scientific appliance you could think of. I was boss of what they called the 'darkroom' in which I had to exhibit a good deal of apparatus. Two Grove's batteries had to be fixed up in the room to work my electrical appliances which were uncommonly pretty in a darkened room. They consisted of spectroscopes to show the spectra of solar light, light of a gas flame, candle etc., an electric fountain, fluorescent tubes, Geissler tubes, electromagnetic star driven by electricity. I had one of the students as assistant and managed to work the affair pretty well. It was rather dangerous work fixing the wires up in the dark as you might get a very nasty shock from the large induction coil I had there. I worked. I explained my apparatus for about 3 hours before a continually changing audience, when I went and had a look round the show myself. Everything was lighted up well and about 800 people were assembled most of them in evening dress, parading in the hall and different exhibit rooms. It was a complete success both financially and practically. Today is Sunday and I have being loafing all day long reading and doing nothing. I hope the girls and Flos are working hard at their lessons. I have received a letter from Jim [and]George, who between them gave me a good bit of news. It is not worthwhile starting a new sheet so will finish.

My love to all. Vale E Rutherford.

[Four years later fluorescence was to be a key element in two of the most remarkable discoveries of all times, X-rays and radioactivity, fields in which Ern first came to world attention.]

One of the best patronized rooms was the refreshment room in the East Wing. During the evening, musical items were given in the Hall, a telephone transmitting the sound through to Prof Bickerton's room. In one consequence of the heated rooms and very cold night, many people caught a cold while crossing the quadrangle. The conversazione started at 7.30 and continued till 11 p.m.. Highly successful, it brought science and the College before the public. It also made the Society relatively rich overnight. Between 500 and 600 people attended, the general public being charged two shillings and sixpence each. The Diploma Day Social Committee, which went into deficit that year, successfully applied for a grant from its rich relation, the Science Society.

The conversazione arrangements possibly make a subtle comment on professorial relations. The new School of Engineering was not on display, nor did the lecturer in charge, Robert Scott, participate. Neither did the Professor of Natural Philosophy and Mathematics, Professor Cook.

Apart from helping with the conversazione, Ern contributed nothing to the Society's first year of operation but his subscription and his attendance.

Practical Physics 1891

At the start of the second term Ernest had added yet another course to those he was already taking – practical physics. This then was his initiation into the world of experimental science. A relatively new course, it had been introduced in 1889 to conform to the University regulation that any candidate in physical science shall furnish to the examiner a certificate showing that a practical examination in laboratory work had been passed. The work covered the use of apparatus in three fields; Heat (thermometers, density measurements, etc.), Sound and Light (spectroscopes, lenses, etc.) and Electricity and Magnetism (electrometers, galvanometers, Wheatstone's bridge, batteries, etc.)

The apparatus sufficed but the facilities did not. Bicky's 'Tin Shed' had been built solely as a Chemistry Department to accommodate twelve chemistry students in its laboratory. In the first term of 1891, 29 students were catered for in practical chemistry by taking them in shifts. No provision had been made for space for physics laboratories. The laboratory department had coped in the past by setting up different apparatus in the lecture theatre, chemical laboratory and the two preparation rooms. None of the appliances could be left where they were used. This arrangement added great difficulties to the teaching of experimental physics, incurring lack of supervision, loss of time and the possibility of damage to the apparatus. With the prospect of thirty-one practical physics students in the second term Professor Bickerton wrote to the Board suggesting that a two-storey physical laboratory be built, with an upper floor able to be darkened for optical experiments, and a lower floor provided with concrete blocks on which to mount vibration sensitive electrical instruments such as galvanometers. His request concluded

> ⋯ *The building should advisedly be of temporary construction, it being impossible to estimate the future requirements of practical physics either as regards number of students or character of experiments. Laboratory work in Physics being in its infancy.*

His plea failed. Instruction in physics practical work continued under the unsatisfactory conditions of previous years. Bicky's assistant, Sammy Page, taught the class. Only very seldom was Bicky called upon to assist the assistant. Though chemistry laboratory classes were scheduled for a four hour period (as well as all day Saturday), physics took two hours per week in the second term only. In practice Ernest Rutherford devoted four or five more hours weekly to this work.

A spark was being ignited.

End of Year Exams 1891

Some Professors set internal College exams which were harder than those of the University, thereby maintaining a high pass rate in the latter which could be sat only after passing the former. One claimed not to have had a failure in the University exams in nineteen years.

In the October College examinations Ernest Rutherford sat and passed in Latin, English, pure maths, applied maths and physics. The following week he sat the College Honours exam in mathematics. Of the five candidates, Ernest came second behind Willie Marris, who topped both mathematics and Latin. As a rule the £20 Exhibitions (prizes) were shared around so that one person took no more than one prize. Marris took that for Latin. The Mathematics Exhibition thereby fell to Rutherford.

Rudyard Kipling, on a brief visit to Christchurch, called out Professor Haslam from supervising an exam. The pair reminisced about the old days. For Kipling the meeting had a touch of sweetness. As he recalled with sarcasm in his none-too-accurate autobiographic notes, after detailing the story of Haslam the schoolmaster acidly telling off Kipling the schoolboy,

··· it pleased Allah to afflict H— in after years. I met him in charge of a 'mixed' College in New Zealand, where he taught a class of young ladies Latinity. "And when they make false quantities, like you used to, they make eyes at me!" I thought of my chill mornings at Greek Testament under his steady hand, and pitied him from the bottom of my soul.

Attendance at lectures and passes in the College exams saw the names of successful candidates forwarded to the University as having kept 'Terms'. Having done so for two years they were eligible to sit the first part of the University of New Zealand B.A. examinations. In 1891, 111 candidates were eligible throughout the country, including thirty students from Canterbury College. For the B.A. degree at least six subjects had to be passed. At least one of the compulsory subjects (Latin and maths) had to be attempted in Part I. In the November 1891 U.N.Z. exams Ernest sat the usual number of four subjects: Latin, English, pure maths and applied maths. (In physics, seventeen were to sit at Canterbury, three at Auckland and three at Otago but seven from Canterbury were to fail.)

The setting and marking of University papers was always a contentious issue. Some, including Professor Bickerton, believed the colonial colleges should affiliate with the University of London (the scientific university), so that their degrees would be widely recognized. Others believed that the University of New Zealand should choose examiners resident in New Zealand. As there were often only one or two people in the country capable of examining most subjects and these people would have taught about half the students sitting that particular subject, this clearly was not yet a viable option. The system in use fell between these two extremes. The University of New Zealand chose its examiners from 'Home'. [The colonists still looked on England as Home, referring to the mails from England as outward and the mails to England as homeward.]

The examination papers were hence sent by fast steamer to England for marking. The tentative pass list would be telegraphed back during the last week of February, the official list following by mail. This system worked well until the S.S. *Mataura*, carrying the 1897 exam papers, missed the entrance to the Magellan Strait.

After the 1891 University exams the candidates dispersed for the summer vacation.

Pungarehu
January   1892.

Dear Father,
            I received your letter
on Friday, and I have made up
my mind to come home by the
coach of Thursday as there is none
of Friday. On Friday Campbell
and I went to Parihaka, and after
that to the light-house. Earnest made
28 gallons of wine the other day,
and he intends to make 5 gallons
of rhubarb champagne soon. -
Mr. Rutherford bought 20 calves.
the other day and we had
great fun branding them.
        I hope you enjoyed the regatta.
I have not tried to ascend the
mountain yet, as the day they
arranged for it was a bad one.

Archie MacDiarmid's letter home

1892

At Pungarehu Ernest filled in the holidays. One day he made 127 litres of wine (possibly blackberry), on another he laid down 23 litres of rhubarb champagne. Assisted by a young visitor, the stalks were passed through the rollers of the washhouse mangle. The juice flowed magnificently. In no uncertain terms did Ernest's parents remind the youths that they had neglected afterwards to wash the wooden rollers! Ern helped brand twenty calves his father had purchased. Quite likely he worked at the mill. Various expeditions took place including one to a favourite place, the Cape Egmont lighthouse. Late in life Archie MacDiarmid, Ern's helpmate in wringing rhubarb, recalled holidays spent at the Rutherford farm; riding to the Maori races; riding to Pungarehu to meet Jim off the coach; and making a mast and sail for a Maori dug-out canoe for use on the mill pond.

When the exam results were telegraphed back from England at the end of February, Ernest had passed Part 1 for a B.A. degree. A few days before lectures started again, he travelled down to Christchurch and enrolled in three French courses, general biology, chemistry laboratory practice, teachers' chemistry, advanced mathematics, practical physics and honours physics.

The overcrowding of the laboratory department was still acute and at last some provision was made for space for physics experiments. As an emergency measure, three tables were erected in the Hall. There Ernest and the ten other students could work undisturbed at electrical experiments. The apparatus available, quite adequate for the pass physics work, did not suffice for the honours physics course. Because of a shortage of good electrical equipment the senior physics students were certainly working under difficulties.

1892 brought the beginning of the end of the old guard. Professor Brown's health broke down yet again, with eye strain leading to headaches and insomnia. He applied for leave to go to England to seek a cure. At the end of his last lecture his classes presented him with an illuminated address signed by over 200 of his students, past and present, including Ernest Rutherford. They wished him a pleasant voyage and a return to full health. Such was not to be. Although he returned to Canterbury, continued ill-health caused him to resign his position in 1895 when not yet fifty-years-old.

A good attendance at the Football club A.G.M. again ensured the formation of three College teams. But Ernest did not have a season to write home about, oscillating between the second team, the third team, and oblivion before settling into a regular place in the seconds, he participated in one forfeiture (due to a recess), two postponements (due to rain), three losses and one win. The second teams' standard is illustrated by its six tries to nil loss to the Christ's College team, in theory a team of schoolboys. The only time he appeared in a winning side Ernest scored a try, one of seven against a Linwood side which could field only thirteen men.

On the scientific side he was nominated and accepted for membership of the Philosophical Institute of Canterbury. Once more he took no prominent role in the College Science Society, nor at its meetings. The Society continued to grow with audiences reaching over one hundred and fifty. Discussion had always been one of the main aims in setting up the Society. Book reviews were initiated and alternate meetings declared sectional meetings. The latter had not been clearly distinguished the previous year but now they were. The programme drawn up at the start of the 1892 year left every second meeting blank, where any member could bring up any matter of interest. At one, Alex Bickerton, one of Professor Bickerton's sons, read a paper on 'The Essentials of Evolution' which treated the subject in *an original manner*. Other sectional talks involved interplanetary communication, the history of the locomotive, and Walter Pye, the secretary, read a note suggesting profit sharing as a means towards industrial conciliation. The regular scheduled meetings also covered a wide range including 'Lyttelton, an Old-Time Volcano'; 'Greek Domestic Life in the Homeric Age'; 'History and Chemistry of Fire'; and a short, lucid paper by Charles Adams on modern developments of electricity, on the lines of Prof. Oliver Lodge. After his paper Adams spoke at some length on new applications of the science, illustrating his remarks with numerous specimens.

In his only recorded interaction with the Society's activities during this year Ernest Rutherford spoke to this paper but what he said was not recorded.

The Theory of Partial Impact

In science, Professor Bickerton's star was on the rise. Observations in Edinburgh on a new star which had suddenly appeared in the sky, a nova, seemed to support a long established theory proposed by Bicky to explain the sudden appearance of such stars.

The event that had initially triggered his interest occurred in November 1876 when a point of light appeared in the constellation Cygnus and grew rapidly in brilliance (Nova Cygni). Bicky, the all-embracing scientist and free-thinker, had turned his attention to this observation. He examined the recent theories put forward to account for the appearance of new or variable stars and rejected them. Instead he proposed his own. Stars were just distant hot bodies which, like our Sun, radiated energy away. It seemed reasonable to Bicky that a star will eventually cool until its surface becomes so dark it cannot be seen. Thus space would be inhabited by numberless dead Suns. Hence there was a chance that occasionally two of these large dark bodies, moving with tremendous speeds through space, would collide. As a glancing blow seemed more likely than a head-on collision, material would be torn from each of the bodies on impact. A fraction of the enormous kinetic energy of the dead Suns would go into heat energy. The torn-off material would therefore form a very hot third body, a 'new' star, a 'nova'. The signature of just such a new star is that it would suddenly appear as a very bright star then slowly decrease in intensity as it cooled.

Other astronomical features could also be accounted for by his Theory of Partial Impact. At the time scientists thought of an old sun as a hard body with a hot interior and a cooler crust. A partial impact would therefore rip off a part of the cold crust of each dead star, thus exposing to view a luminous, deeper, region. The partial impact would cause the two bodies to rotate in opposite directions. Thus were variable intensity stars accounted for, the bright zones showing only when the impact region faced Earth. Professor Bickerton expanded his Theory of Partial Impact until he believed the whole cosmic system could finally be accounted for. It was a steady-state theory, the radiation from stars being absorbed by the dust from earlier collisions and the dust and their energy accumulating into solid bodies again by collision. [We now know that currently the Earth sweeps up 100 tonnes of cosmic debris each day.]

Bicky championed his theory. In the early days he had immediately won local acclaim. Some well-educated people with astronomical knowledge cautioned him to make his theory quantitative. This it was never to be for he lacked the necessary mathematical ability. One serious objection to this theory was the low probability of such a collision. A series of fifteen letters the Prof sent to the English science magazine *Nature* were rejected. English scientists were indifferent to the theory either by its lack of quantitativeness or by the fact of the author being an upstart in the colonies. This official indifference over the years had bred skepticism in New Zealand.

However, the preliminary observations made in Edinburgh on the 1892 nova using photographic and spectroscopic observations suggested the nova had indeed been caused by two stars in partial impact. After a decade of neglect, Bicky was once more hailed as a great man, even by some English newspapers. The Science Society moved, and passed unanimously, the very scientifically worded statement

> ⋯ *that the society views with satisfaction the probability of Professor*
> *Bickerton's Impact Theory being confirmed by high authorities and that*
> *the secretary be instructed to convey to the Professor the congratulations*
> *of the Society.*

During lectures devious students could often sidetrack Bicky by a seemingly innocent question relevant to Partial Impact, the motive being to divert the Prof away from asking backward students questions they should be able to, but could not, answer. Often the ploy worked and away would go Bicky on his hobby horse to the glee of the laggard students but to the disappointment of the serious few who wanted to get on with the work in hand.

Bicky would expound his theory to all and sundry and often worked it into his public lectures. He was a propagandist supreme in full flight. Some Professors and some members of the Board of Governors did not take too kindly to Bicky's rekindled public popularity. Some complained that he should not be pushing his own theories in class. His enemies gathered ammunition. However, much of the euphoria dissipated as further examination of Nova Aurigae cast doubts on the earlier assumption that partial impact had been involved.

Alexander Bickerton thereby continued to be ignored by British astronomers.

Dialectic Society

The Dialectic Society, the oldest student society in the College, met every second Saturday night during term in the English lecture room. Its function was to give students the experience of public speaking and public debate. On the whole, matters were taken pretty seriously with flashes of wit and satire few and far between.

Most meetings took the form of an Essay, when one person read an essay followed by criticism from a second person, or a Debate when two spoke for, and two spoke against, a motion. The subjects were serious and topical: *'That considerable emendations in the regulations for the Pass Degree are desirable', 'That unless the British Empire continue to expand, disintegration is inevitable.' 'That England's refusal to grant India Representative Government is wise and politic.'*

One meeting they reserved for Olla Podrida night. Short, anonymous contributions were read by the secretary, criticised by the members and voted on for best composition. The 1892 winner managed to work Bicky into his verses.

III

Hail to our own illustrious prof!
Who fixed his gaze upon the sky
And though the scorners jeer and scoff
A triple star did there espy.

His theories sound very nice,
But Oh, it would be better by far,
If he would take the bard's advice,
And manage to impact a star.

Then all could see how it was done,
The sneerers then would sneer in vain,
The crown of glory would be won,
And Bickerton with Newton reign.

Like almost all students, Ernest Rutherford had joined the Dialectic Society in his first year at Canterbury College. For his first two years he had been merely a spectator. Now, as a senior student he took a more active role. In 1892 he was elected Treasurer, taking over from Willie Marris. It is also the first occasion on which he appears on the programme, as the in-support speaker for the motion *'That the influence of the Modern Newspaper Press is excessive and dangerous.'* The Prize Essay competition filled the final meeting of the year, the title set being *'The past and future of the Maori'*. Apirana Ngata, with personal insight, won.

Capping Ceremony 1892

With the start of the second term, diploma day preparations had commenced. The students' examination results had been confirmed in May. Their achievements were however not publicly recognised by the College until mid-August when the successful graduates were formally presented with their diplomas and capped at a special ceremony. The graduates were few, the official speeches long. In self-defence the undergraduates would hold meetings to decide how they would celebrate the occasion. Invariably, as they had since 1889, and following the custom at Otago, they chose to write songs for the function or rather, they put their own words to the popular songs of the day. These were anonymous, often pointing out failings and foibles of the staff, students and administrators. The songs were printed into a song sheet and singing practices held.

The day dawned, the afternoon ceremony drew nigh and the College hall filled to overflowing. Eight rows at the front were reserved for graduands and undergraduates in academic dress, with the lady students segregated on the right. Friends, relatives and the general public crowded in behind. With the visitors seated, the male students marched in from their robing rooms with the football banner flying high, singing the hardy annual 'Long Live Canterbury College'. Having taken their seats they lustily rolled forth 'Gaudeamus Igitur', that Latin song still sung uncomprehendingly at graduation ceremonies today, a relic of the days when an educated gentleman spoke Latin.

At the stroke of three the door at the back of the platform opened to extrude the official party; the Bishop, the Mayor, sundry dignitaries, the Board of Governors, administrators, and the professors and lecturers. This august procession was saluted by the male students belting out their time honoured greeting '*The animals came in two by two* ⋯'. The undergraduates summed up their philosophy for the day in the motto of their song sheet '*Dulce est desipere in loco*': a line from Horace exhorting his friends to have fun while they can, somewhere between '*It's fun to fool about at this time*' and '*all work and no play makes Jack a dull boy*'.

With the official party seated, the students moved on to the first of their 'anonymous' songs, one written by Jack Erskine and Ernest Rutherford entitled '*Quot Homines Tot Sententiae*'. [This oft-quoted line, from a play by Terence, means '*there are as many opinions as there are people*'.] Its choice as the opening offering probably arose through its mention of the Professor of Mathematics, Professor Cook. His turn had come around to represent the University of New Zealand so he had charge of the official party and the day's proceedings. To the tune of 'The Vicar of Bray' the students rendered two men's view of the clash between the arts and sciences.

QUOT HOMINES TOT SENTENTIAE.

Air—" Vicar of Bray."   *Erskine & Rutherford.*

WHEN good Prof. Cook holds forth to us,
On surds and conic sections,
Instructs us in the Calculus
We speak with circumspection ;
Say Taylor is our sole delight,
And Parkinson a pleasure,
That English all our hopes doth blight,
And plagues us beyond measure.

CHORUS—

I would that all my trials were o'er,
And I a graduate free, sir,
(From lectures, profs. and all such bores)
And M.A., B.Sc., sir.

When on the scene comes smiling Brown,
And English comes in fashion,
The Calculus is hooted down,
It kills imagination ;
The soul it cabins and confines,
And cripples it most sorely,
Imagination soars aloft
In Mason and in Morley !

CHORUS—

Now Alpers fills the well known place
Of wisdom most platonic,
Much famed for dignity and grace,
Professor embryonic ;
A model youth devoid of pride,
A warrior at elections,
Just 'like the good young man that died'
All free from imperfections.

CHORUS—

[Taylor and Parkinson are the authors of mathematics books used by the students, Brown the Professor of English, and Alpers a recent graduate and Brown's temporary replacement.]

Professor Cook then delivered his loudly applauded chairman's address on the work of the University of New Zealand. Two more songs followed. *'Kill and Cure'* to the tune of *'I've got a little list'* from the Mikado, the first two verses of which went

> As some time it may happen that a victim must be found,
> I've got a little list, I've got a little list
> Of a few Collegiate bugbears, who might well be underground,
> Who never would be missed, who never would be missed.
> There's the awful swot who thinks the aim and end of life is cram,
> Who would never such a crime commit as bunking an exam.
> But worst than he, the specious wretch who swotting does decry,
> But who utilises all his time by mugging on the sly.
> Then that singular anomaly, the would-be pessimist,
> He never would be missed, he never would be missed.
>
> Chorus:
> You may put 'em on the list
> And they'd none of 'em be missed.
>
> There's the Dialectic member to the point, who'll never speak,
> He never would be missed, he never would be missed,
> With irrelevancies dry, who'd go on talking for a week.
> He never would be missed, he never would be missed.
> There's the croaking undergraduate who 'knows' he'll never pass,
> And the student too who comes in late disturbing all the class,
> And the patronising graduate, who though he's been ploughed twice,
> Is for ever boring you to death by giving stale advice;
> Then he that's ploughed – poor wretch! – and would our sympathies enlist
> He never would be missed, he never would be missed.
>
> Chorus:

Then followed one of the all time great diploma day songs, a creation of Willie Marris (Air: 'Trelawny').

> In the days of old, ere the world grew cold,
> When our Universitee,
> Sent monkey graduates marching up
> To a Chancellor Chimpanzee;

Then ourangotang toffs were our only Profs.,
And Palm tree groves our halls,
And Lancaster Park was a jungle dark;
And coconuts made footballs.

Chorus:

O sometimes still try hard as we will,
We sigh for those days again,
When each undergrad. was a monkey glad,
They were palmy ages then!
For a Registrar we'd a gorilla,
But there wasn't a library fine,
And we lay at our ease till noon in the trees,
And we didn't turn out at nine;
And a Board was a thing to be sat upon then,
Not a thing that sat upon you,
And we cracked our nuts with a big stick, which
Was the only Malet we knew.

Chorus:

Matric was a thing of a jump and a swing,
In those days gone by so far,
And we took our degrees in the forks of the trees,
With a leaf for a diploma;
And he bossed the rest who could climb the best,
But he did it without red tape,
O he wasn't so fat you could bet your hat
When F de C. M. was an ape!

Chorus:

Then we learned a date by its flavour sweet,
Not out of a rubbishy book;
And extracted our roots when we wanted to eat,
Nor bothered a jot for a Cook ;
O we cared not a dam for any exam,
And life was worth living then!
'Twas a howling shame when old Darwin came
And turned us all into men.

Chorus:

Yes that was the day when the world was gay!
With our arts, and science and such,
All the pains we take are a great mistake
We've evolved far far too much;
For undergrads, then, whether monkeys or men
Were as they will always be;
Wherever you went, out of every ten,
There were nine at the top of the tree!

[Mr F de C Malet, was the Chairman of the Board of Governors and a dam was explained away as a small Italian coin.]

A spontaneous shout of *'Three Cheers for G G Stead'* acknowledged the most recent member elected to the Board of Governors by the graduates. The College Registrar then read out the results of University examinations held the previous November. For enlivenment the students sang 'Come, here's to Canterbury College' commenting on a peculiarity of each of the Professors in turn followed by another purporting to give a new student's view of the Professors.

Professor Cook then presented degrees to the graduates present – two M.A.'s, eighteen B.A.'s and two B.Sc.'s, followed by a serenade of the graduates by undergraduates which had for a first verse

We rejoice that it's decided,
Happy now their life will be,
For at last they are provided,
With that coveted degree.

Once more the college was praised in 'Our College' to the tune 'British Grenadier' after which a member of Parliament gave another address, amazingly brief and to the point, on the responsibilities the students accepted when receiving their diplomas. Applause and songs followed. One in honour of the rugby team 'The Old Fifteen'; and then one in a language foreign to almost every person present: *Maranga! ranga! ra ki runga!* (Tune: 'Tramp! Tramp! Tramp, the boys are marching')

CHORUS
Maranga ranga! ra ki runga!
Takahia ki raro te mamae!
Whaia ko te mahi pai! ko te matauranganui!
Takahia ki raro rawa te mamae.

Ern took the levels of the soaking pond at the Tipoka flaxmill.
(A Northwood, Taranaki Museum N.5.2 LN 2150, from Auckland Weekly News 28 Feb 1907.)

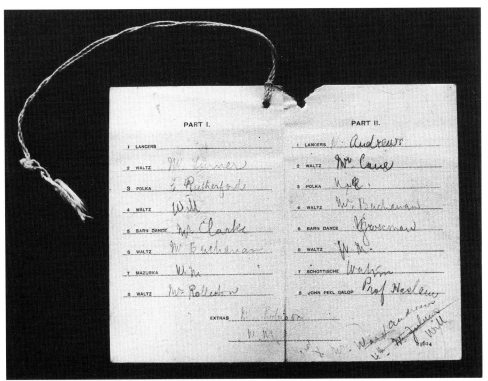

Alice Fordham's dance card for 4th Nov 1892. Will and WM is Willie Marris.
(John Campbell, Fordham Family)

The Tin Shed in later life. Ern carried out his first researches here in 1893.
(S Page, University of Canterbury, Chemistry Department)

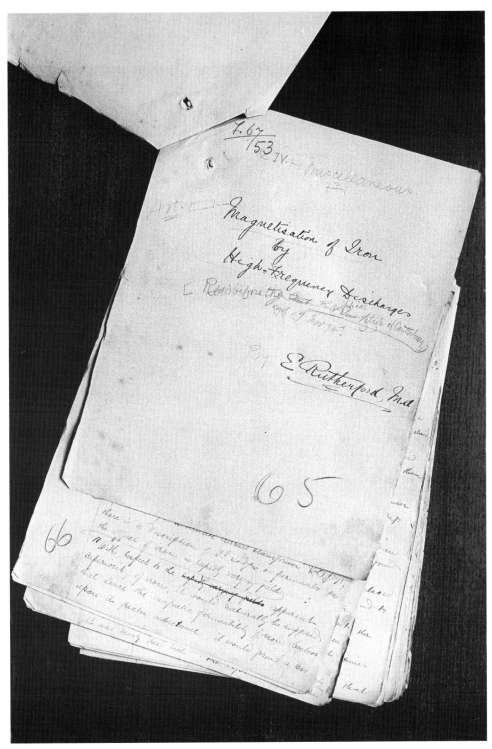

Manuscript of Ern's second research work, his first published paper.
(John Campbell, Hector Papers, National Museum of New Zealand)

A photo for Ern for his exile.
(Rutherford Family)

Jack Erskine.
(pu, Erskine Family)

(Oh rise up, and tread down pain!
Pursue the great task!
It is high learning!
Tread down all pain!)

(Presumably the pain refers to the effort involved in study.)

The author, Apirana Ngata, sang the chorus first as a tenor solo, his voice ringing round the rafters in that hushed hall. The other students joined in to sing the verses, the first of which went

In the college cell I yawn,
Freezing, mother dear, with awe
For I caught the threat and menace in that look
And the professorial eye
It is evil, it is sly,
As the gentle tones come sweetly "Will you please?"

The sight and sound of Ngata's solo remained with many present till their dying days. At the time they applauded loudly.

A short address by the Principal of the Boys' High School terminated the formal speeches and the musical programme concluded with 'The Undergrad's Last Words' (Air: 'There was a young lancer lay dying')

There was a young student lay dying,
His frame was all wasted away,
As his last breath was speedily flying,
These words so pathetic did say

CHORUS —
Wrap me up in my gown old and tattered,
With my books and my cap by my side,
And bear this frail body so shattered,
To the grave where poor students can bide.

Years ago on a bright course I entered,
Bright hopes were enabling my soul,
On success my ambition was centred,
M.A. first class honours, my goal.

Old Brown marked my course out so neatly,
And Cook gave me wholesome advice,
And Bickerton smiled on me sweetly,
Prof. Haslam I thought very nice.

My essays were always much quoted,
And somehow created great fun,
Just because they so aptly denoted
The faults that a writer should shun.

The French I first thought very pleasant,
But those verbs were the ruin of me,
Clarke asked me of Avoir the present,
And I answered of course, It's 'Je suis'.

And then that exam – but why dwell on
The horrors I had to endure;
I retired with the air of a felon,
Who knows that his sentence is sure.

That day I was down with the fever,
A 'rider' pursued me all night,
And my bones they were crushed 'neath "a lever
Of the first order" painfully tight.

A fiend came and took up his station
At my bed, and I tried – (but to fail),
To find by 'quadratic equation',
The length and the 'root' of his tail.

He said he had been a professor
Of algebra, down in this world,
But now he was father confessor
To examiners in the pit hurled.

So now you have heard my sad story,
And I pray, when interring my bones
You'll write – "This fond youth sought for glory
And found it – With old Davy Jones."

So drew to a close a capping ceremony celebrated for many years to come as an example of what a capping ceremony should be: a balance between regrettably long official speeches and the light relief of student boisterousness; a marrying of young world wit to old world melody.

In Auckland the ceremony proceeded less smoothly. The Chancellor had to call for silence to start proceedings. He presented the diplomas to the ten graduates present and introduced the first speaker whereupon the students launched into their first song. After calling in vain for silence and order the Chancellor called the meeting over and stormed out. The students carried through their musical programme.

Such events were to place a shadow over future diploma day ceremonies.

B.A. Final Exams 1892

When enrolling for the second term Ernest Rutherford had had to decide on which subjects to concentrate. He needed to pass only two more to complete a B.A. degree. The regulations restricted him to not more than two science subjects from applied maths, physics, chemistry and natural science. He already had applied maths under the belt from the 1891 exams. Which to choose of the other three? Maybe Ern had no choice. He had had more exposure to, and perhaps preferred, physics. Perhaps the fact that one of his classmates in chemistry had taken the Chemistry Exhibition for the previous two years influenced his choice. We may never know. The records show he enrolled to sit physics and French.

The new lecturer in French, William Clarke, taught Ern and the other twenty students. A Cambridge M.A. graduate and a mere thirty years of age, he had great charm in manner and appearance.

Twenty-two students attended the pass physics lectures while seven took the honours lectures. All had to pass the course of practical work lasting half a year before they could sit their University of New Zealand papers but Ern and the other serious students worked on experiments all year, supervised by Sammy Page.

The October College Pass exams were followed by the College Honours and Exhibition exams. When the results were announced Marris and Rutherford once more dead-heated for the Mathematics Exhibition. The result showed a touch of diplomacy because they were the only two candidates. In physics there were three candidates, first-class honours being awarded to both Ern and Jack Erskine, his junior by one year. Just one student sat chemistry, he also obtaining first-class honours. With only one Exhibition available for all physics and chemistry candidates this was bracketed by Ern and the chemist Edward Buchanan, the latter winning for the third year in a row. Similarly Willie Marris obtained his hat trick in Latin. Thereby the final result was that £20 Exhibitions were awarded to Marris in Latin, Rutherford in Mathematics and Buchanan in Experimental Science.

Following the College exams, Professor and Mrs Haslam held a dance at their house for the students. Ern attended, reserving the third dance, a polka, in the dance card of Alice Fordham, Willie Marris's girl-friend. [So much for Lady Rutherford's reminiscence that Ern would <u>never</u> go to a dance.]

As a result of the College exams, seventeen third-year Canterbury students became eligible to sit their final B.A. exams which they did in mid-November. The students had the option of sitting the University's ordinary pass exams or the harder papers for the Senior Scholarship exams with a standard between that of pass B.A. and M.A. courses. The scholarships were competed for New Zealand wide, with one scholarship available for each of nine fields. These Senior Scholarships, each of value £50, provided the finance for a student to return for the one year Honours (Masters) course in that field. Ernest sat the scholarship papers in mathematics and in experimental science (physical science option; chemistry being the other option available) but not in French as there was only one scholarship available for French, German and English (the most popular of all subjects).

Physics consisted of two papers, one covering heat, sound and light, and the other covering electricity and magnetism. Examples of the Scholarship questions set in the latter by the examiner in England include:

> No 4 *Explain fully the meaning of Ohm's law. To what extent is Ohm's law applicable to electrolytes?*

> No 9 (part) *How would you show experimentally to a class that the tendency of a powerful magnetic field to prevent the motion of a mass of copper is due to electric currents induced in the copper?*

Exam time coincided with Professor Bickerton once more making the news. Throughout the year he had given four series of six public lectures. His second lecture in the 'Recent Chemical Achievements' series had been delivered to the usual crowded room and sparked the typical praise he drew regularly from the reporter in the audience ⋯ *The lecture was interspersed with some humorous anecdotes and the experiments as a whole were brilliant and successful* ⋯. At his final public lecture of the year, Professor Bickerton sorrowfully announced that his public lectures probably would not continue next year. The other professors had demanded this because, in reporting Bicky's public lectures so fully, the newspapers gave the impression that Canterbury College did nothing else.

The Press looked into the matter but could find no cause other than that the Professorial Council (i.e. the other professors) refused to permit their continuance. In a long editorial it deplored this attitude and went further

> ⋯ *We would suggest that the work of extending the usefulness of the college in popular directions should not be confined to one professor. There seems to us no reason why other members of the staff should not deliver popular evening lectures that might be just as useful. It could be no great hardship on these gentlemen, who enjoy five months' holidays in the year, to devote a part of their leisure to such classes. And they would have the satisfaction of knowing that they were rendering our College useful to other and larger classes than those who are privileged to wear gown and trencher* ⋯ .

Correspondents entered the fray with letters of support signed Machinist, the Working Man, etc.

> ⋯ *Perhaps we are not aristocratic enough for Canterbury College* ⋯

No doubt existed of Bicky's popularity amongst the skilled workers, nor of his declining popularity with some of his fellows and members of the Board of Governors.

For Ernest Rutherford, as for the other senior students, the two months wait for exam results had begun. He was, of course, to pass thus gaining the privilege of being entitled to screw the magic letters B.A. to his handle for life.

What he did that summer, and where he went, I have as yet no idea.

UNIVERSITY OF NEW ZEALAND.

EXAMINATION FOR SENIOR SCHOLARSHIPS, 1892.

PHYSICAL SCIENCE.

PAPER **b**.   ELECTRICITY AND MAGNETISM.

Examiner: Principal GARNETT, D.C.L.

1. Make carefully a sketch of the equipotential surfaces and lines of force due to two very small bodies positively charged with 20 and with 5 units of electricity respectively, and placed 6 centimetres apart.   What is the form of the surfaces in the neighbourhood of the point of equilibrium?

2. Describe the replenisher or some other form of continuous electrophorus, and explain clearly the source of the energy of the electrification produced.

3. What is the chief difficulty in the experimental determination of the specific inductive capacity of glass, and what methods have been employed to overcome it?

4. Explain fully the meaning of Ohm's law.   To what extent is Ohm's law applicable to electrolytes?

5. Assuming that 1 calorie is equal to 42,000,000 ergs, that the electrochemical equivalent of hydrogen is ·00001038, and that one gramme of hydrogen burning in oxygen produces 34,000 calories, determine the least E.M.F. capable of continuously decomposing water by electrolysis.

[*Turn over.*

Chapter 6

APPRENTICESHIP IN RESEARCH

Canterbury College 1893

I learnt more of research methods in those first investigations under somewhat difficult conditions than in any work I have done since.

Ernest Rutherford, reminiscing in 1909

about his work at Canterbury College

Bicky Comes to Prominence, Yet Again

1893 saw an Otago man fined for stacking his crop on a Sunday, an offer to light the streets of Christchurch by electricity, the New Plymouth highwayman captured, an officious attendant ensuring that the citizens of Christchurch did not walk or sit on the grass in the public gardens, the reputed artificial production of diamonds in Paris, professionalism in rugby mooted in England, encouragement for New Zealand women to take up professions and to wear rational dress when cycling, the dubious firing of the Professor of Mathematics at Auckland University College, moves to establish a University College at Wellington, the coming of age of Otago University, advertisements continuing for electric belts to cure rheumatism, and New Zealand short of 42,500 females.

Otago's *Taieri Advocate* thought New Zealand would eventually be renamed Maoriland. *The Sydney Bulletin*, the originator of the proposal, was more definite ⋯ *The name NZ will be legislatively altered to "Maoriland" as surely as that the sun shines.*

Professor Bickerton started the year with a bang. Or rather with a series of bangs. He held several public firework displays at Tahuna (meaning sandbank), his home amongst the sandhills of Wainoni, an eastern suburb of Christchurch. His earlier nickname of 'Fireworks', acquired in London, was coming into significance. His son Alex, a scientific apparatus and firework manufacturer, held patents for improving fireworks. The profits from the Tahuna Fire Fetes were to go towards publishing a journal of science ethics to serve as the organ of the Kingsley Club. This club, of around 100 members, dedicated itself to the removal of class distinction.

As usual, Bicky was in demand as a public speaker. The only College Professor to be so, he spoke on a wide variety of topics: 'Bacteria' to the Canterbury Women's Institute; 'Man and His Relation to Society' to the North Belt Literary Society; 'Evolution and Mimicry' to the Kingsley Club; 'Genius and Communism' to the Linwood Football Club; 'Chlorine as a Cure for Consumption' to the Philosophical Institute, 'Science and Religion' to the Rangiora Presbyterian Church; and 'The Photographic Process' for a practical course in photography which Sammy Page held for the Womens' Institute. At the Tahuna Fire Fetes he gave short demonstration lectures on electricity and chemistry. These however could not replace his popular, public, lectures on science and technology.

The College Board of Governors generally appeared to hold themselves aloof from public comment. A letter to the *Lyttelton Times* (signed 'Young Scientist'), asking the whereabouts of a telescope which a Mr Townsend had presented to the College two years earlier, went unanswered as did two follow-up letters. ⋯ *those authorities consider you nobody unless you attend University* ⋯. The second follow-up letter (signed 'Orion') also broached another subject.

> ⋯ (I hear) *Professor Bickerton's popular scientific lectures are to be discontinued by the authorities for no other reason than a little petty jealousy at the success of last year's lectures.*

Another correspondent (who signed 'Student') on the same day raised the same subject.

> *Can it be that the Board wish to prevent the working classes from learning and so raising themselves? I* ⋯ *hope* ⋯ *the Board, instead of preventing the continuance of the Science Course, will insist on all the other Professors giving evening lectures.*

This letter did draw a response. The Board stated Professor Bickerton could give popular lectures; he need only apply to the Board. This he immediately did, for four courses each of six lectures: Technology, The Utilization of Waste Products, The Experimental Science of the Century and The Chemistry and Physics of Organic Life. Bicky was back in his element again, seemingly oblivious of the festering sores left behind.

Whilst he had no competition from his fellow professors in public speaking, Bicky did not have the field to himself. Mr Worthington of the Temple of Truth could draw a crowd of 2,000. [A religious imposter, he four years later drew his largest crowd – 6,000 people, many of whom were intent on lynching him.] The President of the Canterbury Freethought Association, Mr W W Collins, who gave public lectures including some on science, drew crowds of up to 800 people.

Professor Hutton had resigned his Chair in biology and geology to become the curator of the Museum. As he retained the lectureship in geology, the College advertised for a lecturer in biology. This drew a letter to the editor suggesting Mr Collins be offered the position ⋯ *excellent teacher* ⋯ *does not offend religious opinion* ⋯ . Mr Collins promptly advertised a series of popular lectures on biology. The job however went to a respected scientist, Dr Arthur Dendy, of Melbourne University.

In the field of electricity the performance of Professor Richard, M.E. took Christchurch by storm. The M.E. stood for Medical Electrician. Castigated by an evening paper as a fraud and charlatan, praised by a morning paper as a healer and entertainer, he started each show by using electricity to 'cure' rheumatism, deafness, paralysis and even blindness. Each candidate had to be certified by a local minister that he or she was too poor to pay for the treatment. Professor Richard was, after all, primarily in business. The first part of his performance resembled a faith healer's show, the magic ingredient in this case being electricity. The second part was nearer vaudeville, where, in a highly entertaining and mirthmaking way, electrical tricks were performed. One involved handing a lady an orange which had been electrically charged – a shocking trick.

For general workmen 1893 meant a continuation of tough times. Unemployed men petitioned the Mayor and Government for work but there were no Government work schemes near Christchurch. The city mission was crowded out and had a great want of boots and clothing to distribute. Some women even had to borrow boots to wear to the mission when seeking support for their families.

These events had little effect on Canterbury College. The roll however had peaked and, although not then clear, the period of decline was to last a decade. But the majority of students, generally from well-to-do families, carried on as normal.

Student Life 1893

Early in the autumn students drifted back to Canterbury College. Havelock took pride in Ern having attained a B.A. degree. Following the formal confirmation of the previous year's exam results, the *Pelorus Guardian* commented (12 May 1893) ⋯ *His success shows what ability and energy can accomplish in a short time.*

Ern was now one of the elite – a postgraduate student. There were only fourteen in the whole country, of whom seven were at Canterbury. Of the latter, all but Ern studied languages. Throughout the country seven studied languages, one chemistry, one mental science, four mathematics and mathematical physics and two physical science.

The ranks of his contemporaries had thinned markedly; Willie Marris, for example, had moved on. A brilliant scholar, he had been placed first or first equal for the College Prizes (Exhibition) in both Latin and mathematics in each of his three years at Canterbury College. Since students were limited to one prize each, the mathematics prize had therefore each time been awarded to Ern (in 1890 he shared it with Marris), who had twice tied with Marris and once been runner-up. Each year it had been a game with the students to see if Marris planned to concentrate on Latin or on mathematics. Classics won. He returned to Britain, the country of his birth, with the Indian Civil Service in mind.

The results of the University of New Zealand's Senior Scholarship exams had been announced before the term started. Ern had entered in mathematics and in physics. The physics scholarship went to an Otago man. Ern's marks had been so close to those of the winner that the examiner in England had recommended that an extra scholarship be awarded to him. There was no precedent for such action and it proved unnecessary as Ern had won the Scholarship for mathematics. Hence it was his mathematical prowess (and possibly the absence of Willie Marris) which had returned Ern to Canterbury College for this fourth year.

For the first term of 1893 he enrolled in six courses; honours maths, honours chemistry, chemical laboratory practice, practical physics, general biology and senior botany. In mathematics he was in a class of his own; the only Canterbury student taking the Master's course. Six exam papers spanned the syllabus;

geometry, algebra, calculus, solid geometry and differential equations, mechanics and hydrostatics, optics and astronomy. The official title was Honours in Mathematics and Mathematical Physics. Ernest was a good student of mathematics. Of him, Professor Cook later said ⋯ *"He is possessed of considerable Mathematical ability and is endowed with great power of work so that he has been a highly successful student."*

The new academic year spawned the annual meetings of the student groups. Twenty members turned up at the College Lawn Tennis Club meeting which saw Ern elected to the Committee.

For the Football Club he was elected assistant secretary. Canterbury College could field only two teams, with Ern immediately going into the first team as a forward. He played in the first competition game of the season at Lancaster Park before a paying audience (Admission 6d, ladies free). That Saturday dawned with the grounds wet and slippery but the rain held off. College started the season well and in a very even game, much appreciated by the spectators, they defeated Christchurch 10-7. From there on it was mostly downhill. With one game cancelled because of a snow storm, and two forfeited through not being able to raise a team, College finished the season as bottom team. They won two games, drew one and lost the rest, even though most losses were in games described as fairly even contests. The club did not seem very healthy. The original draw allowed for three college teams but only two were fielded, and by the end of the season they struggled to raise even one team. Ern did not stand out in the first team but did receive sporadic mention in the newspapers. Occasionally he assisted or was prominent in the forward rush ⋯ *A College rush, lead by Morris, Rutherford, Haast and Dawson was stopped at the East 25* ⋯ and once ⋯ *the College line was again in danger. Rutherford, however, dribbled to the centre,* ⋯.

The Science Society persuaded Ern to be its secretary but apparently only with difficulty for, being conservative, he thought the society had gone rather too far in its earlier discussions on evolution. Presumably, as secretary, he organized the talks for the year, and he had a duty to turn up to record the minutes of each meeting, even that for June on 'Notes on Recent Science', held during a snow storm. The 'recent science' covered Water Power, Moas, Possible Mode of Mental Evolution, and Aluminium. That year physical science talks were given on ⋯ 'a New Cosmic Philosophy' (Professor Bickerton's Inaugural Address), 'Atoms and Molecules' (E S and A J Buchanan) and 'The Alternate Current Transformer' (C E Adams). At the conclusion of Adams' paper, Ernest Rutherford, whose course covered such devices, spoke on the subject. Walter Pye's talk about bodily organs had Ern record ⋯*special attention was given to the bearing of many of the points on the theory of evolution.* Although attendances at one meeting reached 100, (Laing on 'Our New Zealand Flora'), in general they were down on the previous year. At the year's end, the Chairman was to sound a note of caution in his annual report ⋯ *the Society has not been supported as it deserves by the younger students* ⋯ .

Ern did not again become an office holder for the Dialectic Society. Very few did so for two years running, and his stint as treasurer in 1892 appears to have exempted him from further work for the Society. Once again the printed programme shows the Society's activities to encompass debates, essay readings, a concert and Olla Podrida night. Amongst the essays was Apirana Ngata's on 'A Maori Parliament'. The debates covered the usual wide field of topical issues: 'That an extension of the College terms is both practicable and advisable' (Auckland University College had unsuccessfully suggested this to the New Zealand University); 'That the prohibition of intoxicating liquors is desirable' (opposed by Jack Erskine. Legislation allowing New Zealand voters to control liquor licences was passed later in the year); 'That limitation of the hours of labour is a proper function of the state'; and 'That the franchise should be extended to the women of New Zealand'. Ernest Rutherford's contribution to the 1893 programme was as the second speaker in support of the motion 'That the average value of environment as a factor in the formation of character is greater than that of heredity'.

Irrespective of his arguments in debate, as a boarder away from home Ernest was influenced by both heredity and environment. In Christchurch he lived in the Newton household and that was to have a major influence on his life. He was to marry the daughter.

The Newtons

Arthur Charles Newton entered life as a gentleman and with the help of the demon booze worked his way down. The only child of the last of a line of vicars, he was born at New Radnor in Wales while his Reverend father waited for his Reverend grandfather to vacate the family living as vicar of Bredwardine in Herefordshire. This living had been purchased in 1829 and was one of the best in England. It bordered on the Wye, an excellent salmon river. [Although the last Newton vicar died in 1862, the Newton family in New Zealand continued to have the power to appoint the vicar of Bredwardine until Charlie Newton signed away the right in 1918.]

Programme—Session 1893.

FIRST TERM.

APRIL 8. **INAUGURAL ADDRESS—**
"The Restoration of Philosophy."   PROFESSOR HASLAM.

APRIL 22.—**DEBATE—**
MISS S. HENDERSON will move "That an extension of the College terms is both practicable and advisable.
In Support—MR. W. G. PYE.
Contra MISS VON HAAST and MR. MACKAY.

MAY 6.—**DEBATE—**
Mr. Miss S. A. ATKINSON will move "That the prohibition of the sale of intoxicating liquors is desirable."
In Support—MR. E. S. BUCHANAN.
Contra—MESSRS. ERSKINE and A. J. BUCHANAN.

MAY 20. **DEBATE—**
MR. J. P. GROSSMAN will move "That literature tends to degenerate under modern democracies."
Contra—MR. F. A. PEMBERTON.

JUNE 3.—**ESSAYS—**
"Girton and Newnham."   MISS TODHUNTER.
Critic—MR. ROBISON.

"A Maori Parliament."   MR. NGATA.
Critic—MR. ALPERS.

JUNE 17. **DEBATE—**
MR. H. WARD will move "That limitation of the hours of labour is a proper function of the state.'
In Support—MR. DAWSON.
Contra—MESSRS. GIBSON and BANNISTER.

SECOND TERM.

JULY 29.—**CONCERT.**

AUG. 12.—**DEBATE—**
MRS. BURN will move "That the Franchise should be extended to the women of New Zealand."
In Support—MISS FOSTER.
Con ra—MISS GIBSON and MR. CRADDOCK.

AUG. 26. **OLLA PODRIDA.**

SEPT. 9.—**ESSAY—**
"Tennyson."   MISS B. GIBSON.
Critic—MR. W. F. WARD.

SEPT. 23. **DEBATE—**
MR. PYE will move "That the average value of environment as a factor in the formation of character is greater than that of heredity."
In Support—MR. E. RUTHERFORD.
Contra—MESSRS. SPEIGHT and JACK.

OCT. 7.—**ESSAYS—**
"Lives and Works of Beethoven and Bach."
MR. WATKINS.
Critic—MR. COHEN.

"The future of Art in New Zealand."
MR. CANE.
Critic—MR. VON HAAST.

OCT. 14.—**PRIZE ESSAY—**
"New Zealand, the Colony of Experiments."

Canterbury College Dialectic Society

Arthur received his education at Marlborough College in England, and went to New Zealand as a twenty-year old and possibly as a black sheep. Initially a farm cadet at French Farm on Akaroa Harbour, he later entered a partnership as a wine merchant. Within two years the partnership dissolved, and he lost his money. In the meantime he married Mary Kate De Renzy Gordon, a well educated and reasonably socially well-placed lady, whose father had been the first Town Clerk of Christchurch.

Arthur and Mary Newton had four children and a trip 'home' to England. Arthur's social status appears to have declined, perhaps as his drinking increased – gentleman, telegraphist, civil servant and/or librarian. A charming man when sober, he died in 1888 at the young age of thirty-five – rupture of the urethra of long standing, says the death certificate, alcoholism says the grapevine. [Or was that the hop vine?]

Mary Newton was thus a widow in reduced circumstances, with a young family. Her house at Carlton Mill Corner was a pleasant ten minutes stroll from Canterbury College along the bank of the river Avon. To make ends meet Mrs Newton took in College men as boarders. Only two are known, Christopher Craig and Ernest Rutherford; there may or may not have been others. Craig, also a Nelson College boy, won a University Junior Scholarship and attended Canterbury College from 1891 to 1894. It is not known when Ernest Rutherford started boarding with Mrs Newton. Certainly it was before 1893. Possibly it was in 1891. His previous room mates had moved into College House, the upper department of Christ's College. Willie Marris reminisced that Ern didn't because he was the wrong denomination. When Mrs Newton came into money she kept Ernest on because she liked him.

At the start of 1893 Mary Newton was forty-one years old though the long black dress and widow's cap she wore made her look more severe than she was in reality. Her daughter, Mary Georgina (called May to distinguish her from her mother), was a 16-year-old schoolgirl in the lower sixth-form at the Girls' High School. Sons William (13), George (11) and Charles (9) followed.

Arthur Newton's alcoholism had been hard on his wife. Often she and her younger spinster sister Emma had had to carry a paralytic Arthur home from the Carlton Hotel. In 1885 she had helped found the Christchurch Branch of the Women's Christian Temperance Union, and served as the branch secretary for the next eight years. The Union had many activities. It ran a self-supporting coffee shop in town to allow people to partake of refreshment without having to go into a public house. It ran temperance booths at the agricultural shows in opposition to the beer tents. Mrs Newton held the position of National Superintendent for this activity. She had also contributed to the Litigation

Defence Fund of the Sydenham Prohibition League, as had Mr Jeffries of Spring Grove, Ernest Rutherford's step-grandfather. [In later life she became more militant, going into hotels to turn full glasses of beer upsidedown. She even poured her son Charles' wine cellar stocks down the sink. She was a lady with a purpose, not the battleaxe that she might appear to be from her activities. In fact she had a heart of gold, one grandson describing her as "a real honey". She looked after the wives and children of tramdrivers, an 'at risk group' as they say today, and it is recalled that she never had to pay on trams. Generosity personified, when she died in an old people's home at the grand age of eighty-one, all she had retained were a suitcase, the clothes she wore, and a bible.]

George Rutherford's Visit to Christchurch 1893

Early in the year James Rutherford, now aged fifty-four, handed more of the operation of the firm Rutherford and Son, Flaxmillers, to son George, now aged twenty-six. George then planned a trip to Australia on flax business, travelling on the steamer that ran a regular service between Christchurch-Dunedin-Bluff-Hobart-Melbourne. This gave him the opportunity to visit Ern in Christchurch. To record his journey George purchased a diary. It records the route Ern regularly took between Taranaki and Christchurch.

> *Geo Rutherford*
> *Pungarehu,*
> *Taranaki.*
> *28 April 1893*

Ap 27, Thursday

Left Pungarehu by coach for NP broke down 3 miles from Oakura waited two hours for a brake got into NP at five oclock. Got cheque cashed by McDiarmid and also got bank draft £30. Jim went to Bayly's party. Gave uncles the cheques to cash. He gave me a letter of introduction to Mr Foxlee Chief Engineer of NSW Railways. Dull and showery.

Friday 28th 1893. Left the Breakwater per Mahuiapua at 10.30. Meet old fellow who knew the Nests down at Greymouth. Saw the signals from the house, Captain replied by blowing the Steamers whistle. Had a very bad time, no sleep, pumped out. Weather fine but hazy.

Saturday 29th April. Reached Wellington 8 oclock took my luggage on board Brunner which leaves for Lyttelton at 11 tonight. Met J Glover and Jim Nithir. Spent the afternoon and evening at McGregors. Went down to the steamer at 9.30 and went to roost. Went into the Free Library. Streets fearfully muddy have not seen the sun for a fortnight. Weather very wet.

Sunday 30th April. Weather dull and rainy had a fear passage reached Lyttelton at 7 oclock waited 2 ¾ hrs for the train. Ern came down went up with him to Mrs Newtons. Stopped at the Terminus Hotel. Got to bed at one oclock.

Monday 1st May. Put in the morning in looking over the town. What strikes a stranger most here is the queer style of architecture adopted in building the better class of houses. They are all gables, points and angles. Wrote letters to mother and Jim. The Christchurch horses all very good, the streets are also much cleaner than in Christchurch [Wellington?]. Ern came down to the hotel at two oclock and we went for a walk, went first to Canterbury Coll. It is splendid building it and the museum take up the whole square. Was introduced to Proff Bickerton also saw Proff Haslam. Went to the museum saw some splendid pictures and statuary. Went up to Mrs Newtons to dinner at six, I like her very much ditto Miss Newton who is very sensible and plays very nicely. Mrs N is a good talker and we had a long yarn socialism, Brotherhood of man, prohibition etc Ern went down to a meeting in the evening. The two Miss Gordons Mrs N's maiden sisters came up in the evening, they both strike one as clever women who might have done good to humanity as married women. Miss Gordon has lived in Sydney and says the suburbs are very beautiful. Mrs N offered to get me invitations to two dances if I will only stop in Chch for another week, she is determined that Ern shall attend May Ns first dance to be held at her aunt's Miss G and says that a certain young lady the nicest in ChCh is very anxious for him to come. Ern says he is not going. Mrs N says she would sooner have this young lady for a daughter in law than any one she knows. Mrs N invites me to come down and stop at her place a week before Xmas. She says she looks upon Ern as one of her family. She is very proud of his success. Went home in the tram (steam).

Tuesday May 2nd. Met Ern at 9 oclock in the Cathedral Square walked around got some books sent some music for the girls and left ChCh by the 12.10 train for Lyttelton. When Ern and I reached Lyttelton we found the Tarawera had just arrived and would not sail till six oclock, got the number of my berth after some delay No.110 and took my luggage on board. Saw Ern off by 3.15 train for Christchurch. The *steamer is crowded with passengers mostly for Dunedin. Had dinner at six and enjoyed it, I find my fellow passenger is Mr J Williams commission agent and head of the NZ Freemasons who is travelling over to Australia on the masons business he has got the upper berth is rather stout. I hope he does not come through in the night ⋯ .*

Initiation Into Research

The month-long midwinter vacation had brought with it the football club's biennial visit to Otago University. Fifteen members spent a long Friday on the train to Dunedin. The following afternoon the blues and the maroons once more met on the field of battle. The day was right – fine, with a light breeze that carried dense volumes of smoke across the ground from the local brickworks. The conditions were right – the ground in good order and a fair number of spectators present. The players however, were not right. Otago University, like Canterbury College, graced the bottom of its league. Even though Otago boosted its team with two ex-provincial players the game was tediously slow and uninteresting.

> ⋯ *some life was infused into the game by a capital passing rush, in which Buchanan, Rutherford, Gibson and Dawson participated, which shifted the play into the Varsity quarters where Cresswell obtained possession and nearly dropped a goal.*

Canterbury led 4-2 with five minutes to go but Otago scored two late tries.

Celebrating or drowning one's sorrows probably meant the same thing at the highly successful football dinner that night. Next day the Otago club chartered a steamer for an excursion down the harbour. On the Monday morning the Lawn Tennis teams drew their match. A much enjoyed social in honour of the visitors concluded a very pleasant trip. The Canterbury team then dispersed to various destinations; Ern went by train to Timaru, possibly to visit his Uncle William Rutherford's family who lived in the area.

The mid-winter vacation also marked a period during which Ernest had important decisions to make concerning his future. For the second term he enrolled for honours mathematics, general biology and senior botany only. The last two indicate he had made up his mind about his future career. He planned to go to Edinburgh University to take up medicine.

In mid-year he wrote to John Stevenson, an ex-Canterbury College classmate studying medicine at Edinburgh. The reply did not return until near exam time. ⋯ *I am glad you think of coming here. I have not the least doubt but you will get on all right* ⋯ . Stevenson gave Ern twelve pages of information and advice on Edinburgh, medical scholarships and bursaries, lecturers, lectures, what certificates to bring, which courses to take first (botany, natural history and physics), not to go to the medical school in Dunedin first, and what route to take between New Zealand and Scotland.

It is not known why Ernest Rutherford did not proceed with a medical career. Perhaps it was because of his success at Canterbury. Perhaps he was dissuaded by the drawbacks Stevenson mentioned: medicine now a five year course, living costs similar to Christchurch at £100 per year, large classes, uncouth and selfish Scottish students, and an Australian club that was just a smoking, drinking, gambling hall. Since only Stevenson's letter survives, it is possible Stevenson merely misunderstood a request from Ern for information about Britain in general.

For 1893, Ern had his sights set on a double honours degree. This had not been achieved in science since 1887 when Alfred Talbot of Canterbury College obtained first class honours in mathematics under Cook, and heat, light and sound under Bickerton. (Talbot had gone on to take medical degrees at Edinburgh.) At the start of the year Ern had enrolled in the honours chemistry class. One requisite of this course demanded that a candidate, on presenting himself for examination, hand in a paper, certified by his professor that it contained only the student's work, *embodying the results obtained by himself in some investigation or research in Chemistry*.

For this research Professor Bickerton suggested to Ern a problem of electrical synthesis of nitro-compounds of hydrogen, carbon and oxygen. Ern finally declined this suggestion. He felt he did not possess the intimate knowledge of chemistry required for the project. His only exposure to chemistry prior to the Honours course had been a one-term course for teachers. [There are indications that this project was connected to Professor Bickerton's interests in evolution and partial impact. Could biological chemicals be produced from electrical discharges in basic elements? Stanley Miller and Harold Urey attained great fame when they carried out similar experiments in the 1950s. In July of 1889 Bicky had given a public lecture on the theory of evolution as part of a series on organic chemistry. Even more interesting as far as Ern's future was concerned, in December of 1893 Walter Pye wrote an article for *The Press* entitled 'The Theory of Evolution' in which he stated the various facts of the day. For example, if a body were heated its spectrum of emitted light altered as the body changed from solid to molecule to atoms. There was even one further change at higher still temperatures ⋯ *The inference is irresistible that the elemental atom has broken up into still simpler forms.*]

Honours in experimental sciences could be taken in chemistry or in physical science, the latter either in heat, light and sound or in electricity and magnetism. Ern had not enrolled for the Honours Physics class during this, his honours year. This is no cause for surprise. Senior students did not bother enrolling for, or going to, the honours physics class. Ern had attended the honours classes during 1891 and 1892. The course consisted of but one lecture a week, Bicky's view being that senior students should work independently. He never dictated notes to the honours class. Instead the time was used as a tutorial to cover any points of difficulty the students stumbled over in the set books.

Electricity and magnetism for Honours covered three exam-papers and practical work. The papers were that for Senior Scholarship, another of wider scope and greater difficulty and a third containing questions and problems involved in the practical syllabus. In 1893 the examiner in England set questions in the first paper which required an understanding of electrical meters for measuring currents of up to 100 amperes, the magnetic behaviour of different types of iron, and the effect of an iron core in an induction coil. The second paper included questions such as

> *No.2 Determine the conditions under which an electric discharge, such as that of a Leyden jar, will be alternating.*

and

> *No. 4 Describe the process of electric welding by means of an alternating current transformer. Explain why it is possible to weld a tyre although the continuous portion of the hoop offers much less resistance than the weld.*

The practical paper included

> *No. 4 It is not unusual to specify that an electric-light cable shall have an insulation resistance of 5000 mega ohms per mile after being immersed in water for 24 hours. How may this insulation resistance be measured?*

Other questions covered the determination of the constant of a ballistic galvanometer, the measurement of self-induction and the evaluation of the magnetic properties of an iron sample to be used in dynamo magnets.

Ernest Rutherford and Jack Erskine were both in their third year of practical physics as Ern had not taken practical physics during his first year. Junior by a year, Jack was taking physics for his B.A. finals and for Senior Scholarship. Like Ernest, he had not bothered to enrol for the honours lectures this year.

Earlier in the year the pair probably worked together but later Jack studied optics while Ern worked on the more advanced experiments involving electricity and magnetism such as measuring the coefficient of mutual inductance of coils, the determination of the magnetic permeability of iron and specific inductive capacity (dielectric constant) of materials.

The course of practical work in physics was, for the first time, fully laid out in the College's Calendar for 1893. Surprisingly, at the same time the necessity for an original investigation had been dropped from the requirements for honours in physics. Neither Bicky nor Ern seem to have noticed this change. If they did, they disregarded it. Ernest Rutherford prepared to undertake a project involving original research in electricity and magnetism.

After turning down his Professor's suggestion of a problem in electro-chemistry, Ern opted to extend one of his physics laboratory experiments on the magnetic permeability of iron. This involved winding two coils of wire on an iron core. A current passed into one coil (the magnetizing coil) produced a magnetic field which magnetized the iron core. The second coil (whose output went to a ballistic galvanometer) measured the degree of magnetization. In this way, the amount by which the iron core enhanced the magnetizing field due to the current in the first coil could be readily determined. These measurements were invariably taken as the magnetizing field was slowly changed.

Ern's extension was to determine whether or not the same results were obtained for rapidly cycling magnetizing fields. This covered a problem of some technical importance relevant to the use of magnetic cores in alternating current transformers. Measurements around one magnetizing and demagnetizing cycle yield the energy lost per cycle. This energy is wasted and merely heats the core. Considerable differences in opinion existed amongst electrical workers as to whether or not the energy lost per cycle depended on the speed of cycling.

It may not be entirely unconnected that Professor Bickerton regularly demonstrated Nikola Tesla's experiments with high frequency transformers, and that on the 25th of August 1893 Tesla addressed a public meeting in St Louis, sponsored by the National Electric Light Association, in which he demonstrated how a discharge tube could be lit some distance from his transformer. [In 1936, on the 80th anniversary of the birth of Nikola Tesla, Lord Rutherford wrote, on behalf of Cambridge University, to the Society for Founding the Nikola Tesla Institute in Yugoslavia ⋯ *and in particular I was greatly influenced in my younger days by his experiments on high frequency currents.* ⋯]

For his study Ern devised an ingenious timing apparatus, so simple yet so

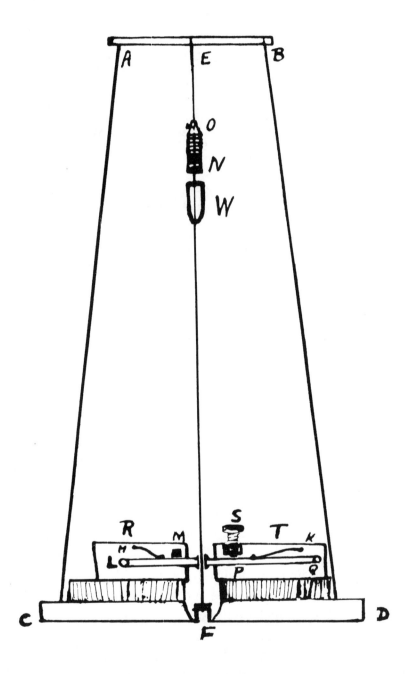

Rutherford's Timing Device

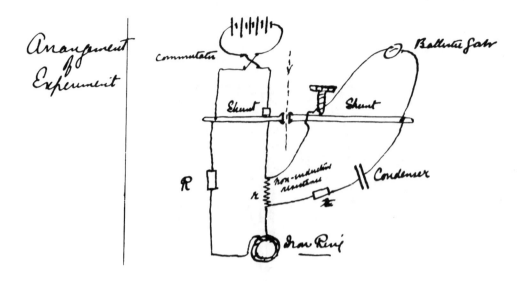

Arrangement of Experiment

Commutator

Ballistic Galv.

Shunt   Shunt

R non-inductive resistance

r

Condenser

Iron Ring

elegant, to study the rise of electrical currents in circuits during time intervals as small as one thirty thousandth part of a second or less. The heart of the device consisted of two horizontal copper rods, pivoted at their outer ends and nearly touching at their inner ends. Springs pulled each rod upwards against a metal stop. One rod had a screw for its stop, by means of which the difference in vertical height of the inner ends of the two rods could be adjusted in a controlled manner. A taut vertical wire, passing between the inner ends of the rods, guided a falling weight. As the weight struck the end of a rod, the electrical circuit involving the rod and its stop was opened.

Knowing the speed of the falling weight and the difference in vertical height of the rod ends, the time interval between both circuits being opened could be readily deduced. The speed could be calculated from the laws of gravity for a freely falling weight. To assist this approximation, the weight was made much heavier than the copper rods; it was released by an electromagnet; the nickel guide wire was well oiled; and the axial guide hole in the weight was constructed so that the weight touched the wire only at the two ends of the hole. Typically the weight fell through a distance of around a metre (three feet and three and a half feet being Ern's standards). With forty threads to the inch on the screw and the screw head divided into twenty divisions, his mechanical device was capable of determining time intervals of one hundred thousandth part of a second.

Ern planned to study several different types of iron and steel, as he had done earlier in his laboratory class. For mathematical simplicity the magnetic cores were in the form of rings. In going to rapidly-changing magnetizing fields a further problem normally arose, that of eddy currents. These are the currents induced in the magnetic core itself whenever the magnetizing field is changing. Such currents could be eliminated if the magnetic rings were fabricated by winding many turns of very fine, insulated, iron or steel wire. This he did. [Modern transformer cores are made of stacked thin sheets.]

Ern had now thought out the investigations he wished to make, designed the apparatus needed and worked out how to reduce the experimental data: a good keen man poised to launch himself into the heady world of original research in competition with the best in the world.

Fate chose this moment to strike. His carefully selected field of research had been pre-empted by a group working at King's College, London. They reported to the Royal Society of London meeting of 20th of April 1893 and the published version, entitled 'Magnetic Viscosity', appeared in Volume 53 of the *Proceedings of the Royal Society of London*. It was by mere chance that a copy became available to Ern.

The Canterbury Philosophical Institute's holdings of *Proc. Roy. Soc.* ceased at 1883. In May of 1893 the Institute ordered the back issues as well as future issues. This action was initiated not by Professor Bickerton, the Institute's President, nor by physical scientists but by a biologist, and the treasurer. Volumes 35 to 53 arrived together prior to the Institute's council meeting of September 11th. To have one's planned research pre-empted must have been a terrible blow to the embryonic researcher. However, Ern elected to carry on because he knew his apparatus allowed him to utilise time intervals very much shorter than those used by the King's College group. [A preliminary account of the work at King's College had appeared in the 9th of September 1892 issue of the '*The Electrician*', a weekly illustrated journal for electrical science and industry. It is not known if Ern saw this at the time. If he did it may have influenced his choice of research topic.]

With his time apparatus Ern studied the times of rise of currents in coils, the magnetic permeability of different types of iron and steel, the effect on the magnetic hysteresis curve of the rapidity of the rise in magnetizing current, the rate of magnetic penetration into magnetic materials and the rate of rise of currents in iron and steel wires. The order in which he performed these experiments, and the rationale for taking on work in this field is not known for sure, except that they followed from standard laboratory experiments, and Ern spent six months elaborating the subject. His earliest laboratory notebooks have not survived. However, the notebook he used for recording botany and biology lectures has. Biology notes start at one end, botany at the other. Ern's heart did not seem to be in these subjects as his notes are sprinkled with doodles, designs based on his initials, an applied maths problem and the odd mind-wandering question: *What does a gown and hood cost?* Both sets of lecture notes peter out with the syllabus not fully covered, leaving about 100 blank pages in the middle of the notebook. These Ern used to record his physics research. The first thirty-five undated pages appear to be notes of his work completed prior to the examinations of 1893. His time apparatus is not described but was being used. The notes are not a record of experiments as they were carried out but appear to have been written after the event. All in all, my guess is that they are a rough draft of the latter part of notes on the research presented to his examination supervisor as evidence of his original work. If that be the case, they would have been written up a month or so before the exams, that is, before November 1893. Ern's summary of his work contains no clear conclusions. Augmented by later experiments his final conclusion was that soft iron and steel exhibit quite appreciable magnetic viscosity in rapidly changing fields.

Diploma Day, 1893

The annual ceremony of presentation of diplomas to the graduates of Canterbury College had been designed by the University to be a formal, dignified ceremony. On the other hand, the undergraduates regarded it as a time of fun and festivity. Not surprisingly these views clashed and this year at Canterbury more so than usual, mainly because the stern Professor Brown presided. He was renowned for being school-masterish, long winded and lacking a sense of humour. An ex-Canterbury student studying medicine at Edinburgh wrote, in a letter to Ern, that during lectures at Edinburgh

> ··· *no mistakes are allowed to pass without interruption* ··· *There are no little gods here like Brown. The fellows would not tolerate such a brute for one moment. They would hoot him out of the room* ··· .

Once more students, friends and relations crowded into the College Hall long before the starting time, the audience spilling out into the porch and quadrangle beyond. Professor Brown, representing the Chancellor of the University of New Zealand, led in the official party which comprised of the Board of Governors, representatives of the clergy, the armed services and the law, the mayor, and the college teaching staff. As usual the students serenaded with their standard ode of welcome 'The animals came in two by two'. There quickly followed an undiplomatic song aimed at Professor Brown, their Chairman for the ceremony. (Tune: Ta-ra-ra-boom-de-ay). A sample will suffice.

You know it always was my rule
To treat them all as though in school,
To show up each offending fool:
But now they murmer calm and cool:
Ta-ra-ra-boom-de-ay,
How near Diploma Day
The time old scores to pay,
Ta-ra-ra-boom-de-ay.

This set the tone of the function. Following the preliminaries, Professor Brown launched into his address. It was typical of the man. Long, far too long. A columnist in *The Press* recorded ⋯ *Long vacations, long lectures, long songs, long speeches on diploma days, long faces on exam days – such appear to be the fashion at Canterbury College.* Professor Brown kept on his feet for at least forty-five minutes. A few days before the ceremony he had tried to curtail the undergraduates' festivities. This was, to say the least, indiscreet but not nearly as foolish as his attempt to stonewall the songs by talking. An editorial in the *Lyttelton Times* condemned the behaviour of both sides but showed sympathy for what was inflicted on the students ⋯ *A long string of semi-detached generalities, however true, is about as interesting as a list of copy-book headings.*

As the speech droned on, the interruptions crept in and escalated. The students attempted to sing their songs, the chairman attempted to stop them. In doing so he showed only that he was absolutely devoid of tact. "I shall name that student", speared one fearful and dire threat thundered from the platform. As one student later said of the Chairman's remarks

It aint exactly what e' sez
But the nasty way e' sez it.

Professor Brown threatened to adjourn the proceedings if the interruptions did not cease.

Throughout this chaos those central to this gathering sat quietly in the front rows – the uncapped graduands. What they thought of threats to stop the ceremony is not recorded. Their presentation followed the Chairman's speech and lasted but a few minutes for they were few in number: twenty-four in all – eight M.A.'s, one M.Sc., two L.L.B.'s and thirteen B.A.'s. One third were women. As they were presented the ladies were heartily cheered. The men were vocally assured that they were good fellows or, if members of the football team, their prowess on the field commented on. The order of presentation being by degree and alphabetically, Ernest Rutherford (new B.A.) rose last but one to mount the stage.

Heinrich von Haast, recently elected to the Board of Governors by the graduates, then delivered the second and final speech of the day. The instigator of the singing of songs at Diploma ceremonies at Canterbury, he himself, as an M.A., LL.B., had been leading the students' celebrations only 4 years previously. Now practising law, he was a favourite of the students. Until, that is, it became clear that he too planned a long speech. Again the students interrupted with their songs. Heinrich von Haast at least had the sense to good humouredly wait until the music stopped each time before continuing. Three cheers for the professors closed the official proceedings. Hardly had the last of the platform party passed through the rear door than the students took over the stage and completed their musical programme.

So ended another Diploma Ceremony. Of this one it could be said that Ernest Rutherford was lucky to be presented with the diploma for his first degree from Canterbury College. For sometime afterwards newspaper reporters and correspondents apportioned the blame for the near fiasco. [It was to be 1903 before the students devised an effective way of controlling longwinded speakers. A banner declared that speakers were allocated ten minutes. When the first speaker reached the ten minute mark a deafening rustle had every undergraduate buried behind a newspaper. That did not work so time was called, then a ten second countdown followed by an eruption of alarm clocks. At this, the speaker nervously sat down.]

By way of contrast, the ceremony in Auckland had, through the tact of their Professor Brown (a chemist) proceeded well enough even though some items would have *been hissed off the stage at any second class nigger minstrel show*. After the officials had left, a skeleton placed in the chair presided over the musical section. This act caused the *Auckland Star* to question, in an editorial, not merely whether the ceremony was worth preserving but ⋯ *Is the University of New Zealand worth preserving?* The University was going to have to look into its Diploma Ceremonies. In the meantime, life proceeded.

Votes for Women

The Women's Christian Temperance Union (WCTU) appreciated that temperance could be achieved only when women had a vote. This fight became their major thrust. Educative work in this cause had been going on since the early days of the colony. The first Women's Franchise Bill had been introduced into, and thrown out of, Parliament in 1878. Skirmishes occurred nigh on yearly with Parliamentary votes going against enfranchisement by about two to one. The cause had its male supporters in Parliament, notably Sir John Hall who used his expertise in parliamentary procedure to advance the cause. Outside parliament Christchurch's Mrs Kate Sheppard, the National Franchise Superintendent of the WCTU, stood out as the real champion. With tact, patience, personality, determination and reasonableness, she always concentrated on converting, not antagonising, an opponent. The WCTU distributed literature, asked debating societies to take up the topic, put in train legislation relevant to home and family and, probably most importantly, presented ever growing petitions to Parliament.

The huge petition of 1893 contained nearly 26,000 signatures. An Electoral Reform Bill once more wound its tortuous way through Parliament. This Bill, which specifically barred women from standing for Parliament, extended the vote to all citizens, not just land owners. Whilst hopeful, supporters did not know what would happen. Previously such bills had faded away but this one did not. Suddenly, it passed the final stages with a majority of two. One last step remained: the formal signing of the Bill by the Governor-General. This could not be taken for granted because he was known to be opposed to women's enfranchisement. Besides, the brewers immediately raised a petition against such signing.

With just two months to go to the elections and time running out, the women of Christchurch once more used their initiative. They called a public meeting to register women in anticipation of the bill becoming law. Both Mrs Sheppard and Mrs Newton addressed the large gathering. Six days later the Governor-General, with a few strokes of his pen, at last granted women the vote. New Zealand was the first country in the world to so do. [They could not however stand for parliament until 1919; the first women member of Parliament being elected as late as 1933. New Zealand later provided one other first. Mabel Howard, an ex-neighbour of Professor Bickerton's, became the first female Cabinet Minister in the British Commonwealth. Also it should not be forgotten that individual states in America had women voting earlier than did New Zealand.]

This enfranchisement raised problems for many people, such as 'Annie S' who wrote to the *Lyttelton Times* asking if it was now in order for ladies to propose to men. The Minister of Education jokingly assured one electoral meeting that the women's franchise would not lead to a tax on bachelors. However, the immediate problem was to register all women in what little time remained before the elections of November 28th. 120,000 new voters were very rapidly added to the rolls. No doubt there was jubilation in the Newton

"Disguise our bondage as we will,
'Tis woman, woman rules us still."
                    Tom Moore.

household, with Mrs Newton being so closely associated with both the movement and Mrs Sheppard. Ernest Rutherford, the boarder, was therefore a close observer of these events. For him the elections were also a milestone. Having come of age the year before, it was the first time he, like the women of New Zealand, was eligible to vote.

Three years elapsed before the College students found cause to work women's franchise into a diploma day song. This was in response to the arrival of Professor Mathew, the new Professor of English from England who appears not to have known that Canterbury College admitted female students. (To the tune of the music hall favourite: 'Wot cher or Knock 'em in the Old Kent Road')

Chorus –

"Wot cher !" all the fellers cried;

> *"Who'll we get to teach, blokes?*
>
> *Now he's out of reach, blokes?"*

"There'll be another prof. inside,

When we come to swot next year."

Then comes Mathew in a steamin' boat;

We says "How do" in our Sunday coat.

'E says, "Lord why female students float

> *Round about the College rooms and quad."*

We says "Gent, I'll let you in the know

Why the girls don't stop at 'ome and sew

We've got female franchise in this show;"

> *So the women "scoop their bits of sod."*
>
> *Chorus –*

"Garn, you beat the Yankees just a bit;

You would make a feller 'ave a fit;

You chaps think you've got a pretty wit,

> *When you tell a feller sich a yarn."*

"Well," says we, "I think we'll let him learn;

Chaps wot live in England can't have hearn

We New Zealanders 'ave passed the turn

> *Where they think that women only darn.*
>
> *Chorus –*

"So now, chapsies let us give the prof.,
A right welcome such as suits a toff,
Who don't sneer and jeer and laugh and scoff
*   At the blokes who weren't brought up at 'Ome.*
"E ain't fell into our groove just yet,
But 'e'll soon be there, that you can bet;
'Ere's 'is 'ealth, so come and 'ave a wet,
*   Tell 'im that we're bloomin' glad 'e's come."*

Professor Mathew lasted but two years at Canterbury College.

Research 1893 continued

Ernest Rutherford pioneered original research in electricity and magnetism at Canterbury College. Mostly he worked alone. Sammy Page, the laboratory assistant, could help in constructing and setting up equipment but not with the actual physics of the problem. Professor Bickerton, while ensuring all his honours students carried out original research, had not carried out any fundamental work in electricity since his early work in England on a new relation between heat and static electricity (*Phil. Mag.* **46**, 450-452 1873). In this study he had used very direct methods to examine why charged bodies discharged faster in hot air than in cold. At Canterbury he had been mainly occupied, as far as physics was concerned, with teaching elementary work. In the meantime he had not lost his skill as an experimenter in electricity for he maintained this through lecture demonstrations. At one public lecture he displayed the brevity of an electric spark by using one to illuminate a rapidly revolving wheel in a darkened room. The wheel appeared motionless. At another he showed that electric waves, when reflected or refracted, obey precisely the same laws as waves of light.

During Ern's research, Professor Bickerton would look in occasionally and would go away satisfied that progress had been made. He seldom interfered. There were two reasons for this. Firstly he recognised that Ern had outstanding ability in original research and could look after himself. It was the Professor's way to devote most time to the less able students who obviously needed help. Secondly, he did not have the mathematical ability to assist honours students in the theoretical aspects of electricity and magnetism.

The University Calendar quite clearly stated that the mathematical level required for honours in physical sciences was that of the B.A. degree. This Bicky could cope with. However, the overseas examiner disregarded the

Calendar and demanded a higher level of mathematical knowledge. Bicky had great physical understanding, and could help the advanced physics students with matters of measurement techniques but he never claimed to be a mathematician. While expert in a graphical method of analysis that gave great insight into the basic physical principles of a problem, he could not solve advanced problems analytically. Besides, this was beyond his field. He had been employed to teach chemistry and electricity and, by default, had extended to cover most of physics. The mathematical side was to be covered by the Professor of Mathematical Physics, Cook. This was so for optics and astronomy but Professor Cook knew little of advanced electricity and magnetism. He did however obtain several books on the subject for the College library.

It was to be two years before a student complained bitterly of the mathematical level demanded by the examiner for honours in physics in defiance of the Calendar requirements. It is very clear though that no student could do well in honours electricity and magnetism unless also taking honours in mathematics. John Chisholm, the Otago student who had beaten Ern for the Senior Scholarship in physical science, took honours only in electricity and magnetism. He was to attain merely a second class degree.

That Ernest Rutherford studied under both Professor Cook and Professor Bickerton was undoubtedly the foundation of his future career. He was influenced both by the imagination and flights of fancy of Bicky, moderated by the down-to-earth approach of the staid mathematician. Not that Bicky failed to emphasise the basic points of scientific research. He was almost certainly the best advocate for research in the country. At one of his public talks on 'Sound and Music' he

> ⋯ *laid considerable emphasis upon the invariability of law, upon the absence of debate in the realm of experimental science and the reliance placed by physicists on observation and experiment as contrasted with the metaphysical mode of attacking problems by thought without work.*

At another he had emphasised that nearly all modern applications of electricity were due in the first place to the painstaking labour of those who loved science for its own sake. Bicky was very much the free thinker when compared with Professor Cook, who confined himself to the narrow path of formal mathematics.

Besides the lack of help on the theoretical aspects of his research, another of Ern's problems concerned the lack of apparatus suitable for the honours course. This was but part of a bigger problem – Canterbury College had no physics laboratory. Students worked where they could. For his experiments

Ern had used a variety of sites in the 'Tin Shed', including the right of way and a store room in the attic. Lack of space where equipment could be left set-up was not the major problem. His work involved measurements with a ballistic galvanometer, a device highly sensitive to vibration. At one stage he tried operating with the galvanometer in the room below his experiments. Much of his work had been carried out in the Great Hall but here too vibrations were still a very serious problem. The motions set up by someone stepping in the front door would disturb the galvanometer for some minutes. The Hall presented another problem, that of being required throughout November and December for examinations, whereas Ern wanted to continue his research as soon as his own exams finished in mid-November. Professor Bickerton suggested a solution to both problems. When the original College buildings were constructed he had reported to the Board on the character of the concrete used. He now recalled that both dens below the lecture rooms had good concrete foundations and would be ideal for mounting galvanometers and other vibration sensitive instruments. So he dictated a letter to the Board of Governors.

> *Canterbury College*
> *Laboratory Dept*
> *Nov 2nd 1893*

Sir,

I have the honour to ask for the use of the cloak room under the Modern Language room for a time during the vacation.

It is required by Mr Rutherford who has commenced a research on the time effect of magnetic permeability. The College Hall has been used to commence the research, but examinations will be there and the floor is not steady enough as Mr Rutherford's experiments are of a very delicate character. He has already recorded time observations of the thirty thousandth of a second and hence perfect steadiness is of the most extreme importance. Mr Rutherford has spoken to the students using the room and they are quite willing to do without it for the time being.

> *I have the honour to be Sir,*
> *Your obedient servant*
> *A W Bickerton*

[It is interesting to note that the den requested is the eastern den, not the western one we now call the Rutherford Den.] In mid-November Ernest sat his honours exams in the Hall. With exams over, and permission given for the temporary use of the den, Ern shifted in. It is not clear which of the two dens he used that summer.

At the same time other facilities improved. The College Library had shifted from its cramped quarters into the Hall. Its holdings were not extensive: 135 books covered the whole of chemistry and physics, while eighty-eight others encompassed maths and mathematical physics. In particular, for Ernest, it had a shortage of modern books on advanced electricity. He had implored the Professor of Mathematical Physics to recommend strongly that the College purchase particular books. This Professor Cook had willingly done. At the end of November, immediately after his exams, Ern took out a new arrival – Lord Kelvin's *Mathematical and Physical Papers*. What he read caused him to head up a new page in his notebook. This is the only dated page in the book so perhaps marks the recommencement of work after his honours exams and thus signals the start of a new research towards the 1851 Exhibition Scholarship.

DEC 5 1893

Experiments on secondary circuits

After reading Lord Kelvin's article on "An accidental illustration of a transient current in an iron bar" page 473 Vol III of his collected works and Lord Raleigh's Article in the Philosophical Magazine for 1886 on "Resistance of conductors conveying alternating currents" it occurred to me that Faraday's statement of the absolute equality of the time integral of the induced current on making and breaking the circuit that this was only true in the case of very fine wires and that the thickness of the wires in the secondary circuit would have the effect of making the current at make and break different since the resistance of conductors increases with the shortness of duration of a transient current.

Kelvin had reported to the Royal Society of Edinburgh in March 1890 on a first-class, but accidental, illustration that transient currents in metallic conductors flow in a very thin surface layer. Lord Armstrong, while connecting up a plant to light his house with electricity, had accidentally shorted the dynamo terminals with a bar of steel he was holding in one hand. His fingers were painfully burnt where they had been touching the bar. No mention of a lordly oath is recorded but he certainly dashed the bar to the ground. An attendant, on immediately picking it up, found the bar to be quite cool.

This article motivated Ern to use his equipment and expertise to study transient currents in iron wires. Exactly how far Ern progressed with this research in his last month before returning home for the summer holidays is not certain. What is clear and undeniable is that by the end of his fourth year at University he was an experienced and accomplished researcher in physics. Ernest Rutherford had found his niche in life.

Application for a Job at Christchurch Boys' High School

Ern's academic successes were not the only ones in the Newton household. May Newton gained third prize in her small lower-sixth form class. She achieved this with third place in English and in Latin but second place in mathematics and in science. The latter two possibly suggest a little coaching from the boarder. A proud Mrs Newton and her household watched as May ascended the platform in the College Hall to receive her prize from the Countess of Glasgow, the wife of the Governor-General of New Zealand.

The following day, the 20th of December, was a very busy one for Ern who had booked a passage on the steamer to take him home to Taranaki. Several last minute jobs were taken care of including returning a library book, volume 3 of Thomson's *Mathematical and Physical Papers*. He also found time to write a letter of application for a teaching job.

The expanding Boys' High School in Christchurch had advertised for another assistant master *to teach the usual secondary subjects, including French and Elementary Science. A knowledge of Sloyd or Shorthand might be an additional recommendation.* The appointment would commence on the 1st of February, the start of the 1894 school year, so applications closed on January 11th.

Canterbury College
Christchurch
Dec 20 1893

Chairman of the Board of Governors.

Sir
         I have the honour to submit my application for the post of teacher at the Boys High School which has been lately advertised.

I was educated at Nelson College and won a Junior University Scholarship in 1889. The last four years I have spent at Canterbury College, taking my B.A. degree and winning the Senior University Scholarship for Mathematics last year. This year I sat for the examination for M.A. with Honours in Mathematics and Mathematical Physics and also for Honours in Physical Science (Electricity and Magnetism). For the B.A. degree I passed in the following subjects – Latin English French Mathematics Mechanics and Physical Science.

Besides these subjects I have also attended lectures in Chemistry and Biology passing the practical examination in both necessary for the B.A. and B.Sc. degrees. I have had no experience in regular teaching but have undertaken a considerable amount of private tuition the last three years. This year also I conducted a class in Physical Science for the B.A. degree.

I have the honour to be
Your obedient servant
E. Rutherford BA.

That evening Ernest sailed home for the long summer holidays to await the results of his examinations and job application.

Because of a tight job market for graduates fifty-eight men applied for the Boys' High position, many of them better qualified than Ernest Rutherford B.A.. Their qualifications ranged widely. Some were experienced teachers from other high schools, for instance Mr Cooke who had taught Ernest at Nelson College, or Henry Kitchingman who, four years previously, had been preferred for a teaching vacancy at New Plymouth High School to Ernest Rutherford the schoolboy. Some were distinguished graduates older than Ernest such as Walter Pye M.A., a founder of the Science Society. Some were distinguished contemporaries like Edwin Norris, B.A., M.A. (Hons), later a registrar of Victoria University College of Wellington, and James Hight who had trained at the Christchurch Training College for teachers as well as at Canterbury College. Some were well known in the community, for example Thomas Cresswell B.A. the captain of the College Rugby team. One had been a contemporary of Ernest's at Nelson College, Charles Major B.A., M.A. (1st Class Hons.) later to rise to be revered Headmaster of King's College, Auckland. No doubt existed that the advertisement had attracted high quality applicants including many from Australia.

Competition would be fierce. The choice lay in the hands of the Headmaster who held an M.A. degree from Oxford. His seven assistant masters consisted of two B.A. men who had studied at Oxford and Cambridge respectively, a junior-form master, two distinguished M.A. graduates from Canterbury College (Grossman and Alpers), and two M.A., B.Sc., graduates in natural sciences from Canterbury College (Laing, the founding President of the Science Society and Speight, later to be Professor of Geology at Canterbury College).

The College Board accepted the Headmaster's recommendation, a man from 'Home'. Thomas Jackson, B.A., had good credentials: tall, athletic, thirty-four years of age and an experienced teacher. During his ten years at Mill Hill School, London, Jackson planned and fitted out a science lecture room and chemical laboratory. Well versed in French, he had spent several vacations in France. Though a graduate in Arts from Manchester, he had mainly taught mathematics and science. To this end he had passed the first section of B.Sc. and M.B. (Bachelor of Medicine) for the University of London examinations. Jackson had left England on medical advice to cure a severe attack of rheumatism. Though a recent arrival in New Zealand, he already claimed to be completely restored to health.

Ernest Rutherford had failed in his second attempt to become a school teacher. Many other good New Zealand graduates had also missed out. The newest member of the College Board of Governors, Heinrich von Haast, suggested to the Board that in the schools under the Board's control teachers should be selected only from colonial graduates. But Jackson's appointment stood.

When the new school year started, 238 boys turned up, a big increase on the previous year's 188. The Board immediately appointed another master from their list of unsuccessful candidates. They chose a graduate of Canterbury College with a first-class Master's degree in Classics, and five years teaching experience at the Timaru High School. They also took on a part-time master, a Christchurch man who was a recent Canterbury graduate with an M.A. with honours in Latin and English. Though not an applicant for the earlier post, he had the advantage of immediate availability since he lived locally.

All in all, Ernest Rutherford was having great difficulty obtaining a job in New Zealand. It was enough to drive a young man overseas.

Chapter 7

PLANNING FOR THE FUTURE

Canterbury College 1894–1895

Rutherford is with me a dim but delightful memory. He was entirely hopeless as a schoolmaster. Disorder prevailed in his classes.

Reminiscence about schooldays of 1894,

by one of Ern's junior pupils at the Boys' High School.

Here Mr Rutherford saw the possibility of supplying the world with light and power with a nominal expenditure of energy and with no waste

Report on Ern's talk to the Science Society,

Lyttelton Times, 28th May 1894

Christchurch 1894

When 1894 opened so too did the New Brighton Pier. After two and a half years in construction, it had reached its full length of 214 metres. Beyond the breakers fishermen could catch large sharks, and excursionists from Lyttelton could land from steamships. Visits to the seaside were promoted as beneficial to the health – one went there 'to take in the ozone'. The pier owners relied not only on the ocean. ··· *to assist visitors to assimilate the ozone, a penny-in-the-slot galvanic battery has been placed on the pier and has been kept going almost from morning to night.* [There still stands at North Beach a building called the Ozone. In fact ozone is poisonous.]

In Christchurch a soup kitchen reopened for the winter to help feed the poor, and entrepreneurs planned a ship canal to link city and estuary. Traction engines on public roads had to have two men to warn horse traffic and to assist in passing the engine safely.

Professor Bickerton's name was, as usual, seldom out of the public eye. As a popularizer of science and technology he proposed to give twenty-four public lectures at the College (these ceased after the first term when the Board asked him to pay for the advertising from the fees he charged); as Government analyst he reported in court on the contents of a bottle found beside a corpse; as noted speaker he addressed the Linwood Literary Guild on evolution; as a man with a social conscience he was on the advisory committee of the Avon Refuge (a shelter for hard-up families); as a consultant to industry he gave a lecture and display on coal at the Canterbury Industrial Association conversazione; and the Kingsley Club held a social in his honour.

Naturally his astrophysical theories were not forgotten. A series of articles which he had written earlier for the *Lyttelton Times* had been reprinted together as 'A New Story of the Stars'. This gave an explanation of temporary stars (novae), variable stars, double stars, star clusters, nebulae and even the origin of the solar system. His final chapter argued against Lord Kelvin's conclusion that the Universe will die as the suns loose their heat. Instead Bicky proposed that the radiated energy would be absorbed by the dust and molecules in space and thereby returned to bodies that collided with them. Hence the title of his last chapter – 'The Immortality of the Cosmos'.

Well after publication, this work came to the attention of newspapers in America. As the *Detroit Evening News* reported: ⋯ *To persons of common education this theory is satisfactory; if it is not satisfactory to the astronomers they ought to tell the world why not.*

The *Lyttelton Times* devoted a sub-leader to this belated recognition ⋯ *The Professor will doubtless appreciate these tardy tributes to his courage.* When the science journal *Nature* reported a bright light on Mars (Is it inhabited? Have our own species strayed there?) Bicky quickly explained the light in terms of a partial impact. He continued on to also explain away the so-called canals of Mars. In his eyes his theory was all-encompassing.

Canterbury College 1894

On the 25th of February 1894 the University of New Zealand's agent in London telegraphed the results of the examinations of the previous November. Each student had a code name to preserve anonymity. Those for M.A. candidates started with the letter A, LL.B.'s with B and B.A.'s with C. Ernest Rutherford's examination scripts were therefore known only to the examiners as those of 'Acute'. On the second page of the telegraphed list appeared

 ··· *first abate abjure acute both subjects* ···

Ern had obtained his desired double first class honours.

It was necessary for the University to release these telegraphed results immediately because lectures for the new academic year were due to start on the 10th of March. However they were subject to confirmation or correction when the full results arrived by mail some two months later at which time an official list was published in the newspapers. This 'official' list credited Ern with first class honours in physical science but only second class honours in mathematics. The following day a hasty correction gave him a first in both.

Ern immediately telegraphed his success to his former teacher, Jacob Reynolds, at Havelock who passed it on to his friend, the editor of the *Pelorus Guardian*. Reynolds needed encouragement at this time because a year earlier both his young daughters had died, and a month earlier a neighbouring schoolteacher had shot himself. Curiously, it was three weeks after Ern's news appeared that George Price, who had probably been responsible for the death of two of Ern's brothers, killed himself.

With the official results from England came the examiner's detailed comments. The physical sciences examiner, Principal Garnett of the Durham College of Science, reported

 ··· *Acute is very excellent.*

At the start of the new academic year Ern had returned to Christchurch. He had no job. Neither had he a scholarship. Financial support came by tutoring struggling students, and possibly from his father and elder brother. He had returned to continue original research with a view of thereby attaining a research scholarship overseas. At the same time he could add a B.Sc. to his stable of degrees by taking two more science subjects. He may have had no other option. Any applicant for the scholarship had to be enrolled for a University course in 1894.

Of the four compulsory subjects for B.Sc.: mathematics, physical science, chemistry and natural science, Ern had already passed the first two for his B.A. He was therefore restricted to taking chemistry and natural science. For the latter he had three choices: biology and either botany or zoology; human anatomy and physiology; or geology. His flirtation with the biological sciences (and a possible career in medicine) had ceased the year before, although he had passed the practical exam in biology. At the start of term Ern enrolled for junior geology, senior geology and chemical laboratory practice. The latter was connected with his research as he had already passed that course the previous year.

Among the new students at Canterbury College in 1894 was one May Newton, his landlady's daughter, who launched her unsuccessful academic career by enrolling for classes in Latin, English and biology.

The college football club elected Ern as a committee member and as a selector. Two teams were entered in the Saturday competitions, and one in the Thursday competition against commercial teams (e.g. Drapers, Hardware). Little success fell to the College teams – they were invariably beaten if not thrashed. Complaints were made that elements of professionalism were creeping into the game in Christchurch – good players were given jobs. But this did not explain College's poor performance. Regrettably, football at Canterbury College was in decline. During the mid-year vacation the college could not even scrape together one team.

The first team finished bottom of the senior competition. Their standard was so low that when they played Otago University at Lancaster Park most of the 1500 spectators watched an adjacent game. Appropriately the university match resulted in a scoreless draw. The game against Linwood was described as not worthy of a senior contest and many spectators wandered off to watch a junior match. Once again Ern played a relatively undistinguished role in the first team. Occasionally, he rated a mention in the newspaper reports.

> ⋯ *Afterwards the maroons, headed by Hawkins, Gray, Rutherford and others, made a determined charge* ⋯ *Dawson, Gray and Rutherford worked well in the scrum* ⋯ *Hawkins and Rutherford best in open* ⋯

He even scored a try against Drapers during one of the team's few wins.

However the true measure of Ernest Rutherford may be found in the last game of the season against Christchurch. College were at the bottom of the table; the day was wet and cold. By half time College were down 0–8. Then their forwards came to life. Ern took the ball to the Christchurch twenty-five and Craddock completed the move by potting a goal. 4–8. Ern picked up at the centre and ran again to the opposition's twenty-five. As he went down in a tackle he threw the ball behind him where Dawson took it on the full and scored. 7–8. Regrettably Craig failed to convert the try. In his last rugby game Ern had given his best exhibition of the season. Perhaps as he played against what most regarded as impossible odds, he had in his mind's eye the image of Porky Littlejohn on the Nelson College cricket field, bowling himself to exhaustion against two first-class batsmen.

The poor performance of the College football teams during the year was not entirely the fault of the team members but part of the general malaise beginning to pervade the undergraduates. A capping day song captured the feeling (Tune: 'All Doing a Little Bit')

> *Oh sacred nine assist me as I sing my modest lay*
> *About a certain College, which is famous in its way,*
> *Successes academical have won for her a name,*
> *Her sons however, sadly lack all love of manly game;*
> *The undergrads have seemingly no stout esprit de corps,*
> *As we return defeated, trailing homewards from the park,*
> *The fops are always ready with some would be smart remark.*

> *CHORUS*
> *They drawl-as they-cadge from you a fill.*
> *"Aw! have you really been put down by 20 points to nil."*
> *But they would not soil their collars,*
> *Oh, no; not for "fawhty" dollars.*
> *The thought really makes them ill.*

This reality flew in the face of a motion debated by the Dialectic Society "The tendency at the present time is to overestimate the value of athletics".

The senior mathematics students, all from out of town and living in digs, had organized the first debate of the year. As the programme recorded for April 7th

> *Mr E. RUTHERFORD will move "That the time has arrived for the establishment of a residential department in connection with Canterbury College."*
> *In Support – MR CRAIG*
> *Contra – MESSRS MACKAY and ERSKINE*

Throughout the year the society put on its usual type of programme but something was lacking; in particular an audience. The capping day song continued

> *Our dialectic suffers from this milk and water state,*
> *Some barely twenty fellows ever roll up to debate;*
> *The visitors and ladies all the vacant spaces breach.*
> *But only in an azure moon they dare to make a speech;*
> *'Tis labour Herculean to attempt to run a dance,*
> *The fellows are so spiritless, you hardly have a chance,*
> *To meet all your expenses what with music, supper, ball ;*
> *The coterie of patriots often have to bear a call.*

CHORUS

> *Oh muse! are we only here to swot.*
> *Can we ever weld our studies here with College life or not.*
> *Let us end this masquerading,*
> *This veneer of lore parading*
> *And pull together on the spot.*

Even the Science Society lost spirit that year. The members elected Ern to the committee. As such, he seconded the motion to make the ever willing Sammy Page a life member, and moved the motion which halted the serving of refreshments at the end of meetings. Ern addressed the Society twice and helped with the conversazione. Of these, more later. The minute book did not record attendances that year but William Dawson, the secretary, gave his, and his committee's, view of the undergraduates in the draft of the annual end-of-year report.

> $\cdots$ *In spite too of the merit of the papers, the attendance during the year has on the whole been far from satisfactory – many of our original members have left and their places have not been filled, for there is at present a plentiful lack of science students at this college. Like other of our college institutions this society has not received the support of the present race of undergraduates who it must be confessed are of a degenerate type. They have either dropped all enthusiasm, or else they reserve it for their text books. If this meeting therefore should be of the opinion that this undesirable state of affairs is likely to be of long duration, it is evident that it would be necessary to consider the question*

of suspension or of reconstruction. If the society is to continue and flourish it must receive the support of some few at least of undergraduate scientific enthusiasts. The rest they leave to you.

'You' did not pull his weight. At the end of 1894 the Science Society went out of existence.

Graduation Day 1894

Ernest Rutherford received his M.A. (double first class honours) with full lack of pomp and ceremony: through the mail. As it had threatened, the Senate of the University of New Zealand banned degree ceremonies. *The Press* deplored this act:

> ⋯ *True, the students were a little boisterous during the proceedings and not always very complimentary to the ultra-solemn person on the platform.* ⋯

But things were no different overseas. As it pointed out

> ⋯ *At Edinburgh we hear that the students resort even to peashooters, possibly owing to the fact that the Scottish youth is not so ready with verbal repartee as the Southerner, and finds a peashooter the most effectual means of conveying an epigram that shall sting.*

The students did not accept the ban and applied to the Board of Governors to be allowed to hold some function to publicly acknowledge those who were the happy recipients of degrees. Granted. The function differed but little from its predecessors. A ticket only audience packed the hall. As a prelude the students, accompanied by piano, violin and drum, sang the first five of their songs. The last concerned the football team, in praise in particular for the man who scores the try. Its final verse enthused:

> *Five minutes yet to time, boys – now just another point,*
> > *O tempora, O mores,*
> *Oh Dawson, Speight, and Rutherford – just sweep them off the ground*
> > *O tempora, O mores,*
> *I told you so – they're over!*
> > *Upon the ball they lie,*
> *Hurrah! Hurrah! Hurrah!*
> > *O tepo – tempora*
> *All glory to them all for all have scored the try.*

A full platform party led by the Chairman of the Board entered to the hackneyed greeting of 'The animals came in two by two'. This day the speeches were punctuated with applause and song. Tolerance and good nature prevailed. The Chairman spoke of this ceremony, the new staff, and various matters including the future career of those in front of him.

> "Many, perhaps, would enter Parliament." (Laughter and applause.)
> "I do not mean the ladies, and hoped they would be content with having
> had the franchise granted them." (Applause and "Ohs".)

Following the Registrar's long winded report, which detailed such minutiae as the number of students in each class, the real business of the afternoon was got down to, the presentation of the graduating students. Ernest Rutherford ascended the stage first. Greeted with good natured banter from his fellow students, he merely signed a register of graduates – the students' answer to the ban on the public presentation of diplomas – in a book which had been made especially for the occasion.

The Exhibition of 1851 Scholarship

The Great Exhibition of 1851, Prince Albert's brainchild, had been held in London as a showpiece of British industry and science. The exhibition hall itself proved to be a modern marvel. Covering ten hectares of Hyde Park, the world's first large prefabricated building had been erected in just 22 weeks. Of iron and glass construction, Punch magazine christened it the Crystal Palace. The name stuck.

On display were more than 100,000 objects from 14,000 exhibitors with half the space allocated to foreign products. During its six month season the Exhibition had been a tremendous success – not the least financially. When the accounts were finalized the net profit exceeded £180,000, a veritable fortune. This windfall helped establish the great cluster of Museums at South Kensington, including the Science Museum and the Natural History Museum.

In 1891 the Commissioners of the fund established a scheme of postgraduate research scholarships for students from Great Britain, Ireland, Canada, Australia and New Zealand. Officially called the Exhibition of 1851 Research Scholarship, but usually shortened to the 1851 Scholarship, each scholarship paid £150 per year for two years. They could be held anywhere in the world by a student who showed evidence of outstanding ability for original research in a field of importance to their national industries.

In 1891 the University of New Zealand had been allocated a nomination for 1892. The research theses of two students were forwarded to the University's examiners in England to choose whom should be nominated. Both candidates were chemists. 'Test', Professor Bickerton's student, had studied the active principle of the native pepper-tree and also the influence of water vapour in causing or accelerating the action of H_2S, HCl, HBr and HI on various metals. The examiner regarded both efforts as lightweight and showing no sign of aptitude for original work. 'Box', a student of Professor Brown's at Auckland, had attempted a much more ambitious project. He tried to discriminate between the physical and chemical theories of solutions.

The nomination, and later the scholarship, went to 'Box' – David Jackson. The examiner cautioned that neither entry would have stood the slightest chance of a scholarship had it been submitted from an English or Scottish University. Deeper study and a more careful write-up were required.

Both Bickerton and Brown were primarily teachers and stimulators. Brown published only one paper while at Auckland, and that on the insulation of cold stores. Both were practical men, Bickerton the Colonial analyst and Brown the consultant to the Auckland Gas Company and the Waihi Gold Mining Company. Both vigorously encouraged and fostered research by their honours men. Naturally many projects they suggested were connected with their own interests.

Jackson had proposed to devote himself to investigating methods of extracting gold and silver from ores – a topic of major importance in New Zealand. In the meantime, Professor Brown had put another student, James Maclaurin, on this work. Jackson studied hyponitrites at Melbourne, the yellow coloured substance canarin at the Royal College of Science in London, and, on having his scholarship extended for a third year, gained his Doctorate at Heidelberg with a thesis entitled 'Synthesen in der Hydrobenzolreihe'. A confidential report on his work stated he had been badly advised in topic at each place and should have stuck to his original intentions. The two-page report concluded

> ⋯ *He cannot be said to have made a substantial contribution to science by research in the slightest degree commensurate with the value of his Scholarship.*

[David Jackson became a private consultant in London.]

The Commissioners offered a second nomination to the University of New Zealand to be finalised by May of 1894. Late in 1893 the University requested that the Commissioners postpone the Scholarship until 1895. This would allow candidates time to perform research during 1894 and to have their work sent to the University's examiners at the usual time of November. The Commissioners agreed.

Research for the 1851 Scholarship

Contrary to popular mythology, Ernest Rutherford's research for the 1851 Scholarship was not motivated by electromagnetic signalling. His interest was still in the magnetization of iron at high frequencies, a subject not only at the forefront of electrical science, but of importance to the electrical industry where alternating currents and iron-cored transformers were the high technology of the day.

As soon as he had once again settled into college life, Ern started taking out library books. He commenced with his favourites from the previous year – Gray's *Absolute Measurements in Electricity and Magnetism Vol 1*, Oliver Lodge's *Modern Views of Electricity*, and the recent arrivals: Lord Kelvin's *Mathematical and Physical Papers Vol 3* and J J Thomson's *Recent Researches in Electricity and Magnetism*. All these books had been recommended for the library by Cook as Professor of Mathematical Physics rather than by Bickerton who taught practical electricity.

The College still had no laboratory for physics experiments. Once more the Registrar received a letter requesting a place where physics research could be carried out undisturbed.

Canterbury College

April, 2 1894

Sir

We the undersigned respectfully request the use of the gown room below the Mathematical Lecture room for the purpose of conducting electrical researches.

At present it is used only by a small number of students and there would be ample accommodation in the other gown-room.

In conducting electrical researches a stone or concrete support for the galvanometers is an absolute necessity; for the vibration of a wooden building is fatal to the accuracy of observations. Even in the large hall a passing vehicle or a step at the hall-door interrupts observations for several minutes and in the Laboratory the effect of vibration is still more marked.

We have the honour to be

Your obedient Servants

E Rutherford

J A Erskine

The College Committee resolved ⋯ *to raise no objection in the meantime, no complaints having been received.*

Jack Erskine held the UNZ scholarship for experimental science. He too carried out electrical research as required for his Honours (M.A.) course. As well he had enrolled for junior geology and honours mathematics. Jack's research had been spawned by Ern's. Often they worked together but mostly Ern worked alone.

Usually Ern laboured on his experiments for half a day at a time. He required constant electrical currents, which meant that before each session a battery of Grove cells had to be prepared. Sammy Page, Jack Erskine and the 'lab boy' Willie Bickerton occasionally helped by preparing batteries, and whenever two people were required to make observations. Sammy Page and Professor Bickerton helped in the design and construction of the apparatus.

Bicky would look in occasionally to see how the work was progressing. Always available for technical advice, he read the new books to keep up with Ern. But he did not interfere with the direction, as Ern had proposed the field himself. Bicky provided support and encouragement, two of the main ingredients required by a young fellow with a good idea.

Later, Jack Erskine was to criticise Professor Bickerton for not checking the mathematics associated with Ern's early work. This appears to be unfair and may be more of a criticism of Cook, the Professor of Mathematical Physics, who does not seem to have been involved in any way other than recommending books on advanced electricity, an extremely mathematical subject, to the library. And in general this was usually a result of a student urging he do so.

At the end of the academic year Ernest Rutherford handed in two theses. Thesis I covered his honours research of 1893 – a full description of the construction and testing of his timing device, and his measurements using this apparatus to study the high frequency magnetization of iron. Iron and steel cored solenoids had been used to determine the depth of penetration of the magnetic field into iron and steel as a function of time. He also showed experimentally that an iron-cored transformer, with its primary and secondary windings on opposite sides of the core, will be very inefficient at high frequencies unless the core is very finely laminated. As he concluded ⋯ *In rapidly changing fields the lines of force prefer to pass through air rather than through the usual path through the iron. This fact is of great practical interest in regard to transformers.*

It is interesting to speculate about this thesis. In itself it met all the criteria asked for by the terms of the 1851 Scholarship. Had the University of New Zealand not asked for a one year postponement of the nomination, Ernest Rutherford would have entered only this work. I don't believe he would have won the nomination for 1894 ahead of James Maclaurin, but if he had, one point is clear. He would not have gone to Cambridge as they did not admit non-Cambridge graduates prior to 1895. What then would have become of Ernest Rutherford?

Ern's researches of 1894 were reported in his second thesis – Thesis II. In it he had extended his earlier work to yet higher frequencies. In this thesis he first reviewed the conflicting conclusions of all the great electrical scientists – Hertz, Lodge, J J Thomson and others – before stating ⋯ *In the experiments that follow it will be shown that iron is strongly magnetic in rapidly varying fields even when the frequency is over 100 million per second.*

For magnetic fields varying much more quickly than his time apparatus could produce, Ern turned to the well-tried method of using the oscillatory discharges of Leyden jars. (These electrical capacitors are made by coating the inside and outside of a glass jar with metal foil. Electrical charge can be forced from one foil to the other so that one foil has an excess of electrical charge while the other has a deficiency by the same amount. This is one way of storing electrical energy.) He obtained the charge separation initially using an old Voss machine (an electrostatic friction machine which works on the same basic principle as the Wimshurst machine) and later with a Ruhmkorff coil. (This is essentially a high voltage transformer. A battery supplies a current to the primary coil, the magnetic field of which then attracts a magnet thus opening a switch in the primary circuit. This causes the field to turn off thereby releasing the magnet which falls back and turns the current on again. A secondary coil magnifies the induced voltage. The device exists today as a car ignition coil.)

When the charged capacitor is discharged through a spark gap in series with a few turns of wire around an iron needle, the needle experiences an oscillatory magnetic field. Ern determined the resulting magnetization of the needle by using a homemade magnetometer – a small magnet supported by a fine fibre. The magnet would initially align itself with the horizontal component of the Earth's magnetic field. Any other magnetized material, such as the needle, brought near it, would then cause the magnetometer to rotate to a new equilibrium position. An optical lever (a light shining on to a mirror cemented to the magnet is reflected to a distant screen) allowed small angles of rotation to be measured very accurately. Such devices are very sensitive to vibration so are usually mounted on heavy stone pedestals.

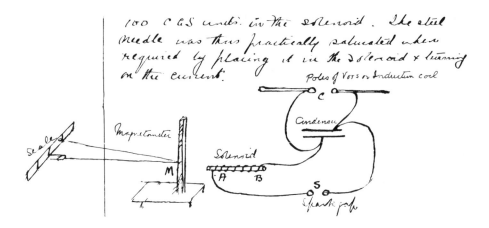

Ern found the magnetometer deflection to be proportional to the needle diameter (and thus to the surface area of the needle). As expected, only a thin layer at the needle's surface was magnetized by a current pulse of short duration.

Ern measured the actual depth of penetration in a most ingenious manner. He monitored the magnetometer deflection as the magnetized needle dissolved away in boiling, dilute nitric acid.

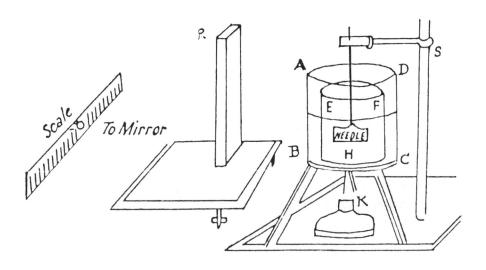

In this way he determined the thickness of the magnetized surface layer to be a quarter of a millimetre. Furthermore, this layer itself consisted of a thin outer layer magnetized in one direction, with a thicker inner layer magnetized in the opposite direction. Ern correctly deduced that this pattern was due to the well-known damped oscillatory nature of the discharge from a Leyden jar. When the spark jumps the spark gap the current flows first one way then in the opposite direction. This oscillation is rapidly damped out, and for his case went through one cycle only. The strong current flow in the initial direction

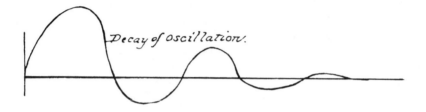

Decay of oscillation.

Magnetisation of Iron.

magnetized the needle to a depth of a quarter of a millimetre. The weaker return pulse magnetized the surface in the opposite direction but predominated for only a depth of a quarter or so that produced by the first pulse. (F Savary had reported these alternating layers in 1827 in *Annales de Chemie*, a journal Ern did not have access to.)

Ern had invented a new method of studying heavily damped, high frequency current oscillations in electrical circuits. The ratio of the current in the second half oscillation to that in the first half oscillation could be readily determined by placing two identical, uniformly magnetized steel needles in two coils in the discharge circuit.

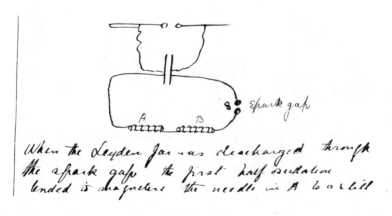

Spark gap

When the Leyden Jar was discharged through the spark gap the first half oscillation ended is magnetised the needle in A to a till

The two coils were wound in opposite senses so that the first, third, fifth etc. half oscillations tended to demagnetize one needle but magnetize the other. With the latter already magnetized to saturation, these current pulses would have no effect on that needle. Similarly, the second, fourth, sixth etc. half oscillations would have the opposite effect on each needle. Hence one needle would be demagnetized by the larger, odd number half oscillations, and the other would be demagnetized by the smaller, even number half oscillations. It was a simple matter to show that for his apparatus the current in the second half cycle was only half that in the first half cycle.

He used the magnetic needle technique to investigate the current pulses in various circuits connected to a discharging Leyden jar. The wavelength of electromagnetic waves could be measured very simply using Lecher wires, whereby a standing wave is established on two parallel wires adjusted in length so that they resonate electrically. [As late as the Second World War this method was the only one available in the Physics Department laboratory at Birmingham University to measure the wavelength emitted by the newly designed cavity magnetron, the high-powered generator of short wavelength waves that made possible high resolution radar for submarine finding, night-fighter aircraft and bomber navigation.] Ern repeated Oliver Lodge's classic experiment of 1888 on the speed of electrical waves along wires, the magnetizing coil and spark gap now being at the end of two long copper wires adjusted in length for resonance.

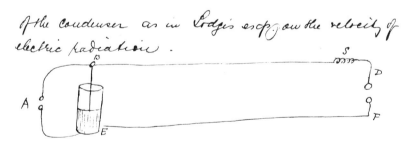

With each wire about 20 metres long (equaling half a wavelength) the frequency of oscillation was several million per second. In each case the previously uniformly magnetized needle was partially demagnetized at these frequencies. Though easily measurable, the effect was quite small since only a thin surface layer of the needle has its magnetism reversed. The magnetometer deflection typically changed from 300 units before the pulse to 285 afterwards.

To study the magnetization of iron at even higher frequencies, when the depth of penetration would be even less, it became necessary to make the detector more sensitive, so Ern built his 'compound detector' which contained a bundle of 24 very fine, glass-hard, steel wires each of length 1 cm. He first dipped each wire in paraffin to prevent eddy currents passing from one wire to another and mounted the bundle in the end of a thin glass tube for ease of handling. This detector was far too sensitive to use in the Leyden jar experiments.

To achieve the higher frequencies Ern turned to Hertz's dumb-bell oscillator.

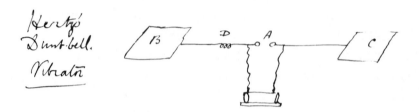

With plates about 20 centimetres square, frequencies of around 100 million cycles per second were generated since this circuit has a much lower capacitance than an ordinary Leyden jar. With his compound detector inside a coil of just two turns in one arm of the resonator, Ern showed that the amplitude of the oscillations for this Hertzian oscillator died away about as rapidly as in the ordinary Leyden jar, and that the depth of penetration at these high frequencies is merely one hundredth of a millimetre.

He repeated Hertz's study of the currents in a resonating circuit that was separated from the generating circuit.

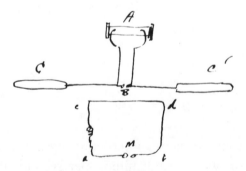

Hertz could observe effects only through the spark induced across the spark gap of the resonating circuit. Ern placed his compound detector inside a coil of three turns of wire in one arm of the resonator. This was an incredibly sensitive method; it not being necessary that a visible spark should occur. Strong effects were observed at the magnetometer even with a resonator spark gap of over 25cm wide.

The second half of Thesis II reported further details of experiments to measure the absorption of energy and the resistance of iron at high frequencies. He also built a balance to compare the currents flowing when shared between two parallel coils.

Ern wound the differential coil very carefully, and with the currents flowing through the two branches travelling in opposite directions. The degree of demagnetization of his compound detector inside the differential solenoid gave a measure of the difference in current flowing in the two arms of the circuit. In England J J Thomson had suggested a qualitative method of studying high frequency currents in various branches of circuits by placing a discharge tube in a coil in each branch. The comparison of currents could be made by the degree of brilliance of the luminous discharge in the tubes. Ernest Rutherford's magnetic detector was far superior in sensitivity and gave very accurate quantitative results. Such was to be a feature of all his later work. Where others devised qualitative methods he devised techniques for quantitative measurement.

Apart from an appendix covering his work in determining the resistance of spark gaps, Ern reported one more experiment in his Thesis II. The aim had been to see if a magnetized needle could be used as the detector of the intensity of waves at different parts of a circuit oscillating freely. He placed a metal plate near one of the plates of the Hertzian dumb-bell oscillator and from it ran a wire about five metres long. Ern used a previously magnetized needle to study the current along the wire, and particularly at the end for the two cases where the end was 'free', and where the end was terminated with a metal plate. This was a standard, oft-repeated, demonstration.

   ··· *The experiment was not proceeded with any further as the subject of distribution of waves along wires has been worked out experimentally by several methods.*

Ern opened his summary page with

   ··· *Before starting this research I was uncertain whether iron was magnetic in very rapid varying fields or not.*

He closed with

> *... It has been shown that iron still keeps its magnetic properties for frequencies of 500 million. On account of the small quantities of electricity set in motion I did not pursue my experiments with still higher frequencies of oscillation but I have no doubt, by the use of very thin steel wires, that iron will be proved to be magnetic for the highest frequencies yet obtained. ...*

Ernest Rutherford's second year of original research had been very fruitful. He had made a contribution to electrical research, and to materials science, of which anyone would have been proud.

With Electricity then at the forefront of science, the local newspapers often reprinted articles from overseas on the new technology. Scientists predicted that light, like water and gas, would soon be conveyed in pipes; that pictures would be conveyed by telegraph; and that moving pictures could be transmitted along electrical wires. Professor Bickerton, like most professors who taught electricity, could reproduce Hertz's experiments whereby an electromagnetic pulse could be sent from a transmitting circuit to a nearby receiving circuit. This was invariably carried out to demonstrate the properties of electromagnetic waves rather than as a display of the possibility of 'wireless' signalling.

Early in March a newspaper report had described the work of Mr Preece, of the British Post Office, who had experimented with electromagnetic signalling by induction across the Bristol Channel. Bickerton knew Preece. They had worked together at the Hartley Institute at Southampton teaching students for the Telegraph Service of India. Bickerton had taught theoretical and practical electricity, and Preece practical telegraphy. In April, another newspaper article had mentioned work by Edison in signalling to a moving train by induction from a wire alongside the train.

Ernest Rutherford ceased his experimental work for the year, early in October. He did not appear to have considered signalling by electromagnetic waves.

His Thesis II records the work he performed, but not necessarily in the order he carried it out. However some clues to his progress and interests in 1894 survive. He had actually started this work in December the previous year, for the few weeks which separated exams and summer vacation. Returning to Christchurch at the start of the academic year in early March of 1894, he once more took up his researches.

Let knowledge grow from more to more,
But more of reverence in us dwell;
That mind and soul, according well,
May make one music as before,
But vaster.
— Tennyson.

Felix qui potuit rerum cognoscere causas
Atque metus omnes et inexorabile fatum
Subjecit pedibus strepitumque Acherontis avari.
— Vergil.

Canterbury College

Science Society

SESSION 1894

HONORARY PRESIDENT:
DR. DENDY.

PRESIDENT:
MR. J. P. GROSSMANN.

HONORARY SECRETARY:
MR. W. H. DAWSON.

HONORARY TREASURER:
MR. C. A. CRAIG.

COMMITTEE:

MISS E. STEVENSON.   MR. E. RUTHERFORD.
MISS S. HENDERSON.   MR. R. M. LAING.

The Society meets in the Chemical Lecture
Theatre, at 7.30 p.m.

Programme—Session 1894

FIRST TERM

MARCH 31—*Annual General Meeting.*
Obscure Life in Australasia...............DR. DENDY

APRIL 28—
Standards of Conduct: A Survey of Ethical Systems
............................MR. J. P. GROSSMANN

MAY 12—
Electrical Waves and Oscillations...........MR. E. RUTHERFORD

JUNE 9—
Science Notes.

SECOND TERM

AUGUST 4—*Conversazione.*

AUGUST 18—
The Subterranean Crustacea of New Zealand.........DR. CHILTON

SEPTEMBER 1—
Limits of Responsibility.................DR. LOMAX SMITH

SEPTEMBER 29—
The Principles of Stereo-Chemistry.............DR. EVANS

In May he addressed the Science Society on the subject 'Electrical Waves and Oscillations'. The minutes record him reading a paper

> ⋯ *in which he dealt with oscillatory discharges in general, referring more particularly to the recent researches of Hertz and Tesla and their bearing on Maxwell's Theory. The paper was fully illustrated by experiments performed by Mr Rutherford with the assistance of Mr Page and Mr Erskine – the most striking of the experiments being a reproduction on a small scale of Tesla's experiments on rapidly alternating currents. Mr E S Buchanan and Mr Erskine spoke on the paper ⋯ .*

The talk received just a brief mention in a Monday newspaper – *The paper was well illustrated by numerous experiments which were well arranged and highly instructive.*

A fortnight later a fuller account, over one column in length, appeared in the *Lyttelton Times*. Ern had started by demonstrating discharges from Leyden jars, pointing out that rotating mirror photography showed the discharge to be oscillating. The work of Hertz and others was covered. The loud crack and flash of the spark, together with the information that the electromagnetic wave travelled at the speed of light along a wire, caused the reporter, (if not Ern), to state that

> ⋯ *This would point to the unity of all forces, and indeed to the identity together of every known variety of force. It would seem to tell us that sound and light and heat and electricity are only moods of one force, just the same as some chemists are thinking that there is only one kind of matter in the universe and that the materials we now call elements are themselves capable of division into atoms that shall all be alike. ⋯*

Following a mechanical analogy using two tuning forks, Ern displayed Hertz's experiment whereby a 10MHz electromagnetic wave was transmitted to an adjacent resonating circuit. Placing ebonite or glass between the two circuits he showed how electromagnetic oscillations could go through any insulating material, but merely stated that even a three foot thick brick wall would not stop the radiations, yet the thinnest metal plate or gauze would. However the main part of his talk concerned electrical power.

He next discussed the production of light by electricity and hinted at inexpensive lighting. A full description of the operation of the transformer was given, followed by the point that overhead power lines were a danger to firemen in America. He displayed Tesla's experiment whereby a discharge tube glowed when held near the Tesla coil, a step-up transformer resonating at a frequency of several tens of thousands of cycles per second. This high frequency method of lighting provided no danger to the human body.

> *… Here Mr Rutherford saw the possibility of supplying the world with light and power with a nominal expenditure of energy and with no waste.*

In saying this Ern merely paraphrased, or pirated, Tesla's public statements. [The Grammar School in Toowoomba, Australia, requested a printed copy of Ern's talk on behalf of a local tradesman but none was forwarded as the Registrar of Canterbury College claimed it was not printed.]

In September the Science Society held another Saturday night conversazione at the College. Festivities started at 7.30 p.m. and admission cost one shilling. A professional string band provided music and the Engineering department displayed its new equipment. The large crowd thoroughly appreciated the Society's efforts.

> *⋯ Later in the evening a modification of Tesla's experiments on high potential currents was performed in the Chemical Lecture Theatre by Mr E Rutherford.*

On neither occasion is Ern's magnetic detector of short current pulses mentioned. It would have been extremely difficult to demonstrate it at these public events because of the sensitivity of the magnetometer to vibration.

The Science Society reserved its June meeting for science notes. Jack Erskine spoke on 'Theories of Matter', William Dawson on 'Synthetic Chemistry', and Mr Laing on 'A New Order of Plants'. In the absence of the other scheduled speaker, Professor Bickerton, Ernest Rutherford gave a short account of the importance of quartz fibres. No details were recorded. A quartz fibre was almost certainly used to suspend the magnet of his magnetometer. The technology was not new to Christchurch. In January 1891 the Australasian Association for the Advancement of Science had met there. Professor Lyle, the President of the Physical Sciences Section, had given a wide-ranging address on 'Advances in Physical Science and its Applications' which had covered electromagnetic radiation, Hertz's experiments, liquification of gases, Langley's Bolometer, the manufacture and uses of quartz fibres, the magnetization of iron, electric dynamos and electric welding. Several of these topics were to be of interest to Ernest Rutherford. There is no evidence that he attended the 1891 AAAS meeting but both Bicky and Sammy Page did so, and Lyle's talk appeared in full in the conference report.

On the 28th of October 1894 Professor Bickerton certified that the work reported in Rutherford's two theses ⋯ *is the result entirely of his own original work* ⋯ and forwarded the theses to the University of New Zealand. Once more the outcome was transferred to the hands of the Gods overseas and candidates faced a wait of several months before their futures would be decided.

In the meantime life carried on and Ern looked to publishing his research work. The *Transactions of the New Zealand Institute* appeared yearly. As a condition of publication, papers had first to be read at a local branch meeting. On the 7th of November the Canterbury Philosophical Institute held its annual general meeting. The retiring President Mr Laing delivered his Presidential Address on 'Marine Algae of New Zealand'. More than twelve other papers were tabled and taken as read including one by E Rutherford M.A. entitled 'Effect of the discharge of the Leyden Jar on the Magnetization of Iron.'

The *Transactions* had been published since 1868. Very few papers on physical science had ever appeared; just the occasional one on earthquakes, seismometers, astronomy, the earth's magnetic field, atmospheric optics, astrophysics and electricity connected with the telegraph system. No fundamental research in electricity had previously been reported there. Professor Bickerton wrote to Dr Hector, the editor and the Director of the New Zealand Institute, in support of Ern's paper.

> *Canterbury College*
> *Laboratory Dept.,*
> *Dec. 18th/94*

> *Dr. Hector*
> *Wellington*

> *Dear Sir,*

> *Mr E. Rutherford M.A. of this college is forwarding for publication a series of researches laid before our local Institute. The Transactions of the Institute have hitherto been very deficient in Physical papers and as Mr Rutherford's paper is of very great merit and quite abreast of the work of leading electricians & also in a direction that is at present exciting a great deal of interest in the scientific world, I should beg you very strongly to recommend its insertion.*

> *Yours faithfully,*
> *A. W. Bickerton*

On the same day he asked for the latest date on which papers could arrive. Dr Hector replied that the end of January would be safe. He continued

> ··· *Of course Rutherford's papers will be printed if sent up through the Society. I glanced over his theses before posting it to London. It seemed very high class work.*

Ern forwarded the draft of his Thesis II. His first publication therefore reported his work of 1894, not his first researches.

It was printed in the Miscellaneous section of the *Transactions*.

Teaching at the Christchurch Boys' High School

Ernest Rutherford had ceased his experiments in good time to write up his theses prior to sitting the university exams in geology and chemistry. Two other events occupied his time. One concerned the Boys' High School.

In early spring one of the assistant masters at the school fell seriously ill with a severe attack of bronchitis. The College Committee Minute Book recorded on the 12th of November 1894

> ··· *Owing to the illness of the Mathematics Master at the Boys' High School, Mr Walton, the Headmaster was authorised to make a temporary arrangement with Mr Rutherford to take up some of his duties, at a remuneration at the rate of about four pounds (£4) per week.*

Thus at last, and by chance, Ernest Rutherford began his school-teaching career.

The Boys' High School bordered the town side of the college site. Governed by the College, its staff of Headmaster, eight assistants and four instructors for drill, singing, drawing and swimming catered to 240 boys. Like all private schools, boys could be accepted from age nine, and earlier with special permission.

The boys were worked hard. Homework was prescribed at the rate of one hour per night for the junior boys but up to three hours per night for the seniors. The school prospectus cautioned that

> ··· *As boys, if not looked after, are apt to dawdle over their work, parents should encourage briskness and concentration of attention in home preparation.*

Play balanced work. Oscar Alpers had just shepherded the school rugby team

on a September vacation trip to Nelson College. The seasick lads were glad
they had a day and night in Wellington while changing steamers. As well as
doing the town, the boys went off to see how the country was governed. Their
scribe reported

> ⋯ *In the afternoon we decided to honour Parliament with a visit. At
> two o'clock we entered the gallery, and shortly afterwards Mr. E. M.
> Smith rose and addressed the house on the New Plymouth (H)arbour
> Board. Then followed a discussion in which some members called other
> members names, and one honourable member regretted that nature
> had not endowed his honourable friend, the member for so-and-so,
> with a few brains. Those who were not engaged in the discussion made
> remarks and interrupted the speakers, or went to sleep, with their feet
> on the top of their seats and their hats on the side of their heads. In fact
> the behaviour of our members is not up to "concert pitch".*
>
> *Having left the Parliament House in disgust, ⋯ .*

Nelson they enjoyed, describing it as a very pretty little place, a Sleepy Hollow,
and where no one seemed to be in a hurry except the boys going to school.

Ernest Rutherford had been offered the temporary position of mathematics
master presumably because he was a well trained mathematician, had tutoring
experience, had taken a College class in physical science and had been a
qualified but unsuccessful applicant for an earlier position at the school. Also,
perhaps most importantly, he was available at short notice.

As a teacher he was not effective. Forty years on, one of his junior pupils,
who later took a law degree, reminisced about Mr Rutherford the schoolteacher.

> ⋯ *Rutherford is with me a dim but delightful memory. He was entirely
> hopeless as a schoolmaster. Disorder prevailed in his classes, not quite
> so overt as the Auckland riots, but far more continuous. I do not
> remember myself following any one of his intellectual processes on the
> blackboard. They were done like lightning. When he detected some more
> than usually noisy boy he sent him sternly for the Appearing Book. All
> the lad had to do to escape the consequences of his misdeeds was to stay
> out of the classroom long enough for Rutherford's enormous mind to
> have bulged in some other direction, sneak back to his seat, and he
> would inevitably not be noticed. He had quite a modern theory, too, of
> giving the boys the answer books, observing that the working was what
> really mattered. I am afraid, though, that he did not really too carefully
> inspect the working, as I got quite good marks personally by filling in*

*the answer correctly and working back a mere mass of x's, y's etc.,
which were put in more for their decorative effect that anything I
understood about. The main characteristic of the mob mind of a
schoolboy class is its ape-like cunning, and we certainly had him added
up as a genial person whose interests were nothing to do with the keeping
in order of small boys. He used to blurt suddenly into anger, which was
succeeded by a desperate calm. This latter mood was hailed with real
joy by all pupils.*

This appears to be the only reminiscence extant concerning Rutherford the
schoolmaster. It may not be relevant to senior classes.

Ernest Rutherford's stint as a schoolteacher lasted but one term.

Inquiry into the Department of Chemistry and Physics

On the 27th of February, 1894, the Canterbury College Board of Governors
had elevated the lecturers in charge of Engineering, French and Law to the
exalted title of Professor. They thereby ranked with those other august
'professorial' members of Christchurch society: Professor Adair the hot air
balloonist, Professor Sylvester the magician and Professor Pannell the swimming
instructor at the Sumner pool.

Sammy Page planned to travel for some years, hence at that same meeting
the Board accepted, with regret, his resignation. This act led to a remarkable
chain of events.

The Board consulted Professor Bickerton for his views about a replacement.
He proposed his eldest son, twenty-four year old Alex, who had supervised a
small factory making technical apparatus, had given many experimental lectures
to various groups and for the past year or so had carried out the routine work
for Bicky, the Government Analyst. He had also assisted in the elementary
teaching laboratory. His second son Willie, the lab boy, would then take over
Alec's analytical work and could be replaced in turn by Joshua Matthews who
had been employed occasionally as an unskilled assistant.

The Board advertised Mr Page's position. Ten men applied including Sammy
Page, his turn around being due ⋯ *to a recent change in my circumstances of a
purely personal character and apart altogether from the College.* (The latter
statement may not be altogether true. He had fallen for a lady student.) The
Board asked Professor Bickerton for his comments on the candidates. He gave
a fair appraisal of each one, ranking Sammy Page first and Alex Bickerton
second. There were difficulties about salary, as Sammy hoped for an increase.

The College Committee recommended to the Board that Mr Page be re-employed at the advertised salary. They further resolved:

> 2 *That in the opinion of the committee an inquiry should be made into the management of the Department of Chemistry and Physics and into the Salary and Duties of the Assistant.*

The Board accepted both recommendations.

The special committee of enquiry consisted of four members of the Board: Henry Webb F.R.M.S., Chairman of the Board, a member of the Philosophical Institute and an ardent churchman; the Bishop of Christchurch, who was powerful enough to use 'C. Christchurch' as his signature; Thomas Weston, a lawyer; and Richard Westenra, a gentleman J.P. The committee, minus Mr Westenra who seldom attended, convened on November 16th. They invited Professor Bickerton to be present ⋯ *if he wishes it.* He did. The inquiry spanned nine meetings over three months generating a confidential report of the proceedings covering 108 printed pages of evidence. This is a truly noteworthy document. The Registrar had been requested to attend to record proceedings – every question and every answer being recorded verbatim.

The inquiry started innocuously enough with the facts of Professor Bickerton's appointment, and an endeavour to sort out the job responsibilities of the Professor, his assistant and the laboratory boy. Fairly quickly though it appeared to be partly an inquisition that had the little professor on the defensive. By the sixth sitting he had cause to seek clarification

THURSDAY, 13th DECEMBER, 1894.

*Present :—*H. R. Webb, Esq. (Chairman); Ths Bishop of Christchurch ; T. S. Weston, Esq.; R. Westenra; Members of Committee ; and Professor Bickerton.

776A. Professor Bickerton :—I should like to ask the Chairman whether there are any specific charges in the matter of this enquiry, as many persons outside have spoken to me on that assumption ?

The Chairman :—There are no charges : we are simply enquiring into the whole department.

On the surface there were two basic problems, the first being that the laboratory was untidy and not clean. Yet Bickerton and Page had been asking for some time for permission to employ an additional boy to do the cleaning. And when the committee had inspected the lab a newly arrived consignment of equipment was strewn about while being unpacked. The crux of the problem Bicky (and others) maintained, was centred on the laboratory being too small. Only two-thirds of the size initially planned, it had no provision for physics, and equipment deteriorated because of the chemical fumes. Many witnesses stated that a physical laboratory was badly needed.

The Chairman attacked Professor Bickerton:

> *756. Except speaking to me personally, and not in an official manner, have I ever known that you wanted a Physical Laboratory?*

Forgotten were Bicky's letter of 1891 requesting that one be built; and that the result of the unofficial approaches had resulted in comment that it could not be afforded. At the time Bicky had stated that he would then soldier on as best he could. It can have been no consolation to him to learn that the Board had recently approved a biological laboratory using funds previously set aside for a Medical School, when physics also was a prerequisite to medicine.

Many witnesses were called by the committee for cross examination, the first being the present honours student in physics – Jack Erskine B.A.. His evidence, while basically factual, mostly counted against Professor Bickerton: he didn't attend honours lectures because they were no help, he never saw Bickerton use apparatus in the lab, Bickerton couldn't help the honours students with higher mathematics, the honours exam is beyond Bickerton's graphical method of solving mathematical problems, the apparatus is insufficient for honours.

In all Jack Erskine fielded 108 questions, some quite leading, for example:

> *104 (Mr Weston) Do we understand you to say that the help in the Practical Department was insufficient, or useless in quality? – I do not know whether Mr Page would be acquainted with the higher practical work.*
>
> *106 Are we to understand that, in your opinion, the practical department is useless, except a student is able to work for himself? – I think it is sufficient for the Pass work.*

The difference in philosophy between professor and student showed during Professor Bickerton's questioning of Jack Erskine.

> *134 If you had an Honours student, such as Mr Rutherford, with his ability and resource, and you had other students who had nothing like that ability and resource, do you not think that the time would be best spent in attending to the other students rather than to him? – I think the best student should be made the most of. I think they are of some importance in the College.*

Mr Weston put a final question to Jack Erskine.

176 So that for time, method, and attention, you do not altogether believe in the practice of this Department? – Yes.

The committee then called its second witness, Mr Ernest Rutherford M.A., who answered seventy-two questions. In contrast to Jack Erskine, his replies invariably supported Professor Bickerton.

191 (The Bishop) Is one hour a week sufficient for Honours Physics in your judgement? – I think it is sufficient for the non-mathematical part of the subject – for the experimental side. In electricity, especially, there is a great deal of mathematics required, of a fairly advanced type, and although it is stated that for the Honours degree no more mathematics will be required than for the B.A. degree, it is still necessary to understand the higher parts of the subject; to have an acquaintance with the Differential and Integral Calculus, and also with Differential Equations.

192 Do you think that the Honours students are receiving all the help from the Department that they are entitled to? – The Professorship in Experimental Science is not one in Mathematical Science. As far as regards the ordinary Experimental Science, I think Professor Bickerton has gone through the course required; but as far as the mathematical part is concerned, which is not his function, we have not had it taught, but it is really necessary for an Honours Course, although it is not definitely stated by the University. Last year the Examiner gave seven or eight questions requiring a knowledge of Higher Mathematics.

194 (The Chairman) Then Professor Bickerton has nothing to do with the semi-mathematical side? – I should understand that it was the province of the Professor of Mathematics Physics.

195 By Mr WESTON:- Who is that? – Professor Cook.

205 By the BISHOP OF CHRISTCHURCH:- The Department has provided you with nothing but apparatus? – Research work is supposed to be my own unaided work, but I have been assisted by the professor and Mr Page in certain mechanical details of apparatus.

206 By Mr WESTON:- Have you wanted assistance and been unable to obtain it? – Only in regard to mathematical difficulties.

233 (Professor Bickerton) Have you found me especially well up in the leading principles of Science? – Yes ; I think it is one of the Professor's strongest points. He has a very clear knowledge of the foundations on which Science rests, of the great principles, I mean, underlying Science, both the elementary and the great.

In Ern's view physics was the most difficult optional subject in the University course; students came from school unprepared, and very few of them took the trouble to work; he had been greatly helped by Professor Bickerton's graphical methods; and there was too much work for one professor to take both pass and honours courses in both chemistry and physics.

Ex-students made the points that both professor and assistant were overworked, and the latter was under paid. They suffered the disease of enthusiasm, and spent a lot of time in connection with science that "was not College work": being consulted by industrialists with technical problems, advising schoolteachers, testing the effectiveness of a chemical fire-engine the Fire Brigade proposed buying, lending equipment to schools, organising displays for the Science Society meetings, running the photographic section of the Philosophical Institute, giving popular lectures, lending equipment to church and other groups for conversaziones, being public analyst and giving talks on his theory of Partial Impact. In short, they supplied the scientific leadership a community should expect from university people.

The committee probed each of these activities, all of which they, and the other Professors, regarded as outside the province of a College Professor. A very narrow, ivory tower attitude prevailed. The crux of the matter was that honours students in Physics were scheduled for just one hour of lectures per week whereas Mathematics honours students had six hours. The thought existed that if the extraneous activities were eliminated, Professor Bickerton would have no excuse for not giving more lectures to the Honours students.

This ignored Bicky's view of a university: help the lower students who were struggling but make the honours men self-reliant. As he remarked to the committee: *Why, the very pith and marrow of University work should be its original researches.* The honours lecture was but a tutorial where Bicky probed the students understanding of their reading. He was freely available at any time to honours students. For their practical work

> ⋯ *I like to guide them almost wholly in their original researches, except in one case, that of Mr Rutherford, who exhibited such unusual capacity for research that although I followed his work all through and have been greatly interested in it he has not been greatly helped. I believe his research will be considered a classic one of extraordinary ability.*

The lack of peer and official support for his efforts to popularize science through public lectures particularly hurt Bicky. Where he was being vilified, the professors at the Royal School of Mines in London had received the thanks of Parliament for their public lectures. Professor Bickerton called eight witnesses and read fourteen letters in his support. All sang his praises for his popular lectures. They included a brass founder, a slow student, the medical expert to the Crown, teachers, a civil engineer, a past member of the Board, the secretary of the Gas Company and an iron founder. Twenty-four employees from one firm attended one of his courses. Although the lectures were usually just an overview, they stimulated interest and developed a taste for further reading on the subject. Many Board members were in favour of these lectures. The main opposition sprang from the other professors.

Bicky's astrophysical theories provided another bone of contention. Was he wasting College time on this work? Was he dissipating students' time by referring to this work during lectures? What today would be regarded as legitimate research, even Bicky regarded as his hobby. The committee probed the witnesses: e.g. The Chairman to Jack Erskine

> 80 The lectures were entirely on physics; no other matter was introduced?- I do not think so.

One witness, the science master at the Boys' High School, considered the theory was of no use to honours students until it had been accepted by most scientific men. In the main though, most agreed there were many applications of physics and chemistry embodied in the theory so that it was a useful talking point.

The committee questioned the time spent as public analyst. Bicky insisted the position took little of his time as his son Alex did the routine work. The students frequently repeated the analyses in the laboratory class thereby working on problems of technical importance. That, Bicky insisted, was the value to the students.

Professor Bickerton provided a fair summing up of the needs of his department that

> ⋯ were funds available, we want first and foremost a Physical Laboratory; secondly, more junior assistance; thirdly a physical assistant; fourthly, more honours apparatus.

Most witnesses testified to there being too much work in chemistry and physics for one professor. They were united that Bicky's department could not help honours students in electricity and magnetism with the higher mathematics needed. This was not necessarily a criticism of Bicky. The examiners in England set questions requiring mathematics at a much higher level than that laid down in the University's own calendar. Furthermore, Bicky had been employed for practical work.

No one regarded splitting the department into two separate departments as financially viable. Usually only one honours physics student came forward each year and a professor cost four or five times an assistant. At a lower level physics and chemistry were intertwined. Hence Bicky asked for a physical assistant, a graduate who was trained in physics and higher mathematics, to take the honours physics work. In his closing speech he made the point

> ··· *Of course, just as it would be unfair to expect Professor Cook to give practical demonstrations of his optical problems, so it could scarcely be expected that I should teach the principle of differential coefficients to physical students ignorant of mathematics, and although Professor Cook's chair is that of Mathematical Physics, yet it would be too much to expect him, with his present work, to prepare himself in such subjects as thermo-dynamics, electric oscillations, etc.* ···

He saw no difficulty in getting such a man:

> ··· *in fact I know of several who would be willing to take such a post at a salary far less than they would take a schoolmastership.*

One such man, Ernest Rutherford, had also suggested this type of split. So had the one witness who, besides Bickerton, had had experience of laboratories overseas. Dr Evans, the science master at Christ's College had obtained an M.A. with first class honours in mathematics and mathematical physics while a student at Canterbury College, and a Doctorate in chemistry in Germany. He recommended that Bicky have two assistants, one for Chemistry, and one for Physics, both to be men with degrees. He thought such men ought to be available in the colony, more and more so with each passing year. Dr Evans' evidence supported Professor Bickerton. As one lay witness told the committee ··· *The master's real work is in those he turns out.*

For its final meeting the committee had a private interview with Professor Cook to hear what he recommended, which was: leave Professor Bickerton with chemistry only, shift practical electricity to the Engineering school, put physics under himself, build a physics lab, give him a lab boy to clean the equipment and an assistant to take physics. The chairman supposed a qualified assistant could be obtained from England. Cook opted for a local ··· *I believe I could get a man here, but time is an important element.* [Presumably he had in mind Jack Erskine or Ernest Rutherford, both of whom were likely to take jobs in the new year.]

When the proceedings of the enquiry were with the printer, Bicky went along to proof-read his closing statement.

Said the printer *"I suppose they are putting you on your trial."*

Bickerton *"I suppose so."*

Printer *"Well all I can say is that they have produced such a statement for you as I have never seen equalled."*

The Board of Governors held a special meeting in March of 1895 to consider the Committee's report. They went into committee and finally adjourned for a month. This stung *The Press* to produce an editorial.

> For the best part of half a year the sword of Damocles has hung suspended over the devoted head of our cosmic philosopher – the Professor of Experimental Science. ···

The writer took issue with the form of the inquiry, commenting sarcastically

> ··· We are aware some of them (the Board) are great scientific experts. Their enthusiasm for science has been fostered in the erudite debates of the Philosophical Institute, where the widest and deepest problems of the age, from the parabola of a flea-spring to the curvature of a chair-leg are discussed with much learning. But we scarcely think that the best way to arrive at the capacity of an eminent scientist was to call in a number of schoolboys and ask them their opinion. Not that all witnesses merit that description. Many of them are level-headed men who know what they are talking about. But some of them were very juvenile indeed, and these did not keep in the background from excess of modesty – a virtue whose ravages are not wont in the person of a young graduate. One young gentleman who has the reputation of being an eccentric genius, in whom the eccentricity predominates over the genius, has let it be pretty generally understood that he gave most weighty and damnatory evidence, and flatters himself he produced no end of an impression upon the Commission. ···

(Jack Erskine was the only eccentric present.) On the 8th of April 1895 the Board reconvened, initially in committee then in the open. The Committee had accepted Professor Cook's scheme. And this in the face of such evidence as Dr Evan's replies to various questions.

> 406 By the CHAIRMAN:- I conclude that you think the Physical Department should be taken by a mathematician, pure and simple?- No, he must be able to lead research or he would be no good at all. He might have a Demonstrator.

408 By Mr WESTON:- That is what I was leading up to. Do you think that Physics, as taught by Professor Bickerton now, can be taught as well as if the subject were in the hands of a Professor of Mathematics?- I do not think a Professor of Mathematics could teach the subject at all.

For Chemistry, the Committee recommended that Mr Page's salary be increased by one third, and stated that they ··· *are not satisfied with the Department of Chemistry as they saw it.*

For Physics they had three proposals

1. That Professor Bickerton be relieved of this subject, and that it be attached to the Department of Mathematics and Mathematical Physics, under the charge of Professor Cook.

2. That a Mathematician of standing be appointed as an Assistant to Professor Cook at a yearly salary of £200 or thereabouts, and that a Junior Assistant at £50 a year be also appointed – subject in both cases to such notice as the Board may consider to be just.

3. That reasonable Laboratory accommodation and apparatus be at once provided for the Department of Physics, and that in addition thereto the sum of £50 be granted annually for three years for such additional apparatus, and for such other things as Professor Cook may require to ensure the efficient teaching of Physics.

Thus the Committee was proposing to give to Professor Cook everything it would not give Professor Bickerton.

Their recommendations were unjust and the Committee members were attacked by other Board members at a full Board meeting. Mr Spackman, a member absent through ill-health, wrote in protesting against the report being adopted on the grounds that the conclusions arrived at by the committee were not fair deductions from the evidence. The Reverend Mr Webster could not put a friendly construction on the report, which appeared to undervalue experimental science in physics. Other speakers were more scathing of the report. It made no mention of those who spoke in favour of Professor Bickerton. As Mr Stead put it:

··· *the only witnesses whose evidence had been referred to at any length were Messrs Erskine and Rutherford, both of whom were hostile to Professor Bickerton, and even a number of Mr Rutherford's answers were favourable to the professor.*

[This is an oddity. From the written evidence Ern does not appear to have been hostile.] After a long discussion, the first clause, to relieve Professor Bickerton of Physics, was put and lost. The others were withdrawn. The meeting rose with the understanding that the College Committee would draft some recommendations that conformed to the evidence.

It was widely thought that Professor Bickerton's enemies had gone off half-cocked and failed humiliatingly. An editorial in *The Star* stated that street gossip said the aim had been to haul Professor Bickerton over the coals.

> ⋯ *the professor is not, and never has been, a persona grata with the Board and the Professorial Council, for the simple reason that he is too much a man of the people, and has always been bent upon popularising scientific knowledge.* ⋯ *It will be well if Professor Bickerton's popular lectures are re-established on a wider basis: it will be better if other of the professors are induced to give courses of popular evening lectures also.*

Apart from Jack Erskine, the students were generally delighted with the outcome. At the Diploma Day ceremony the following month they honoured Bicky in song. (Tune: 'My Old Dutch')

> We've got a Prof.
> An' 'e's about a one'er,
> 'E 's a fine kind old toff
> And 'e's to us a stunner;
> There's many blokes 'ave raised a cry
> To plague old Bick we'll 'ave a try
> Take more than 'em, to wipe the eye
> Of our old Prof.

> CHORUS
> E 's been Professor now for twenty years,
> And 'e ain't done a dirty trick;
> There ain't a scholar livin' in the land
> As could wipe out our old Bick

> 'E 'as 'is fad
> At learning 'e's a buster
> 'E 's a smart cute old lad

But cannot use the duster,

'E ain't an 'ousemaid, 'e can't go

A cleanin' out the bloomin' show!

'E 's just a savant, don't you know

Is our old Bick.

CHORUS

Fine kind old Prof.

We could not do without yer.

Ye'r nature's kind old toff,

And that is all about yer.

There's some who scorn yer simple ways,

From us yer merit nought but praise,

We 'ope to spend yet many days

With our old Prof.

Seven years later, Canterbury College fired Professor Bickerton.

Summer Vacation 1894–1895

The end of the 1894 academic year was a hectic time for Ern. In short order his theses were dispatched, a draft paper tabled at the Philosophical Institute, the College and University exams sat, evidence given at the Inquiry into the Chemistry and Physics Department, students tutored, his paper polished and schoolboys honed for their final exams in mathematics. During this busy period it appears that he performed no more experiments prior to going home for Christmas.

The day before Ern left town, Professor Bickerton wrote his letter to the New Zealand Institute saying that Mr. Rutherford was forwarding a paper. Ern too found time to write a letter, to 30-year-old Sarah Saunders. the daughter of Alfred Saunders, the Member of Parliament for Selwyn, who had given the name Brightwater to the village near Ern's birthplace. Sarah, who had been taking practical physics for two years, and apparently receiving maths tuition from Ern, had just become engaged to Sammy Page. Thus it was probably she who had inadvertently triggered the enquiry into the Chemistry Department.

Cant Coll

Dec 18 / 94

Dear Miss Saunders

I am afraid mathematical study has a very peculiar effect on you if I am to believe what I hear.

I really must congratulate you for bearing away a prize of such value – for it is not only rumour, I have verified by inspection of the prize in question. There is no one I admire more than Mr Page both as regards mental and physical qualities and when accompanied also by a character 'sans peur et sans reproche' you have reason to be proud of your choice.

Yours sincerely

E. Rutherford

Over Christmas, 23-year-old Ern himself looked forward to romance. He had arranged for his landlady's daughter, 18-year-old May Newton, to spend February with the Rutherford family. She did not hit it off with the Rutherford girls who regarded her as spoilt. They found cause to complain to their father when May always accompanied Ern on the ride to fetch the mail from the Pungarehu Post Office. Why couldn't they have a turn?

During the holiday May and the Rutherford family got to know each other. Ern's brothers, George and Jim, were both fine, upstanding young men. As May said to James, "Well Mr Rutherford, if I cannot have your Ern I will have one of your other sons." But it was Ern she was kissing and cuddling in the Lovers' Walk.

The vacation passed quite pleasantly. In mid-February Flo became the fourth member of the Rutherford family to win academic distinction, her name appearing amongst those who had passed the University matriculation exams.

All too soon the time came for May to return to Christchurch for the new academic year. Ern went with her.

1895 In New Zealand

At Canterbury College May Newton enrolled for Latin, English, zoology and French. (Nine months on she failed them all.) Ern again took up tutoring. No longer a student, he could not play football for the college but he maintained a connection by being elected to the club's committee. Members of College House elected him to the Chichelian Senate to represent the district of Pungarehu. College House, officially the Upper Department of Christ's College, stood on the corner of Cashel and Antigua Street (now Rolleston Avenue), opposite the School of Art, and was the only 'hostel' for university students. The Senate met on Monday nights from 7.45 p.m. to 8.30 p.m. for parliamentary style debates which covered topical issues and during which Ern was always referred to as 'the Member for Pungarehu'. All members of College House qualified for a seat, and any former member could be admitted on a majority of votes but anyone else required the approval of three-quarters of the members.

May and Ern had arrived back in Christchurch in time for her mother's court case. Late one Friday night Mary Newton, her sister Emma Gordon and one Theophilus Wake, had nabbed a 13-year-old boy coming out of the Carlton Hotel. (The lad had not been served because he looked under thirteen.) The fearsome trio marched him home to ask his mother why she had sent him for beer at that late hour. Mary Newton remonstrated with the mother, who professed to be ill, to have been prescribed beer by her doctor and to have sent the boy for some as no one else was home. The boy's father later charged Mary, Emma and Theophilus with assault, in detaining the boy. The magistrate dismissed the case but imposed on the defendants costs of one guinea.

The resulting burst of letters to the papers were equally against as for the trio's action. Some called them fanatics. ⋯ *This trio have apparently constituted themselves a species of patrol, who roam the town at night and drop on little boys or girls coming from public houses* One writer gave practical advice to young children.

> *Sir,*
>
> *My son Timothy wears very thick-soled boots, with heavy iron toeplates. When at breakfast this morning I read to his mother a case heard in the court. He listened. After I concluded he remarked, "Call that a magistrate? Well, I shan't trouble him while I've got these", and he held up his foot. Any amateur detectives, male or female, prowling about our neighbourhood had better wear cricketing pads in future.*
>
> *I am etc*
>
> *DURHAM ST*

Meanwhile in England, another skirmish had taken place. For this the University of New Zealand's agent, Henry Eve the headmaster of University College School in London, acted as master of ceremonies.

The skirmish involved the 1851 Scholarship. Two candidates had sought nomination by submitting their work to the University of New Zealand. Ern's two theses were on the high frequency magnetization of iron. The other candidate, James Maclaurin, a chemist from Auckland, forwarded his work on the extraction of gold from quartz. James Maclaurin's research had been an outcome of Professor Brown's consultancy to the gold industry in New Zealand. The earlier part of his work had already been published as 'The Dissolution of Gold in a Solution of Potassium Cyanide' in *J. Chem. Soc. London* Vol **63** 724-39 1893. (Had the UNZ not asked for a postponement of the 1851 scholarship date James Maclaurin would presumably have entered this paper for the nomination in 1893.)

When the theses had arrived in London in mid-December, Mr Eve had immediately passed them for evaluation to the University's examiners: for physical science, Professor Gray of University College of North Wales; for chemistry, Professor Thorpe, the Government Chemist. They regarded both candidates work as of exceptional merit but Maclaurin's as the better. His published papers had already received favourable comment. When Mr Eve telegraphed to New Zealand to report a slight delay in sending the results of the University exams, he appended the news

> ⋯ *Maclaurin slightly better. Thorpe pressing commission for extra scholarship.*

Professor Gray wrote seven pages in support of this request. The author of one of the textbooks Ern had often consulted, he was familiar with the latest researches into electricity and magnetism, and therefore was well able to judge Ern's work.

> ⋯ *They comprise an extensive range of research of an advanced and difficult character, which has for the most part been suggested by a careful and thoroughly appreciative study of the more recent development of electrical and magnetic theory as set forth in Prof. J. J. Thomson's Recent Researches in Electricity and Magnetism (lately published as a sequel to Maxwell's Electricity and Magnetism), and in other works. It appears to me that the results obtained are many of them of both theoretical and practical importance. Some appear to be new, and others which seems to have been independently arrived at by the author agree with results obtained by different methods by other experimenters, for example some of the results of Dr. J. Hopkinson's experiments, and those on the march of induced currents in coils surrounding iron cores described in Prof. T. Gray's paper on the Magnetization of Iron, Phil. Trans. R.S. 1893. As the author is most careful to state his indebtedness to others, and having regard to the date of publication of the latter paper, I infer from his not mentioning*

it, that he was not aware that his results had been anticipated, and that
so far as the author is concerned this part of his work is original.
I mention this as evidence of the reliability of his methods and
conclusions. ···

After describing the essentials of Rutherford's theses, Professor Gray
summed up

··· *Having regard to the objects which the Royal Commissioners for the*
Exhibition of 1851 have in view, the furthering research in subjects
concerned with industrial progress, the value of the results obtained in
these memoirs as bearing on the construction of alternating dynamos
and transformers as well as their theoretical interest, the unmistakable
evidence of capacity for original investigation which they display, I hope
earnestly that a second Scholarship may be bestowed on the author.

To add weight to the application, Professor Gray wrote to a friend, Lord Kelvin,
one of the seven members of the Scholarship's Committee for the
Commissioners. Lord Kelvin, as well as having written one of the books on
electricity that Ern had often consulted during his research, had coincidentally
reported the accident that had stimulated Ern to study the depth of penetration
into iron of a rapidly changing magnetic field, and to enter the one dated entry
in his notebook. A second member of the Scholarship Committee, Professor
Garnett, had marked Ern's anonymous M.A. papers in physics the year before.

The Commissioners could not allow a precedent to be set, as several
Universities had difficulty in selecting a single candidate. They pointed
out to the agent that since the University of New Zealand received a
nomination every second year and since the 1894 nomination had been
postponed a year

··· *The authorities of the University may possibly think it well to*
nominate Mr. Rutherford, if still qualified, for the Scholarship of
1896. ···

The Agent succinctly telegraphed the news to New Zealand

Agent to UNZ   *Maclaurin only.*

A week later the New Zealand newspapers announced the news. ... *The*
Science Scholarship awarded to Mr. J. Maclaurin B.Sc. of Auckland. Mr. Rutherford
of Christchurch was second. [This is the view of an optimist. Since there were
only two applicants, a pessimist could say he came last.]

Such news must have been devastating for Ern. For the third time in his life he knew what it was like to miss winning a scholarship. More importantly, yet another career path appeared to have closed.

In Auckland jubilation prevailed. The University of New Zealand sent Professor Brown the form 'Recommendation to Science Research Scholarship 1895' for him and James Maclaurin to fill in the details. As they sat down to do so, consternation set in. This form was different from the one Jackson had received in 1892. Now one condition of the scholarship stated that the recipient be engaged on research full time and could not simultaneously have other remuneration. In Auckland James Maclaurin held the plum job of government analyst, which paid £180 per year as against the scholarship's £150. Being recently married, and with jobs hard to get, he had no wish to give up his position. He anticipated he could take one year off but in no way would he be allowed two. Prior to receiving the form he had planned to spend one year in Auckland doing both his job and the research required of the scholarship. During the second year he had intended to take leave and go overseas for more research. James Maclaurin explained his position to the University of New Zealand, enclosing the filled-in but unsigned form.

Professor Brown wrote a covering letter and complained that

> ··· *The fact is that the conditions of the Scholarship do not meet the wants of Auckland students who, very generally, have to earn their own living even while attending the College classes.*

The University officials had only one other candidate for the scholarship. All they knew of the merits of the candidates had been obtained via the two brief telegrams from their agent in London. Details had yet to arrive by mail. They cabled to London on the 2nd of April.

UNZ to Agent   *Maclaurin declines. Can you recommend Rutherford.*
Agent to UNZ   *Certainly.*

Even before the telegram was sent they had forwarded the reserve form of recommendation to Christchurch for Ern to fill in. Subject to further enquiries on arrival in England, he proposed to go to the *Cavendish Laboratory Cambridge* [J J Thomson's laboratory] *subject to further enquiries on arrival in England* to carry out research on the *Properties of rapidly alternating currents.*

In the section of the form requesting particulars of the original research the nominee had been engaged in, Ern entered

··· *Research some time effects in the magnetization and demagnetization of iron were investigated dealing more particularly with magnetic viscosity and decay of magnetic force. Also an investigation into the properties of iron under the influence of high-frequency discharges including the resistance of iron wires and the absorption of energy by magnetic cylinders.*

Being involved in only part-time tutoring he had no qualms about signing the same declaration which Maclaurin could not.

Three weeks elapsed before the local papers made the public announcement.

SCIENCE RESEARCH SCHOLARSHIP

Mr. Rutherford M.A., B.Sc., of Canterbury College, has received notice that he has been recommended by the University Senate for the Science Research Scholarship granted by the Commissioners of the 1851 Exhibition. The Scholarship is awarded for a long and valuable research in Electricity and Magnetism. ···

First published in the *Lyttelton Times*, a paper close to Professor Bickerton, the source of the news seems transparent from the last two sentences of the item.

··· *Canterbury College has been especially successful lately in Chemistry and Physics. There have been several first-class honours and senior scholarships awarded by the University, and in these two subjects for the colony the whole have been won by Professor Bickerton's students.* ···

Thus could Professor Bickerton flay his critics.

A reader who may have had an axe to grind replied

Sir, – My attention has been drawn to a paragraph in your issue of this morning regarding Mr Rutherford and the science scholarship, which makes it appear that Mr. Rutherford was the winner of that scholarship. This is quite a mistake, as the scholarship was won by Mr Maclaurin, of Auckland, and, on being refused by him, on account of his inability to comply with one of the conditions attached to it, was awarded to Mr Rutherford, of Canterbury College. I have no wish to detract in the very least degree from Mr Rutherford's abilities, but I think it only fair to let it be known that he was not the winner of the scholarship. – I am etc.

April 27 1895   JUSTICE

JUSTICE was mistaken. The Scholarship had not yet been awarded to anyone. The University of New Zealand had merely sorted out who it would recommend for the Scholarship. The Commissioners in England would make the award.

As the recommendation form could not reach the Commissioners before the deadline of the 1st of May, the University telegraphed its agent to make a formal nomination of Mr Rutherford, and trusted that the delay would not jeopardize the award of the scholarship. Ernest Rutherford could only wait and hope, as the form wallowed its sea-mail way to England.

All his hopes were now based on this scholarship. When the changes proposed by the Committee of Enquiry into the Chemistry Department collapsed so too had the possibility of his being appointed assistant to look after the honours physics students. All in all he had missed out on four jobs in New Zealand. [A month after Ern's departure from Christchurch, Professor Cook was granted six weeks leave provided he obtain a suitable replacement to take his mathematics classes. On the 25th of July Professor Cook recommended Jack Erskine.]

With his B.Sc. degree scheduled to be sent through the mail, Ern had no incentive to stay on in Christchurch. He therefore gathered together a set of references. The Chairman of the Professorial Council, Professor Dendy, gave a general one listing Ern's career, including the optimistic entry 1895 – *was awarded the 1851 Exhibition Science Scholarship for research in Electricity and Magnetism.*

Professor Cook mentioned his record and his mathematical ability.

> *As he is proceeding to Europe with this scholarship he will have excellent opportunities of scientific work and I am quite sure he will make the most of his opportunities.*
>
> *He is a thoroughly conscientious worker and may be completely trusted with any work he may take in hand.*

Only Professor Bickerton correctly stated that he had been recommended for the scholarship. And only Professor Bickerton gave him credit for his research skills and the work already accomplished.

> *⋯ From the first he exhibited unusual aptitude for experimental science and in research work showed originality and capacity of a higher order. Mr Rutherford conducted a long and important investigation into the time effects of electric and magnetic phenomena in rapidly alternating fields and by means of an ingenious apparatus of his own design was enabled to observe and measure phenomena occupying less than*

1/200,000 sec. He also devised other new methods of investigation · · · ·
Mr Rutherford has great fertility of resource, a very full acquaintance
with both the analytical and graphical methods of mathematics and a
full knowledge of the recent advances in electrical science and methods
of absolute measurement. Personally Mr Rutherford is of so kindly a
disposition and so willing to help other students over their difficulties
that he has endeared himself to all who have been brought into contact
with him. We all most heartily wish him as successful a career in England
as he has made in New Zealand.

Gathering up his references, Ern left a message for Jack Erskine to take
over the supervision of his students, and on May 9th 1895 departed north to
visit relatives and friends at Nelson and Havelock before returning to Pungarehu
to await news from England. He had enough confidence in the outcome to
regard his visit to Havelock as a farewell one, and told everyone he would be
leaving in about six weeks for England via Australia, with plans to continue
his work at Cambridge and later on at Berlin. The *Pelorus Guardian* proudly
reported these plans under the heading "Our Boys".

We are glad to see that in health Mr Rutherford looks well after his long
and successful course of studies. His future career will be watched with
interest by scientific New Zealanders, and in a different sense by hosts
of friends in Havelock. We wish him every prosperity.

On the 2nd of June Ern wrote to the University of New Zealand from
Pungarehu seeking clarification – could he proceed to a D.Sc. degree when the
necessary requirement of first class honours in a science had been obtained for
his Master of Arts degree? He added a final sentence.

· · · Please let me know if you have received any further word with
regard to the Science Scholarship.

The University Registrar replied that there was no reason why he could not
proceed to D.Sc. He had a B.Sc. and he had first class honours in a science.

You cannot go up to Honours in Science (i.e. MSc) but that will not
prevent you from taking the degree of DSc five years hence. The agent
in England recommended you to the examiners for the scholarship but
your papers have hardly yet got to London.

Ern waited. Perhaps he now took more of an interest in life overseas through
newspaper reports such as that reputedly of a French duel.

Monsieur Lelache having fired his shot, it was now the turn of Monsieur Beboche to discharge his weapon. He waited calmly for a moment, brought up his pistol, awaited the word and fired in the air. This was not, however, so great an act of magnanimity as might be supposed, for his antagonist had climbed a tree.

On the 9th of July the relevant telegram arrived in New Zealand.

Agent to UNZ   *Rutherford approved.*

Ern later told Mark Oliphant that he was digging potatoes when news of the scholarship arrived. Family history says he threw down the spade saying "That's the last potato I will ever dig.". [It would be reasonable, but not certain, to assume that the scholarship involved was the 1851 and not one of his earlier scholarships.] Overseas travel was imminent. Ern sent for a copy of his birth certificate. For the first time he learned that his official name was Earnest.

Thirteen days after receiving the 'Rutherford approved' telegram, the S.S. *Takapuna* called at New Plymouth on its regular service between Auckland – New Plymouth – Wellington – Christchurch. Six passengers embarked at New Plymouth: Constable Grey, four prisoners and Ern. He had time for a quick visit to Christchurch, just missing the severe weather when Lyttelton harbour had frozen over as far as Ripapa Island. And he just missed Professor Bickerton who, after lecturing in Sydney during the July vacation, had been delayed through a dreadful crossing of the Tasman Sea, after nine of fourteen horses on deck had been washed overboard, cases of acid carried as deck cargo burst and the after-cabins flooded. But Ern did not miss May Newton who joined his ship as far as Wellington, the last port of call in New Zealand.

On the night of Thursday the 1st of August 1895 a steamer carried 23-year-old Ernest Rutherford B.A., M.A.(hons), B.Sc. away from New Zealand. The event passed almost unnoticed, just a brief entry in the Wellington papers.

Mr. Ernest Rutherford M.A., of Christchurch, the Exhibition Science Scholar of 1895, left by the Wakatipu yesterday to pursue his studies at Cambridge and Berlin.

From then on, Ernest Rutherford belonged to the world.

INTERLUDE

Professor Bickerton's genuine enthusiasm for science gave a stimulus to me to start investigations of my own. ⋯ I was very sorry when the Board took the extreme step of dispensing with his services. ⋯ I felt that Canterbury College had not quite done its duty by Professor Bickerton. He had done very good work for the college, and had influenced many men for good.

Ernest Rutherford,

Castigating Canterbury College

on its treatment of Professor Bickerton.

The Growth of Myths

Ernest Rutherford B.A., M.A.(Hons.), B.Sc., left New Zealand as a highly educated and skilled young man. Few New Zealanders at the time, perhaps only Professor Bickerton and one or two advanced students studying electricity, appreciated the quality of his research work, or that he had found his niche in life. However, it must be to the credit of early New Zealand that within fifty years of formal European settlement the country had in place an education system which produced a university graduate destined for immortality.

Unfortunately, after Lord Rutherford had achieved world fame, New Zealanders and others projected his fame backwards, and built a mythology of his formative years that often does not stand close scrutiny. Some aspects are trivial. I visited several schools where locals told me of the pen that used to be stuck in the ceiling, thrown there as a dart by young Ernest. And many families seemed to have had a distant relation who had saved Ern from drowning at sundry locations.

More serious are the fame projections that inflate Ern the schoolboy to superhuman status: for example, the claim that he was a brilliant schoolboy. Only by comparing Ern's marks with the record of his fellow students and following their subsequent careers is Ern placed in perspective. He was undoubtedly a good student but surely he will be more identifiable to present-day New Zealand school pupils if they are told the truth – that Ernest Rutherford was a fairly normal New Zealand school-child who did not stand out at the time to an excessive degree, and that he had two tries at each of the three scholarships he received – Marlborough, University of New Zealand and Exhibition of 1851.

When interviewing the children of people who went to school with Ern at Foxhill and Havelock a typical first response to my question: "What did your parents tell you about Ernest Rutherford?" was: "They were surprised he did well". As a young schoolboy he was a quiet kid and a swot, so does not appear to have imprinted memories on his contemporaries. Twenty years on, his old headmaster at Nelson College described Rutherford the schoolboy as one who *displayed some capacity for mathematics and physics but not to an abnormal degree.* His professors at Canterbury College, apart from Professor Bickerton, regarded Ern as a good student but rated others such as Willie Marris and Jack Erskine as more promising.

Other pointers to his early contemporaries having a more realistic view of Ern than those who got to know him after fame had settled on his shoulders, include the following: Nelson College holds photographs of their rugby team for every year from 1887 to 1896 except for the one year Ern played; each year on Graduation Day the students at Canterbury College had a group photograph taken in the quadrangle but I have so far failed to locate one which includes Ern; and although Professor Bickerton reminisced many years later that he had stored Ern's apparatus in the ceiling of the laboratory because he thought Ernest Rutherford would be famous one day, that apparatus has never turned up.

When later viewed from England, James Rutherford is often implied to be a poor farmer, but James was a skilled tradesman and a flax manufacturer employing many men. As James was never indolently rich, from an early age the elder son's duties were, as customary, to help dad. Thus was George's destiny mapped out for him. As members of a large family with few, and in earlier days no, servants, the older girls naturally helped run the household and raise their younger siblings. Only the latter had the freedom to concentrate on schoolwork.

It is to New Zealand's credit that females never had any formal impediment to equal opportunities in education. When Ernest Rutherford won a Junior Scholarship to attend University, four of the ten scholarship winners were female. When he graduated, thirteen of the thirty-one B.A. graduates throughout New Zealand were female. The problem lay in employment opportunities. Teaching stood out as the largest, and nearly the only, employer of educated women, whereas men had a few other avenues available. In 1893 the *New Zealand Graphic and Ladies Journal*, appreciating that one third of all New Zealand women in the age group twenty-five to thirty were unmarried, encouraged women to take up the professions. Hence it was quite normal for Florence Rutherford to become a schoolteacher, as had her mother and maternal grand-mother before her. The youngest Rutherford girls did not receive the same opportunities because the family's shift to rural Taranaki in 1888 removed them from teachers of quality, and the chance of scholarships to secondary schools.

What of the younger Rutherford boys? Arthur did have two years at Nelson College but was handicapped through receiving much of his schooling from governesses. He had another obstacle to success. As the baby son of the family ever since Percy, Charles and Herbert had died at Havelock, Arthur had been spoiled. So that leaves Jim and Ern. Though academically successful, Jim was never favoured by the vagaries of the flax market in the way Ern had been. Furthermore, Jim preferred sport and the outdoors life, giving up a bank job to become a flax farmer.

Therefore, Ernest Rutherford was a product of New Zealand society of the time. He got to the start line by being born into a middle-class family as neither first son, nor female, and advanced through having parents who believed in the value of education, and through teachers of above-average abilities.

Three teachers had a major influence in the making of Ernest Rutherford. How did posterity treat them?

Jacob Reynolds

Jacob Reynolds arrived in Havelock a year before the Rutherford family and served seventeen years at the Havelock School. He played a crucial role in the education of Ernest Rutherford and other Havelock children. Few country teachers were classical scholars, but some were highly educated black sheep of well-to-do English families. Many a country child in New Zealand received a good education from such a person. Perhaps this partly explains why Jacob Reynolds preferred small schools when many large town schools would have jumped at the chance to have him on their staff. Certainly he liked his booze. He had been known to be carried home in a wheelbarrow or on the shoulders of his mates. Sometimes he went to school with a hangover, and occasionally a boy was thrashed unjustly and too hard. None-the-less, everyone regarded Jacob Reynolds as a good teacher, and Ernest Rutherford remained in touch with him when his school days were long over.

As it had the Rutherfords, Havelock cost Mr and Mrs Reynolds dearly. They lost one son as a five-week-old baby, and in May of 1893 their two daughters died and another son broke an arm. Perhaps this black period helped escalate Jacob Reynolds' drinking. In 1898 the Havelock School Committee called a special meeting to investigate charges laid by a parent (a Mr Ward), that Mr Reynolds had addressed a girl in such a way as to make her a butt of her classmates ⋯ *together with other accusations.* A letter was read from Miss Matthews stating that she had been at the school for fifteen years and ⋯ *had hence seen Mr Reynolds in the condition stated by Mr Ward.* The committee ⋯ *decided that it would be advantageous to both Master and school if a change was affected.*

Moments before being fired 41-year-old Jacob Reynolds resigned, and left unheralded. A friend, the local Member of Parliament, secured work for him as a civil servant in Wellington. He never taught again, apart from a very brief spell twenty years on at the tiny settlement of Cust in North Canterbury, just prior to dying in obscurity. He is buried in the Avonside churchyard, Christchurch.

William Littlejohn

Ernest Rutherford received a good grounding in mathematics, his strongest subject at both school and university, from the very popular William Littlejohn of Nelson College. Finally appointed Principal in 1898, Mr Littlejohn doubled the school roll within six years. In 1903, after twenty-two years on the staff of Nelson College, 'Porky' was appointed Principal of Scotch College, Melbourne, the oldest 'Public' School in Australia. He built Scotch College into the second largest 'Public' school in the British Commonwealth. There too he was revered by staff and generations of students, dying at age seventy-four, the year he planned to retire. Lord Rutherford described him as

⋯ *not only a self-denying teacher of rare powers, but a man of broad humanity and tolerance who laboured unceasingly by precept and example to develop the intelligence and character of the boys under his charge. It is given to few men to have such a wide influence for good on the younger generation. I feel myself fortunate to have come under his influence and guidance in my developing years.*

William Littlejohn is the only one of the three teachers of major influence who happily lived out his chosen career.

Alexander Bickerton

By 1899 Alexander Bickerton had established his 'Federative Home' at Wainoni. Thirty members shared domestic work, which was allocated, so far as possible, by personal preference. Most members had outside occupations but some worked at the fireworks factory. Bicky believed this would initiate a communistic utopia. As Government Analyst he had investigated some appalling tragedies which were the result of unhappy marriages, so much so that he disapproved of marriage as an institution. This did not endear him to the authorities. Also in 1899, after a quarter of a century of service to Canterbury College, 56-year-old Professor Bickerton's health broke down, so he applied for leave of absence for the first time. The Canterbury College Board of Governors fired him. It was badly handled and messy. They granted leave for 1900 but gave notice that his appointment would terminate in twelve months time. The incompetence of the Board and the frankness of Bicky's reply ensured old wounds were reopened. The Board finally decided to establish separate Chairs of Physics and Chemistry, offering the latter to Bicky at a much reduced salary. He accepted, sailing off to spend 1900 in England where he endeavoured to convince British scientists of his theory of Partial Impact. Even a paper in the *Philosophical Magazine*, a talk at the annual meeting of the British Association for the Advancement of Science, and a book of 90,000 words, *The Romance of the Heavens*, failed to do so. In Bicky's view, he had presented the Royal Astronomical Society with a gold mine but they had objected because the gold was nuggety, instead of being minted into sovereigns as they preferred.

Alexander Bickerton arrived back in New Zealand on the day Nova Persei blazed into brilliance in the night sky. Throughout 1901 he taught chemistry with zeal. That year an old foe, Thomas Weston the lawyer, rose to be Chairman of the Board of Governors. In January 1902 Mr Weston moved ⋯ *That in the interests of the College and its students the engagement of Professor Bickerton be terminated by the requisite notice.* Bicky had another book of 35,000 words in preparation. It had been written to explain his Theory of Partial

Impact to new members of the Board, but now he rushed it into print, entitling it *The Perils of a Pioneer*. Incorporated into it was material condemning the Chairman's action, a rehash of the 1894 enquiry and a letter which the Board had found deeply offensive. The unfriendly College Committee once more investigated Bicky. Remarked one student after being interrogated: *"that committee are after Bicky's blood"*. They got it. Alexander Bickerton was fired once more, but this time finally.

Little Bicky retreated to his home, which he expanded into a pleasure garden for the people of Christchurch. Wainoni Park drew large crowds through sideshows, gardens, science displays, animals, firework shows and mock miniature naval battles and sea rescues on a small lake. Had he concentrated on show business Professor Bickerton may have carved out a second successful career. Unfortunately the initial financial success diverted Bicky back to Partial Impact.

He unsuccessfully petitioned Parliament to establish a commission of scientists to examine and report upon the theory. As his finances faded another possibility emerged. A supporter ascended to the Chair of the Canterbury College Board of Governors, so Bicky mounted a campaign to be able to teach again at the college.

Ernest Rutherford always acknowledged the debt he owed Professor Bickerton, and publicly supported him. In writing to the Canterbury College Board of Governors, after they had congratulated Professor Rutherford on being awarded the 1908 Nobel Prize, Ern stated ⋯ *Professor Bickerton's genuine enthusiasm for science gave a stimulus to me to start investigations of my own.* ⋯ Ern counselled against Bicky's request to write on his behalf to the Christchurch newspapers. Instead he wrote directly to the Board of Governors.

Physics Laboratories,
The University,
Manchester.
March 27, 1909

Dear Mr. Russell,

I understand that there is some discussion among the Public and Board of Governors of Canterbury College as to the propriety of giving some official recognition to the services of Professor Bickerton by appointing him Honorary Professor in Astro-Physics or some such title. I take the liberty of writing to you personally to say that I warmly support such a step, and trust that something of the kind will be done for my old

Professor. In a previous letter, I mentioned to you that I found Professor Bickerton a very stimulating and good lecturer on general Physics. I was very sorry when the Board took the extreme step of dispensing with his services. The Theory of Cosmical Impact of Professor Bickerton is in my opinion the only satisfactory theory of accounting for the remarkable phenomena observed at the time of the appearance of a new star. It is not his fault that the theory has not made more headway in astronomical circles but is rather due to the fact that no astronomer of reputation has had sufficient leisure to examine the consequences of the theory in detail.

The theory is a genuine contribution to Science and no doubt will be ultimately taken up and carefully examined by astronomers. I feel that Canterbury College would not be the loser by affording Professor Bickerton an opportunity to lecture on Astro-Physics and allied subjects. I think that his enthusiasm for the subjects in which he is interested is a very valuable quality in a lecturer, and would increase the interest of students in scientific matters generally. I know that this was so in my own case for I still have a vivid remembrance of some of Professor Bickerton's lectures.

I am sure that a suitable recognition of Professor Bickerton's services would meet with the approval of his many old students. I shall be delighted to hear that this can be done by the Board and trust that no difficulties of precedent will stand in the way.

Yours very sincerely,

E. Rutherford.

Such efforts were unsuccessful. However a lecture tour of Australia secured the patronage of the Governor-General of Australia, who gave Bicky the fare to return to England in order to convince British scientists. Ted Howard, Bicky's neighbour and President of the Canterbury Trades Council, established the Bickerton Association whereby the workers of New Zealand would help with expenses by raising £300, to be matched by a pound for pound subsidy from the New Zealand Government. Slow at first, the accumulating sum soon rocketed to the planned total once Comet Halley had safely missed the earth. Alexander Bickerton, together with a daughter to look after him, left New Zealand for England in July 1910, shouting down to the small farewelling group of family and trade unionists "··· *Your motto should be: not solidarity of the workers, but solidarity of the race."* Bicky had walked up the gangplank penniless to prevent the hovering process-servers from seizing the donated funds. As the ship pulled away from the wharf Ted Howard tied the money in a pouch on the end of a long pole and passed it to the now safe Bicky.

His fixation with his lack of recognition turned Bicky into a sad case. A Hungarian friend of Ern's, when reporting on the 1913 meeting of the British Association for the Advancement of Science, stated that

> ⋯ *On the excursion to Kenilworth Castle I met a former teacher of yours, Bickerton. He is a funny old chap and one of the comical figures you find at every congress. Coming back from Kenilworth, we passed Leamington where the Mayor entertained us and saw us off later on. When standing on the platform he happened to start a conversation with Bickerton and seemed to be very much struck by the versatility and nobility of the old man, and after hesitating for a few seconds he lifted his grey top hat and asked him "if he happens to be Sir Oliver?" "Not so famous, but greater" came the prompt answer and the train left the platform. I will never forget this scene.*

May Rutherford, in private correspondence home to New Zealand, was quite brutal ⋯ *The poor old man is quite mad, talks all the time of his wonderful marks in a school of mines exam about 45 or more years ago. It is much as if Ern talked of his marks in the Civil Service Exam.* ⋯ Ern on the other hand was more sympathetic ⋯ *Although he is seventy he is very active and energetic not withstanding his trials in Christchurch.* ⋯ Ern, by now heading a large research team at Manchester University, confided his personal feelings to a young research student from New Zealand, David Florance, who recorded in a letter home

> ⋯ *Rutherford is greatly concerned about the prospects of Bickerton coming this way. He says that the scientific world has no time to consider Bickerton's theory – they are all too busy over their own work – he thinks B will be nothing but a plague. He laughs uproariously at B's oddities. He says he will let Bickerton loose amongst the Research Students but he himself will take a holiday as he would find no peace with Bickerton always around him. He considers it the greatest mistake to send the old man over here.* ⋯

Nonetheless, Ern encouraged Bicky to write a paper on Partial Impact which he edited very strictly and sent off to various scientific bodies. In a covering letter to the Secretary of the Royal Society, Ern explained

> ⋯ *I feel confident the old boy has got hold of a first class idea in his Cosmical Impact theory. He is really very sound in physical ideas and*

without mathematics is able to reach conclusions that look unsupported but I think a close examination will show he is generally on the right track. He is decidedly ingenious and bubbling with ideas. Why not publish some of them? It will do no harm to the astronomers and will certainly cause a good many people to think as well as to blaspheme. Both processes are equally valuable as stimulants. Do the best you can for our N.Z. emanation.

This support was to no avail. In 1914 the highly mortgaged Wainoni Park had to be sold. With lecturing and writing engagements falling off, Bicky lived on in poverty in London. Requests for financial assistance to aid his crusade went to Ern and other famous scientists in England, and to patrons back in New Zealand, such as Thomas Edmonds of Edmonds Baking Powder fame. Ern organised a grant, and later an annuity, from the Royal Society. When Mrs Bickerton died in New Zealand, Bicky wrote home to an old friend to join him, and at the age of seventy-eight married 57-year-old spinster Mary Wilkinson. Several approaches by Sir Ernest Rutherford to obtain Bicky a pension from the New Zealand government came to naught.

Once more a nova had an influence on Bicky's life. In March of 1925 Nova Pictoris flared briefly to prominence. Sir Ernest Rutherford, in a visit to Canterbury College late in 1925 stated publicly that he

> ··· *felt that Canterbury College had not quite done its duty by Professor Bickerton. He had done very good work for the college, and had influenced many men for good.*

Three years later astronomers noticed that the now faint nova appeared to have split in two. Friends swung into action claiming this as evidence of a stellar impact as predicted by Bicky fifty years earlier. At long last recognition flowed. Several journals and newspapers hailed the vindication of his theory. Again this was premature. [Modern astronomers observe twenty to thirty supernova each year, but all but one were due to nuclear processes in old stars, processes not discovered until well after Bicky's death. In 1992 astronomers using the large infrared telescope in Hawaii finally recorded a supernova which was the result of a collision, not of two cool stars but of two galaxies of stars.]

Bicky's old friend Ted Howard, now a member of Parliament and a Governor of Canterbury College, ensured the government of New Zealand immediately dispatched a telegram of congratulations. Professor Brown, on receiving a letter from Bicky in London asking if any steps were being taken to grant him Professor Emeritus Status, wrote to the new Rector of Canterbury College.

> ⋯ *Of course it must not be forgotten that he was ousted largely through the intrigues of that unspeakable disaster to Canterbury College, Haslam; they had almost been successful in 1895 through his getting at members of a commission on Page's salary;* ⋯.

The College Board of Governors, worried that history would regard the Board as having treated Professor Bickerton badly, accepted Ted Howard's motion to appoint Bicky as Professor Emeritus. They also sent a deputation to speak to the Prime Minister who immediately arranged a special state annuity.

Bicky had little time to enjoy these victories. He was dying the morphia-eased agony of cancer of the rectum. His death in London on the 22nd of January 1929 sparked obituaries in newspapers throughout the world. Ern wrote one for *The Times*. When Bicky's ashes were returned to New Zealand, Ted Howard, after failing to get a memorial at Wainoni and against family wishes, arranged for the ashes to be interned behind a plaque in the Canterbury College Hall.

Professor Alexander Bickerton has been the subject of a book *Scholar Errant* (by R M Burdon, Pegasus Press 1956) and is the only academic at Canterbury College (now the University of Canterbury) to have had a musical written in his honour: *Bicky* by John Densem for the Court Theatre, Christchurch, 1986. He is the only Canterbury academic to have inspired a future Nobel prize winner, and the only one to be fired. Regrettably he is remembered today as an eccentric; as a radical at odds with established society; as an old man seeking belated fame via a theory of astrophysics based on the unlikely premise of regular collisions between dead stars. Had he died at the age of fifty-six he would have been remembered by posterity in the way he deserves: as an inspiring teacher; a promoter of original research; an outstanding communicator of science to the general public; an innovator; an educational reformist; a promoter of damming New Zealand rivers to generate electric power; a free thinker and a humanitarian. History and officialdom has not dealt kindly with Alexander Bickerton.

Jack Erskine

Electrical researches at Canterbury College did not cease with Ern's departure. Jack Erskine extended Ern's work to study the magnetic screening of various metal cylinders placed between the magnetizing coil and magnetized needle of Ern's detector of short current pulses. This work appeared in the *Transactions of the New Zealand Institute* **28**, 178–82 1895 and won Jack the 1851 Scholarship for 1896. The University's examiner had stated

··· It showed distinct ability to engage in physical research although not so much ingenuity and skill as Mr. Rutherford displayed.

Jack Erskine chose to go to Germany, much to the relief of Ern who had earlier written home from Cambridge that he was glad that

··· he is not staying in Cambridge for he is too terrible and would get up a name for himself in the Varsity after the first week. My personal impression is that Erskine is not over fond of pure water and his disdain of clean linen and ties is too much for me altogether. Moreover his gait is like a rollecking sailor and generally he looks as queer a card as one could conjure up in imagination. I did my best to put him in a white shirt occasionally but I don't think it will have any effect on the obstinate beggar.

After two years in Germany, where he published several papers on magnetic screening and on dielectric constants of liquids at high frequencies, Jack Erskine spent two years in London, attending classes at University College and translating German works into English.

He spent 1901 attending courses in mechanical engineering at Canterbury College, and until 1920 worked in industry, for General Electric in America, and the Sulphide Corporation and General Electric in Australia. Thereafter he is listed as retired or in private practice, giving the Melbourne Stockbroker's Club as his address. He played the stock market with great success, having one of the finest analytical brains in the business. He regularly returned to his home town of Invercargill for the summer, and competed in the New Zealand Chess Championships, winning the title twice. In 1926 Alexander Bickerton reminisced about Jack Erskine *··· He did not like my substituting graphics for analytics and so did not take my advice. I believe him to be a better brain than Rutherford ···*.

Jack Erskine and Ernest Rutherford kept in touch as young men but seldom had opportunity to see each other when older. Late in life Jack would exclaim *··· Damn fool. He may have split the atom but he didn't make as much money as me.* That is true. As well as making a lot of money, Jack practiced frugality, often reporting to his stock market friends whenever he had found an even cheaper place for lunch. Towards the end of his life he and his sister Daisy (Margaret) shared one room of a boarding house in Melbourne, using a curtain as a divider. When Jack Erskine died in 1960 he left the bulk of his estate, several hundred thousand pounds in shares, to Canterbury University College for the benefit of the Faculties of Science, Engineering and Commerce. The Erskine Fund is today extremely healthy ($32 million dollars in 1999) and the envy of the other faculties and all Australasian universities. When his sister Daisy died in 1969 she left a large bequest to the University of Edinburgh for medical education. It had risen to over £900,000 by the time it helped build the Erskine Medical Library in 1981.

Willie Marris

Willie Marris had initially planned to attend Canterbury College for only one year prior to returning to England to compete for the Indian Civil Service. Instead he had stayed three years, completing a B.A. degree and incidentally providing a strong stimulus in mathematics for Ernest Rutherford. During his B.A. exams Marris had sat for, and won, the New Zealand University Senior Scholarship in Latin, indicating that he had considered staying on in New Zealand for an honours (M.A.) degree. It was not to be. England called. Willie was engaged to a fellow student, Alice Fordham, whose mother had taken ill. Alice, a dutiful daughter, would not leave her, so by mutual consent Willie and Alice parted company. Willie went 'home' for two years, cramming for the Civil Service examination. He was to top the 1895 exam with 3738 marks, a most remarkable effort for a colonial. He opted for the Indian Civil Service. The second candidate ran him close. Those ranked 2nd to 7th opted for the Home Civil Service. The eighth candidate was 895 marks behind Willie. Hence, with rounding up, Willie Marris has gone down in New Zealand folk-lore as winning the Indian Civil Service exams 1000 marks ahead of the next candidate. Willie Marris went on to a distinguished career in the Indian Civil Service, rising to be Sir William Marris, K.C.I.E., K.C.S.I., Governor of Assam. He told his son that his greatest academic achievement was to have beaten Rutherford at mathematics two years running.

The Wireless Telegraphy Myth

Jack Erskine's continuation of Ern's research into magnetic damping raises once again the question of how the myth arose that Ern worked on wireless signalling in New Zealand. I have found no evidence to support such a claim in written material of the time such as newspaper reports of talks, theses submitted for the 1851 scholarship, references from his Professors, advertising for conversaziones, etc., etc. All the contemporary evidence from that time in New Zealand, and in Cambridge, points to his first working on signalling without wires some months after starting research at Cambridge. In New Zealand he had merely repeated Hertz's experiment showing that electromagnetic waves could travel through air to a nearby detector. Such demonstrations were part of the repertoire of Professor Bickerton and all teachers of electricity, and were mounted to illustrate the properties of electromagnetic waves.

The first demonstration of wireless signalling in New Zealand appears to be that given by J S S Cooper to the Philosophical Institute of Canterbury in 1899. John Cooper carried out that research work for a first class Masters degree in electricity and magnetism. (After a brief period as a school teacher in New Zealand he became an electrical engineer in China.)

So why has the first demonstration of wireless telegraphy in New Zealand been attributed to Ernest Rutherford? The earliest sourced reference I have located is in Professor Farr's Presidential Address to the Canterbury University College Science Society in July of 1925, some thirty years later.

> ··· I understand from a friend who worked with him at that time that while working at Canterbury College, in 1892–93, Rutherford succeeded in transmitting signals from the Old Tin Shed, as it was called, which stood about where the present Library stands, to the Great Hall, and in receiving them there by his own receiver, which was an outcome of his previously mentioned experiments in penetration.

[Ern did not use a Hertzian oscillator in his researches until 1894.]

Clinton Coleridge Farr came from Australia and conducted a magnetic survey of New Zealand beginning in 1898. Soon after Professor Bickerton had been forcibly reduced to Professor of Chemistry only, the College Board had rescinded its motion to create a Chair of Physics and placed the teaching of electricity and magnetism under the Engineering School. Dr Farr taught electricity, surveying and mathematics part-time before being appointed Professor of Physics when a Chair was finally created in 1911. Who was Professor Farr's informant? Sammy Page, who retired in 1922 and whose sons had fallen foul of the Canterbury College Board of Governors? No. The evidence points to Robert Laing, the botanist and science master at the Boys High School and a stalwart of the Science Society and Philosophical Institute in Ern's day.

When Lord Rutherford died in 1937 the *Dominion* newspaper in Wellington printed reminiscences of Rutherford collected by Professor Farr some years earlier. Mr Laing, after referring to Ern's published papers in the *Transactions of the New Zealand Institute* stated

> ··· By this time he was able to send Hertzian waves from one end of the old "tin shed", as it was called, to the other and pick them up by means of a detector of his own invention.

Curiously, Professor Farr credits Sammy Page with assisting Mr Laing in drawing up these notes.

On the same occasion *The Press* in Christchurch interviewed, or accepted a written tribute from, Mr Laing now long retired.

> ··· *As a fellow student with Lord Rutherford I would like to add my tribute to his memory. I saw him send a message by means of these waves from one end to the other of Professor Bickerton's laboratory, the old tin shed, as it was called, through various intermediate walls.*

Mr Laing had not been a student with Ern, having completed the third of his three degrees a full year before Ern started at Canterbury College. *The Press*, too, did not interview Sammy Page.

Why do no contemporary records support the claim while many in fact discount it? Was Mr Laing confusing Ern with John Cooper's later demonstration? Was he incorrectly recalling Ern carrying out his vibration sensitive magnetism experiments in separate rooms on separate floors of the 'tin shed'? Had time merged his remembrances of Ern working in the tin shed and later in the den? Or was he correct but no one else ever mentioned such a 'long distance' experiment? Certainly Ern never claimed to have done this work at Canterbury but did claim it for Cambridge.

I have had to reject the wireless telegraphy in New Zealand story, based on the reminiscences of one doubtful 'eye witness', because of all the first-hand evidence against it.

Enough of interluding. We left young Ern on board a ship leaving New Zealand.

Chapter 8

WIRELESS SIGNALLING

Cambridge 1895–1896

I congratulate Mr Rutherford in breaking the record of distance at which electrical waves can be detected.

Professor S P Thompson,

British Association Meeting, 1896

Voyage to England

After a smooth trip across the Tasman Sea, the S.S. *Wakatipu* steamed into Sydney Harbour. The cargo included schnapps, oysters, five boxes of gold and Ernest Rutherford. (Tacked on to the passenger list were ··· *and 4 chinamen for transhipment to S.S. Catterthun*. They drowned when the *Catterthun* was wrecked two days later.)

Thirty years on C C Farr recalled that Ern visited Sydney University and explained what he was doing. A few years after the visit Sydney scientists were reporting on research which utilized Ern's detector of fast current pulses.

The ship on which Ern had booked to England had left Sydney the day before he arrived. As it harbour-hopped around the south-east coast of Australia, he took the train to Melbourne, travelling in the company of Edward Buckeridge who, a few years older than Ern, was also an ex-Nelson College boy from New Plymouth on his way to England. Buckeridge, and most probably Ern as well, joined their ship, the S.S. *Himalaya*, at Melbourne, where it had helped fight the fire on another large passenger ship.

Through the Australian newspapers the two young New Zealanders could catch up with the cabled New Zealand news (Minnie Dean, the so-called baby farmer, had been hanged), and read about their homeland through the eyes of others:

> ··· *for New Zealand the general view of affairs was somewhat gloomy, the future was looked at with a good deal of anxiety* ··· *low prices of wool and other products* ··· *great depression* ··· *with respect to the unemployed, I may say they thronged the towns.*···

and learn that newspapers had to be careful what they printed – the *Advocate* in Victoria had taken a blasting when dynamite had been pushed through its letterbox! They also learned how dangerous sea travel was: *Catterthun* wrecked, *Port Chalmers* struck an iceberg, *Orient* on fire, *Angus* stranded, *Cloncurry* grounded, *Mayhill* lost.

The S.S. *Himalaya* spent two days at Adelaide where Ern visited Professor Bragg who had been to Christchurch for the 1891 Australasian Association for the Advancement of Science meeting. A few days before Ern's visit, Professor Bragg had concluded a series of public lectures entitled 'Radiations' in which he demonstrated the production and detection of electric waves, their reflection from metals and their transmission through non-conductors of electricity such as doors. [In 1897 Bragg and his assistant, Arthur Rogers, gave the first recorded public demonstration of wireless telegraphy in Australia. They used a coherer as detector, not Ern's magnetic needle.] This meeting in Adelaide initiated a life-long friendship.

On the voyage across the Indian Ocean his fellow passengers did not impress Ern. They possessed little musical talent, and he and Buckeridge were the only teetotallers. One jolly card-player type stayed drunk for two days. A ray of sunshine was Miss Groom, the only decently educated girl on board. A schoolteacher aged about thirty, she turned out to be a good chum of a lady student Ern had coached. As Miss Groom spoke German she gave Ern, who didn't know whether he was going to work in Germany or England or both, instruction in the language.

While the ship ploughed its temporary furrow across the Indian Ocean, Ern's thoughts, like many a young Kiwi research student departing for overseas, turned to the girl he had left behind. He wrote May Newton letters which were informative and affectionate. When May complained that they were merely *most platonic,* Ern replied

Ern (standing second left) on a cycling holiday in Lowestoft, Easter, 1896.
Richard Maclaurin (left) was a New Zealander destined to be President of
MIT. Unidentified are two South Africans (De Villiers and De Waal, both
studying law) and an Armenian. (Augustus Young, Lowestoft, Rutherford Family)

Ern in 1896 with Professor
John Brown (right), his
daughter Millicent (later the
mother of James K Baxter)
and Mrs and Mr Collins the
architect.
(pu, Millicent Baxter))

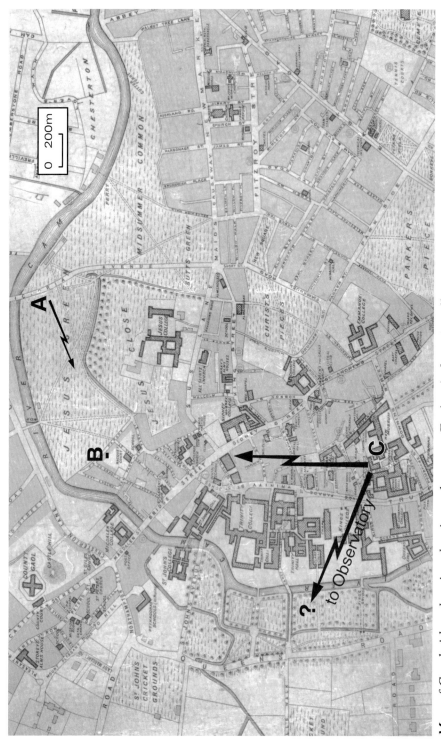

Map of Cambridge showing the sites relevant to Ern's wireless signalling experiments of 1896.
B marks Townsend's digs, C the Cavendish Laboratory.
(*Stephens and Macintosh Street Maps, 53 (2) 89 8, Cambridge Public Library*)

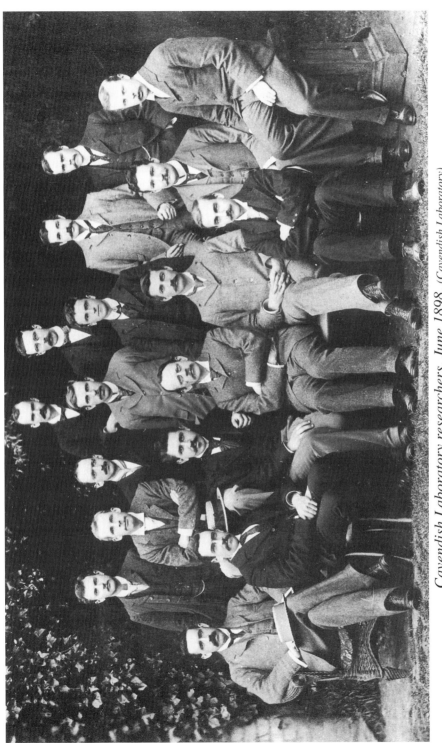

Cavendish Laboratory researchers, June 1898. (Cavendish Laboratory)

S W Richardson, J Henry.

E B H Wade, G A Shakespear, C T R Wilson, E Rutherford, W Craig-Henderson, J H Vincent, G B Bryan.

J C McClelland, C Child, P Langevin, Prof J J Thomson, J Zeleny, R S Willows, H A Wilson, J Townsend.

Ern at Montreal.
(Notman and Son, Rutherford Family)

Physics department, McGill c. 1899 including Ern at right, Harriet Brooks, John Cox (front right) andHoward Barnes (third from right).
(pu, Rutherford Family)

··· I am afraid you will have to get accustomed to that sort for I dont naturally take to being very loving on paper. Such inhibitions didn't stop him signing that particular letter *··· so good bye my ain little darling and don't think I am at all forgetful of our lovemaking in the past for I wish it was continuing at the present Vale ER.*

Three years of separation loomed ahead as a long time to Ern.

While the ship coaled in Colombo he joined a group travelling inland to the coolness of the higher altitudes at Kandy. Here, he reported to May, was an ideal place for their honeymoon. He may have alarmed her with

··· Miss Groom was the only lady in the party and it was my duty to look after her. You need not be the least alarmed for there is not the slightest danger in that quarter. ···

But certainly he mollified her with

··· The result of being in love with a particular young lady makes me rather critical of other ladies for naturally I have not seen anyone to compare with the aforementioned individual.

On his twenty-fourth birthday the S.S. *Himalaya* resumed its voyage. Five days later, as it approached the Red Sea near Aden, Jack Erskine read Ern's two papers to the Canterbury Philosophical Institute
(1) *On Magnetic Viscosity*
(2) *Periodimeter for measuring the periods of rapidly oscillating currents.*
(These were approved for publication. Two months later Jack's own paper *A comparison of the Magnetic Screening produced by Different Metals* was tabled and taken as read. At the following Annual Meeting the Institute resolved to make their meetings more attractive by recommendations such as

··· (1) That all purely technical papers be taken as read unless they contain matter of general interest.)

The S.S. *Himalaya* negotiated the Suez Canal and glided on to Brindisi where the mail went ashore to travel more quickly by train to London. Malta and Gibraltar passed astern. A brief stop at Plymouth allowed more mail to be landed. On the 20th of September 1895 the S.S. *Himalaya* arrived at Gravesend on the Thames on its way to the Royal Albert Dock. Fifty-three years earlier his Scottish grandparents and father had been outward bound. Now officialdom incorrectly recorded: *Mr E Rutherford, Gentleman, English, age 26, embarked New Plymouth, landed London.*

Arrival in England

Ern was at his physical prime: tall, strong, slim and physically fit apart from a dicky knee, the result of an old rugby injury. Blue eyes, fair hair and a well-shaped nose punctuated a face divided by a solid moustache.

London held no charm for him. A service at St Paul's Cathedral did not impress and the *horribly filthy* Billingsgate fish market *smelled vile*. As he was careful to point out in his first letter from England to teetotal May, he took bed and breakfast in a private hotel with no bar. Besides sightseeing, his first week passed in visiting the University of New Zealand's agent to collect the first half-year's instalment of his scholarship, and visiting the theatre, ex-fellow students, the Indian Exhibition and the University's past examiner in Physical Science. The latter gave Ern a letter of introduction to Professor Fleming of the Royal Institution and a promise of further letters. These he did not need, having already practically decided to go to Cambridge. The letter he had written to Professor Joseph John Thomson of the Cavendish Laboratory, enclosing a copy of his paper, drew an immediate and friendly response inviting him to visit Cambridge.

Ernest Rutherford was impressed by J J Thomson (known to all as JJ). Only fifteen years older than the young New Zealander, he was already a highly respected scientist. At their first meeting they discussed research work and general matters. Professor Thomson seemed pleased with Ern's proposed plan of research. Then they adjourned to the Thomson home for lunch where the Professor played with his young son. Ern, with future plans of his own, wrote home to May

> ⋯ *I have forgotten to mention* the *great thing I saw – the only boy of the house – 3½ years old – a sturdy youngster of saxon appearance but the best little kid I have seen for looks and size* ⋯ .

On his return to London a severe attack of neuralgia laid Ern low for three days. Upon recovery he shifted to Cambridge, where Mrs Thomson had arranged lodgings with one of the lodging housekeepers licensed by the University, Sarah Cracknell, a widow of 49 Park Street. Ern had one of the two units (bedroom plus study) offered.

The Cavendish Laboratory – pre 1895

Cambridge University was founded in the Middle Ages to train men for the clergy. Moves to drag it into modern times were made by two of its chancellors: Prince Albert and his successor William Cavendish, the seventh

Duke of Devonshire. The latter, an industrialist and cattle-breeder, was keen to see scientific principles applied to industry and agriculture, and provided funds for a laboratory of experimental physics. It was given his family name to honour the Duke's philanthropy, and also Henry Cavendish's work in determining the gravitational constant.

Initially the role of the Professorship in Experimental Physics was

> ⋯ *to teach and illustrate the laws of Heat, Electricity and Magnetism,*
> *to apply himself to the advancement of the knowledge of such subjects*
> *and to promote their study in the University.*

In 1871, the Scotsman James Clerk Maxwell at age thirty-nine, became the first holder of the position. Eminently qualified, it was he who had carried out many experiments in electricity and combined the known relationships in electricity and magnetism to produce a wave equation.

Maxwell died of cancer in 1879. He was succeeded by 37-year-old Lord Rayleigh, a member of the landed gentry, a Cambridge graduate and an amateur scientist with his own laboratory on the family estate at Terling in Essex. His estate depended largely on his dairy herds, and chain of dairy shops and milk rounds in London where 'Lord Rayleigh's Dairies' cut out the middleman. He briefly entered the life of a professional scientist only because of an agricultural depression and a disastrous drop in the price of wheat.

Rayleigh was an excellent scientist – *"a good instinct and a little mathematics is often better than a lot of calculations."* In six years he published sixty-two papers, many concerned with the measurement of electrical units but others on optics, sound, hydrodynamics, and even the soaring of birds. For more than twenty years he accurately measured the apparent density of gases in attempting to test Prout's hypothesis that all atomic masses were exact multiples of that of hydrogen. He discovered that the density of nitrogen appeared different for nitrogen obtained from air to that from ammonia, and the difference was due to the presence in air of an inert gas which he named argon, the Greek word for 'inactive'. (For this he received the 1904 Nobel prize in physics.) In 1884, trade recovered, so Rayleigh resigned to continue his individual researches at Terling.

The electors chose as his successor the young, 28-year-old, J J Thomson under whose influence the laboratory grew in stature. His predecessors had been individualists whereas JJ led a team. His experimental researches at the Cavendish included the discharge of electricity in gases, the relation between the speed of light in a transparent material and its electrical properties, experimental checks on Maxwell's theory of electromagnetic waves, electrical conductivity of alternating currents in electrolytes, the charge acquired by a jet of steam, and the velocity of cathode rays. By the time Ern arrived at Cambridge, J J Thomson was close to discovering the electron.

JJ was well versed in high frequency techniques using Leyden jar oscillatory discharges and Hertz's vibrator. He had shown that electrolytes were good conductors of alternating currents for frequencies of a hundred million per second whereas Maxwell's theory required them to be insulators at frequencies of visible light (a thousand million million per second). Hence the molecular processes of electrolyte conduction must occur somewhere between these rates. And it was he who had used a rotating mirror while photographing the image of an electrical spark to determine its duration.

So it was no mystery that J J Thomson welcomed the young New Zealander, who arrived at the Laboratory with a scholarship, a magnetic detector of fast current pulses, and a plan of research compatible with his own.

Cambridge

Ernest Rutherford was Cambridge University's first 'research' student. He arrived ten days before the start of the first academic year in which the University lowered its nose and opened its doors to outsiders: to those with degrees from other than Cambridge. For such people a B.A. by research had just been instigated, requiring two years residence and an original research. In the meantime they could wear the Cambridge B.A. gown without strings.

Ern now came under the rules of the University which, for undergraduates, were restrictive: cap and gown to be worn after dark and on Sundays; anyone caught smoking fined seven shillings and sixpence; and in by 10 p.m. The university laid down rules for students living in college and out. Visitors were not allowed to arrive after 10 p.m. and had to leave before midnight. JJ strongly advised Ern to join his own college, Trinity, the best and dearest. Ern did so as a good investment socially, for dining in hall meant not only the bachelors' table, hard forms and waiters in evening dress, but also contact with people encompassing a wide range of interests.

He spent much spare time in the company of John Townsend, a fellow research student, from Dublin. Also a newcomer to Cambridge, he too had no established circle of friends. They occupied adjacent laboratories so helped each other in research. Long cycle rides, walks and rows into the countryside filled in Sundays. On winter Saturdays Ern went to the rugby matches but his playing days were over. The people in the laboratory could only lament that such a large fellow did not play.

Mrs Thomson took Ern under her wing and usually introduced him as *"Mr Rutherford who has come all the way from New Zealand"* which, after all, was as far away from England as it was possible to get on this planet. In return he assisted with her charity work when she organized teas and entertainment for the old folk. In entertaining ladies during afternoon calls, he developed social skills and overcame his natural shyness.

May sent Ern letters and the Christchurch newspaper, *The Press*, to keep him informed about home. His letters to her have survived and show his affectionate side. One letter ended

> ⋯ *It is very sad that all those kisses can't be gone over again. But I go over them in spirit anyhow. With my hearts love my little wife.* He missed May and a hug and kiss ⋯ *a photograph is very mild after the original.* ⋯

He hoped she could come and visit him within a year or so. These letters do not reveal Ern's endearment or pet name for May as most were later cut out (– literally – with scissors) by her when Lady Rutherford. But they do reveal his plans for the future.

> *I hope that Christchurch Professorship is awarded some time during the next two years. If I can't raise enough influence to get it – I will be sadly disappointed. I would be rather a youthful Prof. but I reckon I will make those students sit up in Honours Physics – real good solid stuff for me – none of the Bickertonian stuff. Even if I do get that Prof-ship you will have to wait one whole year till I have settled down as I have a few debts to pay off before I can start in double harness. It is very sad but I am afraid it will have to be so.*

Failing the Professorship there was facetious plan B.

> *The sooner that old aunt of yours departs and leaves her cash to you the better I will be pleased. I will then research and you will have to keep me and the house going – not a care or trouble for me – so be as quick as possible to collar the needful.*

After all, was not research now the main thrust of his life?

Research in Electromagnetism 1895

The day after arriving in Cambridge Ern went to work in the Laboratory. Two days later he purchased a sixpenny notebook, laying claim to the flyleaf with 'E Rutherford Cavendish Laboratory Oct 3/95'.

For the first two months he extended his earlier work in New Zealand to determine the period of oscillation of Leyden Jar circuits. Previously this could be done only by an elaborate and difficult process using the flash of the spark, a rotating mirror and a photographic plate. Ern set up an electrical circuit with two parallel discharge paths.

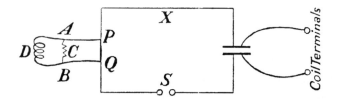

Rutherford's frequency meter ABCD

One used a tube filled with electrolyte to provide a high resistance (R), low inductance path. The other used a standard self-inductor (L). The peak of the rapidly decaying oscillatory current in either path was monitored using his detector, a fine magnetic needle inside a small coil in the circuit. By adjusting the resistance of the electrolyte until equal currents flowed in the two parallel paths, the frequency of oscillation of the Leyden jar circuit could be deduced to be simply $R/(2\pi L)$. The periods thus measured were typically one million per second. By using a Hertzian vibrator as the source of oscillations these were extended to thirty million per second.

His detector of current pulses had thus been turned into a frequency meter. The frequency (f) of oscillation of a circuit depends upon the capacitance (C) and the inductance (L) of the circuit. ($f = 1/2\pi \sqrt{LC}$). Ern experimentally checked this expression before extending his technique to another application. Using a discharge circuit of known inductance and tapping off a small portion of the discharge current for his frequency meter, he could accurately measure the electrical capacitance of two parallel plates. By placing materials between the two plates he showed that ebonite, plate glass, paraffin wax and sulphur had the same dielectric constants at high frequencies as they did for steady fields. However, the plate glass result contradicted an earlier result of J J Thomson.

To check the value for plate glass, Ern also used Lecher's method. High frequency waves generated by a Hertzian oscillator set up a standing wave along two parallel wires some ten metres in length. A capacitor bridging the wires confirmed Ern's value for plate glass.

Experimentation requires perseverance. Seldom does such work proceed effortlessly and problem free. As Ern reported to May on the 21st of November 1895

> ··· *The last fortnight has made me swear more than usual as my investigations have been wasted due to the cussedness of nature for things won't come off experimentally in the way theory points. However I must expect to have to work away without result occasionally.*

The letter had been headed *My darling little girl* and continued

> ··· *It appears to be an age since I left NZ and a fearfully long time since I had my last hug and kiss and the lord knows when I expect to get another. You remember the old quotation "Caelum non animum mutant qui trans mare currunt"* [From Horace meaning: Those who cross the sea change their sky but not their heart.] *I think there is a great deal of truth in the same – at any rate it is very applicable in my case.* ··· *I think of you very often* ··· .

Prior to the introduction of research students, much of the original research work was carried out by demonstrators. These men were Cambridge graduates who stayed on, earning a living by demonstrating in the undergraduate laboratories and carrying out research in their spare time. Not all of the three demonstrators accepted Rutherford and Townsend, the outsiders who had bypassed the Cambridge route. For the first two months the demonstrators ignored them, knowing the pair had no friends in Cambridge. As they passed Ern's door, they invariably sniggered. Ern countered by politely asking them in, telling them he was having some difficulties with his experiments and would be grateful for their help. They quickly realized it was very advanced work of which they had not the faintest idea. Thereafter they left Ern alone, but even after five months at Cambridge Ern would comment ··· *many of them are my enemies* ··· and ··· *There is one demonstrator on whose chest I would like to dance a Maori war-dance.* Friendship was extended only after several months when Rutherford and Townsend were names widely known and acclaimed. Even so, three years later, when new students wanted to invite the demonstrators to the Research Students' Dinner, the earliest research students absolutely refused to allow this.

One can have some sympathy with the demonstrators (Lionel Wilberforce, George Searle and Sidney Skinner), and assistant demonstrators (Thomas Fitzpatrich and Percy Bateman). Their ordered world was being turned upside-down and their planned pathway to fellowship and remuneration looked to be under threat. In 1898 John Townsend wrote back to Dublin that ⋯ *There is great rivalry between the research men here and the former occupants of the laboratory.* He noted that even then each group attempted to put the other down.

By arriving at the Cavendish with an invention and a proposed plan of research which fitted into the laboratory's interests, Ern had an early step up the ladder. His first researches there merged his interests and experimental methods with the Professor's. The latter had quickly recognised Ernest Rutherford as an exceptional researcher. Wider recognition soon followed. JJ asked him to address the Cambridge Physical Society during the first week of December. The notice board announced '*A method of measuring waves along wires and determination of their period – with experiments by E Rutherford.*' Ern claimed he had been the first member of the Cavendish to give an original paper before the Society – a great honour indeed. The audience consisted of Sir George Stokes, lecturers, demonstrators, students and various wives. No one asked questions, the work being mostly over their heads. As Mrs JJ commented to Ern over tea

> ⋯ *"You kept us ladies very interested indeed, and I am sure it was sufficiently deep for the more scientific members of the society."*

Wireless Signalling 1895–1896

During the first week in December of 1895 Ern modified his detector. Two reasons seem to be involved. One was to make it more sensitive in order to extend the dielectric measurements of solids to even higher frequencies. The other was to test the ultimate sensitivity of his detector with the bolometer method of studying standing waves along wires. Since high frequency currents affected only a thin surface layer of the magnetic needle, very fine needles were needed. The sensitivity could also be increased by using several such needles inside a magnetizing coil of several turns. Hence he made his sensitive (or compound) detector from a bundle of a dozen or so fine steel wires, each insulated by shellac to reduce eddy currents. [One of these detectors is today proudly preserved by the Cavendish Laboratory].

The main check of the sensitivity of his compound detector involved repeating the brief experiment carried out at Canterbury where, with his single needle detector, he had detected Hertzian waves some two metres from the oscillator, as had Hertz and many subsequent teachers of electricity. In 1894 Oliver Lodge, using a coherer as detector, had publicly exhibited the sending of wireless waves some hundred and fifty metres through stone walls of buildings. By the 8th of December, Ern could detect electromagnetic waves over a distance of twenty metres using his compound detector .

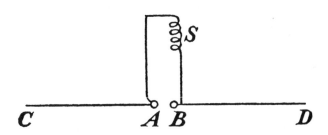

Rutherford's receiver of electromagnetic waves

These results impressed JJ who urged him to continue. By Christmas he could detect waves which had travelled some forty metres through three walls and two floors of the laboratory. Ern asked about publishing the work. JJ recommended the prestigious Royal Society. That was not the only accolade. When the grand old man of British Science, Lord Kelvin, visited the Laboratory he told one demonstrator he wished he had been taken to see Rutherford's work.

Thus exhilarated, Ern departed for Edinburgh to spend Christmas with the New Zealand contingent there. During this holiday he saw the sun just once.

Returning to Cambridge Ern increased the wavelength of the Hertzian oscillator and by mid-January could detect waves over ninety metres with plans in hand for an experiment over half a mile. John Townsend mentioned the work to a fellow Irishman, Sir Robert Ball, Director of the Observatory, who immediately made an appointment to see the apparatus and experiments. Until 1892 Sir Robert had been Astronomer Royal in Ireland and scientific consultant for the Commissioners of Irish Lights, the group responsible for maintaining and improving the system of navigation lights in Irish waters. In the latter position he had conducted tests of the relative efficiency of different types of lights for penetrating fog. The young New Zealander's project excited him. He saw it as a way of solving the problem of the uselessness of lighthouses in fog. With a vibrator in a lighthouse and a receiver on a ship, the presence of an invisible lighthouse (and hence danger) could be detected over a safe distance. Ern's technique was also timely for the Royal Commission on Electrical Communication with Lightships.

Ern saw fame and fortune if he could push the technique to a range of ten miles. As he wrote home to May ⋯ *I see a chance of making cash rapidly in the future* ⋯ . He never did. [Incidentally the principle of having the receiver detect a reflection from a metal object, later to be called radar, had been known since Hertz's earliest experiments. In 1904 a German, Christian Hülsmeyer, finally patented, in England, this idea for detecting ships or trains.]

Sir Robert Ball became an enthusiastic publicist of Ern's work. He invited Ern and John Townsend to dine with the Fellows at his college (Kings). Invitations by others followed. JJ declared to all that the new research students were a great success, and that the work Ern had done had shown the wisdom of the University in opening its doors. The magnetic detector of fast current pulses, conceived independently in distant New Zealand, eased the path for many future research students entering Cambridge.

Meanwhile J J Thomson had become heavily involved in the amazing new photography of Röntgen which overshadowed Ern's work. As the latter reported to May Newton ⋯ *The air here is full of the new photography, till I myself feel rather tired with it* ⋯ .

He planned an experiment to detect signals over a long distance. Ern's lodgings were surrounded by houses whereas Townsend, who lived nearby at 23 Park Parade, overlooked Jesus Green and Midsummer Common beyond, and had a clear line of sight for nearly a kilometre. Hence Townsend tended the sensitive detector in his rooms while Ern tended the transmitter on the common.

Ern's first attempt at long distance detection of electromagnetic signals was almost a fiasco. The firm from which Ern hired two men to transport the transmitting apparatus to the common had botched the arrangements. Two men and a handcart were hunted up from the street, delaying proceedings by a couple of hours. The first experiment at 500 metres gave no effect. Reducing the distance progressively still gave no effect by which time Ern knew he had a break in the detector coil. A rough, not so sensitive, detector replaced the faulty one, giving a large effect up to 350 metres. Of his scientific assistants, Townsend and McLelland, Ern reported ⋯ *They both worked like Britons, and I could not have done without them.* It was a rush to get the equipment back to the laboratory by the pre-arranged lock-up time of 11.30 p.m.

The following night, the 22nd of February 1896, the experiment was repeated with a repaired detector and more comfortable bases. Effects were detected between the Laboratory and Townsend's digs, a distance of over half a mile. Sir Robert Ball called on Ern the next morning to hear how the experiment went. Months later when the news reached New Zealand, the *Taranaki Herald* printed a small item.

> *Mr E.G. Rutherford, son of Mr J. Rutherford, of Pungarehu, who it will be remembered, went home some time ago to pursue his studies in electricity at the Cavendish Laboratory, has again distinguished himself and has attracted the kindly interest of Sir Robert Ball, Astronomer Royal, Ireland, who has offered Mr Rutherford the use of his observatory for his experiments.*

Ern thought he would make use of the observatory as it was over a mile from the Cavendish. [Whether or not he ever did is unclear. The lack of first-hand evidence implies not. In a June 11th report on this work he claimed only the half mile from the Cavendish Laboratory to Park Parade. In September a newspaper reporter quoted three-quarters of a mile. In 1942 John Strutt stated that Ern did transmit between the Cavendish and the Observatory.]

When he had reported these events to his parents he also sent them two of the new X-ray (Röntgen) photographs, one of a frog and one of a hand. These were possibly the first X-ray photographs to reach New Zealand. [The first X-ray photos taken in New Zealand were probably those exposed in June of 1896 by W E Thompson of Christchurch. In May the following year, after Sammy Page displayed a large number of X-ray photographs to the Canterbury College Dialectic Society ⋯ *Special mention was also made of Mr Rutherford, part of the apparatus being the result of his work.*]

The new photography featured as the highlight of the Science Conversazione to celebrate the March opening of the new buildings at the Cavendish Laboratory. About 700 guests crushed through the rooms and displays which included most of the Cavendish research. For example, C T R Wilson showed his experiments on the condensation of clouds in dust-free air. Mr Kelsey displayed the spectrum of helium and Mr Wilberforce the wonders of Röntgen rays. Ern, in a new dress suit, demonstrated experiments with Hertzian waves. He had the vibrator in one room and his detector in another, forty metres and five solid walls away. He and John Townsend took turns at either end. Many distinguished people visited him, principally through the efforts of Sir Robert Ball and Mrs Thomson. As he wrote proudly to May ⋯ *Some people were very interested and reckoned it was the thing worth seeing in the Lab.*

The *Cambridge Chronicle and University Journal, Isle of Ely Herald,* and *Huntingdonshire Gazette* (all one paper) did not have the same view. Its reporter never got past the illustrated lecture on the new photography using Röntgen rays. By public demand it had to be repeated. The climax involved taking an X-ray photograph of a lady's hand.

During the Easter vacation of 1896, Ern spent three weeks at Lowestoft with fellow students – one Armenian, two South Africans and the New Zealander Richard Maclaurin who was a mathematician, a future President of the Massachusetts Institute of Technology and the brother of the man who couldn't accept the 1851 scholarship nomination. They loafed and were happy. Walks, bike-rides, sailing, eating, carriage-rides with legs dangling out behind and generally playing the goat were the order of the day. And swimming. As their house faced the sea they had an early dip. Next morning a policeman turned up saying he had been specially sent by the superintendent to tell them to go further down the coast as one of the nearby landladies had objected. Two mornings later another policeman hinted they should move even further down as another modest female had complained. As Ern reported to May ⋯ *The alarming modesty of the British Female is most remarkable – especially the spinster,* ⋯ . Not so the four girls who promenaded the Esplanade to coincide with the swim.

Ern and three others cycled back to Cambridge, a distance of some 140 km, against a strong head wind the whole way. With most of his wardrobe still in Lowestoft and not due to return to Cambridge until later with Richard Maclaurin, he passed the next morning in visiting shops to purchase collar studs, braces, boots etc., dressing as he went.

The new term heralded several changes. Ern's spending outran his allowance so JJ arranged for him to tutor undergraduates. The pay was good ⋯ *if I could get half a dozen men for three terms I could nearly make a living for one, if not for two* ⋯ . He turned down a job in India for which JJ had been asked to recommend someone. And JJ took Ern for his first game of golf. (⋯ *I don't think, however, I am quite old enough for golf yet – at any rate to take it up with much enthusiasm* ⋯ .) But the major change involved his research for he switched to working with JJ and the new Röntgen rays. ⋯ *I am a little full up of my old subject and am glad of a change. I expect it will be a good thing for me to work with the Professor for a time. I have done one research to show I can work by myself* ⋯ .

Henry Dale later recalled a meeting of the small Natural Science Club held in Ern's rooms. The members sat around the living room table upon which, in pride of place, sat the detector of electromagnetic waves. Ern had arranged for someone at the Cavendish to start the Hertzian oscillator and had carefully synchronised his watch with the laboratory clock

⋯ *We all sat round the table waiting for the great moment, like a racing-boat's crew counting the seconds to the starting gun. Exactly at 9 o'clock the bell began to ring, and we greeting the demonstration with cheers; and then Rutherford gave us a short talk on the nature of the transmission which we had been witnessing.*

[More than thirty years later the Club held a dinner celebrating the completion of some number of hundreds of meetings. Sir Henry Dale, speaking after dinner, recalled the incident and suggested that Ern had probably placed a bell-push under the carpet, to press with his foot at the appointed time. Sir Ernest Rutherford, ⋯ *in rollicking mood replied: "I have little doubt that my friend Dale's unworthy suspicions were fully justified."*]

Ern retained some interest and did not stop all involvement with long distance 'wireless' signalling, for he had put his mark on the field. A talk at the British Association for the Advancement of Science (BAAS or BA for short) conference was planned. Sir Robert Ball and other prominent men broadcast his work. JJ used Ern's magnetic detector in his lectures and offered to communicate Ern's work to the Royal Society. As a result a paper describing his work entitled 'A Magnetic Detector of Electrical Waves and some of its applications' was accepted for publication in the *Philosophical Transactions of the Royal Society*. The referees were to state:

> Oliver Lodge – *I am of the opinion that the magnetic detector for electrical waves is a step in advance and that Mr Rutherford's paper is suitable for the Transactions. It is neither needlessly long nor over illustrated.*
>
> C V Boys – *The method employed by Mr Rutherford is an exceedingly beautiful one and it has been turned to excellent account and varied information has been obtained by means of it. I am clearly of the opinion that it should be printed in the Transactions.*

Ern wrote to May ⋯*If my paper was a novel, I would dedicate it to you* ⋯ . He turned down a request to exhibit his detector at a conversazione of the Royal Institution on the grounds of notice being too short.

On the basis of Ern's work, J J Thomson made enquiries in the City as to the possibilities of developing commercially a system of wireless communication. Those whom he consulted were of the opinion that while the scheme would form excellent subject-matter for a prospectus, it was not likely ever to be of real commercial use. This discouraged JJ, and presumably Ern also.

Cost wasn't a concern for Henry Jackson, the commanding officer of HMS *Defiance*. As a torpedo officer in 1891 he had first thought of using Hertzian waves to communicate between torpedo boats and friendly ships, but it was the end of 1895 before he could start experiments on perfecting a coherer detector. [These detectors consisted of a tube containing metal particles. A spark passing through the powder lowered its electrical resistance. A physical tap shook the particles back to their original state.] In August of 1896 he could send and receive Morse code messages by wireless. By the end of the year he could send messages over distances of several hundred yards. Had he known of Ern's sensitive detector early in 1896 history might have been changed. But history shows that Jackson had only Marconi to align himself with, and in 1900 Marconi wireless telegraphy apparatus was installed in a number of ships of the Royal Navy.

On the 30th of May 1896, Ernest Rutherford forwarded a yearly account of all his work to the Commissioners of the 1851 Exhibition, covering the work with the magnetic detector and the work undertaken since April using X-rays. But it also included a since forgotten experiment.

Scientists had invented the ether, a mythical solid filling all space, to explain how electromagnetic waves travelled in a vacuum. That theory predicted a displacement of the ether in the neighbourhood of an electrical vibrator. JJ suggested to Ern that this be investigated. They set up an optical interferometer, following Professor Lodge's earlier work, of four mirrors arranged so that light from a source could travel in opposite directions around a closed path. The interference pattern produced by the two beams is capable of detecting any changes of the path length down to about one tenth of the wavelength of light (i.e. to 50 millionths of a millimetre). A spark gap served as both the light source for the interferometer and the electromagnetic wave source, so both had the same duration. As Ern concluded

> ⋯ *Not the slightest movement of the interference bands could be detected when the discharge passed round the mirrors, so that as far as the experiment goes, it proves there is no movement of the ether in the neighbourhood of a vibrator.*

British Association Meeting – 1896

This annual jamboree of British Scientists convened in Liverpool for the week of September 17th to 23rd 1896. Professor Gray, the examiner in physics for the University of New Zealand, attended, later reporting to the University's agent that he had met Rutherford there.

··· *He seems a nice fellow and to be getting on very well. I am glad to find my view regarding him so completely confirmed.*

In his opening Presidential address, Sir Joseph Lister, who revolutionized the surgeon's art through cleanliness and antiseptics, used recent advancements to illustrate the interdependence of science and the healing art. In the forefront came the newly discovered X-rays. When used with photographic plates, a halfpenny lodged in a boy's gullet for six months had been located, a dislocation distinguished from a broken bone, and a bullet found in a hand wound. However, long exposures to X-rays were already predicted to produce ··· *according to the condition of the part concerned, injurious irritation or salutary stimulation.*

Physical scientists had concerned themselves more with trying to determine the nature of these rays. As J J Thomson pointed out in his address as President of the Mathematical and Physical Science section, there was as yet no direct evidence that they were a kind of light wave. However if they were, the already known fact that a beam of X-rays did not change direction when incident obliquely onto a block of material, whereas a light beam did, implied they were waves of very high frequency indeed. One peculiar property of X-rays concerned how they caused gases to change from electrical insulators to electrical conductors. This formed the subject of the first of two papers reporting Ern's researches at Cambridge. It was read by J J Thomson to an audience of several hundred.

Three days later Ern described to a smaller audience his magnetic detector, and how it had responded to waves produced three-quarters of a mile away. Professor S P Thompson, the author of one of the electricity and magnetism books which Ern had used back at Canterbury College, ··· *congratulated Mr Rutherford in breaking the record of distance at which electric waves can be detected.*

When discussion of papers re-opened the following day Mr W H Preece F.R.S. of the Post Office rose to his feet. This was the same Mr Preece who had taught practical telegraphy at the Hartley Institute with Professor Bickerton, who had written the text book *A Manual of Telephony*, who had experimented with using ground currents to signal across bodies of water, and who regularly reported the excessive 'noise' on telephones which occurred during solar sunspot maxima and displays of the Aurora Borealis. Mr Preece pointed out to the meeting that he was assisting a young Italian, Signor Marconi, who was transmitting signals over distances of one and a quarter miles on Salisbury plain. Furthermore, at the receiving apparatus, the signals actuated a relay and produced Morse signals. True wireless communication had been born.

[Guglielmo Marconi had first had the idea of using Hertzian waves for sending messages in the summer of 1894 on reading an article marking Hertz's death. By the following December he could use wireless waves travelling a few metres to start a bell ringing. He, or others on his behalf, later claimed that by the end of 1895 he could transmit Morse code messages over a range of three kilometres, including receiving messages sent out of sight below the brow of a hill. The Italian Minister of Post and Telegraph expressed no interest in wireless telegraphy. Marconi realised that wireless signalling appeared to have its future in communications where telegraph cables did not exist, such as between shore and ship. So, noting that England was a sea power, Marconi and his Irish mother arrived in London in February of 1896. His work soon came to the attention of Mr Preece who had long been seeking ways of giving early warning of impending storms to lighthouses and to lightships. His work in Italy had preceded Ern's but was unknown to scientific circles. On his arrival in England he claimed a reception distance of only 400 metres. So maybe Ern can claim just the 'English' world record for the period February to September 1896. In 1895 Carl Braun at Strasbourg also started experiments in this field. Braun and Marconi received the 1909 Nobel Prize in Physics for their development of wireless telegraphy.]

The following day, Mr Preece read his own paper concerning the proposed telephone line to Germany. At the close of proceedings Professor Oliver Lodge

> ⋯ *referred to the statement of Mr Preece on the previous day that an Italian had transmitted Morse signals by means of Hertzian waves. He invited members of the section to witness in his laboratory an experiment in which, at an hour's notice, his assistant had arranged apparatus to do an exactly similar thing. He regretted that all the resources of the Government should be open to foreigners, while so little encouragement was given to workers in our own country.*

Ern's interest in Hertzian waves as a research field, dormant for the past few months, now died.

Chapter 9

THE NEW PHYSICS

Cambridge 1896–1898

We've got a rabbit here from the Antipodes, and he's burrowing mighty deeply.

Andrew Balfour,
Advanced Student, Cambridge.

The Mysterious Fourth State of Matter

By the latter quarter of last century science was beginning to make sense of the world around us. Chemistry was becoming an established science with indivisible atoms as its cornerstone. Atoms could join together to form different types of chemicals, and it was well known that if an electrical current was passed through acidified water then oxygen gas formed at the positive electrode, and hydrogen gas at the negative electrode. Because such electrolysis always produced the same mass of hydrogen gas for each unit of electrical charge which had flowed, it seemed that each hydrogen 'ion' carried a fixed but tiny electrical charge.

Some amazing electrical properties of solids had been known for millennia. The ancient Greeks had learned that rubbing fossilised resin on cloth produced a spark, an electrical discharge in air. [Most of us have had an electrical shock on dry days after walking across synthetic carpet or sliding across a car seat.]

The solid resin, which we know as amber, the Greeks called ηλεκτρων. A letter by letter translation yields 'electron', one word which caused the introduction into the English language of possibly more derived words than any other during this past century.

By the middle of last century physicists had divided all materials into three quite distinct subgroups: solids, liquids and gases, and they had a puzzle. When a high electrical voltage was placed across two metal electrodes inside a glass vacuum tube, in which the gas pressure had been laboriously reduced to less than a thousandth of the atmosphere around us, the gas became a conductor of electricity instead of an insulator and glowed with a colour characteristic of the type of atoms present, for example red for neon gas. [These tubes were the forerunners of today's neon advertising signs or household fluorescent lamps.] Physicists were so impressed with this change that they regularly talked of this as a new, fourth, state of matter.

The beauty of the colourful gas discharge had been known for two centuries and was a regular feature of scientific lectures from the 1830's. Heinrich Geissler, a glass blower at the University of Bonn, made improvements to vacuum pumps so that the glow broadened from a narrow thread into a diffuse column. Such tubes were usually called Geissler tubes in his honour.

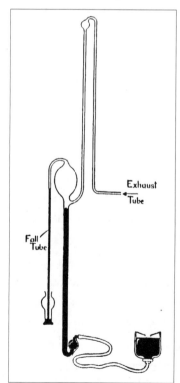

A striking feature was that at the lowest of pressures then possible, the gas discharge broke up into striations: regions of bright light separated by darkness. (We now know that when a high speed electron collides with an atom, ionizing it and causing it to glow, the electron comes to a halt and must be accelerated by the electric force until its speed is once again high enough to knock an electron out of an atom. Between those regions there is no light emitted by the gas.) The length of the first dark region increased away from the negatively charged electrode as the gas pressure was lowered.

The crude vacuum pumps of the day were manually operated mechanical pumps which used mercury in an elaborate series of glass tubes over two metres tall. Half a day's hard-labour was often required to reduce the gas pressure sufficiently for the more delicate experiments. As J J Thomson was to pervert, "Nature abhors a vacuum".

Early Töpler vacuum pump

Those who persevered could finally produce a low enough gas pressure so that the first dark gap (the Crookes' dark space) expanded until the whole tube between the negative plate and the positive plate was a dark space. Curiously, it still conducted electricity.

This advance in effort led to the next discovery. In such tubes the glass at one end of the tube now glowed brightly. Clearly, invisible rays, called cathode rays because of their origin at the negatively charged electrode (the cathode), were travelling the length of the tube before smashing into the glass. Because the invisible cathode rays caused glass walls to glow, physicists soon learned to 'see' the invisible cathode rays by placing known fluorescence materials in their path. Typical fluorescent materials were uranium salts in glass, and barium platinocyanide soaked into a small sheet of cardboard. [We can see here the foundations of the bright face of TV and computer screens.] They also learned that cathode rays darkened photographic plates so cathode rays could be photographed.

The positive metal plate (the anode) was often placed in a side-arm of a pear shaped tube so that a large area of glass wall was available to study these rays unimpeded.

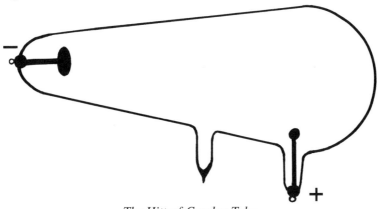

The Hittorf-Crookes Tube

Physicists placed obstacles in the path of the cathode rays and showed they were stopped by a thin sheet of metal. Heinrich Hertz, the discoverer of the electromagnetic waves which we now know as wireless and television waves, showed that cathode rays could go through very thin sheets of metal. Philipp Lenard made a 'window' of aluminium foil in his glass tube to allow the cathode rays into the air. Though they travelled only a few centimetres in air they could be studied far more easily than in the closed cathode ray tubes. (Lenard received the fifth Nobel Prize in physics, that for 1905.)

By the mid-1890's British scientists knew the cathode rays to be electrically negatively-charged particles because they could be deflected with a magnetic field and could rotate a miniature 'windmill' placed in their path. Other than that they were a mystery, one worthy of serious scientific study.

A Revolution in Science – The Discovery of X-Rays

X-rays had a meteoric rise in public interest which is unparalleled in the history of science. Yet their background was one of missed opportunities and missed fame.

At the University of Würzburg a 50-year-old physicist, Wilhelm Röntgen, who had been born in Germany, raised in Holland and educated in Switzerland, switched his researches from that on solids, liquids and gases to the new fourth state of matter, cathode rays. After familiarising himself with standard effects of cathode rays, he reasoned that maybe some cathode rays pass through the glass walls of a discharge tube but were never noticed because of the bright light emitted by the phosphorescing glass. Therefore he took a standard glass tube (a pear-shaped Hittorf-Crookes tube), covered it with thick black cardboard, darkened the laboratory and on the 8th of November 1895 switched on the tube and gained world fame.

Luck was on Willi Röntgen's side. In the darkness of the laboratory, and with dark adapted eyes, he could see that no light from the tube penetrated the cardboard shield but he was very startled to notice a glow a metre or so from the tube. Striking a match he saw that it was the little barium platinocyanide screen which he had used in studying cathode rays. It was far beyond the reach of the cathode rays in air. A new type of ray was in the air. Willi Röntgen was to call them X-rays (x is the unknown in mathematics) while a proud nation called them Röntgen rays, the name by which they are still known in Germany and countries upon which Germany had a marked influence, for example Turkey.

Willi Röntgen knew he briefly had a field all to himself so told no one (initially not even his wife) of his discovery, but quickly and quietly worked away. He showed that X-rays readily penetrate lighter materials but that a millimetre or so of lead stopped them. [We now know that X-rays interact with the electrons around atoms so metals with few electrons per atom (eg beryllium and aluminium) are used as transmitting windows while cheap metals with the most electrons per atom (eg lead and uranium) are used to shield X-rays.] On holding a lead disc in his fingers between the tube and the screen he was startled to see a shadowgraph of his bones. Like others to follow he regarded seeing his living skeleton as a grisly sight, a glimpse of death. He halted his experiments, afraid he would be ostracised. But curiosity forced him back to the lab.

He showed that X-rays came from where the cathode rays hit the glass wall, that X-rays couldn't be deflected with a magnetic field, and that X-rays did not change direction when passed into liquids or solids. He also found that a permanent record could be obtained using a photographic plate instead of the fluorescent screen. He photographed various hidden objects including weights inside their storage box and a compass inside its brass housing. His photo of his wife's hand and ring is one of the most famous of all X-ray photographs.

All this was done in secrecy. Then Willi Röntgen wrote an account of his experiments for the Würzburg Physikalisch-Medizinische Gesellschaft, a society in which physicists and medical doctors exchanged ideas, and on New Year's day of 1896 he posted copies and photographs to scientific colleagues. An account in the Vienna newspaper *Wiener Presse* of the 5th of January 1896 caused a sensation and was wired around the world. X-rays seemed so amazing that the *Presse* felt compelled to

> ⋯ *assure its readers that there is no joke or Humbug in the matter. It is a serious discovery by a serious German Professor.*

Five days later Professor Röntgen was called to Berlin to demonstrate X-rays to the Kaiser who promptly awarded him the Prussian Order of the Crown, Second Class. This was the first of many awards which were to include the first ever Nobel Prize for Physics (1901).

By late January of 1896 X-rays had been used to treat dermatitis and a cancer. By February Professor Röntgen's preprint was into its fifth printing. Within three months X-rays were routinely used for medical purposes in Vienna. The world soon followed. A sliver of glass in a heel explained a dancer's pain. A German who had been committed to a mental institution 10 years earlier, for claiming that his head pains were due to a bullet in his brain lodged there during a failed suicide attempt, because doctors could find no evidence of an entry or exit wound, had his sanity proven when an X-ray photograph of his head revealed the bullet. Magazines published all the latest X-ray photographs, including a hand riddled with lead shot. The owner, an American, had been walking on an English friend's country estate when he noticed what appeared to be a small cannon in the undergrowth. On bending down to examine it he tripped the trap set by game-keepers to deter poachers. The newspaper account stated that, by mistake, a live shotgun shell had been loaded instead of the usual blank. [If you believe that apology then I have this nice bit of swampland on the Chatham Islands which you may wish to purchase.]

Satirists had their day with one account of a romance which collapsed when a photographer finally succeeded in photographing the skeleton in the cupboard. And within 20 days of the first public announcement, the fortnightly magazine *Punch* published a poem entitled *The New Photography* for which the first three verses were:

> *RÖNTGEN, then the news is true,*
>   *And not a trick of idle rumour,*
> *That bids us each beware of you,*
>   *And of your grim and graveyard humour.*
>
> *We do not want, like Dr. Swift,*
>   *To take our flesh off and pose in*
> *Our bones, or show each little rift*
>   *And joint for you to poke your nose in.*
>
> *We only crave to contemplate*
>   *Each other's usual full-dress photo;*
> *Your worse than "altogether" state*
>   *Of portraiture we bar* in toto!

Cartoonists, of course, had a field-day showing possible uses of X-rays: a husband checking the thoughts of his sleeping wife, a boarder checking to see if his land-lady was snooping behind his door, John Bull displaying his backbone to the German Emperor, a family portrait showing skeletons only, metal clothes to prevent unauthorised X-ray photographs being taken of one's body, and, predicting the future, a customs' border guard examining the contents of a traveller's locked luggage trunk.

THE NEW PHOTOGRAPHIC DISCOVERY.

THANKS TO THE DISCOVERY OF PROFESSOR RÖNTGEN, THE GERMAN EMPEROR WILL NOW BE ABLE TO OBTAIN AN EXACT PHOTOGRAPH OF A "BACKBONE" OF UNSUSPECTED SIZE AND STRENGTH !

Technology quickly followed. Within six months Thomas Edison in America had invented a fluorescent lamp which produced light ten times more efficiently than incandescent lamps. X-rays emitted from the metal anode of a cathode ray tube caused a powder on the inside wall of the tube to fluoresce. [Nowadays we use ultraviolet light from electrically excited mercury atoms to fluoresce the powder coating the inside wall of fluorescent lights.]

There has never been a scientific discovery to match X-rays' immediate assimilation into science, medicine and public knowledge. It was a simple discovery missed years earlier by many men well known to science but who missed real immortality by their failure to wonder in the same way Wilhelm Röntgen wondered. Any number of world class scientists (including Hittorf, Crookes, Hertz and Lenard) could have, with a bit of luck, made this discovery several years, if not decades, earlier. [If they had, would there then have been anything left for Ernest Rutherford to discover in 1896?] Less notable people also missed it. The first X-ray photograph in the world appears to be that taken on the 22nd of February 1890 by Dr Goodspeed of the University of Pennsylvania while photographing cathode rays. This he had merely put aside as a curiosity, so consigning himself to scientific oblivion.

The Discovery of Radioactivity

Over the channel in France another revolution had taken place, though this time it was merely scientific.

A mere 15 days after the public announcement of Wilhelm Röntgen's discovery of X-rays, Henri Poincaré described the new photography to a weekly (Monday) meeting of the French Academy of Sciences in Paris. Since X-rays came from the luminescent area where the cathode rays struck the wall of the glass vacuum tube, he wondered aloud if X-rays were also emitted by other luminescent bodies.

Materials which glow other than by heating are referred to as luminescent, so this is the all-encompassing term. Those that glow while being irradiated by photons of higher energy (eg sunlight, blue light or ultraviolet light) are referred to as fluorescent while those which continue to glow after the excitation ceases are referred to as phosphorescent.

One man in the audience was uniquely placed to investigate this suggestion. Henri Becquerel, was professor of physics at the Museum of Natural History in Paris, as had been his father (Edmond) and grandfather before him, with an interest in mineralogy. Luminescence of minerals was widely known but not understood. Some uranium salts had exceptionally bright phosphorescence.

This had attracted Edmond. Henri first started publishing on phosphorescence in 1883 and had written 20 subsequent papers in this field. Uranium was well known commercially for its use in coloured glazes and in coloured glass. [In the 1960's waste uranium was used to produce a bright orange tableware.] So Henri Becquerel had unique knowledge and a large number of fluorescent minerals and salts already on hand.

His first experiments were simplicity itself, readily achievable by any scientist of the day. Henri wrapped a photographic plate in black paper, placed a known fluorescent mineral on top and put the combination on an outside window-ledge to expose the mineral to strong light from the sun.

At a meeting five weeks after the first, he claimed success, reporting that several fluorescent materials emitted penetrating rays which fogged the photographic plate. Crystals of potassium uranyl sulphate, well known as a phosphor, seemed particularly effective. He even took transmission photographs of a coin and other objects but these were nowhere near as sharp as X-ray photographs so that subject excited few people.

After that meeting Henri Becquerel prepared several sets of minerals and wrapped photographic plates. Each had thin metal objects between to examine the penetrating power of the rays. However the Parisian winter was not providing the necessary sunlight so these resided in a dark drawer awaiting the Sun's next appearance in strength. On the 1st of March 1896, the day

MÉTÉOROLOGIE NATIONALE   PARIS (PARC DE SAINT-MAUR)

NEBULOSITE , en 1/10.

Dates / Heures		FÉVRIER 1896							MARS 1896				
	23	24	25	26	27	28	29	1	2	3	4	5
5 h.		0	0	0	0	10	10	10	10	0	10	10	1
6		0	0	0	0	10	10	10	10	0	10	10	10
7.		0	0	0	0	10	10	10	10	0	10	5	10
8		0	0	4	0	10	10	10	10	0	10	1	9
9		0	0	2	0	10	10	10	10	4	10	9	10
10		0	0	5	1	10	10	10	10	10	10	10	10
11		0	0	3	7	10	10	10	10	6	10	10	10
12		0	0	2	8	10	10	10	10	8	10	8	9
13		0	0	4	8	5	10	10	10	6	10	10	9
14		0	0	7	7	4	10	10	10	7	10	7	6
15		0	0	8	9	0	10	10	10	8	10	6	8
16		0	0	7	9	0	10	10	10	10	10	10	7
17		0	0	10	0	10	10	10	10	10	10	10	3

Cloud cover in Paris Feb–Mar 1896. Note the total cloud cover prior to March 2nd.

before the next meeting of the Academy and after three totally cloudy days, Henri developed the plates anyway, expecting at best a weak exposure from the diffuse exciting sunlight. Instead he found strong exposure and reported that potassium uranyl sulphate appeared not to need stimulation by sunlight before or during the experiment.

This association with luminescent minerals was to bias European scientists' thoughts on the nature of radioactivity for years to come, even though Becquerel immediately moved on to uranium minerals that didn't luminesce and to uranium metal itself.

Over the next year or so Henri Becquerel showed uranium rays were in many respects similar to X-rays. They affected a photographic plate, passed through metals, caused gases to conduct electricity and discharged electrified bodies. (In 1903 Henri Becquerel was awarded half of the third Nobel Prize in Physics.)

Ern's Researches Using X-Rays – 1896

Soon after the discovery of Röntgen rays, J J Thomson had his assistant, an excellent glass blower, construct a Röntgen ray tube. JJ had two aims: to try to understand the nature of Röntgen rays, and to use them to assist his research into the nature of electrical conduction. Several assistants and students worked in this field. Irradiating a gas with X-rays changed it from an electrical insulator into an electrical conductor. Hence X-rays were to be a very valuable tool in the study of the fundamental mechanisms involved in gaseous conduction.

Ernest Rutherford had started his research with JJ in this field during mid-April of 1896. For the first six weeks he had laid the groundwork by studying the leakage of charge from charged conductors illuminated by X-rays, the effects of pressure and temperature on the rate of discharge, and searched for electrical polarization effects of X-ray irradiated gases and solid dielectrics. Some exciting possibilities were reported for the actions of X-rays on substances. He wrote home to his mother ⋯ *I see by the papers a few days ago that a blind person ⋯ can see when the rays fall on the retina.*

Many such amazing claims surfaced in these early days. For example, a French doctor claimed to have photographed thought. The Temperance movement hailed X-rays because they expected to be able to show drunkards and cigarette smokers the steady deterioration of their systems.

After the British Association meeting in Liverpool, Ern returned to

Cambridge for the new academic year. Research people now crowded the Cavendish. ⋯ *I am very glad I came last year, as I have got a good start* ⋯ . Ern worked in the Professor's rooms ⋯ *an unheard of thing up to the present, and it is very handy there to have Everett, the Professor's assistant, alongside to give me a hand occasionally.*

Ern would arrive at the laboratory at 10 a.m. and leave at 6.30 p.m., returning to his digs for lunch at 1.30. JJ invariably visited him at 12 noon and 5 p.m. to assist and see how things were progressing. The evenings were for reading and coaching.

His researches went well. During the first half of the long vacation, JJ and Ern completed their collaboration, which was reported to the BA meeting and published in the *Philosophical Magazine* under the title 'On the Passage of Electricity through Gases Exposed to Röntgen Rays'. This was Ern's fourth research paper. A fifth was sent off before the year's end, showing that the electrical current flowing in an irradiated gas had an upper limit. By measuring the current and the speed of the conducting particles he determined that only one atom in every million million or so conveyed the electrical charge. After measuring the relative absorption of X-rays in many different gases he concluded

> ⋯ *that the discharge of electrification by the Röntgen rays is due to a process going on throughout the volume of the gas, and is not due to the disintegration of charged dust from the electrodes.*

Also in hand were preliminary attempts to separate the positive and negative ions of the hydrogen molecule. To Professor Thomson, Ern's absorption results indicated that Röntgen rays were similar to light, that is to say, electromagnetic waves.

Their joint work had helped transform the new research field from one being merely descriptive to one based on accurate measurement. As a fellow student stated, "We've got a rabbit here from the Antipodes, and he's burrowing mighty deeply".

Life Outside the Lab – 1896

During the long vacation, July to October, Ern had to shift into Trinity College. He possessed no furniture and utensils of his own. His bed-maker went on the scrounge. As a result Ern could recline in Lord Acton's best armchair.

Before Ern left New Zealand he apparently gave May Newton three promises; that he would avoid wild women, would be teetotal, and would not smoke. During the summer vacation he had to admit to her that his willpower had failed.

You know what a restless individual I am, and I believe I am getting worse. When I come home from researching I can't keep quiet for a minute, and generally get in a nervous state from pure fidgetting ⋯ .

He had started smoking.

⋯ Every scientific man ought to smoke, as he has to have the patience of a dozen Jobs in research work ⋯ .

He was probably gently forewarning her as she was due to visit him in less than a year's time. They became engaged but he would await her arrival before sorting out an engagement ring.

⋯ Your mother wrote me a very nice letter welcoming me as a future son-in-law and generally saying things very nicely. ⋯ I am told Charlie calls you Mrs R so you will get used to the title by degrees. He always seemed to be cute over the matter and had evidently seen more than he was intended to.

One diversion from his research involved going with an ethnology expedition to a village in East Anglia to photograph children playing old games and to record measurements such as the dimensions of the head of all the males.

⋯ You can't imagine how slow-moving, slow-thinking the English villager is. He is very different to anything one gets hold of in the colonies.

He spent part of the latter half of the summer vacation having an excellent holiday in Cumberland with the colonial students. The group included the New Zealander William La Trobe, an engineering student from Auckland who later rose to become superintendent of Technical Education in New Zealand.

There is a degree of confusion concerning the various science groups at Cambridge. The Cambridge Philosophical Society was high-powered, long-established and had its own rooms. Its journal collection today forms the basis of Cambridge University's periodical library. JJ was President when Ern was elected an associate in January of 1896. The Cambridge Physical Society comprised all physical scientists in Cambridge. The Cavendish Society consisted of a few people interested in science. The Cambridge University Natural Science Club had a select membership of about 20, including no more than twelve undergraduates. Normally less than a dozen people met each Saturday night in one of the members' rooms to hear a scientific paper and to converse socially.

Ern, elected to this club in May of 1896, addressed the members on the 25th of July 1896 on the topic 'A New Method of Detecting Electric Oscillations'.

Ern attended most meetings and participated in discussions such as 'What should be and what are the motives which induce men to do research work', and 'The Age of the Earth'. At the meeting of the 27th of February 1897

> ⋯ *Mr Rutherford and others occupied the time of the club until 9.40 by (casting aspersions)* [crossed out] *drawing attention to the delinquencies of the secretary* ⋯ [who arrived late] .

Ern was elected Secretary for the long vacation of 1897, Vice-President for the Michaelmas term in 1897 and President for the Lent term of 1898. For his Presidential address to the other eight members present he initiated a discussion on 'Science and the People', stating that he thought

> ⋯ *harm was done to the cause of science by the part that newspapers were taking nowadays in posing as its exponents; he also deprecated the diffusion of scientific knowledge among the people by means of popular lectures.*

In the ensuing discussion some members opposed his views, supporting their arguments with personal experiences.

Another group was formed in November of 1896, the Physical Science Club, which consisted of Trinity research men, and met in one of their rooms on a Tuesday night. Ern gave the inaugural talk in his rooms, supplying coffee, biscuits, baccy and cigarettes.

At JJ's request Ern again addressed the Physical Society, this time on their joint work involving X-rays. Mrs Thomson, who could not follow much of the talk, passed the time idly wondering if there was a girl in his plans. After the meeting JJ was busy with an experiment, so Ern walked Mrs Thomson home. He took this opportunity to tell her he was engaged, and that May would visit him next year. Mrs Thomson was delighted. This exchange may have been what led JJ to steer more paid work towards Ern. For instance Ern took over from the Professor the examination of military candidates in practical physics at Woolwich and Sandhurst. JJ also passed on to Ern, now a recognized authority on X-rays and gases, two books to review for the science magazine *Nature*.

Ern spent Christmas at Eastbourne after which he dropped a hint to May.

> ⋯ *At the dinner I mentioned, some of the dresses worn were very decollete.* [i.e. a lot of skin showed.] *I must say I don't admire it at all. Mrs X., wife of a Professor wore a 'creation' I dare say she would call it, which I thought very ugly, bare arms right up to the shoulders, and the rest to match. I wouldn't like any wife of mine to appear so, and I am sure you wouldn't like to either.* ⋯

Cambridge 1897

Pressing forward with the study of X-ray induced conduction in gases, Ern measured the rate at which the ions recombined. Irradiated gas flowed down a long brass tube along which were insulated electrodes at fixed intervals. The known speed of the gas flow allowed estimation of the time of its travel between the electrodes, each of which monitored the degree of ionization of the gas. Most ions recombined within a second of being ionized.

This technique worked well for cheap gases such as air. For more expensive gases Ern developed a closed method. A metal bell jar containing gas had a central wire connected to an electrometer to measure the rate at which charge leaked away from the wire. The gas could be irradiated through a thin window below the bell jar.

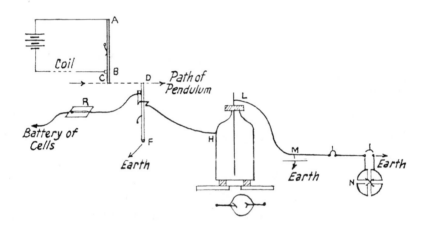

The X-ray tube needed to be turned off before the sensitive electrometer could be connected. Ern used a pendulum switch to break and make the contacts. This device had some similarity with the periodimeter he had developed at Canterbury College, only now, instead of a falling weight, a swinging pendulum broke the circuit powering the X-ray tube and quickly connected in the electrometer. He found the time of ionic recombination to be dependent on the type of gas used. The experiments sound simple but initially some confusion reigned until gases denuded of dust particles became standard.

To uncover the mechanism of conduction Ern needed to separate the positive and negative charge carriers. This he did by irradiating the gas between two metal plates. A battery of several hundred cells between the plates attracted positive entities toward one plate and negative entities toward the other.

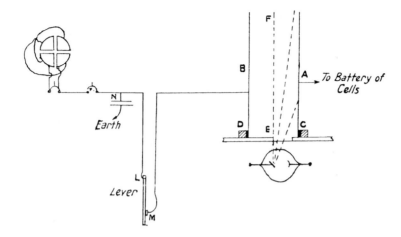

The speeds of either species could be measured by irradiating only half of the gas and measuring the time delay before a discharge current flowed in the electrometer. From the theory of diffusion of one species of molecule in a gas of another, the measured speeds implied that the carrier of the electric charge was no larger than a cluster of about a hundred molecules.

In an extension of this work Ern initiated similar experiments using the recently discovered radiations from uranium in place of X-rays to ionize the gas.

With the coming of spring a young man's fancy turned to May Newton which wasn't surprising as she was visiting England. Based in Cambridgeshire to be near Ern, her outings included the boat races on the Cam and seeing Ern capped as one of Cambridge's first B.A. research students. Ern visited her at weekends during her three week stay with friends near London. On a visit to the Crystal Palace, the horseless carriage caught Ern's attention. Capable of travelling at a racy twelve miles per hour, they were noisy and rattly but cheaper to run than a horse. They did not impress him as vehicles ⋯ *but I expect they will come into very general use shortly* ⋯ . [On the 28th of January 1896 Walter Arnold of Kent had already gone down in history as the first motorist convicted of breaking the speed limit, a heady 3.2km/hr. He was fined one shilling.]

May had several relations to visit around the country. She and Ern went with friends to Ireland, to Clonmel where her mother's family came from, and then to Scotland. In the northern autumn, May returned to New Zealand and separation.

Of the University college proposed for Wellington she reported to Mrs Rutherford:

··· Wellington College seems as if it were going to be an accomplished fact, but I hope they wont advertise for a physics Professor before eighteen months or more, as I feel sure Ern would not apply before that, if he did at all which I much doubt.

Ern's finances improved dramatically. The Commissioners of the 1851 Exhibition renewed his scholarship for a third and final year. Such extensions were common but not automatic. More importantly Ern had entered for the Coutts Trotter Scholarship by sending in his published papers and a resumé of his unpublished work. His winning this scholarship caused great excitement among the research students but near anger among others who had never accepted the idea of non-Cambridge graduates being allowed into Cambridge University. Their privileged, ordered, world of eventual advancement had gone forever.

No doubt Ern's great ability at experimental physics had carried the day. One example of his inventiveness concerned his accurate measurement of the speed of the carrier of negative charge. He mounted a shiny zinc plate above another metal plate (the base plate) so they were accurately parallel but with a variable separation.

Ultraviolet light shone onto the zinc plate, through a metal-gauze-covered hole in the base plate, thus releasing negative carriers from the zinc. Connecting a 100 volt alternating potential between earth and the base plate meant that

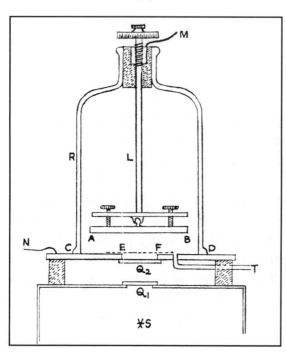

the negative charge carriers were attracted to the base plate but only during each half cycle when it went positively charged. With the plates close together the negative charge carriers had time to reach the base plate. By shifting the plates apart until he no longer observed charge transfer from the zinc plate, Ern could readily measure the speed of the negative charge carriers travelling in the gas. The plates were mounted in a bell jar which could be partially evacuated or filled with gases other than air.

Ern and May's wedding, 28 June 1900. The only Rutherfords present were Martha sitting left and George on Ern's right. The rest are Newtons, Gordons and girl friends of May's. Mary Newton is sitting to May's left. (pu, Rutherford Family)

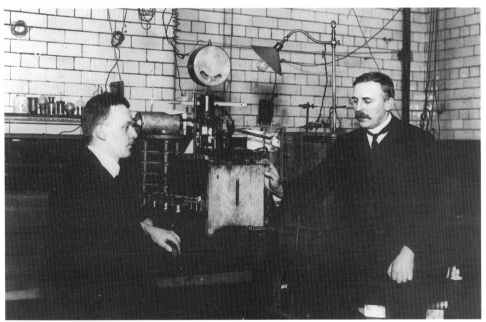

Ern and Hans Geiger at Manchester. The Rutherford-Geiger detector of ionizing particles revolutionised nuclear research. (pu, Rutherford Family)

Physicists celebrating the 20th Anniversary of Clark University, Massachusetts, 1909. Special guests included two recent Nobel Prize winners, Ern (second row, third from left) and Albert Michelson (front row fourth from left).

(pu Clark University Archives)

Going for a drive in the 1910 Wolseley-Siddeley purchased with Nobel Prize money. (pu, *Rutherford Family*)

The first Solvay Conference, 1911. (*Solvay Institute, Rutherford Family*)

GOLDSCHMIT PLANCK   RUBENS LINDEMANN   HASENOHRL
NERNST   BRILLOUIN   SOMMERFELD   DE BROGLIE   HOSTELET
           SOLVAY   KNUDSEN   HERZEN JEANS RUTHERFORD
                   LORENTZ   WARBURG   WIEN   EINSTEIN LANGEVIN
                          PERRIN   Madame CURIE   POINCARÉ KAMERLINGH ONNES

Professors Bragg, Rutherford and Strutt engaged on Admiralty war work, 1915.
(pu, F1212, Press Association)

Sir Ernest Rutherford in court dress, 1914. Eileen thought he looked a rather superior footman.
(pu, Rutherford Family)

The conclusions? Firstly, negative charge carriers must be very small, certainly no bigger than a gas molecule. Secondly, the negative charge carriers produced by the action of Röntgen rays on gases, and by ultraviolet light on zinc, were possibly the *same in the two cases or in any case not greatly different.*

It was an elegant piece of work not without its difficulties. The town electricity supply varied widely during the day in both voltage and frequency whenever other users switched on or off. So much so Ern planned to produce his own alternating high-voltage by using a rotating commutator to reverse the sign of a high-voltage battery.

After the summer of 1897 Ern moved to new digs in Trinity territory – the house of Charles Levett, a tailor, of 16 St John's Road. The University's Lodging-House Syndicate licensed lodging houses and kept strict control over the house and the conduct and morals of the lodging-house keepers. The Syndicate issued Mr Levett with a formal warning after his front door was found unlocked at 10.10 p.m. on October 23rd but, as it was a first offence, they resolved to take no further action. Had the door been left unlocked for Ern? The Natural Science Club met till late that night, and although he is not listed as present, a club rule prevented the secretary from recording any latecomers as present. [A year later the daughter of the lodging-house keeper over the road at number 19 was reported as having unsatisfactory associates. Though claims as to actual misconduct could not be substantiated the lodging-house keeper was ordered to ensure her daughter absented herself from the house during term-time.]

The ranks of the Cavendish research students had swelled considerably. So much so that William Whetham, a Trinity College lecturer and ex-demonstrator, complained

> *T-T-T-T-The English that was so-sp-sp-sp spoken in the laboratory in my time is no the s-s-s-s-s-same as is spoken now!!!*

Craig Henderson had come from Glasgow, Paul Langevin from France, John Zeleny from America, Harold Wilson from Yorkshire, John Henry from Ireland. Many happy evenings were spent together in one or other of their rooms. They decided to have a Research Students Dinner on December the 9th of 1897, before the Christmas breakup. John Townsend proposed the toast 'Our Guests', to which JJ responded. Craig Henderson toasted 'Our Old Universities.' The latter reminisced:

> ⋯ *JJ presided, and was as happy as a sand-boy, and at the laboratory on the following day remarked that he had no idea that the laboratory held such a nest of singing birds.*

This boisterous event at the Prince of Wales Hotel attracted the attention of the University Proctors who hastily withdrew, mystified and without entering the room, on being assured by the landlord that it was a scientific gathering of Research Students presided over by the Cavendish Professor of Physics!

The success of the evening ensured that an annual dinner became a Cavendish tradition, an event of great hilarity incorporating songs written especially to honour guests and their foibles and latest discoveries.

The Electron Unveiled 1897

It is usually forgotten that X-rays and radioactivity were stumbled on by mistake, by curious people probing false trails who had the wit to recognise the scientific importance of what they saw.

These remarkable discoveries diverted researchers away from cathode rays and the nature of electrical conduction in gases. J J Thomson was not wholly diverted. Ern and several other research students, notably John Townsend, had helped him in this work. John Townsend had started research at the Cavendish on a topic of his own choosing, one suggested by his old professor back in Dublin, the magnetization of liquids by induction. Then he too switched to work on the conductivity of gases, attempting to measure the charge per atom in hydrogen gas, both from electrolysis and when subjected to X-rays.

However it was J J Thomson himself who carried out the crucial experiment. It had long been known that cathode rays were electrically charged particles because they could be deviated by a magnetic field. JJ constructed a vacuum tube in which this magnetic deviation could be compensated for by an opposing electric deviation. [This tube is not dissimilar to the modern TV tube.]

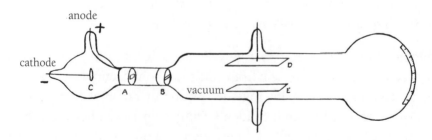

J J Thomson's e/m tube

In February of 1897 J J Thomson announced that the cathode ray, if it carried the same unit of charge that a hydrogen ion carried during electrolysis, was a particle about a thousand times less massive than a hydrogen atom. (J J Thomson received the 1906 Nobel Prize in physics.)

The sub-atomic age was born. Ernest Rutherford was an immediate convert, unlike many chemists who regarded objects smaller than atoms as heresy.

That one discovery of that tichy little entity spawned not only the sub-atomic age, but also today's multibillion dollar electronics and communication industry, and our rocketing information-rich society. From little acorns do mighty oaks grow.

Ern's Research using Radioactivity 1897–1898

Many researchers entered the new and puzzling field that was to be called radioactivity. In Paris, Pierre and Marie Curie put aside their researches in magnetism to pursue what became their life's work. Schmidt in Germany was to show thorium gave out similar radiations. Thus Ern's knowledge of French and German proved useful when he too joined the quiet race to understand these new phenomena.

Pierre Curie was already well-known for his co-discovery of the piezoelectric effect in crystals [the basis of ultrasonic fishfinders, disc record players, buzzers in computers, the frequency control of radio receivers and modern electronic watches] and for his work on magnetism (the temperature at which a ferromagnetic material, such as iron, reverts to a paramagnetic material, which is only weakly magnetic, is called the Curie Temperature). In 1895 he had married his student Marie Sklodowski, nearly ten years his junior, who initially worked on the magnetism of tempered steel. For her doctorate she selected to work on uranium radiations. Uranium ore was several times more radioactive than uranium so, in miserable working conditions, they (mostly she) chemically treated uranium ore (pitchblende) until they identified two more radioactive elements which they named 'polonium' (honouring Marie's homeland, Poland) and 'radium'. (Pierre and Marie Curie shared half of the 1903 Nobel prize in Physics.)

Ernest Rutherford's work on the speed of negatively charged 'ions' in irradiated gases led him to the conclusion that uranium radiation and X-rays were similar. However Becquerel had reported a difference – uranium radiation could be polarized and refracted. Ern repeated similar experiments and found that no such effects occurred. For example, a thick lead plate with a narrow slit cut in it passed a narrow beam of radiation from uranium compounds spread beneath the plate. Prisms of various material placed over part of the slit produced no deviation of the beam at all as shown by a photographic plate above the lead sheet.

The photographic method required long exposures: up to 7 days for weak sources. Therefore, where possible, Ern used the much faster detection method of monitoring the rate at which charge leaked away from a charged body. Electroscopes, in which a thin metal foil is attached at one end to a vertical metal plate, had long been used in static electrical studies. Like charges repel. The angle between the flexible foil and the plate allowed the relative size of the charge on the electroscope to be measured.

By placing different numbers of very thin aluminium foils, each of thickness five thousandths of a millimetre, between the uranium compound and the charged plate he showed that uranium emitted two distinct types of radiation – one that could be readily stopped and one much more penetrating.

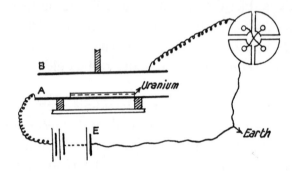

For convenience he called these alpha (α) radiation and beta (β) radiation respectively, names still in use today. [Alpha rays are stopped by a piece of paper or a few centimetres of air. They are used in modern smoke detectors in houses. When smoke particles block the alpha particles from reaching a charged plate, the fire alarm is triggered.]

Ern found that all compounds of uranium gave out rays of similar penetrating power. He also showed that the rays from thorium were similar though more penetrating, but they behaved in a very capricious manner. For thorium the rate of leakage from his electroscope varied by up to a factor of five at different times. [This led to his later discovery in Canada of a new, radioactive element which was a gas – radon.] He studied the rate of leakage for different gases and pressures. Many of his measurements on the recombination rates and speed of charge carriers in gases ionized by X-rays were repeated using uranium rays to show that the conduction mechanisms were the same.

In a little over a year Ernest Rutherford performed very many experiments to quantify the effects of uranium radiation. Even so, at that stage, he had to conclude that

> ··· *The cause and origin of the radiation continuously emitted by uranium and its salts still remain a mystery.*

Last Months at Cambridge 1898

CAMBRIDGE PHILOSOPHICAL SOCIETY.

———

THE next Meeting of the Society will be held on Monday, February 21, at 4.30 o'clock. It is expected that the following COMMUNICATIONS will be made:

I. *By* Professor FORSYTH :
  On some differential equations in the theory of symmetric algebra.

II. *By* Mr E. RUTHERFORD :
  Discharge of Electrification by ultra-violet light.

Several of Ern's uncles had been volunteers in the local militia in the Nelson province and had an interest in rifle shooting. In England he continued the family tradition.

The Trinity Rifle Club comprised those members of the Cambridge University Rifle Volunteers in Trinity College. Any other Trinity man could become an honorary member by paying at least one guinea (twenty one shillings). I do not know to which category Ern belonged but he appears once in the register of rifle matches as Private E Rutherford of E Company.

Ern fired in only two competitions. In March of 1898 he shot on only one of the three days of competition and with the help of a generous handicap finished 10th of the eleven competitors. These contests involved firing over 200, 500 and 600 yards on each day. His best results were always at 500 yards.

In the spring he once again entered. Of the fourteen competitors only four shot on all three days. Ern fired on just two days coming sixth of nine entrants on the first day, and third of five on the second. Having the advantage of the second highest handicap of all competitors raised him to fourth place over the whole three days for which he received a £1 prize – the Nursery Prize.

Higher financial rewards were in the wind. The junior professor of physics at McGill University in Canada had been appointed professor in London. With the possible prospect of a job in Canada, Ern confided to May Newton that he doubted JJ would want him to apply, that there would be a lot of competition for it and the salary wasn't much. To her he partially lied,

> ··· *Personally, next to New Zealand I would rather like Canada, as I believe things are very jolly over there.*

In successive letters Ern vacillated about the chance

> ··· *I don't think I shall go in for this Montreal Chair. JJ does not appear to wish me to ··· I have made up my mind to go in for the McGill Chair, chiefly as a business matter, because it will probably do me much good even if I don't get it ··· I am not very keen on getting the appointment, as I have my scholarship going and the possibility of a Fellowship, but it is as well to keep to the fore in these things. ··· If they want research a great deal I may be in it, but if experience in teaching, I must take a back seat ··· my chances are 'up a spout ···'*.

Ern had John Townsend write to Dublin to see if two good people there were applicants.

He thought that his application might at least make JJ act in regard to getting him an appointment in Cambridge. With the 1851 Scholarship of £150 per year due to cease in a couple of months, thus leaving only another year's worth of the Coutts Trotter Scholarship at £250 per year, Ern's financial future looked bleak. He had counted on getting a Trinity Fellowship, worth £300 per year for six years, but had just discovered a rule which required four previous years in residence. None of the research students would be eligible for another year. Beside he held little hope of success.

> ··· *There is a good deal of friction over this research business, which was intensified by my getting the Coutts Trotter. I know perfectly well that if I had gone through the regular Cambridge course, and done a third of the work I have done, I would have got a Fellowship bang off ···*.

[The following year, possibly as a result of losing Ernest Rutherford, Cambridge University altered its Fellowship rules so that research students could apply for Fellowships as early as after their second year.]

For the McGill position another old boy network swung into action. The remaining McGill Professor of Physics, John Cox, an ex-Fellow of Trinity, had appointed the former McGill professor, also an ex-Fellow of Trinity. Professor Cox and Dr Peterson, the Principal of McGill, returned to England and Cambridge to interview the candidates. Ern didn't have the field to himself. On the 24th of May John Townsend could report that

> ··· *There are two candidates from here Rutherford and Skinner one of the demonstrators. J.J. has a good deal to do with the appointment so there is great interest taken in it as it will be a kind of test case of proficiency in research versus experience in teaching.*

Ern liked both interviewers and his interview went well. During the waiting period Ern attended dinner at another college where a member let slip that all the arbitrators had sent in recommendations in Ern's favour. This unsettled period interfered with his research. He wrote a long letter to May Newton. His prospective duties had been mentioned by Professor Cox who had called Ern in for another chat.

> ⋯ *I am expected to do a lot of original work and to form a research school in order to knock the shine out of the Yankees! The physical laboratory is one of the best buildings of its kind in the world and has a magnificent supply of apparatus* ⋯.

Domestic matters were not forgotten. McGill had two terms which finished in early April leaving a six month summer 'vacation'. As he would have to start work in September, the following April would be the earliest he could come home for May Newton. However he still owed money to his father.

> ⋯ *Am I to go to New Zealand to fetch you to look after me and become Mrs Professor, or am I to wait another year to get enough cash to do it in style?*

Ern knew this letter would arrive in New Zealand weeks after any official announcement. So when word came from Montreal that he had been appointed he made sure the Press Association cabled notification to New Zealand newspapers. *The Press* in Christchurch announced the news, then devoted a leader to him under the headline 'A Clever New Zealander'. It concluded ⋯ *we shall look forward to watching his career, which can hardly fail to be brilliant, with interest and pride.* In response, the couple who were caretakers at Canterbury College wrote to Ern congratulating him on his Professorship.

Ern wrote a follow-up letter to May,

> ⋯ *Rejoice with me, my dear girl, for matrimony is looming in the distance. I got word on Monday, from Dr Peterson, to say I was appointed to Montreal. All my friends are of course very pleased, and I have to submit to being called professor without having a boot to throw at their heads.* ⋯

He would be sorry to leave Cambridge yet it was best he did on account of the prejudice there.

> ⋯ *It sounds rather comic to myself to have to supervise the research of other men, but I hope I will get along all right. There are about four men doing research in the Lab. some of whom are as old as myself, so I will have to carry it off*

Ern received a friendly letter from Professor Bovey, the Dean of the Applied Science Faculty, inviting him to stay with the Boveys on his arrival. Among the many congratulating letters was one from the Master of Trinity College

> ⋯ *It is not everyone of our countrymen who has, so to speak, in his veins the blood of Scotland, New Zealand, Trinity and Canada.*

Frantically Ern wrote up his research on the electrical conduction of gases induced by radiations from radioactive uranium and sent it off to the *Philosophical Magazine*.

J J Thomson's admiration for the young New Zealander's abilities shows in the reference he had written for McGill.

> ⋯ *I have never had a student with more enthusiasm or ability for original research than Mr Rutherford and I am sure that if elected he would establish a distinguished school of Physics at Montreal. I should consider any Institution fortunate that secured the services of Mr Rutherford as a Professor of Physics.*

On the 11th of June 1898 Ern addressed five members of the Natural Science Club on the topic of Cathode Rays. ⋯ *In a paper of the greatest interest, which was illustrated with blackboard diagrams,* ⋯ Ern sketched what was known about them and reported on work by J J Thomson, himself and other members of the Cavendish. Ern ⋯ *discussed the extremely interesting speculations as to the ultimate constitution of matter which have arisen from Pro Thomson's research.*

The ground work for Ern's future discoveries had been well and truly laid. In a remarkable six-year-period from 1893 to 1898 he had worked at the forefront of six major areas of physics: the magnetic properties of iron at high frequencies, the dielectric properties of materials, the detection of electric waves, electrical conduction in gases, the nature of Röntgen rays and radioactivity.

On the 8th of September, 1898, five hectic weeks after receiving news of his elevation, 27-year-old Professor Ernest Rutherford ensconced himself in a first-class cabin of the S.S. *Yorkshire*, a Canada-bound ship.

Another phase of his life had passed most fruitfully.

Chapter 10

NATURAL ALCHEMY

Canada 1898-1903

"For Mike's sake Soddy, don't call it transmutation. They'll have our heads off as alchemists".

Ernest Rutherford to Frederick Soddy,
On confirming the transmutation of atoms.

McGill 1898–1900

A stormy sea voyage rolled Ernest Rutherford across the Atlantic to Canada, where he landed at Montreal on the 20th of September 1898. There he found the physics building at McGill University to be well designed, superbly equipped, and only five years old. Four floors and a basement housed lecture rooms, teaching laboratories, research laboratories, mechanical workshop, lecture preparation room and so on. Even the mathematical lecture room had an adjoining storeroom, housing apparatus for illustrating mathematical physics. It is doubtful that a building better devoted to physics existed anywhere in the world.

Both building and equipment had been provided by one of McGill's most generous benefactors, the non-smoking tobacco magnate, W C Macdonald. As he himself lived on the equivalent of £250 a year, he reckoned that a Professor should be able to live on £500. Since he had accepted the position more because of the facilities for research than for the salary of C$2500, the newest holder of a W C Macdonald Physics Professorship could make do with that. He could have earned more in New Zealand but he had explained to May Newton, when she passed on the news that the new College in Wellington expected to appoint a physics professor at £700 a year,

> ··· I think if I were offered the New Zealand Chair at £700 and McGill at £500, I would take the latter as my chances of advancement are much better in McGill, than if I got out to New Zealand. There is also a certain amount of satisfaction in having a swell lab. under one's control, and probably in New Zealand my chances of research work would be very small.

Ern rented a room in a boarding house and took stock of his situation. As he still owed money in New Zealand he informed May Newton she would have to wait eighteen months before he could come home to fetch her because the round trip would take nearly half a year's salary. Then he settled into the new job.

Being an authority on the subject, Ern taught Electricity and Magnetism (officially called Wireless Telegraphy) to a large class of second year engineering and science students. His standards were unrealistic, the course and its mathematical content being pitched well above the level of the class. To the majority he left the image of a nervous lecturer who had little ability in handling undergraduates. Subsequent classes immortalized him in verse.

> Ernie R-th-rf-rd, though he's no fool,
> In his lectures can never keep cool,
> And his methods, I fear,
> Are not meant for here,
> But would work much "more better" in school.

Or, paraphrasing a popular music hall act,

> There was once a New Zealander came to McGill,
> Alone! Alone!
> His knowledge of students was practically nil,
> Alone! Alone!
> For whenever a student chanced to be late,
> It caused much excitement, but sad to relate,
> The request for a note met a horrible fate
> Alone! Alone!

In attempting to keep order he sometimes found the wrong words. Like the time a slight disturbance occurred at the rear of the lecture room. Said Ern in a dignified manner:

> "*I do not require an ass in this lecture room to keep me company*"
> Pause. "*Gentlemen, I guess the joke is on me.*"

Some students were however influenced by his insistence on their striving to build knowledge on fundamental principles established by experiment. The ability to apply these principles and to reason by using them was paramount. A few students, caught by his enthusiasm for research, altered their choice of career to one in physics. Others merely felt his scorn at their memorizing of electrical formula, their imagined path to success if not knowledge.

Luckily Ern had been engaged principally to supervise research. This he did well while his fellow professor, John Cox, a good teacher who was not a research person, took the bulk of the elementary teaching and administration. For instance, Professor Cox served on the Committee of Management of the Macdonald Physical Building as it was he who had been sent on tour of the best physics laboratories in America, prior to his designing and equipping McGill's. Ern apparently served on just two university bodies during his time at McGill. He replaced Cox for two years (from 1903) as an elective fellow of the Faculty of Arts, and served one year (from 1906) on the new Committee on Graduate Studies.

By 1904 Ern's reputation as a skilled researcher had diffused world wide so that Sir Oliver Lodge could write:

> *I trust you will not waste your time lecturing but will go on with your experiments and leave lecturing to others!*

McGill revered Ern's predecessor, Professor Hugh Callendar F.R.S., who had moved to University College, London. By establishing a tradition of earnest work in the true spirit of research, Callendar had made the Macdonald Physical Laboratory well known in the scientific world. An instrument man, he developed equipment rather than investigated basic principles; his forte being accurate measurements concerned with heat. For this he was renowned. Before his departure, the faculties had passed a resolution honouring Callendar while the University awarded him a LL.D. at a typically rowdy degree ceremony.

As a young fellow of twenty-seven, Ern initially became fed up with the frequent references to the greatness of the man he replaced. J J Thomson hadn't had to hide his feelings. When told by Professor Bovey, the Dean of the Applied

Science Faculty, how sorry McGill was to lose Callendar, he had retorted: *"I don't see why you should be, you got a better man anyway."*

Ern had to be more humble, at least until an early court case corrected the situation. Some residents sued the street railway company over the vibrations caused by the powerhouse when the electric dynamos were running. The company engaged Ern to measure these vibrations. He constructed instruments far more sensitive than earthquake detectors but presumably not as sensitive as the delicate quartz fibre galvanometers and magnetometers with which he had so much previous experience. Vibrational amplitudes typically of 25 thousandths of a millimetre were mechanically amplified and recorded by a pen writing onto a rotating drum. Each day he and two witnesses would visit the power station to change the paper and sign the record. Ern thereby gained local fame and acceptance since it was considered that only the great Callendar could have tackled such a job.

Within three months of Ern's arrival at McGill, the University of New Zealand's agent in England could forward Professor Cox's assessment of Ern. *I am very happy with Professor Rutherford, and the more I see of him, the more I find we have secured a very strong man – perhaps the strongest available.*

With the coming of his first spring in Canada, Ern purchased a bicycle and joined a tennis club. There was no mail from his brothers George or Jim for six months. He wrote regularly to his mother and May Newton, but through a mistake in dates his letters continually missed the mail steamer from San Francisco. This state of affairs lasted until he received a worried cable from home asking if he was well. The reassuring telegram in reply set him back eleven dollars.

A long distance telephone message from Ottawa brought better news. A prominent American entomologist had caught a bug. As he was the planned speaker for one of the Royal Society of Canada's Popular Lecture in two day's time, the Society now needed a last minute replacement. Professor Cox had suggested Ern discoursing on wireless telegraphy. Could he do it? Definitely. With one day preparing equipment, a morning train ride and an afternoon setting up the experiments, he was rushed, but he was there and ready to deliver.

Ern explained that wireless telegraphy was a misnomer. Properly speaking it was telegraphy without connecting wires because the sending and receiving ends have wires. He explained the principles involved, gave the history of electric waves and surprised the audience by using his apparatus to ring a bell. That privileged audience were shown a taste of the future: Marconi had already transmitted across twenty miles. But lack of privacy was one of the principal drawbacks. Furthermore, Ern cautioned that by using the present methods it seemed that people would be able to communicate over distances of no more than 200 miles. For the present at least, it would not affect the telegraphic cable systems laid worldwide. All in all, he thought it

> ⋯ *not safe or politic to invest very much capital in a company for the transmission of signals by wireless telegraphy.*

May Newton received a first hand account of the meeting.

> ⋯ *Everything went off very well and the applause was great. It was a very fair audience in a large hall and was the biggest show I have attended so far.* ⋯ After describing a tour of a research farm he returned to a regular theme of hoped for honours. ⋯ *I think it is quite probable I may be elected a member of the Royal Society of Canada next year – an F.R.S. on a small scale,* ⋯ .

Prior to Ern's arrival, the hot topic of physics research at McGill concerned X-rays. With their splendidly equipped laboratories they had an X-ray tube working shortly after Röntgen's first announcement and immediately applied it to locate a bullet in a man's leg, the first surgical application on the American continent. Within a year scores of surgical cases had been photographed, including a nine-minute exposure to locate a bullet lodged in the centre of a girl's brain. It had been there two years without impairing her faculties.

Recently their interest had been more in elucidating the nature of the mysterious rays themselves. One experiment had shown the speed of X-rays to be not less than 150 kilometres per second and probably enormously greater. Such evidence pointed towards X-rays being electromagnetic radiation rather than particles. The other main field of research encompassed Professor Callendar's first love: heat and thermometry.

Three demonstrators and three graduate students had worked under Professor Callendar in these fields. Ern regarded one of these demonstrators, Howard Barnes, to be the best of the McGill researchers. Of similar age to Ern, he was due for a D.Sc. degree particularly for his work on the formation of frazil ice in rivers. These fine ice crystals could clog the intake pipes to hydro-electric power plants during winter so this was a problem of some economic, as well as scientific, importance.

Ern introduced research in radioactivity to the laboratory. He now had the responsibility for suggesting fruitful lines of investigation to others and supervising their work. The new professor of electrical engineering, a young American, R B Owens, undertook the investigation of the radiations from thorium. The detection method used the same electrical technique with which

Ern had studied the radiations from uranium. Two parallel metal plates were oppositely charged. When a radioactive material was placed on the bottom plate, the charge on the top plate leaked away due to the conducting paths set up between the plates by the ionized trails left by the alpha and beta particles. An electrometer monitored the leakage current. One of Ern's first tasks at McGill had been to improve the sensitivity of the electrometers by many hundred times.

Professor Owens quickly elucidated the properties of the thorium radiation, finding them more penetrating and complicated than those of uranium. Early on, he too observed the very curious phenomenon which Ern had observed in England. The radiation from thorium, when examined by the electrical discharge method, varied in a most capricious manner. It was not constant. [In one test they blew tobacco smoke into the chamber whereupon the current flow in the electrometer fell to one tenth its initial value. The modern smoke detector, a major saver of lives in house fires, had its origins in this simple experiment.] Tests showed this variability to be due to draughts or the opening or shutting of doors. A lesser experimenter would have eliminated the problem by keeping conditions constant through exclamations such as "Shut that door." Not Ernest Rutherford. Here was something needing to be understood. This wasn't a property of thorium, air, alpha or beta rays. Careful experiments, using controlled air flows in closed apparatus, eliminated those possibilities. The thorium apparently emitted a radioactive 'emanation'.

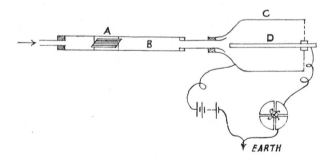

Ern flowed slow moving dust-free air over a thin layer of thorium oxide enclosed inside two sheets of paper which cut off the radiations but passed the emanation. The current in the electrometer rose, becoming constant after a few minutes. When the flow of air was stopped the current decayed exponentially (geometrically), falling to one half of its initial value after an interval of about one minute. The problem seemed more puzzling when he found that any object placed near thorium became radioactive itself. What was going on?

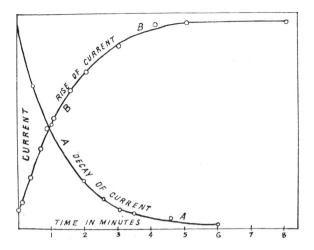

He carried out a beautifully conceived series of experiments to clarify the evidence. This involved hard work and long hours, usually until eleven or twelve o'clock at night, five nights a week. The experiments showed that radioactivity induced by thorium emanation was the same for all materials, falling to half its initial value in some eleven hours. The common factor was the thorium emanation. After one year at McGill, Ern sent his preliminary results to J J Thomson for publication in the *Philosophical Magazine*. His fuller paper two months later coincided with reports in *Comptes Rendus* of similar, but less detailed, work by Pierre Curie on emanations from radium and polonium. The effect appeared to be universal but still highly puzzling.

[As we now know, a heavy radioactive nucleus emits an alpha particle, thus becoming a new, less massive, nuclei which may itself be radioactive. In one link of these chains, radium decays to radon, an inert gas in the helium, neon, argon series. This gas can diffuse out of the parent sample before itself radioactively decaying to radioactive polonium, a metal, which is deposited on any object nearby, thus making the object temporarily radioactive. Similarly the thorium decay chain contains a different isotope of radioactive radon. The discovery of radon is wrongly attributed to Ernst Dorn. Naturally occurring radon has recently come to be recognized as a major contributor to environmental radiation. It diffuses out of earth, stone, concrete and bricks and occurs in worrisome concentrations in some localities which have higher than normal concentrations of naturally occurring uranium in rocks and soil, and also in well-sealed, energy-efficient houses made of these materials.]

Another year of great effort was to pass before Ern could confidently talk of the emanation as being a gas of a new element, and a further year before the radioactive decay chains were begun to be worked out. At the time it all seemed quite mystical and contrary to common sense.

Ern now had four demonstrators and students assisting, or being trained to assist, with his research. One, R K McClung, worked on measuring the energy of X-rays and radioactive emissions, thus turning McGill's specialist skills in X-ray and heat measurements towards Ern's research interests. Ern was to conclude that the large energies involved in radioactivity could not be obtained from the chemical regrouping of atoms.

In June of 1899, Professor Brown, a member of the Senate of the University of New Zealand and Ern's old Professor of English at Canterbury, had briefly visited McGill. At that time he had confided in a letter home to his wife

> ⋯ *Mr Rutherford went with me to the post office. Nobody could be more attentative and kind than he was. He went about everywhere with us and was my constant companion the whole three days we were in Montreal. We went over the university with him and it has splendid buildings indeed; poor Canterbury College is a mere nothing beside it ⋯.*

Yet a few months later he wrote to Ern, sparking the latter to confide to May Newton

> ⋯ *He seems to think I might want to go in for the chair at Christchurch but I don't feel very keen about it. There is no lab and it would be very difficult to get much of a lab and I would have to stay there all my days. I am afraid I would be very discontented there without a good Lab and I still have a certain amount of ambition. It would of course be near for you there but I don't think the Chch staff would be a very interesting lot of collegues. I can't imagine myself being on special friendly terms with any of them that were there in my day. Moreover, the salary isn't enough if one is to go in for complete* [cessation?] *of all thought of research. I don't think you will mind Canada for a few years for between you and me I don't regard myself as finally settled here but hope to get over to England someday. With much love from your own hubbie, Ern.*

England, the centre of scientific activity, beckoned. Perhaps other events helped seed the idea that the divided city of Montreal would not be his permanent home. A month after Ern wrote the above letter, English troops fighting the Boers in South Africa, relieved Ladysmith. The McGill students celebrated wildly. They raised Union Jacks on the City Hall and the French newspaper offices, whereupon an enraged French mob lowered the flags and tore them to shreds. Some McGill students went to the French university (Laval) and asked politely but stupidly for the Union Jack to be flown there. The request unleashed a chain reaction. The French students turned fire hoses on them; they retaliated by throwing snowballs at the windows, smashing many; the police charged with batons. The following day a French crowd burnt the English flag and proclaimed they were going to smash McGill, upon which the latter's students armed themselves with iron bars. Ern entertained no doubts that had these two mobs met, civil war would have followed.

Overall, Ern could be quite pleased with his first eighteen months at McGill. He had discovered new effects of some importance, sent off four scientific publications, made friends for life of many people, laid to rest the bogey of Callendar, introduced postgraduate lectures to McGill (a course of Electrical Waves and Oscillations), been awarded a B.Sc. degree (ad eundem) from McGill, trained four demonstrators and students to assist him in his research, and had plenty of mysteries yet to solve.

Now, however, was the time to fit in the long planned visit home and matrimony.

Visit to New Zealand 1900

With the time of his bachelorhood drawing rapidly to a close, Ern thought of his future.

> ⋯ *I had a vivid dream about you the other night. You were sleeping with your head on my shoulder – I remember distinctly you waking up and kissing me. Hope it isn't too long before it is verified ⋯ .*

With Ern being such an eligible bachelor, his friends in Montreal were curious about the girl to be fetched from New Zealand, that distant South Sea country at the bottom of the world. He reassured May that he had prepared them for her arrival.

> ⋯ *The prevailing impression I have instilled in the staff is that I spent most of my time in NZ basking under a palm tree and that my clothing could have been covered by a postage stamp ⋯ .*

and warned her that she would be asked to display her native dress to the ladies and to speak in her native tongue.

In like vein, after observing a friend with a domineering wife, Ern had laid down his rules for the marriage.

> ··· *You had better resign yourself to your fate for I have come to the conclusion that I do not belong to the hen picked variety of men so you must be prepared to be humble and meek and do what you are told in a proper manner* ··· .

He expressed concern about the wedding.

> ··· *I hope you are not figuring on a public wedding for me to make an ass of myself as all men do. I am not keen on those functions. However you have a free hand over my movements up to the wedding day and then your turn comes. Goodbye my own love with as many kisses as is good for you.*
> *Your own Ern.*

Travelling by the Royal Mail steamer via Honolulu and Apia, Ern arrived in Auckland on the 8th of May 1900. A few hours later the old faithful S.S. *Takapuna* steamed out of the Manukau harbour, rushing the southern portion of the mail on to its destinations, and Ern to his parents in Taranaki.

A week later he continued on down to May in Christchurch. So far his plans for a quiet trip had held. But then C C Farr returned to town having just carried out a magnetic survey of the West Coast of the South Island. Whoever told the *Lyttelton Times* of his return and results also probably reported Ern's arrival.

> *Professor Ernest Rutherford, formerly at Canterbury College, and at present Professor of Physics at M'Gill College, Montreal, is now in Christchurch on a visit. Professor Rutherford, who has had a very distinguished career, succeeded Professor Callendar at M'Gill College, and has been devoting his attention principally to the study of radiations from such bodies as uranium and thorium. Some of his original researches there attracted the attention of the scientific world, and are quoted by the highest authorities.*

Ern was known in Christchurch only through the Newton family and Canterbury College circles. Dr Dendy, his old biology lecturer and currently the Secretary of the Philosophical Institute, immediately asked Ern to address the Institute. To the next council meeting he reported his initiative. This action triggered *considerable discussion*. Ern had never addressed the Institute before, but Jack Erskine's reading of Ern's paper to them in 1895 had caused the Institute to ban highly technical papers and to seek speakers of wider appeal. Perhaps they were thinking back to his last paper? Perhaps they were discussing the problems of altering the set date of their meetings? The minutes merely record that Mr Laing (the science master at the Boys' High School) *be authorized to interview Prof. Rutherford on the subject and if possible make arrangements to suit his convenience.*

Robert Laing and Ern walked in a garden, chatting of old times. Ern peered over a fence to see that no one else was within hearing range then, in an awed whisper, told Mr Laing the latest scientific heresy: he believed there were pieces of matter a thousand times smaller than the hydrogen atom (J J Thomson's electrons).

As for a possible lecture Ern turned the Institute down. He had his own arrangements to make. May Newton wrote of these to Mrs Rutherford.

> *North Belt*
> *May 22nd*
>
> *My dear Mrs Rutherford,*
> *Mother is writing to ask you to come down and see Ernest and myself married. Of course it will be only a very short and comparatively uninteresting affair as there will be no guests beyond my grandmother, Uncle Tom, and Uncle Sam and his wife and my mother and brothers and Mr Rutherford and yourself and George whom Ernest is asking to be his best man. I have finally decided to wear my ordinary sunday costume, a coat and skirt and hat. We are unfortunately very short of room here, Ernest has Gordon's room already so I am afraid we cannot offer to put you up but there are nice boarding houses quite near where you would be very comfortable indeed. We are going away for a short trip and then after ten days in Chch to pack and say goodbye to all my friends, we will come up to you, for ten days or so, if you will have us, before going on to Auckland. We are going to be married at Papanui about 9.30 a.m. in the last week of June the date is not quite fixed more than that. Hoping to hear from you soon.*
>
> *I am*
> *Yours affectionately*
> *Mary Newton*
> *Love to all at home.*

Shortly thereafter Ern returned north to the rural seclusion of Pungarehu, to his large family and to Rutherford and Son, flaxmillers. George and Jim were flaxmillers, Flo a teacher. Ellen, Alice, Ethel and Evelyn did domestic duties. Arthur, the baby of the family, had already reached nineteen years.

A visit to New Plymouth may then have been the trigger for the brief, and not strictly accurate, mention appearing in the *Taranaki Herald*.

> *Mr E. Rutherford, who holds a professorship in Electricity in Canada, is spending a few days with his people at Pungarehu. Mr Rutherford is to be married at Christchurch towards the end of the month and then returns to America.*

He wasn't the only Professor in town. Professor Besant, a London palmist, had arrived to make money.

With all his brothers and sisters still single, Ern's marriage appeared to be an important family milestone. Yet few were to witness it. Possibly finance was the problem. Flax lay unsold in England causing many New Zealand flax mills to close down. Four days before his wedding Ern led the tiny Rutherford delegation of just his mother and George back to Christchurch where, on the 28th of June 1900 at St Paul's church in Papanui, Ernest Rutherford married May Newton. (Or, as George Rutherford's wife would rather cuttingly tell her children later in life *May married Ernest, Ernest did not marry May*.) Following poor photographs and a temperance reception at the Newton house, the shy couple departed for their honeymoon at the southern lakes.

Ern had succeeded in keeping it a quiet affair. The wedding announcement appeared six days later in just one newspaper, although this was seen and broadcast by Dolly Vale, the Christchurch correspondent to the lady's social columnist of the *New Zealand Graphic*. At the Canterbury College graduation ceremony the day after the wedding, the Chairman of the Board of Governors commented

> ··· *that he had hoped that a distinguished visitor would have been present that afternoon, but he had since learned that he had just received another diploma in the shape of a marriage certificate.*

Around the time the brand new Mr and Mrs Rutherford arrived back in Christchurch, the Canterbury Philosophical Institute presented a popular lecture open to all. The Institute had grown in stature and public interest over the intervening years since Ern had been a member. Hence at this lecture Professor Easterfield, the new Chemistry professor at the new college in Wellington, used flashes and bangs to enthrall an overflow audience on the subject of 'Modern Explosives'. Entertainment sweetened the pill of instruction. In his concluding remarks Professor Easterfield became serious. Who was going to perfect the physics and chemistry of explosives to study problems raised by Nobel and other workers? He had no doubt

··· *that it was absolutely wrong of them to allow any person to issue*
from our Universities and University Colleges as graduates in science,
until they were qualified to take up a piece of research, and they should
be enthusiastic in taking up investigations. I fear that as long as they
made examinations one of the ideals of University education, instead
of regarding them as being a thing by no means to be worked for, but
only as a temporary test of the proficiency of the student for the time
being, so long would it be true that our laboratories, however well
equipped they might be, instead of being workshops, would be
playgrounds, and graduates ornaments rather than useful members of
society. The country, in supplying these workshops, required that some
work should be turned out. I do not mean that the work turned out
should bear the mark of usefulness, but the training he has had should
show that he is able to do good work.

These sentiments were also held dear by Ernest Rutherford. On this visit
he gained an academic title. His name was well known to the officials of the
University of New Zealand, as a distinguished old boy, one of six double-first-
class honours graduates. In addition, the Chancellor had been editor of the
Transactions of the New Zealand Institute for Ern's first two papers, and the
Registrar had been his headmaster at Nelson College. As the requisite five
years had elapsed since his master's degree, Ern entered for the November
exams, submitting all his published papers to be considered for a D.Sc. degree.
The University's examiners in England evaluated his case along with all other
exam papers. From February of 1901 Ern could call himself Dr Rutherford,
his sixth degree and fourth from the University of New Zealand.

The first mass use of new scientific words introduced into a language is
often in advertising. [For example, consider the names given to some cars –
Pulsar, Laser, etc.] This is no new trend. While in Christchurch Ern could read
in a local newspaper, of the latest sensation.

The unassuming Röntgen ray
Appears to burn the flesh away
And leave the white and ghostly bones
The cause of shudders, sighs and groans;
So like a man who is ill and cold
Who thinks he's dead until he's told
The way to health in manner sure
By taking Woods Great Peppermint cure.

After ten days bidding farewell to their friends in Christchurch, another ten days with the Rutherford family at Pungarehu, and three days in Auckland, May Rutherford launched into the unknown as a university professor's wife in a foreign land. She, even more so than Ern, never cut her ties to New Zealand.

I know of no personal accounts of this first visit home to New Zealand. However the honeymoon must have been a success. A baby arrived nine months later, almost to the day.

McGill 1900–1902

The Rutherfords arrived back at McGill for the new academic year and a round of social engagements designed to introduce May to Ern's friends. One, Professor Owens the electrical engineer, had moved out of his boarding house and taken a flat with the express purpose, so he said, of preparing suppers for the Rutherfords. Ern and May rented a terraced house with a small rear garden at 152 St Famille Street, a short walk from the laboratory. [The house has survived although its neighbour on one side has been demolished. Due to renumbering of the street it is now number 3702.]

Ern, with the help of his students, pushed forward with his researches into the nature of the emanations from thorium and radium and the radioactivity induced in any material they came in contact with.

By March 1901 he had four or five papers in hand which May would type. Now in the final stages of pregnancy, and busy knitting for the baby, she wrote to Mrs Rutherford with the telegraphic code to be used: 'Waihini' would mean she and daughter both doing well. 'Tipoka' would mean she and son both doing well. Tipoka (dried leaf) was the name of the Maori village near the Rutherford flax mill as well as the mill itself.

The telegram sent to mark the March 30th birth signalled Waihini. Ern wrote home to his mother giving details of her first grandchild.

> ··· *You have probably been aware for several days that you have now the honour of being a grandmother. I hope Father feels correspondingly dignified after reaching the stage of grandfather. The baby, much to May's delight, is a she, and is apparently provided with the usual number of limbs. There is much excitement in the college and on the night of her arrival I was toasted at a whist party. It is suggested I should call her 'Ione', after my respect for 'ions' in gases. She has good lungs, but I believe uses them comparatively sparingly compared with most babies.*

The baby is of course a marvel of intelligence and we think there never
was such a fine baby before. I hope Pater is well – enjoying life – and
meditating on the probable number of his grandchildren.

They named the baby Eileen Mary.

Ern's salary was not large. He had the expense of May's maid, the enlarged family, and of upholding his social position as Professor. Earlier in the year he had turned down a job offer from the University of Columbia as it would not have been an improvement on McGill. Finance was not his only concern. Scientific isolation from Europe would always be a drawback in any colonial or American appointment. He wrote to J J Thomson expressing these sentiments; seeking his advice on whether to apply for the Edinburgh Chair. JJ, with his finger on the pulse of physics in Great Britain, advised him to go ahead – he wouldn't get it as the selection committee comprised local men who knew nothing of physics and they had a local candidate, but Ern's application would let people know he was willing to leave Montreal.

He obviously used the situation to his advantage, as shown by the minutes of the meeting of McGill University's Board of Governors held on the 19th of April 1901:

⋯ the cases of Dr Adams and Professor Rutherford, whose services
might be lost to the University were referred to the Principal, with power
(on consultation with the Chairman) to arrange – if possible – for such
increase of salary as might induce these Professors to continue in their
present posts.

(Dr Adams was the Professor of Geology.) Sir William Macdonald, the chairman, gave the money to increase both salaries to C$3000. Ern's was to take effect in July but Adams' was immediate and came with an agreement for a further increase to C$3500 after three years. [Four years later, from May of 1905, the University increased Ern's salary to a very healthy C$4000.]

One of Ern's earliest co-workers at McGill was Harriet Brooks. She had graduated in 1898, the winner of the Anne Molson Gold Medal in mathematics and physics, and become Ern's first female research student and May's good friend. Initially she examined how the damping of electrical oscillations was affected by altering the spark gap in the discharge circuit. Ern held her in high regard and they remained lifelong friends. Harriet later carried out research at the Cavendish Laboratory and with Marie Curie in Paris. After her marriage in 1907 to a fellow McGill physics demonstrator, Frank Pitcher, she gave up scientific research. I have been told the marriage was not entirely happy. Lord

Rutherford wrote her obituary for *Nature* (17 June 1933) and after detailing her scientific achievements concluded

> *… A woman of much charm and ability, she was a welcome addition to any research laboratory and left in all who met her a vivid impression of a fine personality and character.*

With the help of Harriet Brooks and Howard Barnes, Ern had shown the emanation from radium to be an inert gas with a molecular weight of 40 to 100 or so. Its chemical properties, together with that of the induced radioactivity, were still unknown. Previously, all radioactive emissions had been independent of physical properties such as temperature and pressure. Surprisingly, the emanation from thorium increased as the thorium salt was heated. (Showing the international nature of science, Ern published this work in German). All appeared most puzzling. Obviously a lot of work would be required to sort this out.

Another strong line of research encompassed the production and motion of ions in gases, a continuation of his earlier work at Cambridge. JJ's corpuscular theory, that there were bodies (electrons) smaller than atoms, excited physicists but worried chemists. To them whole atoms begat chemistry and most dismissed Thomson's new theory.

The McGill Physical Society called a meeting on March 28th 1901 to resolve these differences or, as Ern saw it, to demolish the chemists. Ern chaired the meeting and the subject under discussion was: 'The existence of bodies smaller than an atom'. Frederick Soddy, a young Oxford chemistry graduate who had come to Canada hoping to get a professorship at Toronto but had settled for a demonstrationship at McGill, was to be the chemist's champion against *Physical Heresy*. In his address, entitled *Chemical Evidence for the Indivisibility of the Atom*, he attacked physicists for abandoning the accepted notion of the structure of matter, for accepting the idea of particles smaller than atoms, and for attacking the atomic theory.

> *"Thus Prof J.J. Thomson in a paper I shall revert to and Prof Rutherford – to whom we all owe so much in introducing us to, and inspiring us with this fascinating subject – have been known to give expression to opinions on chemistry in general and the atomic theory in particular which call for strong protest."*

In his view there had been undue levity about things chemical on the part of the Physical Society of late.

Ern could do no more than reiterate the wealth of experimental evidence for electrons as fundamental particles some thousand times smaller in mass than a hydrogen atom. With the hour late and the arguments not concluded, the meeting resolved to adjourn the discussion until the following Thursday when the chance to attend a spirited argument drew a large attendance. John Cox reviewed the physicist's evidence. Frederick Soddy and Ern again spoke in the general discussion, both unbudging from their stands.

Ern needed help with the chemistry of his work on radioactivity. His good friend Professor James Walker, who had joined the McGill staff at the same time as Ern and Professor Owens, had earlier declined an invitation to collaborate as he specialized in organic chemistry. Frederick Soddy on the other hand specialized in gas analysis, having given a course of lectures on this topic and he was currently working on the action of light on chlorine. This work involved delicate temperature measurements and hence had been mainly carried out in the physics building. He had recently failed to get the chair of chemistry at his old university, Aberystwyth, so was available for other work. Thus after the summer vacation of 1901 began the remarkable Rutherford-Soddy collaboration, between two young men who just a few months earlier had held quite opposite views on the atomic theory of matter.

In general, Frederick Soddy carried out the chemical processes in the Chemistry Building. He had taken a course in physical measurements of radioactivity under Ern's guidance, so either man could study the radioactivity of the samples in the Physics Building. Not to be outdone, Ern sometimes carried out the chemical preparations.

Within three months they knew that the emanation was indeed a chemically inert gas of the newly discovered argon series; that a highly radioactive component thorium X had to exist in very small quantities in any thorium sample, and they were endeavouring to chemically isolate this unknown element.

Within those brief three months Soddy now accepted phrases such as

> ⋯ *The two considerations force us to the conclusion that radioactivity is a manifestation of sub-atomic chemical change*

Soddy later reminisced that at the moment of discovery, he turned to Ern and blurted

> *"Rutherford, this is transmutation: the thorium is disintegrating and transmuting itself into an argon gas"*

Ern rejoined *"For Mike's sake Soddy, don't call it transmutation. They'll have our heads off as alchemists"*. He then waltzed around the laboratory, booming an off-key rendition of his theme song, *Onward Christian Soldiers*.

With the Christmas break imminent, Ern and Frederick Soddy wrote up their work to date and for the first time Ern sent a paper to a chemistry journal. He wrote a covering letter to Sir William Crookes, a noted chemist who worked in the field, who had studied uranium X and who admired Ern's work. In replying, Professor Crookes mentioned a curious observation by Professor Becquerel in France. After separating the active component away from a sample of uranium nitrate, he found that the radioactivity of the remaining, initially inert sample reappeared and grew in strength. A puzzled M Becquerel asked Professor Crookes if he could verify this completely unexpected observation, and so Professor Crookes was re-examining the radioactivity of some 'inert' compounds which he had prepared in the past.

Soddy had been busy trying to separate thorium compounds into radioactive and non-radioactive fractions. Unlike uranium compounds, it had not been possible to produce an essentially non-radioactive fraction. However, one fraction had an activity of only one-third that of the original thorium compound. These samples were left to stand for three weeks over the Christmas holiday whereupon Ern and Frederick Soddy found the radioactivity of this fraction had increased back to its original value prior to separation. Perhaps it was this first observation of this amazing phenomena that was to be recalled in a 1933 reminiscence of Soddy's. One Saturday he had gone for lunch leaving Ern hard at work over a separated sample. He returned to find Ern waiting for him, pacing about in front of the building with a smile that carried further than words. As he got within hailing distance the inspiring message thundered across: *"Soddy, the darned thing's going up"*.

The years 1901 and 1902 were incredibly productive for Ern who intermingled research in several fields; sometimes alone, sometimes with collaborators. Ions in gases and thorium emanation have already been mentioned. With S J Allen he extended the work of the Germans, von Elster and Geitel, who had discovered low concentrations of radioactive emanation in atmospheric air. Ern thought this could be an important source of atmospheric electricity.

He also reactivated his development of wireless telegraphy.

Wireless Telegraphy

Professor George Fitzgerald of Dublin had suggested to Ern, while he was doing his original work in Cambridge, that instead of using a magnetic needle for his detector, why not use a long iron wire? By drawing the wire through the solenoid, a continuous recording of a message could be made. [The forerunner of the modern taperecorder.] In May of 1900 Fitzgerald wrote to Ern pointing out a paper in the *Electrician* reporting Poulsen's use of this technique for recording telephone messages. Fitzgerald recommended that Ern return to this suggestion as it would be a very rapid way of receiving wireless telegraph messages.

Ern had never given up his interest in wireless telegraphy, having taught courses in it since his arrival at McGill. Therefore, in January 1901, he had reported on Poulsen's invention to the McGill Physical Society. When Marconi, in a lecture to the Royal Institution, later claimed this invention for his wireless work, Ern wrote a matter-of-fact letter to the *Electrician* describing his own early work developing the magnetic detector and his 'long' distance detection experiments. He concluded:

> ⋯ *These results were obtained before Marconi began his well-known experiments in England. From experimental data on the subject, I have come to the conclusion that the 'magnetic detector' was inferior in delicacy to the coherer, and in the press of other scientific work, I have not devoted much further attention to the subject. I have, however, used in the laboratory, for more than a year, a device very similar to that employed by Marconi in his latest form of receiver – viz., an endless moving band of steel wire passing through the solenoid in which the electric oscillations are set up. Instead of using a telephone to detect the magnetic changes in the iron, I used a magnetometer needle close to which the steel wire passed. Marconi has, apparently, applied to the method the principle used by Poulsen for recording telephonic messages with very succesful results. It is to be hoped that further success will attend his efforts to utilise this magnetic receiver, which has many advantages over the erratic coherer.*
>
> Yours, &c.,
>
> E. Rutherford.
> McGill University, Montreal, July 5 (1902).

In October Ern and Howard Barnes became the first to use wireless telegraphy to signal to a moving train. Travelling at over 100 km per hour, they detected signals up to twelve kilometres from the station.

[Eight years later, in a sequel to this letter and work, a firm of solicitors wished Ern to be an expert witness in a big court case. After interviewing Ern, their agent reported back in a letter of which the rough draft is extant.

Nov. 5th, 1910.

Messrs G.F. Hudson, Matthews and Co,
Solicitors,
32, Queen Victoria Street, E.C.

Dear Sirs,

I beg to report herewith the result of my interview with Professor Rutherford of Tuesday Nov. 1st.

Prof. Rutherford is most emphatic in his desire not to be associated with either side.

He says that he is retained or subpoened by either plaintiffs or defendents, he would then be apparently appearing in the interest of one side or the other. His position is one of complete detachment and disinterestedness, and he feels that his independence would be surrendered if he assumes the position of expect witness, a role to which he is most averse.

[The following paragraph was crossed out of the draft. *He told me in confidence (but I feel bound to inform you of this) that the Marconi Company had approached him with a view to retaining his services, but for the reason given above he refused.*]

Professor Rutherford adheres to his statements as set out in his letter to the 'Electrician', quoted by us, and he tells me that he has never exploited any of his scientific work for commercial purposes, or with a view to patenting and thereby securing for himself alone the benefit of such research. He fully and freely publishes the result of all his scientific work, and therefore his research possesses the greater value, in as much as it is not done behind closed doors, but it is done with a view to adding to the world's knowledge.

He cannot definitely say that a particular experiment or apparatus, such as the use of the moving band in his magnetic detector was shown to any particular person, but any addition to his work on magnetic detectors as published in his Royal Society paper was undoubtedly treated as openly as his other experimental work, and was on his own showing used by him a year prior to his letter published in the 'Electrician' in Oct [July JC] 1902.

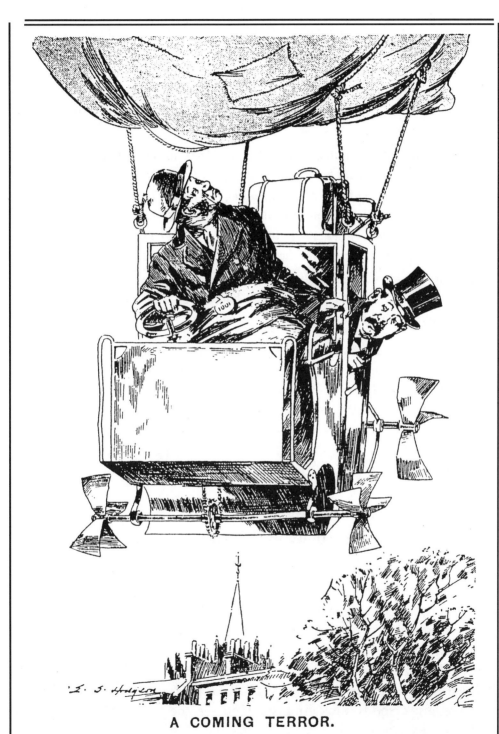

A COMING TERROR.

Fare. "I SAY, WHAT'S GONE WRONG? WHY ARE YOU GOING DOWN HERE?"
Santos 1001. "GOT A PUNCTURE, SIR! ONE O' THEM 'ERE WIRELESS TELEGRAMS, I EXPECT, GONE SLAP THROUGH MY BALLOON."

Punch, 9 Jul. 1902 p18. E.S. Hodgson

He tells me that when he saw Marconi's paper of June 1902, which he referred to the use of a moving band, he thought it only right to (draw the attention of the scientific men to his previous work and his achievements with moving steel wires). [The brackets show where the original had been altered from ⋯ *let the world know that he had openly used in his laboratory a detector of the kind described by Marconi in his paper.*]

I told Professor Rutherford that I was bound to report to our legal advisors, and should have to leave it in their hands as to whether they would trouble him further in the matter, but I know he would strongly resent any attempt at compulsion in securing his evidence on the historical facts of the case. I feel that we, and he also, must regret that his evidence cannot be obtained without the intervention of any interested party.

I hope you will appreciate from the foregoing Professor Rutherford's attitude, and I would leave it in your hands to do what you think right under the circumstances.

[Being a draft corrected by Ern, this letter is disjoint. Also it is the source of the often quoted statement that Ernest Rutherford refused on principle to ever patent his work. However, he does appear in the British Patent Office lists though just once, in 1919, for apparatus concerned with his war work.]

Marconi's progress with wireless telegraphy was such that by 1904 Punch magazine could publish a spoof letter from Winston Churchill MP to Signor Marconi asking for a pocket receiver to listen to the Parliamentary debates as he played golf.

Radioactivity Explained 1902–1903

To escape the heat and mugginess of Montreal, Ern hired a house beside the St Lawrence river for the summer of 1902. Frederick Soddy, one of the few university people left in town, remained behind to carry out a few experiments. The two men kept in touch by mail. Ern heard how some pieces of apparatus had been improved and others broken. Wrote Ern ⋯ *Get yourself in trim for working like the devil when I get back* ⋯ Came the reply ⋯ *You are quite right that I should get myself in trim for working with the devil, I mean like the devil _with_ you.* ⋯ Frederick Soddy took August off to see the Rocky Mountains and Yellowstone Park.

Some of Ern's spare time that year passed in addressing a church society on atmospheric electricity, displaying electrical discharge effects at the Physical

Society conversatizione, going to the theatre, reading books from the Booklover's Library, and writing his own book to be called *Radioactivity*.

The start of the new academic year saw the annual migration back to McGill. Frederick Soddy had already arranged to leave McGill after Christmas to work with Professor Ramsay in London. With the thorium emanation being a new member of the inert gas series and another member, helium, seeming to occur in association with radioactive ores, knowledge of the methods of identifying the inert gases appeared important. As Professor Ramsay was the world authority in this field, the planned shift seemed eminently sensible.

The chemically inert emanation could be identified only through its physical properties. Using gas diffusion methods, Ern and Harriet Brooks had earlier obtained a rough range of values for its molecular weight. Ern and Frederick Soddy however needed a physical parameter which could be measured more accurately. Why not the liquification temperature? They had already passed the emanation through a tube cooled by solid carbon dioxide and ether to the lowest temperature they could reach. The emanation had not liquified.

To reach even lower temperatures they needed a machine for liquifying air. These were new and expensive. A word in the right ear (or it could have been the left) and Sir William Macdonald, McGill's patron saint, donated one. Its first application showed that the emanation condensed and vaporised at a fairly sharply defined temperature.

The *Montreal Gazette* of the 6th of November 1902 reported the discovery under the headline DISCOVERY IS IMPORTANT and continued

> ··· *Where this discovery will lead to it is as yet quite impossible to say, but taken in connection with the recently established existence of radium, thorium and uranium, an entire revolution in physical theory may be within reasonable distance. The science is at present based on the assumption that every molecule is composed of a vast number of atoms, which are, of course, utterly invisible to the naked eye, and are in rapid motion round each other in much the same way as the solar system resolves* [sic] *on itself.*
>
> *Professor Rutherford and Mr Soddy may perhaps succeed in subdividing each of these atoms into a solar system of itself and proving that each atom is composed of inconceivably smaller sub-atoms that are also in rapid rotation. To the layman unused to regard himself as an aggregation of an inconceivable number of inconceivably small atoms rotating at an inconcernably* [sic] *rapid pace, this may seem of somewhat slight interest, but when it is understood that X rays and*

other important phenomena as yet unknown to the public may be cleared up by the new knowledge, it will be seen that advances, not only in scientific theory, but in practical usefulness as well, may wait upon the skill of the two distinguished scientists of McGill.

By the time Soddy left Canada in February of 1903, their collaboration of less than eighteen months had revolutionized mankind's view of the nature of atoms. Nature herself was an alchemist. The most massive atoms all radioactively decayed, emitting particles of very high energy and transmuting into chemically different atoms. This occurred naturally and the rate of transformation could not be influenced by the observer. Ern and Soddy identified five separate steps in each of the radium and thorium decay chains but had not yet chemically identified the atoms at most steps because of the small quantities involved. However, they did know that the rate of disintegration of an atom species depended on the number of those types of atom present, and that the relative rate was a unique characteristic of the atom species.

The concept of half-life, the time taken for half the number of a species of radioactive atoms to decay, had been used by Ern as early as September of 1899 (*Phil. Mag.* **xlix** 1–14 1900). More recent work reported in *Physical Review Letters* **60** 2246–9 1988 shows that the exponential decay law holds for times as short as one ten thousandth of a half-life, and for times as long as forty-five half-lives.

In 1939 Frederick Soddy recalled going to Professor Ramsay's laboratory in 1903 where

> ⋯ *I propounded to the mathematically-minded research students there, a problem of the average life of the radioactive atom and it was evolved correctly by J K H Inglis* ⋯ *the first as far as I know to show period of average life was the reciprocal of the radioactive constant.*

[John Inglis, a New Zealander, had attended Canterbury College from 1894. His work there in 1897 resulted in a first class Masters degree in mathematics. He continued in mathematics and chemistry at Edinburgh and Leipzig before being awarded an 1851 scholarship to work with Professor Ramsay. Following a short spell as Professor of Chemistry at University College of Reading, he returned to New Zealand to serve as Professor of Chemistry at Otago University.]

Rutherford and Soddy deduced that radium had a 'life' of only a few thousand years. It thus followed that since radium occurred in small quantities in minerals it must be continually produced by the radioactive decay of a heavier, naturally occurring, atom species (later shown to be uranium). Hence methods of dating rocks were on the horizon. They laid the foundations of

Rutherford at McGill. Pastel portrait by R G Matthews, 1907.
(Rutherford Museum, McGill University.)

Derelict Rutherford homestead near Pungarehu, 1979, not long before it was demolished. (John Campbell)

Rutherford Flaxmill, near Pungarehu, 1890, painted by the mill cook. Whenever a Rutherford was aboard the New Plymouth to Christchurch steamer, signals were exchanged.
(*T Leggatt, watercolour, ATL A-036-017*)

Professor Alexander Bickerton 'Bicky'.
(C Bickerton, University of Canterbury, Chemistry Department)

radio-chemistry by noting that the electrical method could detect very small numbers of disintegrating atoms whereas the minimum mass detectable by a balance contained some 10^{14} (100,000,000,000,000) atoms. Even the sensitive spectroscopic detection of the small quantity of radium occurring naturally in the mineral pitchblende required Marie Curie to use hundreds of kilograms of pitchblende and health-sapping chemical methods to extract the amount needed.

Another important revelation covered the enormous store of energy contained inside an atom, far higher than the energy stored in the chemical bonding of two or more atoms to form a molecule. ⋯ *It must be taken into account in cosmical physics. The maintenance of solar energy, for example, no longer presents any fundamental difficulty if the internal energy of the component elements is considered to be available, i.e. if processes of subatomic change are going on.* ⋯ [This statement is not as surprising for the time as it appears. After all, helium was 'discovered' in optical spectra of the Sun before it was isolated on Earth – hence its name from Helios, the Sun. And helium occurred in radioactive ores. However, we now know that the helium in the Sun comes from another, then unknown, nuclear process, the fusion of hydrogen nuclei.]

Seldom can one brief collaboration have had such a profound effect on so many fields of science. Frederick Soddy summed up their success in an article entitled *An Account of the Researches of Professor Rutherford and his Co-workers* printed in the *McGill University News* of December 1902. The key to the development at McGill of a new and fundamental view of the nature of matter

> ⋯ *is summed up in one word, measurement. Not perhaps of extreme accuracy, for pioneer work rarely requires it, but sure measurement so the consideration of a curious set of phenomena in a small corner of science has led to a view, which correct or not, has already outgrown the facts it was put forward to explain.*

It should not be forgotten that during this period Ern also wrote a book, developed wireless telegraphy between train and station, gave his usual lectures and worked on other projects, both by himself and with others. To his credit two of his collaborators were women, at a time when very few women carried out original research.

For several years Ern had been trying to determine the nature of alpha rays. These were very easily stopped (a piece of toilet paper will do) yet were highly ionizing and had high energies. Unlike beta rays (electrons), they did not seem to deviate in a magnetic or electric field. Alpha rays therefore seemed to be much heavier particles than electrons. Under the impetus of the key role played by alpha particles in radioactive transmutation, Ern returned to the problem with better equipment. He had a much stronger radium source through the kindness of Pierre Curie in Paris and the use of a much stronger magnet through the kindness of Professor Owens. He then built a special apparatus, a deviation chamber, to allow the detection of small changes in the direction of alpha rays.

An electroscope sat above a layer of radium salts. Between were vertical plates of metal forming channels so that only those alpha particles travelling vertically upwards from the radium could reach and discharge the electroscope. With a magnetic or electric field applied, the alpha rays could be deviated into the vertical metal plates, thus stopping them reaching the electroscope. Small lips on one side of the top of each plate allowed the direction of deflection, and hence the charge on the alpha particle, to be determined.

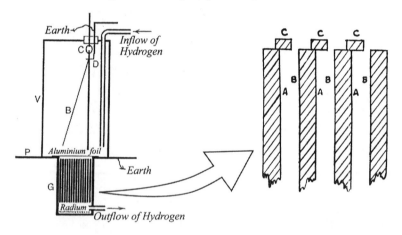

With this simple apparatus Ern showed that alpha particles were positively charged (the opposite charge to electrons), travelled at the incredibly high speed of about 30,000 km per second (a tenth of the speed of light) and had a mass of the order of the lightest atoms. [Soddy later recalled that during one of these experiments Ern danced wildly around the laboratory yelling loudly in what Soddy took to be the Maori language. Not in joy but pain. Ern had picked up a deviation chamber without first disconnecting the high voltage supply from the plates.]

In June of 1903 Canadian newspapers announced Ern's latest honour – his election as a Fellow of the Royal Society of London: *PROF. RUTHERFORD FIFTH CANADIAN TO BE ACCORDED HIGHEST DISTINCTION TO WHICH A SCIENTIST MAY ASPIRE.*

An honour overdue, according to Ern. He had first made overtures to J J Thomson on this matter more than two years earlier and had missed election the previous year, even though proposed by the famous JJ. One reason he coveted the F.R.S. had been mentioned by May in her letter to Martha Rutherford of the 16th of January 1902 ⋯ *Once he gets it, Ern feels that he will be able in say about 3 years, ask for a further increase here.* ⋯ After all, that same letter had mentioned that he had been approached to apply for a chair in London. Though declining to, because they had no reasonable laboratory and he regarded London as a fearfully lonely place, he nonetheless showed the letter to Dean Bovey who borrowed it to show the Principal of McGill and Sir William Macdonald. There is always more chance of your bosses giving you a rise if they know other places are trying to recruit you.

Visit to Europe – 1903

Early in the northern spring of 1903 May, Ern and Eileen went to England to join May's mother, Mary Newton, over on a visit from New Zealand. They spent a month on the continent, principally in Switzerland.

In Paris, Ern and May attended a small dinner given by Paul Langevin, a friend from Cambridge days, in honour of Marie Curie having obtained her Doctorate. Pierre Curie, Jean Perrin and his wife completed the group. At this meeting of great physicists, each of whom held the others in utmost respect, the conversation naturally centred on radioactivity. Said Ern to Marie, *radioactivity was a splendid subject to work on.*

As the warm evening progressed convivially they adjourned to the garden. In the dark, Pierre Curie took from his pocket a tube of radium. Coated in part with zinc sulphide, the tube luminesced brilliantly because the Curies had the world's strongest sources of radium. Ern was amazed at its strength. Pierre Curie had previously studied the effects of the radiations on human tissue by placing a radium source on his own arm. His reports to the academy told of the progression of the 'burn' over fifty-two days. In that Paris garden, Ernest Rutherford could see by the ghostly green light that Pierre's hands were raw and inflamed with radiation damage. This was the last time Ern saw Pierre Curie alive. Three years later he was dead – run over by a dray.

Frederick Soddy, in order to return to England the previous February, had borrowed money from Ern. At the end of the voyage he survived a two-day stranding of his ship while a gale pounded it.

Settling down to research, Frederick Soddy quickly demonstrated to Professor Ramsay that none of the usual rare gases were radioactive while Ramsay in turn confirmed that radium emanation was indeed a new rare gas, albeit radioactive. The big problem was the small amounts of radium available through the Curies. But Soddy got lucky. Walking past a London shop one day he saw an incredible sign advertising 'Pure radium compounds on sale here'. Professor Giesel in Germany had initiated a rival source of supply. On purchasing a few milligrams of radium bromide Frederick Soddy hurried back to the laboratory to check its authenticity. A test with a fluorescent screen used in X-ray studies would have satisfied him but to his absolute horror Professor Ramsay stuck a moistened platinum wire into the bottle, removing a large fraction of the treasure and held it in a Bunsen burner to see if it gave the red flame characteristic of radium free from barium. The vaporised radium settled throughout the laboratory, permanently contaminating it so that no future delicate radioactive measurements could be carried out there.

Before Frederick Soddy had left McGill, Ern had planned ahead to prevent overlap of effort. Soddy was to tackle the chemical problem of whether radium 'grew' in a newly purified uranium sample while Ern, when sufficient radium could be purchased, would examine whether helium was produced from radium. In London Ern visited Ramsay's laboratory one morning to find an experiment in preparation. Twenty milligrams of Soddy's solid radium bromide was to be dissolved in water to release the trapped radium emanation, the evolved gas purified of common gases and the residual passed into a gas discharge tube of very small volume. Hence the unique fingerprint of the radium emanation, its optical spectrum, could be obtained. Frederick Soddy mentioned to Ern that he would take the opportunity at the same time to follow up Ern's earlier prediction and see if any helium gas was released from the radium, using liquid air to rid the residual gas of radium emanation. That afternoon the presence of helium was detected by its characteristic spectrum.

This transgression disappointed Ern. However science came before personal feelings. Having purchased 100 milligrams of radium bromide through the generosity of Sir William Macdonald, he left thirty milligrams of this with Soddy to allow for confirmation of the experiment. JJ later consoled Ern, emphasising

> ⋯ *I always when speaking on the subject point out how you had foreseen and planned the experiment and that if it had not been for you it would never have been made.* ⋯

[In 1962 Georg von Hevesy reminisced that Ramsay and Soddy were the only two men Ern did not like.]

Ern usually based all his conclusions on sound experimental evidence, but occasionally he digressed to speculation, usually in private. With Ern's permission, W C D Whetham recorded one such in his 1904 book 'The Recent Development of Physical Science'.

Professor Rutherford has playfully suggested to the writer the disquieting idea that, could a proper detonator be discovered, an explosive wave of atomic disintegration might be started through all matter which would transmute the whole mass of the globe, and leave but a wrack of helium behind. Such a speculation is, of course, only a nightmare dream of the scientific imagination, but it serves to show the illimitable avenues of thought opened up by the study of radioactivity. ⋯

When addressing the Physical Society on the radioactive process, Ern had finished with the statement that from Pierre Curie's measurements, of radium being warmer than its surroundings, it could be deduced that each gram of radium gave out sufficient energy over its lifetime to raise 500 tons a mile high.

It seems probable that the internal energy of atoms in general is of a similar high order of magnitude.

Sir Oliver Lodge, his old champion, congratulated him on his work but other physicists present were more sceptical. However this was nothing compared to the scepticism he anticipated from the wider audience expected at the upcoming meeting of the British Association for the Advancement of Science.

The Rutherford party went on holiday to Chester. There they were joined for a week by Frederick Soddy and Robert Laing, the botany master from the Christchurch Boys' High School, and all three men proceeded to the British Association meeting at Southport.

Ern led the sectional discussion on the emanations from radioactive substances. He summarized the evidence and mentioned Sir William Crookes' spinthariscope, a magnifying glass focussed onto a fluorescent screen, which allowed the effect of individual alpha particles to be seen⋯*the first time probably that we have observed any single atom effect.* One elderly chemist, in supercilious tones, remarked that ⋯ *Rutherford wants us to believe that the atoms are possessed with incurable suicidal monomania.* ⋯ Ern also emphasised that the evidence to date supported the view that the energy of radium came from inside of the atom. Once again Sir Oliver Lodge congratulated Ern and then proceeded to read, unbelievingly, a communication from Lord Kelvin who sided with the French view that radium received its energy externally, by absorption of ethereal waves. Such an idea followed quite naturally from the explanation of fluorescent materials which absorbed light from the Sun thus storing the energy until releasing it some time later. Two decades later Robert Laing recollected the meeting. *The physicists generally accepted his statements with a certain amount of confidence but the chemists on the other hand generally refused to believe him.*

Ten days after the meeting Ern and family returned to Canada.

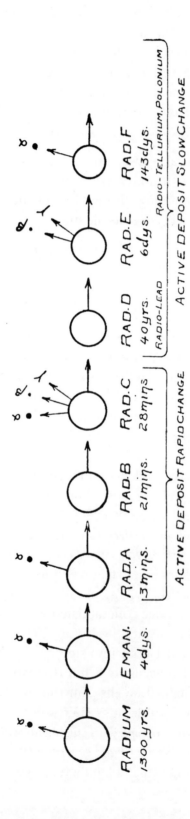

The radium decay chain as known by 1904.

Chapter 11

CONSOLIDATING A NOBEL PRIZE

Canada 1903-1907

*Here was the rarest and most refreshing spectacle – the pure ardour of
the chase, a man quite possessed by a noble work and altogether happy
in it.*

John McNaughton,

Professor of Classics, McGill University, 1904.

Ageing the Earth

Since the beginning of human time the wrinkled Earth had appeared old
and inscrutable, unless one was religious. With the advent of science it started
to unveil its secrets. This led physicists and geologists to a major disagreement
concerning their respective estimates of the age of the Earth. In 1862 William
Thomson, a Scot who was later to be Lord Kelvin, and by the turn of the
century the grand old man of British science, had worked out that the Earth
could be no older than a few tens of millions of years. He had based his
calculations for when the Earth's crust had first formed on the well-known
temperature gradient at the Earth's crust (it is warmer down deep mines), the
rate at which heat is conducted through rocks, their melting temperatures
(he started with a white-hot molten planet), and their thermal properties on
solidifying.

Geologists, for example, working from sedimentation rates and the thickness of sedimentary rocks, needed far longer than Kelvin's estimate. Most physical scientists, if they thought about it at all, went with Kelvin's estimate as that was based on sound physical principles.

Ern reconciled the physicists and geologists views by suggesting that the heating effect of radium gave the Earth a lifetime of hundreds of millions of years since it was formed and before it could cool to extinction. (One journal reputedly greeted the news of Ern's extension of the lifetime of the Earth with large headlines: "DOOMSDAY POSTPONED". *Punch* magazine trusted Ern's statement would put a stop to jerry-building.)

Ern had been invited to deliver the prestigious 1904 Bakerian Lecture to the Royal Society of London so once again he crossed to England where he spent a pleasant May mostly with J J Thomson in Cambridge. The long Bakerian lecture on 'The Succession of Changes in Radioactive Bodies' went off well except that Ern's voice failed him for five minutes. Whether or not the granulated throat would last through a lecture was always a source of concern but it was a weakness with which he just had to live.

The following night, the 20th of May 1904 was more fun. Ern gave the Royal Institution's weekly Friday night popular lecture on the topic 'Radiation and Emanation of Radium.' Such talks were expected to be illustrated with demonstrations.

Presently, in the half dark, he spotted Lord Kelvin and knew he would have trouble at the end when he aimed to discuss the age of the Earth. Luckily, Lord Kelvin drifted off to sleep but as Ern come to the age of the Earth he saw *the old bird sit up, open an eye and cock a baleful glance at* him. What to do? The grand old man of British science didn't believe that the energy of radium was internal to the atom and would no doubt, once again, say so. Lord Kelvin had even bet John Strutt five shillings on this matter. Ern saved himself with sudden inspiration, as he regularly reminisced with glee.

> I said Lord Kelvin had limited the age of the Earth, provided no new
> source of heat was discovered. That prophetic utterance refers to what
> we are now considering tonight, radium! Behold! the old boy beamed
> upon me.

Ern clearly had diplomatic skills.

The account in *The Times* confirms this reminiscence. After reporting that a cubic inch of radium emanation would probably melt its container, the reporter finished his account of Ern's talk with radium's effect on heating the Earth, and thus on the calculation of the age of the Earth:

In that case the date, as calulated by Lord Kelvin, when this globe would have so far cooled as to be uninhabitable might possibly be postponed for a few million years, and an end put to the troubles of the biologists about a little extra time in the past. The lecturer specially invited the audience to admire the foresight, almost amounting to prophesy, which had made Lord Kelvin qualify his calculations with the words "provided no new source of heat is discovered."

Ern spent the following weekend at Lord and Lady Rayleigh's family home in Essex. Their son, John Strutt, had been a fellow student at Cambridge. Other guests included Professor Schuster from Manchester and Lord and Lady Kelvin. As Ern reported back to May:

Lord Kelvin has talked radium most of the day, and I admire his confidence in talking about a subject of which he has taken the trouble to learn so little.

Kelvin took another year before he came to agree with Ern's long-held view that the energy of radium came from inside the atom.

In retrospect it turns out that heat from radioactivity wasn't the whole answer. Had Lord Kelvin carried out his calculation transferring heat in the Earth's mantle by convection (as he did for the Sun), rather than conduction, he would have obtained a more reasonable result.

Geologists hadn't been specific about the age they needed, just that geological processes needed longer times than Lord Kelvin's original calculation allowed them. What was needed was a way to date geological processes. Ern gave them that.

Since the turn of the century Julius Elster and Hans Geitel had shown that radioactivity was present in air, ground water and soil, while John Strutt had shown that radium occurred in many rocks. During the spring of 1904 Ern lectured at Yale. In the audience was Bertram Boltwood, a consultant chemist skilled in the analysis of ore samples for a mining engineer. These ores included monazite which contains uranium and thorium. Thus began another lifelong cooperation between Ern and another, to the benefit of science.

In September of 1904 the International Congress of Arts and Sciences at St. Louis invited Ern to be the featured speaker for their Canadian day. The chairman introduced Ern

⋯ as the man who had done more successful experimenting along the line of radioactivity than any other man in the past, and as one, he was sure, who would do most in the future.

The young scholar was received enthusiastically and was frequently interrupted by applause. Such was the interest in his talk, on current problems in radioactivity, that it was published in French before an English version appeared. Late in the talk he discussed the age of the Earth and suggested this could be accurately determined by measuring the helium content of uranium minerals. With the crude data at his disposal he estimated the age of a sample of fergusonite at 40 million years old. In so doing he initiated the technique of using the known rate of decay of radioactive elements to accurately date geological samples, a technique of immense value today to geologists and Earth scientists. He and Boltwood developed other decay chains to improve the accuracy. The Earth is now recognised as having been formed some four and a half billion years ago.

McGill 1903–1905

With the start of the new academic term following the summer break of 1903, Ern had pushed on with both his research and his book as a matter of urgency. Back in England, Frederick Soddy planned to give a series of lectures on Radioactivity. By letter to Ern came the disturbing news that the *Electrician* wanted to publish these lectures and put them together as a book. He immediately telegraphed Frederick Soddy that this would interfere with his own book. A compromise was reached. Soddy would delay submitting his articles so that Ern's book could come out first.

McGill's Professor of Classics, after attending one of Ern's talks on radium to the McGill Physical Society, recorded for posterity Ern's enthusiasm for research.

> Here was the rarest and most refreshing spectacle – the pure ardour of the chase, a man quite possessed by a noble work and altogether happy in it.

A first year engineering student recalled his 1904 view of Rutherford the lecturer, in a 1945 letter to the *Nelson Evening Mail*. M G Hepburn had been delegated by his class to ask Professor Rutherford if the last lecture of his elementary course on heat, light and sound could be devoted to the excitingly new topic of Radium. Ern obliged.

> ⋯ At the given time not a student was absent. For the next hour we were bombarded verbally with alpha, beta and gamma rays. The blackboard became covered with intricate equations solved by calculus,

> *a subject the rudiments of which another professor was then trying to ram into our heads. Every now and then Rutherford, with a wicked twinkle in his eye, would turn round and say "Don't you understand that? It's quite simple. You only have to do this, that or the other." By the end of the hour, none of us was able even to appear to take an intelligent interest in the subject. And so he had his revenge on us for having the temerity to ask him for a lecture on such a subject. I have often wondered what learned society gained by this rehearsal of their lecture.*

[Mr Hepburn's analysis surprises me. I would have guessed that Ern had honestly, but badly, misjudged the level.] The letter concludes

> $\cdots$ *In case this letter should give a wrong impression of Rutherford, I should like to add that when the subject fitted our mental development, I have never sat under a more lucid lecturer.*

Ern, a proud son of distant New Zealand, supported the Australasian Association for the Advancement of Science when it met in Dunedin during January of 1904. He sent a paper, for someone else to read, on his latest research entitled 'The Heating Effect of the Radium Emanation'. In it Ern reiterated that the energy resident in atoms was enormous compared to that released in chemical reactions.

> $\cdots$ *This energy has not been observed on account of the difficulty of breaking up the atoms by the physical and chemical processes at our disposal.*

He received two other mentions at the Dunedin Conference. In the paper following Ern's, O U Vonwiller of Sydney reported the use of a Rutherford detector in measuring dielectric constants in high frequency electric fields. And the President of the Physics Section, Professor Bragg of Adelaide, in giving the opening address 'On Some Recent Advances in the Theory of the Ionization of Gases', said

> $\cdots$ *One of the names best known in connection with these researches, and with other great researches to which they have led, is that of E. Rutherford, who, having won an "1851 Exhibition" scholarship, left this Colony of New Zealand in 1896 (sic) to pursue his studies at Cambridge. It is a happy coincidence, and I realise the fact with great satisfaction, that, in speaking to you on a subject which owes so much to him, I am addressing his own friends and kindred $\cdots$.*

They certainly were, the joint secretaries for the physics section being Dr Farr of the Magnetic Observatory, Christchurch, and J S S Cooper, a teacher at the Dunedin High School. The latter had followed Ern through Canterbury College, taking double first class honours in Maths and in Physics with thesis work in wireless telegraphy. Showing once again the feedback from expatriates, Ern had sent Mr Cooper a sample of radium. This was later shown around the country at appropriate events, for example in Auckland in conjunction with a lecture on electricity. [Curiously enough, this occurred about the time Frederick Soddy passed unannounced through the city. Having delivered a series of lectures in Western Australia he had squeezed in a quick climbing holiday in southern New Zealand and a tour of the thermal region of the North Island.]

Ern and May had a stream of visitors from New Zealand during the summer of 1904. Mr Joynt the University Registrar; Ern's sister Ethel and family; May's mother and brother Charlie; and Jack Erskine, Ern's associate while at Canterbury College. Charlie later reminisced about their holiday in a farmhouse on a lake in the Laurentian Mountains: bathing, canoeing and fishing.

> As well as trout and white fish we caught edible frogs which took the trout fly readily and played well. Rutherford became quite expert at this new sport! The frogs were excellent eating and we all liked them.

Jack Erskine had a job with the General Electric Company in Schenectady. An earlier planned visit to the Rutherford's while in transit to Schenectady had been cancelled when he had to remain in New Zealand while his brother died of consumption. Jack Erskine, a friend of both Ern and May, stayed with them three weeks as he hated Schenectady.

Amongst Ern's honours at this time was an unusual one. Charles Baskerville, an American chemist who had long been involved in separating elements in thorium compounds, wrote a book 'Radium and Radioactive Substances – Their Application Especially to Medicine'. The book was fascinating. It summarized all the known facts about radioactive substances; for example, that through the electrometer method, radioactivity was a detectable property a million times more sensitive than spectral analysis which was itself a thousand times more sensitive than the most delicate balance for measuring mass. As Berthelot had commented, radioactivity and odours had similar delicacy of detection. A sensitive nose could readily detect 1/100 billionth of a gram of smelly iodoform. In reviewing the field the book described several interesting inventions such as Strutt's Radium Clock and reported the confusion of theories proposed to explain the various observations. J J Thomson had speculated that the large amount of energy per atom emitted during the radioactive process could come from a contraction of the atom. The Curies thought it a release of energy which had been the accumulation of small amounts over a long time. Baskerville himself favoured the dynamo theory, whereby a current is generated in a conducting coil rotated in the earth's magnetic field, which fitted in with J J Thomson's view that an atom consisted of charged particles in rapid oscillatory or orbital motion. Other theories merely confused the issue, reflecting their proposers background rather than reality. For example, the chemist du Pont proposed that radioactivity was a manifestation of catalytic action while Schenck proposed that the gaseous emanation from radium was nothing but ozone.

Baskerville was obviously a fan of Ernest Rutherford's down-to-earth experimental approach to such a confusing field.

> ⋯ *Before giving the theories of those who have done most, experimentally, (Rutherford and his co-workers), toward an elucidation of the difficult problem,* ⋯ .

Not surprisingly the book carried a dedication:

TO

ERNEST RUTHERFORD

WHOSE INVESTIGATIONS ON RADIO-ACTIVITY

ARE WORTHIER OF A HIGHER TRIBUTE.

May and Ern planned a family holiday in New Zealand during the summer vacation of 1905 so May went off several months ahead with her mother while Ern stayed on in Montreal with Professor Morin, the Professor of French. Professor Morin often translated the Curie's publications for Ern, while Mrs Morin converted Ern's handwritten scrawl into a typed manuscript for his book. In 1946 Professor Morin reminisced

> ⋯ *I remember him as a tall, slim man, slightly bent, with very long arms, causing a kind of ungainly gait. He seemed to look fixedly, with large blue eyes; a wellshaped long nose, a good crop of fair hair, light complexion, a man of ready speech, a sonorous, deep voice, bursting often in loud laughter; A more amiable and accommodating man, we never had met before. Eating sparingly, he would be quite satisfied if he had for breakfast his bacon and eggs, his toast and strong french coffee, after which followed, one after the other many a cigarette. He was nervous and very active, devoting all his time working in the physics laboratory. Sometimes, I should say often, he got up during the night and went to his laboratory.*

Golf twice a week provided some relaxation but May gleefully reported to Martha Rutherford how Ern badly needed a wife to look after his manners. In her absence he had arrived half an hour late for one dinner party after falling asleep over a book. At Professor Walker's for supper one night he had fallen asleep in the study. On awakening he found that the others had quietly left him and gone back to the drawing room.

His hard work was paying off and May missed the excitement that followed the award of another honour. In November of 1904 the Royal Society of London awarded Ern its prestigious Rumford Medal. As the first Colonial to be so honoured, the McGill students cheered him into the physics building on his arrival the following morning. The Medical Faculty conveyed its congratulations and a speech was made in his honour at the Chemical Society. He felt obliged to report to May

> ⋯ *My hat, however, still remains of the same dimension.*

Some prominent staff planned a small celebratory dinner in his honour. When Sir William Macdonald heard of the plans he offered to finance the whole show for as many as the University wished. After all, he declared, it was his Physics Building and his Professor and he was going to do it in style. The guest list rocketed to 120. Held at the Windsor Hotel, it lasted until 2 a.m. Everyone enjoyed it but Ern, who wrote to his mother

> ⋯ *I naturally did not over-enjoy myself as I had to look pleasant for three hours while speeches describing my virtues were hurled at me.*

The meeting sent telegrams of honour to his mother and his wife in New Zealand. When Ern rose to respond he was greeted with a demonstration such as the Windsor had seldom seen. Several minutes of cheering preceded his speech in which he mentioned his birth in New Zealand, his early work in England and that there was still plenty of work to be done.

A reporter from the *Montreal Herald* interviewed Ern.

> ⋯ *Attentive Blue Eyes. The one thing that fascinates you when he is talking is his eyes, which have always an extraordinary attentive and penetrating look* ⋯ *Prof Rutherford can explain abstruse scientific phenomena to the lay mind as no scientist of the second rank can ever do* ⋯ *He is a New Zealander as a matter of fact, but they are very English in New Zealand. His tongue is the tongue of middle-class England, middle-class London even, not that of the universities; it has no drawl and is sharp rather than broad. It is rather soft voiced and*

quite pleasant to listen to, but not in the least thrilling. The impression
you get from half-an-hour's conversation with him during which you
had with almost superhuman exertions kept the talk to the subject of
Prof Rutherford for sometimes as much as two minutes at a time, is
that the man probably never thinks about himself at all.

The headline used stated:

RUMFORD MEDAL GOES TO·MAN WHO IS ALL FOR
SCIENCE, NONE FOR SELF.

Such sentiments were echoed by H L Bronson, a young American graduate,
who, after hearing Ern lecture at Yale, applied to join him.

Rutherford proved to be all I had hoped for, not only stimulating but
considerate and helpful. He seemed to have an uncanny ability to see
any problem as a whole and the most direct way to attack it. He never
tried to use the work of his students and younger associates to feather
his own nest, but always made certain that they received more than
their fair share of the credit for any work done.

Ern criticised Bronson for the excessive care he took in determining the decay
constants of members of the radium decay series. *We should leave it to the other*
fellow to get the next decimal place. When Bronson stood his ground, insisting
on ensuring the data was correct, Ern neither pressed the point nor took offence.
However he was noted for the odd shout: *Get on with it* at signs of delay in the
work of his junior associates.

The electrical method of examining the radioactivity of a sample involved
the rate at which a nearby electroscope would discharge its initial electrical
charge. These instruments consist of a vertical metal
rod supported by an excellent electrical insulator.
When the rod is electrically charged so too are two
thin metal foils connected to the bottom of the rod.
These foils then repel each other (because like
charges repel) and the angle between them gives a
measure of the charge on the electroscope.

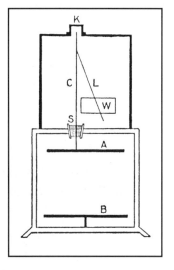

Alpha-ray electroscope devised by Rutherford

On one occasion Ern became frustrated at the inability of Arthur Eve, a recent appointment to the Mathematics Department who had drifted over to physics, and the mechanic to make a sensitive, small-capacity electroscope whose gold leaf would retain a charge for two or three days. These had been readily made at the Cavendish but the McGill ones would lose their charge in less than twelve hours.

One sleepless night, Arthur Eve got up at his lodgings and made an electroscope using a tobacco tin, the amber mouthpiece of a tobacco pipe and some dutch metal foil. On being charged by rubbing it with sealing wax, in a similar way to which dry hair can be made to stand up by running a plastic comb through it, this home-made electroscope retained its charge for three days. The problem turned out to be that all materials in the physics laboratory were coated with the radioactive deposits from the disintegration of radon gas. These deposits discharge any electroscope made from materials which had been stored around the laboratory. Steps were immediately taken to prevent the future escape of radon from the radioactive sources. Arthur Eve's reward was a glowing "Good boy", even though he was Ern's senior by some eight years.

Ern returned to Yale in March of 1905 to give the well-paid and ill-named Silliman lectures. Yale hoped to recruit Ern on practically his own terms. May had reported to Martha Rutherford that Ern was seriously considering the offer. During the train journey back to Montreal he discussed the pros and cons with Mr Bronson:

> "Why should I go there? They act as though the University was made
> for the students"

Besides, when McGill had learned of the Yale offer they increased his salary to C$4000. It was doubted that anyone else would ever rise so high.

The proofs for the second edition of his well-received book were slow in arriving from the printer. Ern consequently put back his departure to New Zealand by three weeks. The new book was already half as thick again as the first edition, and if the publication of the book were to be delayed until his return in the autumn, it would need further updating and rewriting. The other reason offered to May for their delayed reunion concerned the necessity of also sending off papers covering all of his completed researches.

> ⋯ It is very important I should write it up as they are all following my
> trail, and if I am to have a chance for a Nobel Prize in the next few
> years I must keep my work moving.

Considerable time and effort had been squandered on experimentally refuting other physicists who muddied the field. For example, Paschen in Germany had concluded that the heating effect of radium was primarily due to the highly penetrating gamma rays. Ern brought in Howard Barnes and his expertise in heat measurements to show this was not so. ⋯ *the heating effect of radium is largely due to the bombardment of the alpha particles expelled from its own mass.* Arthur Eve helped Ern show that the rate of decay of radium did not depend on the radium concentration as implied by Voller in Germany.

Ern had used chemical analysis to clarify more steps in the uranium decay chain, and, with the American chemist Bertram Boltwood, experimentally deduced that one atom of radium is in radioactive equilibrium with approximately 1,350,000 atoms of uranium.

Using an electrometer in a vacuum to measure the total charge collected from the alpha or beta particles emitted by a known mass of radium, Ern could obtain the number of particles emitted per second from one gram of radium. From these figures he could deduce the half-life of radium (now known to be 1600 years), the volume of radium emanation produced, the average kinetic energy of an alpha particle, the number of ions produced by an alpha particle in a gas, and the energy required to produce an ion.

Bragg in Australia had shown that the alpha particles emitted by radium salts could be grouped into four distinct sets, each from one member of the decay series, and each of a fixed initial speed characteristic of the parent atom. Now, for his studies into the nature of alpha particles, Ern could use a source of constant speed (monoenergetic) particles produced as follows. When a fine wire, negatively charged to attract positive ions to it, is placed in a gas of radium emanation a thin but very active layer of radium A is deposited on the wire. After fifteen minutes or so the radium A atoms practically all decay away leaving only the longer living radium C on the wire as a source of monoenergetic alpha particles. A narrow slit placed well above the active wire produced a fine beam of alpha particles. Using a strong electromagnet Ern could deflect the beam by a small amount as recorded on a photographic plate well above the slit. Since collisions with air molecules progressively slow down an alpha particle (those from radium C stop in 67 mm of air or about 0.04 mm of aluminium), the radioactive wire, slit and photographic plate were housed inside a vacuum chamber.

The electrical effect of these short-lived elements, and the extraordinary sensitivity of radioactive measurements, is put into perspective by mentioning that if a thousandth of a gramme of radium C [now know to be an isotope of bismuth] were shared amongst all the people in the world, each person would have enough to discharge several electroscopes every second.

Following J J Thomson's work on the electron, Ern wished to measure the ratio (e/m) of the charge on the alpha particle to its mass. To do this accurately the magnetic deflection should be exactly cancelled by an opposing deflection produced by an electric field. The latter part of the experiment was giving trouble due to electric arcing in the poor vacuum available. This could not be fixed before Ern was to leave for New Zealand. Hence he could only estimate the charge-to-mass ratio by roughly determining the speed of the alpha particles through the heat output of radium and concluded

> ··· *When the experiments at present in progress on the electric deflection of the rays from radium C are completed, it is hoped that the value of e/m will be obtained with sufficient accuracy to settle definitely the important question whether the alpha particle is a projected helium atom.*

His departure for New Zealand was decidedly rushed.

Visit to New Zealand – 1905

In San Francisco Ern boarded the mail steamer *Sierra* for its fast seventeen day voyage to New Zealand. A 24-hour gale with very high seas gave way to fine weather for twelve days. Roughening seas then increased until at the height of the gale the ship's engines had to be slowed for ten hours. Long sea voyages provided occasional discomfort due to the weather or despotic stewards seeking tips.

On the evening of the 5th of June 1905 the *Sierra* glided to its anchorage in Auckland harbour. May Rutherford, after a separation of nine months, welcomed her husband, having travelled up from Wellington where she had been staying for a few days. They had just the one night in Auckland, at the Grand Hotel.

No longer was it possible for Ern to slip into his homeland unnoticed. Not so much because of his fame, his recent F.R.S. and Rumford medal, but more his use of the title Professor in shipping lists. A representative of the *Auckland Star* interviewed him under the headline:

A FAMOUS NEW ZEALANDER
A CHAT WITH PROFESSOR RUTHERFORD

Though the Professor was but a youthful 33 the knowledgeable reporter realised his name would

> *⋯ go down in history inseparably associated with that scientific marvel*
> *of the century, radium.*

Through leading questions he had Ern explain the current knowledge of radium; that uranium transformed into radium, that no physical or chemical process could alter the rate of transformation, that the heat of the Earth was due to radium, that knowledge of radium and its uses in medicine were both in their infancy. Ern wouldn't concede that the New Zealand secondary school system compared unfavourably with the Canadian system but he did think that the University of New Zealand should conduct its own exams, as did Canadian and American Universities, and not use English examiners. The reporter concluded the full column article by stating its value was not only

> *⋯ the fascinating scientific problems on which it bore, but because of*
> *the personal interest attached to the work and the career of perhaps the*
> *most distinguished and successful of all the graduates on whom the*
> *New Zealand University has conferred its degrees.*

Ern didn't see the report published. The day before that issue was printed he and May had taken the train to Rotorua for a holiday in the thermal region then travelled via Lake Taupo and down the Wanganui River to Wanganui.

Vanishing into the wilderness did not stop news of his arrival being sent around the country. The Marlborough Education Board sent him a message:

> *⋯ Your success which has given great stimulus to every scholar in the*
> *country is, we believe, but the dawn of further brilliant achievements.*

The New Plymouth High School Board moved to

> *⋯ tender to Sir Ernest Rutherford a hearty welcome on his return to*
> *the land of his birth, and congratulates him upon the brilliancy of his*
> *career and the high position he has achieved in the scientific world.*
> As the seconder stated, *⋯ the Professor was practically a New*
> *Plymouth boy.*

Local enthusiasm may explain the premature elevation to a knighthood.

The sombre news of the day concerned the injury that befell Mr Wright, the electrical instructor at the Thames School of Mines. He had overexposed his hand in an X-ray machine. The wound would not heal, creating great medical interest as the first case of X-radiation injury in Australasia. The newspapers ghoulishly reported that Edison's assistant in America had his hand amputated after a similar accident. Mr Wright was granted six months leave with pay to go to England for treatment. However the pain was too great. He had his left hand amputated at the wrist before departure.

From the Wanganui river, Ern telegraphed ahead to New Plymouth, giving his date of arrival by train. Hence a number of friends met him at the railway station then entertained him at the Taranaki Club. In the morning he left for Pungarehu and a family reunion.

His father James, now 66, suffered badly from arthritis, spending periods in the hot baths at Rotorua. George ran several flax mills, living at the Raglan one. George, Ellen, Alice, Jim and Ethel had all married since Ern's last visit and twelve days after Ern's arrival Arthur also took the plunge. A photo taken during the wedding breakfast at the White Hart Hotel in New Plymouth shows dignified James, aging Martha, Ern in his prime, George with a receding hair-line and a pretty good feed in front of all. Only Florence (aged twenty-nine and known in the family as Flo, Floss or Florrie) and Eve (twenty-seven) had yet to marry. Flo, a schoolteacher, had a broken heart and a worrisome arm which had been injured four years earlier. A botched operation had made it worse. More than once the only solution seemed to be amputation. May had been horrified at the thought. She had already badgered Mrs Rutherford to allow Florrie to go back to Canada with them to consult with expert surgeons and committed Ern to pay all Florrie's expenses. His recent prize money, book royalties, lecture fees and rise in salary would allow for this. Florence Rutherford's arm was operated on successfully in Canada and she spent a year there with her brother and sister-in-law before returning to New Zealand.

Ern had promised Dr Farr to give a talk while in Christchurch. This had to be scheduled for the end of July after the students returned from mid-winter holiday. Hence in mid-July Ern took the train south to Wellington. The capital's population of Nelson College Old Boys met, dined and entertained him since time did not allow a visit to Nelson itself. Mr Joynt, his old headmaster and now Registrar of the New Zealand University, took the chair. Several people spoke including an earlier headmaster who expressed pride that he had taught Ern for one day, and Charlie Mills, the MP from Havelock. The informal meeting concluded with the singing of the College song.

Ern spent three days in Wellington including attending an afternoon tea cum civic reception for the city's latest Rhodes scholar. Ern sat next to the Mayor but was a silent unit on this occasion. Then he caught the overnight ferry to Christchurch, arriving early on Sunday morning, the 16th of July 1905.

The town had been forewarned of his visit through a full, two column article published in the Saturday edition of both papers. Almost certainly written by Dr Farr, it described Ern's reputation ⋯ *today he stands forth one of the most notable planets in the scientific constellation* ···, his career and work. On the Sunday a reporter from each morning paper wangled a brief chat with him. Ern relaxed on his mother-in-law's sunny verandah, smoking and talking of his work. Occasionally he broke off to ask after journalists who had been students with him. He avoided material to be covered in his lecture but touched on the theory, long held by J J Thomson and others, that the mass of a charged particle depended on its speed although the variation only became significant as its speed approached that of light. This raised a philosophical question concerning radioactive atoms.

> ··· *These bodies are throwing off electricity in motion, and consequently the question which arises is whether there be any such thing as matter as distinct from electricity in motion.*

Leaving scientific questions the reporter asked about Canada: ··· *exceedingly prosperous and didn't wish to leave the British Empire* ··· and the changes in New Zealand since his last visit: ··· *The country seems to be growing, and strikes me as being very prosperous just now. I notice many new buildings in Christchurch also.*

On Monday morning, the Mayor of Christchurch held a small civic reception for the city's distinguished son. Thirty people, including city councillors, fellow ex-students, board members and staff of Canterbury College, gathered at the Council Chambers to honour him.

Professor Bickerton was there. Little Bicky had recently been on a tour of Australia, lecturing about his partial impact theory of cosmology. An editorial in the *Lyttelton Times*, on receipt of the news that a recent astronomical survey had located hundreds of variable stars, had praised Professor Bickerton and stated that he must now be a happy man. But he was not. His son, the firework manufacturer, had gone bankrupt. Since being fired from the University in 1902, with neither pension nor investments, Bicky had eked a living by opening his home to the public. A newspaper advertisement detailed its attractions.

WAINONI PARK
for winter picnics
Sandy Soil
Sunny Glades
Warm Shelters
Pine Needle Carpets

Wainoni Park, designed by Professor Bickerton, approached by river, road, tram. Always open. Admission 6d; Tea 6d. Wainoni Hall may be engaged for evening parties.

No, Professor Bickerton could not have been happy, except for the success of one of his old students whose ability he alone seemed to have recognized in those early days a mere decade ago.

In his speech of welcome the Mayor, repeating notes from Professor Farr's article, enthused ⋯ *Professor Rutherford's birthplace, Taranaki, was proud of him* thus initiating New Zealand's tendency to disseminate incorrect information about her most famous son, a failing that continues unabated today. Professor Cook recalled how Professor Rutherford had been one of a good group of students.

> [He] ⋯ *had done a good deal of his work at Canterbury College under his (the speaker's) direction ⋯ indeed, he was by far the most successful of the Australasian students who had attempted original work ⋯*

In reply Ern

> ⋯ *feared they had exaggerated somewhat unduly his claims to scientific distinction – (the Mayor : No, no) – but in any case what he had done was very largely due to the very excellent system of education provided by the colony. Thanks to the assistance of the professors at Canterbury College – and he was glad to see present Professor Cook, Professor Bickerton and Mr Page, from whom he had received a large amount of useful training – he had been able to compete on approximately equal terms with the graduates of the Old Land.*

After describing developments at McGill, including the railway-financed school of railway engineering, he raised the question of technical education currently under discussion in Christchurch and concluded

> ⋯ *I am of the opinion that universities should endeavour to assist in the development of the citizen as a whole and I think that if they did not control technical education they should supervise it.*

The *Lyttelton Times* reported these remarks slightly differently stating that he regarded technical education as

> ⋯ *one of the very greatest importance to any university that was supported largely by the people. The university could do no more useful work than to increase the knowledge of the general members of the community.*

After being entertained that evening at the Canterbury Club by Councillor Hurst-Seager, Ern had a free week to catch up with friends and May's relatives.

His next official function involved the governors, professors, graduates, and students of Canterbury College and members of the Philosophical Institute. They welcomed him back by way of a conversazione in the College Hall. The Chairman of the Board gave a glowing speech containing just one small faux pas, reinforcing the escalating trend in New Zealand to give out wrong information about Ern. ··· *Professor Rutherford had begun in one of the Christchurch Primary Schools* ····. His old maths teacher, Professor Cook, now Chairman of the Professorial Board, seconded the motion of welcome. He kept Ern's feet on the ground.

> ··· *There had been in the college several students whom the professors regarded with great pride, students who had distinguished themselves in various ways in the Old Country.*

Had not *The Press* editorial featured three distinguished New Zealanders – Rutherford, Marris (Indian Civil Service) and Greenwood (a classics scholar)?

In reply Ern stated how pleased he was to be back since it was at Canterbury College he received his education and there had spent five happy years. He had often been in the Hall though mostly down below (laughter), and especially did he remember those occasions when the students tried to do honour on the Diploma Day to their various professors (loud applause). He expressed his gratitude for the help he had received as a student from the staff, gave the students sterling advice for their success in their respective careers, hoped that the College would stay free of political control, gave a modest account of his recent work and pleaded for the staff to be given sufficient time for original research. He noted that Physics was still under the Professor of Chemistry and ended with a concrete suggestion close to his heart. Canterbury College should establish a Chair in Physics and build a physical laboratory. His proposal put sound, light, heat and pure electricity under the Professor of Physics leaving applied electricity with the Engineering School.

After several musical items the meeting dissolved into supper and conversation. As an example of why the College should avoid political control, he told of American universities where professors had to lobby the local Legislature for funds to keep their institution going. In particular he mentioned how one professor explained his hours and periods of work to a new member of the Legislature. The latter asked why he wanted so many holidays.

> *"To keep in touch with modern advances."*
> *"What", retorted the legislator, "not finished with your lessons yet!".*

There was no way they would let Ern escape without giving a preview of the wonders of radium. In order to observe the fluorescence of a zinc sulphide screen near radium, the gas lights were turned right down. One gentleman took advantage of the darkness by reaching out to caress his lady love's hand. Stroking it gently, he became puzzled then horrified. So too was its owner, a bearded gentleman standing in front of the oblivious lady.

The Philosophical Institute of Canterbury had scored a coup in getting Ern to agree to address them, the only scientific talk he gave during this visit to New Zealand. Dr Farr, the President, remembered missing out with a last minute approach during Ern's previous visit. This time, forewarned of the visit by May Rutherford's presence in Christchurch, he had written months ahead. How could Ern, recently elected an honorary fellow of the New Zealand Institute, refuse? The Institute had obtained the use of the College Hall and printed tickets to be distributed to members. The subject of the talk – Radium and its Transformations.

Radium certainly seemed the marvel of the century judging by newspaper accounts. A report that it had successfully been used to cure a cancer patient had cancer sufferers besieging a New York hospital. Radium could be utilized to alter the colour of yellow diamonds to blue. J J Thomson reported its presence in tap water and flour. [Perhaps it was this report which caused the miller who had taken over John Rutherford's flour mill at Brightwater to rename his product RADIUM BRAND FLOUR.] But the most startling newspaper report, also from the Cavendish, described Mr John Burke's experiments whereby radium placed into sterilised bouillon (basically beef soup) developed cultures which, he declared, had the appearance of the spontaneous generation of life.

No wonder that some members of the public were disappointed as word leaked out that Professor Rutherford was to lecture on Radium but to the Philosophical Institute only. One wrote to *The Press*.

> Sir – I have it on good authority that Professor Rutherford is going to lecture on radium to a select few in the College Hall. Would it not be a better plan for the Philosophical Society to take a larger Hall and charge admission? I am sure that a great many of the public are just as eager to hear the professor as I am.
>
> Yours etc.
> RADIUM.

No alterations were made to the plans. Ern delivered his talk to a select audience in an overcrowded hall.

He gave a full account of radium, including how it caused the internal heating of the Earth, how it could be used to estimate the age of rocks and that

PUNCH, OR THE LONDON CHARIVARI.   [JULY 12, 1905.

A LITTLE LEARNING.

He. "A MARVELLOUS DISCOVERY, MY DEAR LADY! THAT LIFE CAN BE PRODUCED IN STERILISED BOUILLON BY THE ACTION OF RADIUM. WHAT TRAINS OF THOUGHT IT GIVES RISE TO! WHY, THIS MAY HAVE HAPPENED IN THIS WORLD OF OURS, MILLIONS OF YEARS AGO!"

She. "ER—YES, OF COURSE! I UNDERSTAND THAT THERE MIGHT HAVE BEEN *RADIUM* THEN, BUT—ER—*WHERE DID THEY GET THE BEEF TEA?*"

28

the alpha particle it emitted was helium. At one point Ern mislaid his sample of radium, bringing the lecture to a halt for five minutes while he and Dr Farr frantically searched the table and floor. Members of the audience even joined in with suggestions of where it could be. Finally it came to light exactly, and embarrassingly, where Ern so carefully had placed it. [A year later Ern did lose a radium sample while travelling on a Canadian railway.]

Public exhibitions of radium were fraught with hazards. Sir Oliver Lodge once passed a sample around during a slide lecture in a small town. In the darkened room the small self-contained unit of radioactive sample, fluorescent screen and magnifying glass allowed the fluorescent flashes to be readily observed. During the unit's passage from person to person in the audience it passed to a small boy. As the previous recipient of a steady flow of chocolate chunks, he popped it into his mouth. A lady's shriek startled the audience, awakening some. However all's well that ends well. The unit had progressed no lower than the mouth.

After a final weekend in Christchurch, Ern, May, Eileen and Florrie took the ferry to Wellington to spend a week visiting friends and relatives in the lower North Island. They left Auckland for Fiji to pick up the Canadian-Australian Royal Mail line boat bound for Honolulu and Vancouver, travelling second-class to save money. On the latter leg they found the food so poor that Ern and others complained to the purser.

The *Herald* interviewed Ern on his return to Montreal. He told the reporter how New Zealand was a pioneer in social reform and a wave of prosperity still flowed across the land thanks to a thriving dairy trade. He declared

> ··· *that the extension of the political franchise to women had not had the disturbing effect in politics that had been predicted of it, and its effect, in so far as the cause of temperance and prohibition was concerned, had been strongly felt on the side of the reformers. He believed that the next election would show a large extension of the prohibition areas in New Zealand, where the people voted upon the liquor license question when they voted for the members of the Legislature. If the temperance movement continued its present rate of progress the probability was that the whole country would in ten years be prohibition. In that case it would be an ideal place for the demonstration of the efficacy of the principle in the people who, separated as they were from those of other states, would be able to give it a better trial than most countries could give.*

He spoke of the progressive education in New Zealand, of Fiji's inaugural sugar exports to Canada, of New Zealand's awakening interest in Canada, and of the desirability of a direct shipping route between Canada and New Zealand. The newspaper's chosen headline roared:

NEW ZEALAND WILL HAVE PROHIBITION IN TEN YEARS
Woman Suffrage To Blame.

What May Rutherford thought of such bigoted choice of headlines is mercifully unrecorded.

McGill 1905–1907

The international nature of Ern's laboratory expanded with the arrival of the Pole, Tadeusz Godlewski, and the Germans Max Levin and Otto Hahn. The latter, an organic chemist initially destined for an industrial career, had spent a year in Ramsay's lab in London chemically separating radium and thorium compounds. In the process he discovered a new radioactive element which he named Radiothorium. To learn about this new subject of radioactivity, Otto Hahn had written to Ern, mentioning his discovery and requesting that he be allowed to work with him for a time. Ern replied with a friendly letter and on the day Otto Hahn arrived, immediately questioned him closely about the new element. Ern was sceptical of any 'discovery' reported from Ramsay's laboratory, it being widely believed that Professor Ramsay had lost his touch after his brilliant discoveries of the inert gases. Indeed, Bertram Boltwood had initially thought radiothorium ⋯ *to be a new component of thorium X and stupidity.* Otto Hahn soon convinced Ern and went on to a career which Ern later summed up: *You seem to have a special smell for discovering new radioactive elements.*

Many years later Otto Hahn reminisced about the year he spent at McGill.

The atmosphere and spirit in Rutherford's laboratory were extremely happy. The number of his research students was not yet large, and so he was able to give individual attention to each of them, which he did almost every day. These students all contributed to the rapid development of the new subject of radioactivity ⋯ Rutherford's enthusiasm and abounding vigour naturally affected us all. To work in the laboratory in the evening was the rule rather than the exception, particularly for us Germans, whose stay in Montreal was limited. Frequently we would spend the evening in his house, when naturally little but 'shop' was talked, not always to the pleasure of the hospitable Mrs Rutherford, who would have preferred to play the piano. He had a

*great, hearty laugh which echoed through the whole laboratory ··· This
gay and youthful unaffectedness was one of the qualities which made
contact with Rutherford so enjoyable.*

On return to Germany Otto Hahn encountered the conservatism of
traditional chemists. He described the disintegration hypothosis at the Bunsen
Congress in Hamburg in the spring of 1907. One professor declared against
radium being an element. Otto Hahn contradicted him

*··· in a rather spirited manner – because after all I had, through
Rutherford, attained a pretty good knowledge of the process. During a
break a friend of mine, Max Levin, advised me to exercise a little more
discretion when arguing. He had just overheard one professor ask
another who I was and the other answer: "Oh, he's one of those anglicised
Berliners!" We had never been expected to exercise discretion of that
kind in democratic Canada.*

Professor Becquerel in France took exception to Ern's conclusion that alpha
rays slow down as they collide with air molecules, believing instead that their
mass increased in passing through air. Once more Ern had to perform
experiments to refute another's incorrect conclusions. In doing so he noticed,
before 1905 closed, that his beam of alpha particles was wider in air than in
vacuum. The alpha particles were scattered by air molecules. He therefore
initiated experiments to see if the scattering also occurred when the alpha
particles traversed a thin solid. He placed a thin sheet of mica over half of the
slit in his activated wire-slit-photographic plate apparatus and in June of 1906
reported that some of the alpha particles passing through the mica had been
deflected through an angle of two degrees.

*··· It is possible that some were deflected through a considerably greater
angle; but, if so, their photographic action was too weak to detect on
the plate.*

To produce such a deflection over the 0.03 mm thickness of the mica would
take an average transverse electric field of about 10,000 million volts per metre.
Ern concluded:

*··· Such a result brings out clearly the fact that the atoms of matter
must be the seat of very intense electrical forces – a deduction in
harmony with the electronic theory of matter.*

The age of probing the entrails of atoms had begun in a rather quiet way.

Ern broke off in the middle of this work to represent the New Zealand Institute at the Franklin bicentennial celebrations in Philadelphia where he was awarded an honorary degree. The attitudes in that city failed to impress him; the exclusiveness of it all being typical of Philadelphia with no hall ever full. Impressed by Benjamin Franklin the scientist, he held reservations of Benjamin Franklin the man ⋯ *Franklin was not much on the moral side, he added wonderfully to the population of London, Paris and Philadelphia.*

The science journal *Nature* ran a series of articles on famous laboratories. Three years earlier Ern had contributed an article on the Cavendish laboratory. Now it fell to A S Eve to do the same for McGill. A photographer commissioned by *Nature* arrived to freeze Ern at work, posing with his alpha particle deflection apparatus in his basement laboratory. The first negative showed the photographer that Ern was not elegant enough to grace the journal's page. In particular no shirt cuffs showed below his coat sleeves. Luckily Otto Hahn wore detachable cuffs which were promptly borrowed. In the second photo not enough showed but the third was declared sartorially satisfactory. Thus the photo on page 273 of *Nature* for July 1906 immortalized Ern, his alpha particle deflection apparatus and Otto Hahn's detachable cuffs.

A S Eve's comments about Ern included:

> ⋯ *Rutherford's extreme care of verifying every step by thorough experimental evidence has saved him from error to an extent quite exceptional. It is fortunate that so much of the development centred on a man to whom the remarkable instinct is possessed of rarely following side issues ⋯ Most noteworthy of all is the extreme simplicity and directness of his experimental methods ⋯ Rutherford selects some ingenious, straightforward attack ⋯ Professor Rutherford inspires research students with some of his own enthusiasm and energy. He follows their results closely and is as delighted with any of their discoveries as with his own. He is generosity itself in giving a full measure of credit to those who do research work under his guidance.*

The original method Ern proposed for determining when the Earth's crust had first solidified involved the alpha particles emitted from radium. These particles travelled only a few micrometres in solids, being then trapped as helium gas. By measuring the amount of helium released in dissolving a radium-rich rock, the age of the rock could be deduced. Typical results were 500 million years, these being lower limits for it seemed probable that some helium gas would diffuse out of the rock over such long time scales. With the realization that lead was the end of the uranium decay series, Bertram Boltwood and Ern used the lead-to-uranium ratio in uranium-rich ores to date the formation of rocks. Ernest Rutherford was thus the key figure in establishing radioactive dating of geological samples.

During the summer break of 1906 Ern lectured at the University of Illinois before crossing the continent to give a summer course at the University of California. On the way he picked up an LL.D. degree in Wisconsin and food poisoning in the Berkeley Faculty Club. A free pass on the Californian railway system helped him to see the countryside, the Lick Observatory, the Grand Canyon and the devastation caused by the San Francisco earthquake.

After a family holiday, the great radium controversy caught up with Ern. This followed Frederick Soddy's confident statement, when opening section A of the British Association for the Advancement of Science's meeting at York, that his work had shown that the concept of the gradual evolution of one element into others could not be seriously questioned. Lord Kelvin, on holiday in France, disagreed and immediately wrote a letter to the editor of *The Times* (9 August 1906) to say so. For some two weeks the correspondence column reverberated with letters fired off by many scientists. Sir Oliver Lodge's intemperate letter, which had a certain similarity to Ern's earlier, private, criticism of Lord Kelvin, declared Kelvin's

> ··· *brilliantly original mind has not always submitted patiently to the task of assimilating the work of others by the process of reading, and our hope has been that before long he would find time and inclination to look into the evidence more fully.* ···

The Times replied with a leading article defending Lord Kelvin. On the 11th of October Ern wrote to *Nature* finalizing the matter.

Such a delay emphasised one problem of being away from England. Another concerned the lack of researchers available to help with his work. Ern had only one person available who could spend all his time at research. A graduate school had been inaugurated at McGill but most PhD enrolments were in Chemistry. Therefore, though seemingly settled in Montreal and having recently purchased land on which to build his own house, Ern made it known that he was open to tempting offers from elsewhere. Several people had sounded him out for various positions which were becoming available.

He had not followed through that of Director of Research (Secretary?) for the Smithsonian Institute (too much administration and social life), or of Professor at Kings College, London (not a good lab), but a well-timed death opened another opportunity. Professor Schuster at Manchester inherited a large fortune so offered to vacate his chair. With the prospects of a good lab in

England, a salary of £1000 and possibly a rich benefactor, Ern let it be known he would be willing to accept the chair. Once more May wrote to Martha Rutherford in New Zealand to alert her to a possible change and giving the telegraph code to be used – 'Manchester'.

Manchester University never advertised the position which they offered to Ern. Not surprisingly, he accepted the Manchester chair. On the 4th of January 1907, the Board of Governors of McGill university accepted Professor Rutherford's resignation with regret. Principal Peterson proposed he be given an honorary LL.D. degree for *outstanding achievement in science and valuable service to the university*. This was duly awarded after all faculties of the university had agreed.

John Cox had a further honour in mind for Ern. On being invited by the Nobel Foundation to make a nomination for the 1907 Nobel Prizes, Professor Cox had nominated Ernest Rutherford adding

> ⋯ *Professor Rutherford is leaving us in the autumn to occupy the Chair of Physics in the Victoria University, Manchester, England. It would indeed be a satisfaction to his friends here, if he should receive so great an honour while still a member of the University where during nine years he has completed so many researches.*

Alas it was not to be. John Cox's letter was written a week after the February 1st closing date so could not be considered in 1907.

As a memento of his time in North America, Ern was presented with an album containing a signed photograph of nearly every prominent chemist and physicist in Canada and the United States of America. Each was a friend to him.

McGill's period of international glory was over. Under Professor Rutherford, physics had flared. So too did medicine and engineering when an arsonist burnt down both buildings.

Ernest Rutherford's last month at McGill passed in dread of a late night phone call which might report the torching of the physics department.

Nobel illuminated address 1908 —Front Cover. (Rutherford Family)

Nobel illuminated address 1908 —Inside Left. (Rutherford Family)

Nobel illuminated address 1908 —Inside Right. (Rutherford Family)

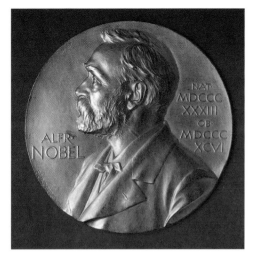

Nobel Medal for chemistry 1908 (gold 75mm).
(Duncan Shaw-Brown, University of Canterbury)

Rumford Medal of the Royal Society 1905 (silver 75mm).
(Duncan Shaw-Brown, University of Canterbury)

Chapter 12

THE NOBEL PRIZE

They gave Ern the Chem. prize because his subject is on the borderland. They had a good many physicists to draw from but few good chemists so were glad to be able to work it in this way. He was told on all sides that he would probably get the physics some day!

May Rutherford,
Stockholm 1908

The Nobel Prizes

Alfred Nobel converted unstable nitroglycerine into safe dynamite and gelignite. Inventor, chemist, industrialist, developer of smokeless gunpowder, sufferer of ill health, unrequited lover of a peace activist, novelist; he willed his fortune to fund annual prizes for physics, chemistry, medicine, peace and literature.

First awarded in 1901, the science prizes were for the biggest advance during the previous year. In Physics this stipulation had been immediately bypassed to cover the great advances since 1895: Röntgen for X-rays; Becquerel, Pierre Curie and Marie Curie for radioactivity; Lenard for cathode rays; and, in 1906, J J Thomson for his studies of the conduction of electricity by gases. Prize winners in Physics and Chemistry were recommended by the relevant committee of the Swedish Royal Academy of Sciences. They accepted nominations from members of the Academy, members of the committee, previous winners, professors in the Nordic countries, up to six foreign professors and an unspecified number of scientists, the latter two groups being named annually.

The 1907 Awards

With JJ out of the way, Ern was nominated for the 1907 prize: in Physics by seven Germans (Emil Fischer, Adolf von Baeyer, Philipp Lenard, Max Planck, Emil Warburg and Hermann Ebert), and in Chemistry by Svante Arrhenius, the Swedish director of the Nobel Institute for Physical Chemistry and 1903 Nobel Prize winner.

At the end of September the Swedish Royal Academy of Sciences received a report from the Nobel Committee for Physics summarizing their deliberations.

> There is no doubt that the experimental work that _Rutherford_ has carried out with radioactive substances are of the greatest importance in this field and that he to a large degree has contributed to widening our knowledge of radioactive phenomena. But on the other hand several of these experiments, which are quite new, would probably require further investigation and can on the other hand be called in question, if the discovery for which _Rutherford_ mainly has been nominated by several nominators, i.e. his demonstration of the disintegration of a chemical substance (Radium) should be awarded the Nobel Prize for Chemistry rather than for Physics. Because of this we are not of the opinion that _Rutherford_ should receive this year's Nobel Prize for Physics.

Hence although Ern had the most nominations for physics that Prize went to the American spectroscopist Albert Michelson with only half as many nominations.

Ern was also a serious contender for the chemistry prize. The Nobel Committee for Chemistry requested one of their number, Henrik Soderbaum, a chemist at the Academy of Agriculture, to produce a three page resume on Ern's work. Their report to the Academy stated:

> ⋯ Rutherford's working methods fall within the field of physics while the results obtained, as they deal with the question of the nature of the chemical elements, must be seen to be of fundamental importance also for chemistry. ⋯ As, however, Rutherford's research of the radioactive substances as yet in no way can be considered to be concluded, it seems a delay of the question of its being awarded a prize is well motivated, so

much more as the same field is still the subject of keen research from other directions, the result of which would be easier to survey after the elapse of some time.

So the Committee for Chemistry had no hesitation in unanimously recommending Edward Buchner of the University of Berlin for his studies of the fermentation process.

The 1908 Awards

As soon as the 1907 prizes were presented the Nobel Committee sent out letters requesting nominations for the 1908 Prizes. For the Physics Prize J J Thomson nominated Ern ⋯ *whose work on Radioactivity and allied problems seems to me to be of the highest merit.* Though written two days before the deadline it reached the committee after the February 1st deadline so was not considered in 1908. However, John Cox's late nomination for 1907 had become an early nomination for 1908. Ern was also nominated for the Physics Prize by Svante Arrhenius of Sweden and Max Planck, Emil Warburg and Philipp Lenard all of Germany. Once more Dr Arrhenius nominated Ern for the chemistry prize as did the physical chemist Rudolf Wegscheider of Vienna and Oskar Widman of Uppsala.

With official announcements held back until the December presentation ceremony, early leaks were impossible to stem. The *New York Times* reported the physics prize going to Marconi which must have confused readers of the *Leipzig Neuste Nachrichten* as this paper had interviewed Max Planck as the winner. In reality both were wrong.

The paths to the final choices were tortuous. Back in 1903 the awarding of the physics prize to the two Curies and Henri Becquerel caused a demarcation dispute between the Physics and Chemistry committees. While this issue was resolved by deleting the discovery of radium from the citation, the chemists none the less made it clear that in future they would assert their right to make awards in the field of radioactivity.

In 1908 the Physics and Chemistry committees initially held a joint meeting to consider the assignment of two candidates who had been nominated for both prizes. Dr de Laval, the Swedish inventor of the cream separator, the steam turbine and a device for measuring the butter fat content of milk, was assigned to Physics whereas Ernest Rutherford's work was assigned as of fundamental importance to Chemistry.

The Physics committee considered the remaining twelve nominees (who included Marconi and Planck) and quickly focused on two major possibilities. Gabriel Lippmann of France for his method of colour photography and the joint nomination of the Germans Wilhelm Wien and Max Planck for their work on radiation from a heated object. Wien had measured the wavelength dependence of the radiated energy and, using standard physics, produced a theoretical expression quite at variance with experiment. Planck showed that by assuming radiation was emitted in discrete bundles of energy (quantized), he could modify Wien's expression to agree with experiment.

Dr Arrhenius encouraged the awarding of a Nobel Prize for recent work. Having made major contributions himself to the physics and chemistry of ions in solution, he knew his goal could be achieved by supporting recent advances in the atomic theory of matter. Since Planck had been able to use his radiation formula to determine values for two atomic constants, the charge on the electron and Avogadro's number (the number of atoms in a gramme-mole of the material), which agreed with values obtained by Ernest Rutherford through radioactivity, Dr Arrhenius envisaged the physics prize for Planck and the chemistry prize for Rutherford. To this end he wrote a report for the physics committee recommending they award their prize to Planck alone. All members except Dr Arrhenius expressed doubts about rewarding only the theoretical side of the work. The accurate experimental work was in fact in the process of being carried out by people who had not been nominated.

In attempting to get two atomistic Nobel prizes, Dr Arrhenius had not pushed Ern with the physics committee. However with the chemists he did not hold back.

There were sixteen nominations remaining to be considered for the chemistry prize encompassing work as diverse as that on atomic weights (Morley of Cleveland and Richards of Boston), guncotton (Lunge of Zurich), protamine (Kossel of Heidelberg) and plant pigments (Willstatter of Zurich). These candidates were quickly discounted as were several others nominated for general work, and also that of the physical-chemist Ostwald of Gross-Bothen, whose main contribution, the committee once again decided, was in *his general activity as a teacher and author rather than in any particular 'discovery or improvement'*. The Chemistry Committee focused on two candidates; Sir William Crookes and Ernest Rutherford. Professor Crookes, at age seventy-six, was proposed for his life's work but both points were against the spirit of the Nobel Prizes. By the spring of 1908, the chemistry committee had 36-year-old Ernest Rutherford as its candidate, either alone or, as one nominator had suggested, with Frederick Soddy. Prior to the summer recess, the committee again commissioned one of its members, Dr Soderbaum the agricultural chemist, to write a report on the two to be used as the basis for a prize recommendation. This report, thought to be substantially written by Dr Arrhenius who served on the Physics Committee, favoured Ern alone. The report mentioned twice that Ern's experimental work belonged to the area of physics and only once did it mention any significance for chemistry; that the foundation for chemistry had radically changed as the disintegration theory showed the immutability of the elements no longer held.

After the chemistry committee agreed to recommend Ern for the award, the proposed citation stressing the importance of the disintegration theory for the chemistry of radioactive substances went before the chemistry section of the Academy. They endorsed the committee's choice. At the meeting of the full Academy Dr Arrhenius arranged that the chemistry prize be considered before that for physics, a reversal of the usual order. The Academy accepted the recommendation of the Chemistry section, thus awarding the 1908 Nobel Prize in Chemistry to Ernest Rutherford. The official announcement cited Ern

> ··· *for his investigations into the disintegration of the elements, and the chemistry of radioactive substances.*

NOBEL PRIZE AWARDS.

ENGLISHMAN'S SUCCESS.

STOCKHOLM, Dec. 9.
The Nobel Prize Committees have decided to award the prizes this year as follows:—
Chemistry: Professor Ernest Rutherford, of

NEW ZEALANDER HONOURED.

RUTHERFORD WINS NOBEL PRIZE.

(Recieved 8.49 a.m.)

LONDON, November 24.
Professor Ernest Rutherford, who was born and educated in New Zealand, and

Prof. Rutherford Fifth Canadian to Be Accorded Highest Distinction to Which a Scientist May Aspire.

Prof. Rutherford, of McGill University, who has just been confirmed in his election as a Fellow of the Royal Society of London, Eng., is the fifth Canadian to be accorded this distinction as the highest in the realm of science.

The Lull before the Storm

At least one member of the physics section felt they had been tricked into handing their best candidate over to the chemists. The physics prize was not as clear cut. A mathematician spoke against giving the award to Planck alone so the Academy decided to hold over that decision and to award the 1908 Nobel Prize in Physics to Gabriel Lippmann. (Wien and Planck were finally rewarded with the 1911 and 1918 prizes respectively.)

Ern knew of the impending award as early as November the 17th when he wrote to Dr Arrhenius:

> *I am naturally very pleased at the award though I feel very unworthy to be included in the chemical list of prize winners. It was quite unexpected for I did not hope that I would be considered as a candidate for several years to come.···* He also requested that he would ··· *be very glad of any information in regard to procedure etc that you might think useful for an Englishman (or rather a New Zealander!) to know beforehand.*

Sworn to secrecy until the presentation on the December 10th, Nobel's birthday, he could not even telegraph his family in New Zealand.

When yet another, but this time correct, leak sprung forth from Stockholm on November 24th, the cable service flashed the item to newspapers on the far side of the world. The *Nelson Evening Mail* devoted a large space to the news many readers eagerly awaited – the result of the 34th week of the Nelson Poultry Association's egg laying competition. Ern's Nobel Prize rated a brief mention amongst the cabled news.

Christchurch didn't let the event pass unnoticed. The Press Association interviewed Professor Bickerton about Ern's time at Canterbury College.

> *··· Professor Rutherford was all through a brilliant student, and showed a good deal of resourcefulness in his investigations. He had also a splendid physical and mathematical ability. ··· When Professor Rutherford was last in Christchurch he made the remark that doubtless a good deal of his resourcefulness was due to the fact that he had to make shift with much less complex apparatus than he would have used in a better equipped laboratory, and he looked upon it as having done him no harm in working with apparatus not quite up to the standard of work he was doing. ···*

Once more radium hit the news. Scientists seem to love a bit of doom and gloom prediction. Lord Kelvin had predicted the earth would eventually cool to where life would die. Ern, through radium heating, had merely postponed doomsday. Now Professor Joly of Dublin, after measuring the concentrations of radium in tunnels and the sea bed, postulated: ⋯ *Is the Earth getting hotter?* ⋯ *the internal heat of the Earth is increasing at what may be a dangerous rate.* Charlatans are more positive. The advertisements in the *Manchester Guardian* for Dr Shower's Radium salve claimed it cured cancer, portwine birth marks and removed wrinkles.

Even honorable men leapt on the bandwagon. Once more a proposal, ⋯ *warmly advocated some years ago by Professor Ernest Rutherford* ⋯ went before the Canterbury College Board to establish a Chair of physics and erect a physics laboratory. The Professor of Engineering vigorously opposed the move as he wished to keep electricity and magnetism under engineering.

> ⋯ *Whilst admitting that special facilities for research work did not exist, he suggested that they might be provided by the extension of existing buildings and additions to equipment. He added that research work in physics at Canterbury College was not likely to be of a character which would directly benefit the Dominion, and could only be carried on in this country under many disadvantages. It could be done far better and more cheaply in the laboratories of the Old World, supported by their extensive libraries and facilities for the manufacture of special apparatus.*

As the chair was established by a bare majority of one vote, the timely award of the Nobel Prize to Ernest Rutherford may have tipped the balance.

Messages of congratulations over the Nobel Prize poured into Ern and to his family. Mrs Newton, recently returned from a visit to England, wrote to Martha Rutherford

> ⋯ *I know how hard he works and that he richly deserves his honours and I can assure you he takes them lightly and his head is not a bit turned by the long list of honours.* ⋯

At the Canterbury Philosophical Institute meeting Dr Farr stated that Ern

> ⋯ *would be recognized as one of the greatest scientific experimentalists that had ever lived. He had a splendid scientific imagination, which seemed to guide him in his experiments and the results he clothed in a language which was simplicity itself.* ⋯

A quick whip round raised the money to send telegrams of congratulations to Ern, and to his mother.

A telegram from George Rutherford told Ern and May that the news had reached the family at home so May wrote to Martha Rutherford.

17 Wilmslow Road
Withington Manchester Nov 27

My dear Mother,

Since I last wrote great things have happened. Ernest wrote telling you the news of the Nobel Prize as far as we had it then – telegrams only I think it was. Next came the formal letter announcing it and inviting us to go to Stockholm and insisting on strict secrecy. That is why we could not cable you for fear of its leaking out. This went on for ten days or so, it seemed horrid to be bottling up such great news. Then one morning it appeared in the papers, leaked out from Stockholm unofficially. Ern cabled to Arrhenius to ask if it was being announced but he still says "rumours all guesswork". So now we are going round evading where possible and lying sometimes in an open way but no one believes us. They say the papers are good enough for them! It is a very silly business altogether, the idea is to publish the awards the day they are presented. This is of necessity told to the candidates two or three weeks before so that they can make arrangements to go away from home so far and then with so many knowing it on the quiet in Sweden it is bound to get out. The papers have in the past made wrong guesses though.

In a PS to a letter to Svante Arrhenius, Ern had stated

⋯ *I would like to put the offending reporter in oil with a slow fire under him.*

Letters and telegraph boys besieged the Rutherford household but only guarded replies could be dispatched. To good friend Otto Hahn in Germany Ern replied

⋯ *It is of course quite unofficial but between ourselves I have no reason to doubt of its correctness.* ⋯ *I may tell you in strict confidence* ⋯ .

The secrecy was indeed a nonsense. How could Ern plan to visit Otto Hahn in Berlin and Hendrik Lorentz in Leiden on the return journey from Stockholm without letting them know?

May had a new wardrobe to purchase after Mrs Thomson had advised her on what clothes she should need. Ern attended the Cavendish dinner on the 5th of December. JJ, or rather Sir JJ since the King's birthday honours list, expressed immense pride in one of his men getting the Nobel Prize even if that man was supposed to be denying all knowledge of the award. Alfred Robb had composed a special song in Ern's honour.

AN ALPHA RAY

Air : 'A Jovial Monk.'

1. *A alpha ray was I, contented with my lot;*
From Radium C
I was set free,
And outwards I was shot.
My speed I quickly reckoned,
As I flew off through space,
Ten thousand miles per second
Is not a trifling pace!
For an alpha ray
Goes a good long way
In a short time t,
As you easily see;
Though I don't know why
My speed's so high,
Or why I bear a charge 2e.

...

4. *But now I'm settled down, and move about quite slow;*
For I, alas,
Am helium gas
Since I got that dreadful blow,
But though I'm feeling sickly,
Still no one now denies,
That I ran that race so quickly,
I've won a Nobel Prize.
For an alpha ray
Is a thing to pay,
And a Nobel Prize
One cannot despise,
And Rutherford
Has greatly scored,
As all the world now recognise.

The Nobel Prize Ceremony 1908

The following day Ern and May embarked on the Harwich to Hook of Holland ferry. May wrote a sixteen page account of their trip for her mother, badly typing a ten page copy for the Rutherford family. These accounts give an interesting insight into the social side of early Nobel Prize ceremonies.

Arriving in Stockholm via Hamburg and Copenhagen at 9.30 a.m. on Wednesday the 9th of December, they were met by Professor Arrhenius, members of the Nobel committee and Professor and Mrs Taylor. The latter were Californian friends of Ern's, on sabbatical leave in Stockholm. After breakfasting, the Taylors took the Rutherfords for a drive to see the city. After lunch, their first experience of a smorgasbord, May went for a look around the shops with Mrs Taylor while Professor Arrhenius took Ern to pay the official calls expected of a visitor in a European country. That evening all the prize people attended a large dinner party hosted by Professor Retzius. May sat between him and the British consul and enjoyed herself. Her earlier fear that the little French and German she and Ern spoke would not suffice was unfounded as the Swedes generally spoke English.

All the prize men stayed at the Grand Hotel.

> ⋯ *The hotel lays itself out very much for the Nobel people and incidentally of course rooks you well. The coach that took us to the Retzius was truly royal I could not call it a cab. It was very big almost all glass red plush lined two horses, fur caped coachman and I suppose about three times the price of an ordinary but we did not enquire. The maid used to take away Ern's clothes every night to brush them.* ⋯

Ern and May become privy to some of the background of the current prizes. The physics award was popular but the literature prize had been given to a third candidate when the committee split over the two main candidates. As for chemistry:

> ⋯ *I think that Ern was the most popular of the prize winners because of his work and also because he was so young and his was the only award that there was no opposing candidate for. Everyone felt that it was really carrying out Nobel's intention.* ⋯ *They gave Ern the Chem. prize because his subject is on the borderland. They had a good many physicists to draw from but few good chemists so were glad to be able to work it in this way. He was told on all sides that he would probably get the physics some day!* ⋯

Nobeldagen.

Festen på Musikaliska akademien.

Nobeldagen, Nobelföredragen, Nobelfesten.

Från Nobelhögtidligheten i går.

Thursday December 10th, Nobel's birthday, saw the presentation ceremony at the Music Academy.

> ⋯ *This is a fine hall, the stage upon which was a good orchestra, all decorated with palms ferns and flowers. Along the front of the audience was a row of gilt arm chairs for the Royalties. To one side were the four prize men and slightly behind but higher were we wives so that we could see perfectly. The audience was very select it was evidently a great privilege to be there. We were all in full evening dress. At 4 pm the Royalties arrived – the King, Crown Prince his wife, Prince Wilhelm and his wife (Czar's niece) and some others. Then the ceremony began with some music which also was performed between the presentations of the prizes. Then the head of the Nobel Institute got up and spouted a long oration in Swedish. When he got to the particular part for each man the recipient stood up. One could tell by watching when he turned to the man. Then he came down off the stage and led the 'subject' over to the King who shook hands and murmured something and presented him with a gold medal and a leather book beautifully tooled outside and illuminated inside. Ern's is in turquoise blue with gold tooling. Inside is a long dedication or whatever one would call it. ⋯*

The Latin inscription on Ern's Nobel medal was adapted from Virgil's Aeneid. *Inventas vitamuvat excoluisse per artes* – It is a good thing to have brought life to perfection by skills/knowledge that have been discovered.

The royals departed as soon as the prizes had been awarded. After a wild scramble for cloaks a subset of the audience dashed by cab to the Grand Hotel for the official banquet. The King did not attend. As May was to be escorted in by the King's second son, a 19-year-old sailor, she was initially shown into a small saloon to chat with the Royals. The wife of the Crown Prince came over, saying "*I think you are Mrs Rutherford. You look like the English one,*" which wasn't necessarily an astute observation with 32-year-old May being the only prize-man's wife under age sixty or so. At dinner she sat between her Prince and the Crown Prince with the Crown Princess opposite.

> ⋯ *I felt rather alarmed at my position of loftiness but soon got over it, they were all as pleasant as possible. Ernest was three or four places along to my left. This all sounds very conceited but I know you are interested to hear it and it was only because I was wife of the chemistry prize winner and it is the only time I am likely to move in Royal circles. I was most agreeably surprised they put me absolutely at my ease and were extremely interesting people to talk to. ⋯*

During the Dinner the Crown Prince rose and toasted the King's health. Teetotal May noted with interest that all the royals drank mineral water. At intervals each prize man was toasted and each responded, mostly at length, dull and in German. Professor Petersson toasted Ern's health in English.

> ⋯ *He referred to Dalton and Joule of Manchester which gave Ern something decent to answer. Everyone says he made the speech of the evening and was rather amusing. He said he had dealt for a long time in transformations of varying length but that the quickest he had met was his own transformation in one moment from a physicist into a chemist! He was in very good form. The royalties all congratulated me and said what a relief to hear someone not altogether serious and heavy.* ⋯ *Ern looked so ridiculously young among the other prize men.*⋯

The following day, Friday, Ern spent the morning fixing up experiments to illustrate his Nobel Lecture.

> ⋯ *The lecture went very well indeed, though I suppose a good many could not quite follow in English. His experiments went well and I think it was a success.* ⋯

May spent the day with New Zealand friends. In the evening she joined a party for dinner and the opera *Aida* while Ern and the other prize winners dined with the King and members of the royal family.

> ⋯ *He says they were very pleasant. The queen seemed to know a good deal about his work – she had got up the subject well for the occasion I suppose.* ⋯

On Saturday Ern and May lunched at the British Embassy. In the evening they attended a dinner for sixty at a country house, being taken there by special electric train. On Sunday Ern went to Uppsala to see the University while May stayed with the Taylors; sightseeing, chatting and talking them into a fishing holiday in New Zealand. Monday passed in shopping, a round of ceremonial farewell calls and an impromptu dinner party with Professor Arrhenius. Culture swallowed Tuesday, with a visit to an art gallery and a guided tour of the prehistory section of the Nordiska Museum. That night they left Sweden by train.

Otto Hahn showed them Berlin before taking May shopping for toys for Eileen. Ern they left at the University talking with the scientists, including Dr Marckwald who had named a mineral in his honour – Rutherfordine, a yellow uranyl carbonate UO_2CO_3 from German East Africa, not to be confused with the earlier Rutherfordite named after Rutherford County, North Carolina. After a meeting of the physical group, a professor invited thirty men to meet Ern and May over supper at a fine hotel.

> ⋯ *we were delighted with it. They are all so cordial and glad to see Ern, they could not have been nicer.*

Stopping off in Leyden, Ern saw the apparatus with which Kamerlingh Onnes could liquify helium, a far harder proposition than liquefying air or radium emanation.

Acknowledgements

Their return to England brought reality. The Sunday train took over nine hours to travel to Manchester. The university threw a dinner in honour of Professor Rutherford, Nobel Laureate. Sir J J Thomson delivered the tribute, describing how Ern had never received the credit that he should have for his radiotelegraphy work at Cambridge.

> ⋯ *His success was so great that I have since felt some misgivings that I persuaded him to devote himself to that new department of physics that was opened by the discovery of Rontgen rays.* ⋯ *But the change of direction had been fruitful.* ... *Of all the services that can be rendered to science the introduction of new ideas is the very greatest. A new idea serves not only to make many people interested, but it starts a great number of new investigations.* ⋯ *There is nobody who has tested his ideas with more rigour than has Professor Rutherford. There can be no man who more nearly fulfils the design of the founder of the Nobel Prize than he does.* ⋯

Letters of congratulation flooded in from around the world. To the Board of Governors of Canterbury College Ern replied:

> *Jan 21 1909*
>
> *Dear Mr Russell,*
>
> *I must thank you personally as well as the Board of Governors of Canterbury College for the kind congratulations to me on the award of the Nobel Prize.*
>
> *I am very pleased that those connected with my "alma mater" wish me well on this occasion. I have a happy remembrance of my old college days and of my first researches in the basement of one of the lecture rooms. I learnt more of research methods in those first investigations*

under somewhat difficult conditions than in any work I have done since.

If there is any credit to be apportioned for winning a Nobel Prize, I think that Canterbury College may take a fair share; for it was there that I was well trained in Mathematics and Physics by Professor Cook and Professor Bickerton. Both were excellent teachers and Professor Bickerton's genuine enthusiasm for science gave a stimulus to me to start investigations of my own.

I may mention that the Nobel Prize was awarded to me in Chemistry and not in Physics. I was rather startled at first at my sudden transformation but the work I have been engaged upon the last two years may be called physics or chemistry at will.

Please convey to the members of the Board of Governors my sincere thanks for their resolution of congratulations.

Yours very truly,
E. Rutherford

He also found time to write one unsolicited letter of genuine thanks, to his old school teacher Jacob Reynolds who had been effectively fired from the Havelock school ten years earlier.

University, Manchester
24th December, 1908

Dear Mr Reynolds,

You will have seen some time ago that I was awarded a Nobel Prize, and am sure you will be pleased at the success of your old student ⋯

After summarizing his trip to Stockholm, Ern continued

In these later days I have not properly thanked you for the way you initiated me into the mysteries of Latin, Algebra and Euclid in my youthful days in Havelock, of which I still have a very keen remembrance. The start I got with you stood me in good stead when I went to Nelson. As the Nobel prize has a considerable pecuniary value, I hope you will accept from your old pupil a little Xmas box in the form of the enclosed draft for £20. It may be helpful to you to take a little holiday or get some little thing you want. We are all very well. With kind regards to Mrs Reynolds, and with best wishes for a happy New Year.

Yours sincerely,
E. Rutherford

This generous gift had a value in excess of one weeks salary for a University Professor in New Zealand, no small sum. The Nobel Prize money of £7680 equalled over seven years of Ern's higher-than-average professorial salary of £1000. Ern purchased some radioactive materials for his researches. May had written to Martha Rutherford of their plans:

> ⋯ *We are not going to launch out very much. Ern will certainly get an assistant and we shall invest most of the money so that it will be some time before much interest comes in. As soon as we get it we shall be able to send your Xmas presents which I have delayed this year.* ⋯

Ern sent his mother, father and Mrs Newton £50 each. His brothers and sisters received £30 together with a note:

> *From your momentarily wealthy brother.*

George, Alice and Jim each named their next born son Ernest.

Chapter 13

COUNTING ATOMS

Early Days at Manchester 1907–1908

He'd try a rough experiment himself on the little things, d'you see, and then he'd turn it over onto somebody and they'd get quite a nice theory about it, ⋯ you see, he never put his name in conjunction with that paper, you know. I think he was a great man that way.

William Kay,

Ern's lab assistant reminiscing in 1957.

First Impressions

"*By thunder!*" roared Ern, smiting the table a mighty blow. Prior to his arrival in Manchester, the Chemistry department had annexed some rooms previously used by physics. This, his first senate meeting, had condoned the action. Having gained the attention of the meeting, Ern launched into a vigorous speech of protest, capped off by pursuing the Professor of Chemistry back to his study denouncing him as being ⋯ *like the fag end of a bad dream.* [Arthur Eve recorded that whenever this story was recalled to Ern in later years he was quite unrepentant and hailed it with delight.]

First impressions often left a permanent memory. On his first visit to the physics department Ern saw an assistant at the head of the stairs.

"*Where is the Professor's room?*"
"*Here.*"

Ern bounded up the stairs three at a time, shocking the assistant who regarded such behaviour as beneath the dignity of a Professor. Ern continued to be amazed and highly amused when people considered him Lord God Almighty.

The six-year-old physics building he thought suitable, though not as opulently equipped as McGill's. It housed a surprise or two. Ern found Mr Petavel had constructed a closed steel bomb to study the pressures developed during explosions. With an internal diameter of about ten centimetres and a wall thickness of five centimetres, small explosions of cordite could be contained within the bomb. At the peak of such an explosion the internal temperature would rise to over 2500 degrees Celsius and the pressure to 1200 times atmospheric pressure. Such figures were far higher than could be obtained in static experiments.

One of the factors distinguishing radioactive transformations from ordinary chemical reactions was that the rate of change of the former appeared to be independent of any physical parameter such as temperature. Once again Ern tested this observation. The bomb was filled with radium emanation which, after four hours, came to equilibrium with its daughter products. The bomb walls stopped all alpha and beta particles but not the highly penetrating gamma rays. An electroscope outside the bomb could thus be used to monitor the radioactivity inside the bomb before, during and after a cordite explosion. Ern observed no change in activity due to these enormous pressures and temperatures:

The dampness of Manchester suited the spinning and weaving industry but not humans. It wasn't unusual in winter fogs for men to miss their way and fall into canals. Harry Moseley, a young research student, was to write to his mother on the 30th of November 1910

> ⋯ *Today the fog is so thick, that I shall probably get lost on my way to the College; it tastes acrid and tickles the throat. Yesterday the tram in which I came back lost itself badly, and I finally got out somewhere and groped for a side-street on which to find a street name which luckily I recognized. Monday the fog was thinner but more yellow. Sunday it poured all day, ⋯.*

But the town and university had a number of advantages in Ern's eyes. He wrote to Arthur Eve at McGill:

> ⋯ *I find the atmosphere good to work in and it appears to agree with me pretty well. Everybody seems jolly and anxious to help and I find a most enjoyable absence of convention. In fact, it is better in that respect even than Montreal* ⋯.

He expressed his first impressions another way to an American friend: ⋯ *a good set of colleagues, a hospitable and kindly people and no side anywhere* ⋯, the latter his way of saying people were not stuck up; snooty; putting on airs and graces. This embracing conclusion had obviously been reached before one particular reception at the Vice-Chancellor's house. Lady Moberly, in showing the guests over her new home, pointed out with pride they had four bathrooms.

> "*Four bathrooms!*" said Ern. "*What do you need four bathrooms for? In fact what do you need one bathroom for? Why, when I was a boy in New Zealand we had a bath once a week in a tub on a Saturday night in front of the kitchen fire with water that was specially heated. And look at me now!*"

Ern called regularly on Professor Schuster at home to discuss University and laboratory matters. He seemed to like the pleasant family atmosphere. The five Schuster children certainly liked him, finding him very cheerful and amiable. He played games with them, being particularly good at word games and with an excellent memory for quotations.

Having arrived in England on the 24th of May 1907, the Rutherfords had quickly settled in at Manchester. They leased a house at 17 Wilmslow Road. Situated less than four kilometres along a main road from the University, it boasted a garden where both Eileen and plants could grow. [The house still stands but due to renumbering is now 409 Wilmslow Road. It is currently owned by the Union of Communication Workers and a plaque on the wall recalls the Rutherford association.]

Ern had little to do with running his own household, leaving that completely in May's hands, who in turn had a nurse to look after Eileen. In writing to Arthur Eve in Canada to congratulate him on the birth of his first child, Ern stated

> ⋯ *You will find a child in the house the most satisfying of all possessions. So speaks one who is old in experience.* ⋯ In the following letter he was more realistic. ⋯ *I suppose you now get exercise without golf – I allude to midnight perambulations with the baby. I only did it once but then I am not the model you are.* ⋯

For May Rutherford the return to England brought her back into the family fold. Several aunts resided there still, her brother Charlie was studying medicine at Edinburgh University and her mother arrived for a long visit. On a trip to Edinburgh to visit Charlie, Mrs Newton suffered partial paralysis. Six months later she walked eleven steps on her way to recovery.

Re-stablishing a Research Group

For Ern the return to Britain meant close proximity to the principal centres of science. Within a few hours train travel from Manchester he could be at the Cavendish Laboratory in Cambridge or a meeting of the Royal Society in London. In his first month back he attended a Royal Society meeting, its soiree and a meeting of the Chemical Society.

After a short family holiday at Mullion Cove, Cornwall, Ern went off to the British Association meeting at Leicester. He reported his work with the 'bomb' but more importantly opened the discussion on 'The Constitution of the Atom'.

In accepting the Manchester chair Ern had sought assurance that there were sufficient staff to cover the bulk of teaching and committee work:

> ⋯ *I should be prepared to give five lectures a week but no more, as otherwise there would be a serious curtailment of time and energy for research.* ⋯

Without question research was his forte. He gave a special series of lectures on radioactivity to raise interest in his field of study.

Another main advantage of Manchester concerned the number of co-workers available to Ern. He anticipated several locals, probably fifteen Germans and a Japanese. Ern's relative youthfulness at the time is highlighted by a chance meeting. Baron Kekuchi, the Japanese Minister of Education, visited Manchester. Professor Schuster introduced him to 36-year-old Ern. Said the Baron later to Professor Schuster: ⋯ *"I suppose the Rutherford you introduced me to is the son of the celebrated Professor Rutherford ?"*

Finding the projects and facilities for all his co-workers was no small task. The Royal Society lent him the actinium residues from about a tonne of pitchblende. This allowed one line of research into the origin of radium. For other avenues of attack he needed radium of which Manchester University possessed a mere twenty milligrams. Not enough. Ern applied formally to the Kaiserliche Akademie der Wissenschaften of Vienna for the loan of half a gram of impure radium. If successful:

> ⋯ *I should at once commence a series of experiments to investigate in particular:*
>
> *(1) Physical and chemical properties of the emanation.*
>
> *(2) Ionization of gases exposed to very intense radiation.*
>
> *(3) Final product of transformation of radium.*

Publication of the German edition of his Silliman lectures could only have helped his cause. The Academy lent 350 mg for the joint use of Ern and of Professor Ramsay in London. Unfortunately this was transported to England by a man who planned to work with Ramsay.

One of the great chemists, Sir William Ramsay had deficiencies as a physicist. He had recently confused trusting chemists with outrageous claims for transmutation based on poor scientific technique: that mixing radium emanation with water produced neon; mixing radium emanation with copper sulphate solution gave argon and lithium; that electrons radiating from radium contained in glass tubes transmuted nickel into some other substance. The latter, for example, turned out to be due to a leak of radon gas. Of the first two claims Bertram Boltwood, the American chemist, wrote to Ern: ··· *I wonder why it hasn't occurred to him that radium emanation and kerosene form lobster salad.* Ern had very little regard for Sir William Ramsay. [May Rutherford was more brutal. In a letter to Martha Rutherford she confided that Ern had been doing his best work for years:

> ··· *He has been upsetting Sir William Ramsay's work – to his great joy – the latter is an awful scientific thief.*]

Ern wrote to Professor Ramsay who, with possession being nine tenths of the law, suggested the radium not be divided but all retained by him. He offered two alternatives. Either Ern could have full use of it after a year or so, or he could have some of the accumulated emanation sent up by train every few days. This development placed Ern in an intolerable position. He made the most of a bad job by using the emanation to produce radioactive sources for all his co-workers while raising the matter with the Vienna authorities. They appreciated the problem. Early in 1908 they lent Ern a similar sample for his exclusive use, a gift Ern long remembered and appreciated. [He repaid this kindness after the Great War.] Now the Manchester group could carry out radioactivity research on a wide front.

Counting Atoms

The fluorescent screen method of observing alpha particles had the problem of being very fatiguing to the eye and thus limited to observations of no more than two minutes duration or so. Hence Ern sought an electrical method of tirelessly detecting individual alpha particles. Since each alpha particle produced a trail of some 80,000 ions in a gas before stopping, estimates showed it should be possible to just detect the effect of one alpha particle using the most sensitive electrical apparatus. However, from his knowledge of ions Ern knew this effect could be magnified. Had not his old friend J S Townsend shown that an electron ionized from a gas at low pressure accelerates in a strong electric field and thereby produces more ions by collision with the gas molecules?

As luck would have it, Ern had inherited the perfect assistant for this work. Dr Hans Geiger had studied electrical discharges in gas tubes for his 1906 thesis before moving from Germany to Manchester to work with Professor Schuster. Using a brass tube containing an insulated axial wire and air at low pressure, they increased the voltage between the tube and wire to just less than the value required for the passage of a spark, being about 1000 volts for their apparatus. Each alpha particle entered the tube through a thin mica window at one end and produced many thousands of ions. The resultant momentary charge flow between tube and wire could easily be observed using an ordinary electrometer.

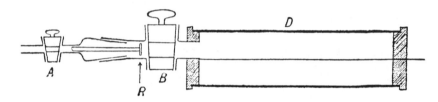

Later a permanent record was obtained by reflecting a spot of light off the electrometer to a moving strip of photographic paper.

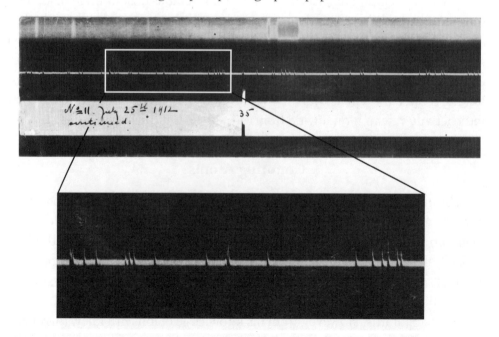

The Rutherford-Geiger detector was later improved by Geiger and by Müller. It is still used today as the standard method of detecting nuclear radiation. Called the Geiger tube or the GM (Geiger-Müller) tube, this invention perhaps emphasises the hesitant recollections of the former laboratory steward at Manchester, taped in 1957 when approaching eighty years of age.

> ··· [Rutherford would] *tell you what he was going to do ··· and then we would do a rough experiment, and get one or two curves ··· and then straightaway button it on to somebody else to do the real work ··· He'd try a rough experiment himself on the little things, d'you see, and then he'd turn it over onto somebody and they'd get quite a nice theory about it, ··· you see, he never put his name in conjunction with that paper, you know. I think he was a great man that way ··· .*

During Ern's time at Manchester the Physics Department concentrated on two main areas of research, radioactivity and spectroscopy, with a smaller group working in electrotechnology. Some 230 papers were published on radioactivity of which Ern produced 73, half as a sole author and half jointly. Excluding those for which he was sole author his name appears on only 37 of the other 200 or so papers. These figures reinforce the many reminiscences that Ernest Rutherford gave more than full credit to his junior collaborators. [Today, in the era of publish or perish, it is not unknown for the leader of a research group to have his name on all papers published by the group members, even in those cases in which his involvement is close to zero.]

Ern quickly put the counting tube to use in obtaining the decay of activity curves for radium C and actinium B and to study the statistical nature of radioactive decay. However the main reason for its development was to tackle fundamental questions. How many alpha particles were emitted each second from one gram of radium? What was the charge on the alpha particle? Was the alpha particle basically a helium atom?

At McGill Ern had measured the charge-to-mass ratio of the alpha particle and the rate of charge collection from alpha particles emitted per gram of radium. The former cannot distinguish between a doubly charged helium atom and a singly charged hydrogen molecule. By direct counting, Rutherford and Geiger could now show that one gram of radium expelled 34,000,000,000 alpha particles per second, thus establishing the first standard for radioactivity. Combined with the McGill data they found the charge on each particle corresponded to twice the value on an electron, once again pointing to the alpha particle being a doubly charged helium atom.

To remove all doubts about the nature of the alpha particle Ern and Thomas

Royds, an 1851 Scholar, carried out the decisive experiment. Thomas Royds already had experience in preparing samples of radium emanation and measuring its spectrum. The laboratory had an excellent glassblower associated with it, Otto Baumbach, who, after many attempts, blew glass tubes with very thin walls of about a hundredth of a millimeter thick. Alpha particles from emanation contained in the tube could then pass through the walls into an outer evacuated space, where the emission spectra characteristic of helium built up over a few days. From then on there could be no doubt at all that alpha particles were helium atoms stripped of their electrons.

A young student, Ernest Marsden, recalled that crucial experiment years later, when reminiscing about 'Rutherford the Man' at the opening of the Rutherford Memorial Appeal in 1951:

> *He could flash fire on occasions when unreasonably thwarted. Perhaps I could record one of many instances. It was the time that Rutherford was engaged on that beautiful experiment on the spectrum of radium emanation and the proof of the production of helium from it by collecting the alpha particles fired through a thin-walled container of radium emanation. I remember the details so well because the spectroscope was set up in the same room as that in which I worked. Photographs of the spectrum of radium emanation and helium were taken at daily intervals as the emanation decayed and the helium spectrum appeared. One day someone had been too inquisitive in looking at the apparatus. Rutherford came into the room and, noticing that the prism had been displaced, flew into a towering rage. He came over to the bench at which I was working and placed his hand round the back of my neck, only moderately gently, and said, "Did you move the prism?" I knew and trusted him too well to have the slightest fear of him and answered "No." I was sufficient of a schoolboy to enjoy the 'boss' in a tantrum. Half an hour afterwards he came back to the room and sat deliberately on a stool alongside me and quietly expressed his apology for getting his 'dander' up and accusing me of the misdemeanour. He must have found the culprit in the meantime. Then we went on to one of those helpful, and on his part, non-condescending discussions of the progress of my work, which all who had a similar privilege treasured as their happiest recollections. I never knew him to bear malice. You will appreciate his action when I add that I was only 19 at the time.*

One reason Ern had pushed the development of the electrical method of detecting single alpha particles concerned the doubt that a zinc sulphide screen fluoresced for every particle. Now he and Hans Geiger returned to investigate these doubts.

> ··· *Geiger is a demon at the work of counting scintillations and could count at intervals for a whole night without disturbing his equanimity. I damned vigorously and retired after two minutes.* ···

They found that the two counting methods did indeed agree.

Ern's first year at Manchester had been highly productive. In March of 1908 he received a surprise telegram. The Turin Academy of Science awarded him the Bressa Prize – a medal and £384. He found that it was awarded every two or three years to the man who, in the opinion of the society, has done the best work or published the best book during the preceding period in experimental science, archaeology, history or statistics. In honour of this event the *Manchester Guardian* interviewed the University's janitor about Ern's hours of work:

> ··· *You can never tell when he'll leave his lab and go home.* ···

When the laboratory steward William Kay retired in 1945, after 51 years of service, he too was interviewed.

> ··· *in his younger days Mr Kay had considerable success as a short distance runner ; "but not after Rutherford came" he said. "Once he came you hadn't time to do anything else – you just worked. We worked whenever the spirit moved him. Saturday afternoons, Sundays, Bank Holidays, any hours. If you were on the point of getting something out you just kept at it. You didn't notice time. You were completely absorbed."*

The hard work had taken its toll on Ern. At the youthful age of thirty-six he started to wear glasses when reading.

But the hard work also yielded rewards and honours: the Bessa prize, Honorary D.Sc.'s from Dublin and Giessen, appointment as corresponding member of the Physico-Medical Society of Vienna and a write-up in the *New York Times* of his work on detecting individual atoms.

These were just the start. Even after the award of the Nobel Prize he didn't rest on his laurels. Further discoveries awaited the right person.

Ernest

went down to Lord Kelvin's funeral he said it was very impressive. He has been having a little bother with Ramsay. They both wrote to the Vienna Akad. for some radium & were both promised it. They sent it all over to R. & said he was to divide with Em. R. calmly wrote to E & said he preferred to keep it all – virtually insisted on doing so & said he would send along emanation whenever Em wanted it. E was very annoyed but possession is 9 points of the law & it was plain that nothing would get it out of Ramsay. Then the emanation began to come – both irregularly & less than he promised. Em wrote to Exner & casually remarked that they needn't expect to see any very startling results published from the ~~fac...~~ radium which he hadn't got. Exner has now written & is going to send Em a whole lot for himself alone! He of course saw what had happened though Em didn't say so. Of course the Vienna Akad expects to see results from the radium possessors. He is not going to tell Ramsay anything about this new offer of red. But doesn't think any more of him than he did needless to remark. Don't mention this. Schuster is a old dear. They go away for a trip to India on Jan 2. for 9 months. Charlie has

May Rutherford to Harriet Pitcher (neé Brooks) 28 Dec 1907

Chapter 14

THE ATOM UNVEILED

Manchester 1909-1914

Dr Rutherford is the one man living who promises to confer some inestimable boon on mankind as a result of the discovery of radium. I would advise England to watch Dr Rutherford; his work on radioactivity has surprised me greatly.

Marie Curie, 1913

Manchester 1909–1914

The British Association for the Advancement of Science went to Winnipeg for its 1909 Annual Meeting. J J Thomson led as President, with Ern the President of the Physics section. This gave Ern and May a chance to catch up with Canadian friends. In his Presidential address to the section, Ern commented on the ease with which alpha particles could pass through very thin barriers of metal or glass which would not pass helium gas. The alpha particle must be not only swift but small:

> ··· *The old dictum, no doubt true in most cases, that two bodies cannot occupy the same space, no longer holds for atoms of matter if moving at a sufficiently high speed.* ···

Ern also travelled down to the U.S.A. to participate in the 20th anniversary celebration of Clark University at which the university gave him an honorary

Doctor of Laws. (Another New Zealander, Richard Maclaurin, was also recommended for one but he doesn't appear to have attended.) The reporter for the *Springfield Republican*, after describing the maths and astronomy talks, enthused:

> ⋯ *In physics was presented the spectacle of a conjunction of two stars of the first magnitude in Prof Albert Michelson of Chicago and Prof Ernest Rutherford of Manchester, Eng., Nobel prizewinners of last year and this, respectively.* ⋯

Ern entitled his talk 'History of the Alpha Rays from Radioactive Substances'.

> *In the brief interval of an hour the enthusiasm of the speaker relating the results of over 60 papers published in 10 years and some not yet carried his auditors with him to the culminating feat of capturing a single particle of the millions of millions flying off per second, and seeing it, not only with the minds eye, but with the eye of sense.* ⋯

The University awarded Ern yet another honorary degree, its brand new Doctor of Physics.

Such celebrations weren't allowed to interfere with research. Now that he was certain each alpha particle caused a flash of fluorescence when it hit a zinc sulphide coated screen, Ern returned to an old problem first noticed during his researches at McGill. When a beam of alpha particles is passed through a thin slice of matter the beam became fuzzy – the alpha particles were scattered indicating that atoms were seats of tremendous electrical forces. His assistant Hans Geiger studied this small angle scattering by thin foils of metals.

One of Geiger's duties concerned the training of students in basic techniques of measurements concerning radioactivity. (His book, co-authored with Dr Makower, entitled 'Practical Measurements in Radioactivity' was printed in 1912). One undergraduate, Ernest Marsden, helped Geiger with the scattering experiments. When Geiger reported to Ern that Marsden was ready for a research of his own, Ern turned to Marsden:

> "See if you can get some effect of alpha-particles directly reflected from a metal surface."

Young Marsden quickly observed that a very tiny fraction were reflected straight back from a thin gold foil. This surprised even Ern. As he later put it:

> It was almost as incredible as if you had fired a fifteen-inch shell at a piece of tissue-paper and it came back and hit you.

He was to puzzle over this observation for two years.

As usual Ern's researches were on a wide front. Sometimes he worked alone such as on a more accurate determination of the boiling point of radium emanation. When Professor Joly of Dublin attributed the microscopic halos observed in mica as due to alpha particles emitted by small inclusions of radioactive material, Ern confirmed the result by studying the inner wall of a glass capillary tube which had held radium emanation. During the next four years they combined to show how the halos could be used to date the formation of rocks (*Phil. Mag.* **XXV** 644-57 1913). This technique eliminated the defect in the method of dating rocks by the quantity of helium gas trapped in the rock, which is that some of the gas could have diffused out over geological time.

Ern enjoyed giving lectures on elementary physics to the students of engineering because in them he could conduct exciting lecture demonstrations common to first year classes. Besides, the engineers were a rowdy lot and only Ern and one other person in the department could keep them under control. James Chadwick, a young student who had suffered poor lecturing in his first year of physics, had a lucky break in his second year. One of his better lecturers received an appointment to London University so a stopgap had to be found. And that stopgap was Ern. James Chadwick thereby received the first stimulating lectures that he had ever had in physics, though on topics not necessarily connected with the syllabus. Ern could talk as if the subject matter was alive, a faculty that few people have. In magnetism he talked of his work in New Zealand on the residual magnetism of a steel needle after a high frequency discharge: ⋯ *Take the skin off and see if the magnetism is gone.* In such ways did Professor Rutherford stimulate James Chadwick to consider a career as a researcher in physics. He worked with Ern on a balance for the radium standard.

Besides research and some teaching Ern had other duties to attend to, for example helping the Cavendish Laboratory celebrate the 25th anniversary of J J Thomson's appointment. Ern wrote a chapter of the book *A History of the Cavendish Laboratory* which covered the three years he spent there.

Ern believed in working hard and relaxing hard. He and May took regular holidays and travelled widely. To assist this mobility, Ern, with the new year of 1910 hardly started, ordered a car. A four-seater, 15-horsepower Wolseley-Siddeley. Their excitement mounted until three months later the car arrived from the factory, complete with chauffeur. For three days Ern practised turning and reversing. Then, as an experienced driver, he set off with May on a fortnight's tour looping down to the South Coast. They cruised at a heady 25 miles an hour:

> ⋯ *A car is very easy to manage and far more under control than a horse.* ⋯ *We can go 35 or 40 if we want to, but I am not keen on high speeds with motor traps along the road and a ten guineas fine if I am caught. These are the woes of motorists that I hope to avoid.*

Other woes he did not avoid. To house the car Ern surmounted much red tape before paying a firm to erect a shed. He was fleeced. The firm didn't exist. The man to whom he had paid the money couldn't be found.

Ern made two new appointments; Charles Darwin, a grandson of THE Darwin, as the mathematical physics fellow and Henry (Harry) Moseley, the son of an Oxford Professor, as demonstrator. May Rutherford commented

> ⋯ *It is nice to get men of good social standing occasionally. Last years were all a dull lot and the former are easier to push for a chair later on.* ⋯

Twenty people worked with Ern, of whom about a dozen held doctorates. They came from all parts of the globe and some could hardly speak English: Japanese, Russian, German, American, Canadian and Australian.

One visiting researcher came all the way from Christchurch, New Zealand. D C H Florance held B.A., M.A., B.Sc. and M.Sc. from Canterbury College but he too had failed to get an assistant master's position at the Christchurch Boys High School. However he had been selected by the University of New Zealand for the free, first-class passage to Europe offered by a shipping company.

David Florance wrote home to his mother giving his first impressions of Professor Rutherford.

> ⋯ *Afterwards met Rutherford – a fine man and the more I see of him the more I like him.* ⋯ *Rutherford is essentially a big man. Big and strong physically and a big intellect. Of an afternoon we have afternoon tea and he sits there and we research students stand around and he is ready to answer questions – explain difficulties – make jokes – laughs and never seems to know what worry is although I've no doubt he gets through more work than anyone at College. A week later his first impressions had not changed* ⋯ *I feel I can't speak highly enough of Rutherford he is the life of the institution and even to see him – it has been worthwhile making the journey.* ⋯

On another occasion word went back to New Zealand that ⋯ *He keeps us in shrieks of laughter.* Also

··· To be with Rutherford is like spending a weekend at the seaside. It is exhilarating. We talked of all sorts of things. He knows Physics knows Radioactivity as no other man does yet his views on many other subjects seem rather vague and he is in the dark just like most of us. You learn that he too has a limited range. He says he never could memorise things — he can reason out everything. He also can understand why some men are lazy he says. He used to as a young fellow dig in the garden at home and he always after an hours work had back ache and would do anything to sneak into a shady spot and rest. We saw his daughter a pert little girl of 10.

At the fortnightly Physics Colloquium Ern introduced David Florance to May Rutherford who invited the young man to Sunday afternoon tea. Florance wrote home of a later visit to the Rutherfords:

··· After church I slipped along to Rutherfords where a big supper was indulged in, then we adjoined to his study for a quiet smoke. There were three others beside myself. On the wall hangs a picture of Canterbury College which bought back old memories. He says he smokes because it keeps him from doing too much work and thinking too hard. ···

Florance was invited another evening when May Rutherfords youngest brother, Charlie Newton, visited. They had been in the lower third-form Latin class together at Christchurch Boys High. Though they had detested each other at school, as young men they got on well reminiscing about school days.

··· He was not as good as me in those days but here he is a full blown doctor and is at present working at the Manchester Infirmary. That's one of the advantages of money. ···

Position also gave power. The prospect of Florance getting into the Manchester Degree Ceremony looked bleak. Tickets were unattainable as far more people wished to attend than there were seats available.

··· there was no chance for me. But fortune always favours the brave and at the last minute Prof Rutherford came in and asked if I was going to the function — said I couldn't get a ticket — he immediately gave me a note to the Registrar — that opened the doors and the Registrar took me into the Hall without a ticket. When the big man speaks the thing is done.

Everyone in the lab benefited from Ern's new car. In groups of three he took them for motor rides into the countryside. Florance's turn came one Friday afternoon with a sixty mile ride through many picturesque country villages.

> ··· *It's a tip top motor car runs so smoothly and quietly the motor is quite a hobby of the profs. He has only recently bought it. But he is already putting it to good use as he has been taking us in turn for a spin. We ended up at his place for afternoon tea and we had a thoroughly enjoyable afternoon.*

At times though the car was an impediment to research. Harry Moseley wrote to his mother:

> ··· *Remaking the apparatus took a long time, as the Laboratory Assistant spent his time mending Rutherford's motorcar, and I had to make everything myself.*

During a visit to Liverpool University Florance looked up two chemistry research students, friends from Canterbury College. One, Fred Farrow, had worked his passage to England. He told of another Canterbury College winner of a free first-class shipping passage who, having no confidence in his social graces, asked the company for a second-class ticket. This reminded David Florance *of Prof Rutherford's opening address at the Physical Colloquium. In it he said to his mind modesty carried to excess is a vice.* Florance worked on gamma-rays at Manchester. Later he became the long serving physics professor at Victoria College, Wellington, New Zealand, succeeding Ernest Marsden.

In the summer of 1910 Ern had a family holiday in the Lake District followed by a pleasant fortnight in Munich. Then on to Brussels for the Radiology Congress where he had a good deal to do with establishing a radium standard. With the unit named in her honour, the task of preparing an international standard fell on Madame Curie. [The unit of one curie refers to the number of nuclei decaying during one second from one gram of radium, a number first accurately measured by Ernest Rutherford. Initially the curie was used only for radium. The general unit of radioactivity was the rutherford (rd), the amount of any radioactive isotope which disintegrates at the rate of a million disintegrations per second. So one rutherford was 1/37 millicuries. The rutherford was made redundant in 1953 and the curie in 1975. Today the standard unit is the becquerel defined as one disintegration per second. One rutherford equals a million becquerel.]

Ern has left a description of Madam Curie at this congress.

> ··· *She looked very wan and tired and much older than her age. She works much too hard for her health. Altogether she was a very pathetic figure.* ···

Not that he himself would relax except on holiday or Sunday morning golf. May and Martha Rutherford regarded the British Association meeting planned for Australasia in 1914 as being too far in the future so they pressured Ern to visit New Zealand during 1911. He, not wanting to interrupt his researches, held out for a cheap trip in 1914.

In an event invoking the past, Ern went up to Dundee to open the University's new electrical engineering laboratory. Thirty-nine-year-old Ern joked to Arthur Eve ⋯ *It impresses the fact on me that I am now regarded as elderly and respectable.* During the opening he carefully mentioned that his father came from the neighbourhood of Dundee. The rowdiness of the students made the newspapers but Ern didn't mind. Having been a student once himself he regarded the affair as a mere frolic.

Back in Manchester May and Ern threw a big party for 105 people. Ern showed slides of New Zealand while May described each scene. Ern helped choose the inaugural mathematics and physics professor for the University of Queensland in Australia but refused to testify as an expert witness for the British Radio Telegraph and Telephone Company. He worked on a third edition of his book, and gave undergraduate and advanced lectures. New people were started on original work. He joined the Council of the Royal Society, adding another dozen visits to London to his crowded annual schedule. The National Academy of Sciences in America awarded Ern the 1910 Barnard Medal for Meritorious Service to Science. Presented every five years for a landmark in scientific progress, the medal was brought to Ern in England, along with a generous job offer from Columbia University.

Thus passed another summer and autumn in the life of a busy man. With winter came understanding of Ernest Marsden's observation of large angle scattering.

The Nuclear Atom

By January of 1911 Ern could write to Arthur Eve in Canada:

> ⋯ *Among other things I have been interesting myself in devising a new atom to explain some of the scattering results. It looks promising and we are now comparing the theory with experiments.*

Several laboratories had studied the absorption and scattering of alpha and beta particles. Sir J J Thomson had extended Oliver Lodge's proposed model of the atom which consisted of a uniform sphere of positive electricity embedded with the same quantity of negative electricity in the form of electrons. He

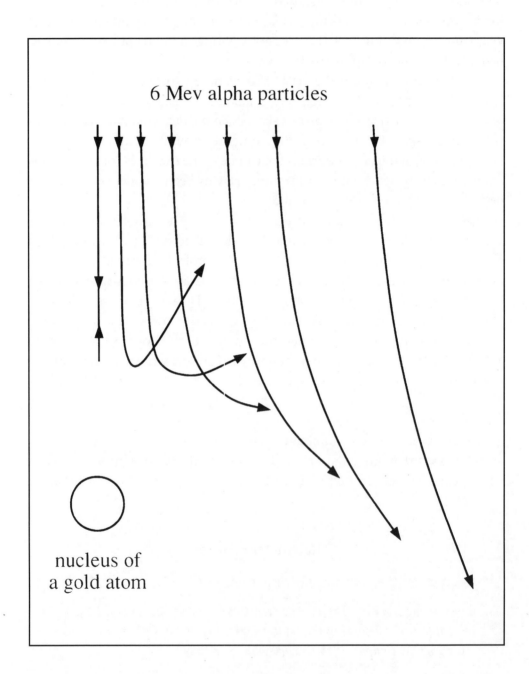

6 Mev alpha particles

nucleus of
a gold atom

worked out a theory of scattering through small angles and one of his students, J A Crowther, examined beta scattering experimentally, finding good agreement between experiment and theory. Scattering through large angles was assumed to be consecutive small angle scatterings by many charges distributed throughout the atom. As Ern wrote to W H Bragg on the 9th of February 1911:

> ⋯ *I have looked into Crowther's scattering paper carefully and the more I examine it the more I marvel at the way he made it fit (or thought he made it fit) JJ's theory.* ⋯ *I believe it is only the use of imagination, and failure to grasp where the theory was inapplicable, that led him to give numbers showing such an apparent agreement.* ⋯

As evidence of his helpfulness to young scientists in distant parts Ern, perhaps recalling how his own first planned research had been overwritten before he could complete it, wrote to J P V Madsen in Australia:

> ⋯ *I had intended to test my theory by experiments with rays along very similar lines to that which I understand you are doing. I shall be glad, however, to leave the matter to you if you will be able to get through the work in reasonable time.* ⋯

Ern had his own theory of the structure of the atom deduced from sound observations. The statistics of Hans Geiger's careful experiments pointed to large angle scattering of alpha particles being due to a single encounter. Therefore, in order to obtain large angle scattering, the alpha particle must approach very closely a large electrical charge. Ern assumed all of an atom's positive charge to be concentrated at its centre. An alpha particle fired directly at the centre of the atom would slow to a halt before being accelerated back to its source. The distance of closest approach of an alpha particle to a gold nucleus could be worked out by equating the potential energy of the alpha particle while momentarily at rest with the known initial kinetic energy of the particle. This simple calculation showed the distance to be some 10,000 times smaller than the radius of an atom. The nuclear atom had been born. If an atomic nucleus were enlarged to be the width of this page then the outer reaches of the atom, the surrounding electrons, would be over a kilometre away. Put yet another way, the volume taken up by the nuclei of all the atoms in a human body is about equivalent to that of a fine grain of sand.

In order to account for such a simple observation as large angle scattering Ern had, for the second time, completely changed mankind's view of nature. In the best of spirits he went to Geiger's room and announced that he knew what the atom looked like. Using his nuclear model of the atom Ern had also worked out the relative numbers of alpha particles as a function of scattering angle. Hans Geiger immediately began the careful experiments which confirmed the relationship and thereby the model.

Placing the Electrons Around the Nucleus

There were some nagging details that needed attention. When Ern announced the work in his brief paper entitled 'The Scattering of Alpha Particles by Matter and the Structure of the Atom' he stated that

> ··· *It will be shown that the main deductions from the theory are independent of whether the central charge is supposed to be positive or negative. For convenience, the sign will be assumed to be positive. The question of the stability of the atom proposed need not be considered at this stage, for this will obviously depend upon the minute structure of the atom, and on the motion of the constituent charged parts.* ···

Having captured such a scientific gem, no wonder Ern was in fine fettle as he travelled down to Cambridge to be guest of honour at the annual Cavendish Laboratory Dinner. Jovial and dominant, he was scheduled to say a few words on his latest discovery. The chairman, in introducing Ern, told the audience that Professor Rutherford held another distinction. Of all the young physicists who had worked at the Cavendish, none could match him in swearing at apparatus. Ern's booming laugh reverberated around the room. A young Dane present took an immense liking to the hearty New Zealander and resolved to work with him.

Niels Bohr quickly visited Manchester to meet Ern who had only weeks earlier attended the First Solvay Conference in Brussels. This forerunner of international physics conferences was financed by Ernst Solvay, a Belgium chemist who had made a fortune from the economical production of sodium carbonate. Twenty-one of the finest physical scientists in Europe had accepted the invitation. Thus Ern, as one of two people from Britain, had joined the pioneers of the quantum theory, Max Planck of Germany, Maurice de Broglie of France and Albert Einstein of Austria, to discuss the topic selected for the conference: 'The Theory of Radiation and the Quanta'. Enthused by Ern's account of the meeting Bohr gratefully accepted an invitation to join him from the following Spring.

At Manchester, Niels Bohr used the new quantum ideas to place the electrons in stable orbits around Rutherford's atomic nucleus. Their friendship was close and lifelong. When Bohr later established the Institute for Theoretical Physics (now the Niels Bohr Institute) in Copenhagen he modelled it on Rutherford's system and later installed a plaque of Rutherford above the fireplace in his study.

Ern also had friends in New Zealand. A letter to the editor appeared in the *Pelorus Guardian* of the 30th of June 1911.

NO OUTSIDERS NEED APPLY.

TO THE EDITOR

SIR, – Looking down the long list of honours that have been New Zealand's share this year I am struck with the fact that with one notable exception (i.e., Sir J.S. Williams, a most worthy recipient) all the others are political and receive their honours through influence. Now, surely in our bright island home there are some others outside of this zone who are worthy of being honoured by our beloved sovereign King George V.

I have in my mind one who by his brain-power, grit, and perseverance has forced his way to the top rung of the ladder, until he now ranks amongst the highest, if he is not the highest, in the scientific world. I mean Professor Ernest Rutherford, a truly great man, who, amongst his many other achievements, is the youngest man who has ever won the great Nobel prize; he I believe won his first scholarship in our small village school.

Not that I think a title would appeal to a man of his calibre and achievements; but an honour it undoubtedly would have been to one so worthy of it in this Coronation year. He is a New Zealander bred and born, and we should be so proud to claim him; but owing to our neglect he is drifting away from us. Surely it should have been the proud privilege and duty of those in authority to have had his name on that noble list, and to claim him as one of our noble sons.

However, Professor E. Rutherford's name and work will be known and honoured long after some selfish self-seeking politicians are forgotten. – I am, etc.,

HAVELOCK

Maybe wheels were slowly set in motion.

Family Life

Professor Rutherford invited young Niels Bohr to join his monthly dinner meeting with an historian, an anthropologist, a philosopher and an organic chemist, Chaim Weizmann, who made perfume for May Rutherford. Later Weizmann, a leading member of the Zionist Movement, became the first President of Israel. Ern often pulled his leg about Zionism but they were good friends and later in life Ern spoke at dinners arranged to assist the formation of the Hebrew University of Jerusalem.

Eileen Rutherford was highly strung and often in ill-health. Looked after by servants and seldom disciplined by her father she had a reputation as a spoilt child: one schoolgirl friend describing her as a real brat. At one tea time May produced an iced cake decorated with walnuts and cherries. Eileen entered and the guests watched in horror as she stuffed all the decorations into her mouth. May said nothing.

Alice Hopkinson, a contemporary of Eileen's, recalled that Ern loved children. They first met when she went as a violet to a childrens' fancy dress party at the Rutherford house. The children had been warned not to go into one of the rooms but during a game of hide and seek Alice slipped in.

> ··· *The room seemed empty but then the most enormous man I had ever seen boomed out :-*
> *"And who are you little girl ?"*
> *"A violet – a very modest violet."*
> *"And what do you want ?"*
> *"I want to hide."*
> *"Well come over here then" and he put me under the knee desk where he was working. I was never found.*

Ern seemed to charm little girls. One weekend in the summer of 1912 he visited Majorie Stevenson's father, a schoolteacher of chemistry. Tea was set under a tree in the garden. Ern raised Majorie onto his knee and asked her what she would like on her bread. The three-year-old couldn't pronounce the letter J properly so jam came out as 'dam'. Ern noticed her father approaching, teapot in hand. Mischievously he asked her to say it louder so her father could hear. 'DAM,' shouted Majorie at the top of her voice. She was too young to know her father could not abide swearing and had sacked a laboratory assistant for just such a crime. After tea Ern said to the tot: *"Majorie, you are a very determined little person – I would like you to become a scientist. Will you promise me that?"* She did and she did.

After Ern's sister Alice died in 1910 her youngest child, Ernest Elliott, had been looked after by James and Martha Rutherford. Hearing (wrongly) that at last young Ernest was to be reunited with his family in Invercargill, his father having remarried, May wrote to Martha Rutherford. She expressed gladness that young Ernest was to grow up with his brothers:

> ⋯ *Besides it is so hard on a child to be brought up as an only child when it is not necessary. I always feel so sorry for Eileen being an only one, but that's not from choice!*

There has been much speculation as to why Ernest and May Rutherford had only one child. Reminiscences of friends and family range from *May regarded sex as a very messy business* to the more likely *May could not have any more children after Eileen* which may also explain why Ern, from a family of large families, spoilt Eileen, an only child. [In her turn, Eileen was to be warned by doctors to have no more children.] May gave a newly married relative a book on birth control.

For her 12th birthday Eileen Rutherford received a parrot called Polly. She had narrowly missed gaining a brother called Paul. When Ern's sister, Ethel Sergel, and her family visited Manchester, May described to Martha Rutherford

> ⋯ *how delighted we all were with the Sergel children, particularly Paul who was favourite with all of us.* ⋯

Everyone liked five-year-old Paul, the Sergel's second son, even Ern's chauffeur, who would take him for a drive. One day Ethel and Henry Sergel lifted Paul up to sit on a table and presented him with a proposition. Would he like to remain behind in England, to stay with his Uncle Ern and Aunty May and receive a good education? Paul liked his Uncle Ern but looked at his own pleasant mother and his formidable Aunty May. He returned to New Zealand with his family. Paul was later told that May and Ern couldn't have any more children and Ern badly wanted a little boy.

How Colleagues Viewed Ern

Reminisces of Ernest Rutherford at Manchester abound. After a hard day's unproductive experimenting Ern could enthuse young colleagues with statements such as ⋯ *Robinson, I'm sorry for those fellows who haven't got laboratories to work in* ⋯ Not that his own was other than functional. Hans Geiger later recalled:

> ⋯ *But I also see the gloomy cellar in which he had filled up his delicate apparatus for the study of the alpha rays. Rutherford loved this room.*

One went down two steps and then heard from the darkness Rutherford's voice reminding one that a hot-pipe crossed the room at head-level, and to step over two water-pipes. Then finally, in the feeble light one saw the great man himself seated at his apparatus and straightaway he would recount in his own inimitable way the progress of his experiments, and point out the difficulties that he had to overcome.

Ern's drive and singlemindedness of purpose is illustrated by the incident involving a foreign woman researcher who showed no outstanding aptitude. As an ardent feminist and somewhat of a man-hater, she elected not to ask a man to open a bottle of sulphur dioxide whose valve was stuck but to go into a very small room and wedge it in the door to open it herself. The sudden rush of gas into the enclosed space rendered her unconscious but luckily she was discovered and revived. On hearing of this Ern sent for her.

"What's this I hear Miss X? You might have killed yourself!"
"Well if I had, nobody would have cared."
"No I daresay not, but I've no time to attend inquests."

Edward Andrade described Ern as a boisterous, inspiring friend, undoubtedly the leader but stimulating rather than commanding, full of fire and infectious enthusiasm and always generous in his acknowledgement of the work of others. On his daily ramble around the laboratory Ern talked to the researchers as a friend and equal. He often gingered up (a favourite expression) individuals by exhorting them to "get on with it".

Around the laboratory he was known as Papa, usually pronounced with the peculiar intonation used by Harry Tate's 'son' in a famous music hall sketch entitled 'Motoring'. Edward Andrade received a high accolade via the laboratory steward who told him *"Papa says you'll do."* Ern had seen him making a photographic plate holder out of cardboard thus saving time and money.

Every day the group had afternoon tea together where discussions ranged widely. One discussion on the merits of electromagnets started getting out of hand with exaggeration. Albert Wood recalled:

⋯ Rutherford, who had remained quiet, then told, with his knowing smile, the story of a magnet at Montreal which would take a bunch of keys from a man's pocket as he came into the room – in fact the magnet was strong enough to draw the iron out of a man's constitution.

An outsider's view of Ern shows in a conversation with a friend Samuel Alexander, the Professor of Philosophy:

"When you come to think of it, Alexander, all that you have said and all you have written during the last thirty years – what does it all amount to? Hot air! Hot air!"

"And now, Rutherford, I am quite sure that you will like me to tell you the truth about yourself. You are a savage – a noble savage, I admit – but still a savage."

Lewis Richardson recorded for posterity his assessment after hearing Ern lecture on 'The Electrical State of the Atmosphere':

··· *A clear orderly account of experimental work, classified and illustrated. No mathematical connections beyond such as current = charge per unit time etc. Spoken extempore in a clear flowing manner with a certain amount of err-r.* ···

Afterwards they discussed University lectures with Ern stating that too much teaching is bad, people must learn to think for themselves, knowledge is no use unless people can apply it. When the suggestion occurred that people might read text books in lecture time Ern replied:

"Well, my idea of a lecture is to get them interested."

Lewis Richardson is one of the people we don't normally hear from. To him Ernest Rutherford was too domineering so he went into meteorology.

Civil Honours

Among his other duties Ern invariably served on selection committees appointing physicists to New Zealand colleges. In 1913, the long-serving Professor Frederick Brown retired from Auckland College. Like Professor Bickerton at Canterbury College he had been Professor of Chemistry and Experimental Physics. The College council advertised separate chairs. For physics the committee passed over the young New Zealander, David Florance, in favour of the Welshman, Dr Gwilym Owen, described by Ern as ··· *a keen and good experimenter.* Dr Owen's book, albeit written before, but published after, he went to New Zealand, was the first physics book to be published by a New Zealand academic. Ern's work featured in this but was incomprehensible to the average New Zealander, the book being written in Welsh.

Ern and May motored down to Aberystwyth where Ern gave a talk to the student society (and perhaps interviewed Gwilym Owen). May reported to Martha Rutherford that the talk

··· was a great success. All his experiments went off perfectly and I never saw such an enthusiastic audience. After the lecture they carried him on their shoulders out into the hall and put him on a radiator for a speech.

The 1913 British Association for the Advancement of Science meeting at Birmingham gathered together the recent remarkable advances in physics and the people who had made them. Aston had proved that chemically identical elements could have different masses by separating the two isotopes of neon through diffusion. The nucleus of an atom appeared to be more complicated than initially thought. The quantum theory stating energy exchanges must take place in discrete amounts gained general acceptance following Bohr's work. However of all the great scientists present the press sought out the shy, retiring Madame Curie. She deflected questions about herself by praising others:

Dr Rutherford is the one man living who promises to confer some inestimable boon on mankind as a result of the discovery of radium. I would advise England to watch Dr Rutherford; his work in radioactivity has surprised me greatly. ···

Obviously the right people were watching. The 1914 New Year's Honours List raised Ern to a knighthood – Sir Ernest Rutherford. Notes of congratulations flowed to Wilmslow Street. John Cox, his colleague from McGill days, cautioned with tongue in cheek:

··· But I say ! You must draw the line somewhere. Remember Lamb's dreadful speculation about Lord Lamb, Prince Lamb, King Lamb and even Pope Lamb. We will allow you the O.M. in due course. But never think of Pope. ···

Ern telegraphed "Received Knighthood" to his parents in New Zealand. Martha Rutherford spread the news to family and friends.

··· I do not think the Honour will spoil him in any way, as he is too unassuming for that; but I think his wife will be more elated than he. Reflected honours after all. ··· we thought he would receive a title some day in recognition of his spark of genius. Research Work and Perseverance, without which one cannot expect to excel. We are glad and thankful that he has received the honour while young and for his own work as influence has not been brought to help him forward and its gratifying for him to receive it before revisiting the land of his birth. ···

To Arthur Eve at McGill Ern wrote:

> ... it was very unexpected and not altogether desirable, for I feel such forms of recognition are not very suitable to people like myself. However, I am, of course, pleased at this public recognition of my labours, and hope that my activity will not be lessened by this transformation.

While in Southport Ern and Mary had lunch with Arthur Eve's mother who reported:

> ··· I was so pleased to see them especially <u>him</u> ··· we had a good laugh together – she is more delighted at her title than he is. He is as nice and natural as of old.

Harry Moseley, who had used the X-ray emission from atoms to initiate a fundamental understanding of the table of elements, had recently taken a position at Oxford University. On the 7th of December 1913 he had written to Ern:

> ··· I want you to know how very much I have enjoyed the three years spent in your department. When I came my brain was full of cobwebs left by reading for examinations, and even if this time has only served as an education it has been well spent. Especially I want to thank you and Mrs Rutherford for your kindness in interesting yourselves about me, and for the debt I owe you for personally teaching me how research work ought to be done.

A mere month later he wrote again.

> Dear Sir Ernest,
>
> Please accept my heartiest congratulations on your knighthood. I know well your views on the sorrows entailed by a title in the guise of blackmail levied by servants and so forth, and I am all the more glad therefore that you have sacrificed yourself for the sake of the public reputation of science.

To Bertram Boltwood, his chemist friend in America, Ern wrote:

> ··· I shall have to go to a Levie before long to be properly knighted – velvet breeches and coat, cocked hat – a sword and buckles galore. I am now in the hands of the tailor to fit me up – damn'd expensive but highly humorous ··· .

Ern reported 12-year-old Eileen's reaction to a colleague.

··· Eileen was very pleased with the news, and was greatly excited on New Year's Day with the succession of telegrams. She is of the opinion that neither of her parents has the 'swank' and natural dignity for such decorations.

With honour came expense. Ern had to have court dress, a black silk tail coat, white silk waistcoat, knee breeches, black silk stockings, cocked hat and sword. Eileen thought he looked a very superior footman.

The first half of 1914 flashed past, a blur of work and engagements such as: opening a Royal Society discussion on the structure of the atom, presentation at court, and lecturing in North America at the National Academy of Sciences, McGill, Columbia, Yale, and Princeton. During the nostalgic visit to a freezing, snow-covered McGill, Ern ··· *"thanked God I did not have to live in Montreal permanently."*

He emphasised, in his illustrated lecture entitled 'The Detection of Atoms and Their Structure', the public perception of the inaccessibility of the atom due to its smallness:

··· If the whole population of North America were to count for some thousands of years day and night continuously, making three counts to the second, they would not any more than have arrived at the number of atoms in a cubic centimetre of gas. ···

Through photographs taken with Wilson's cloud chamber he showed how scientists were now able to follow the trail of an individual atomic nucleus.

Late in 1913 Ern, wishing to test his nuclear model of the atom, had asked Ernest Marsden to play marbles with nuclei. He found what Ern expected, that a light hydrogen nucleus struck by an alpha particle flew off at very high speed. A new avenue of research had opened.

But the forthcoming, long delayed, family visit home to New Zealand overshadowed all.

Chapter 15

THE WORLD AT WAR

1914–1919

Fortunately at the present time we had not found out a method of so dealing with these forces, and personally I am very hopeful we should not discover it until man was living at peace with his neighbour.

Sir Ernest Rutherford,

On the prospect of a nuclear bomb, 1916

BA Meeting – Australia 1914

One aim of the British Association for the Advancement of Science (BA) was to communicate the progress of science to the general public. Occasionally they travelled further afield to the British Empire – to Canada in 1884, 1897 and 1909 and to South Africa in 1905. Australia won selection for the 1914 meeting. Five years of planning went into this important antipodean event. A Federal Council formed under the Prime Minister. Events were scheduled for five states so each formed a committee under the State Governor. Each state gave free rail travel and the Federal Government granted sufficient money to cover not less than 150 first-class shipping passages for the official representatives who were to include selected Dominion and foreign scientists. Around 300 overseas scientists attended and 5000 Australians joined the BA as local members thus making the Australian meeting the most successful BA gathering ever.

The New Zealand government extended an invitation for 25 of the visitors to go on to New Zealand for meetings in Wellington, Christchurch and Dunedin. Ernest Rutherford served on the British Committee which allocated funds to the travelling scientists, the bulk of whom came out on three ships.

One young physicist, Henry Tizard, received the chance of a lifetime when, three days before sailing, he was invited to join the party as a last minute substitute. He joined Ern, May, Eileen and many doyens of the scientific elite on the S.S. *Euripides*. Henry Tizard fondly remembers the friendship and encouragement extended by Ern. Also he could later boast how he had shared in at least one of Rutherford's triumphs – they won the deck tennis doubles. Ern:

> ⋯ *stood at the back of the court where he was worth a good many points to the side by keeping up a running commentary on the looks and behaviour of the opponents.*

For some the voyage was not a complete holiday. One zoologist collected plankton specimens while a Manchester physicist measured the force of gravity over the oceans. Ern gave a lecture on radium, dwelling on its rarity, its value and the danger of keeping it for any length of time near one's skin. "*Now in order that you shall all know what radium bromide looks like I will hand round this glass tube.*" Gingerly it passed rapidly from hand to hand returning safely to Ern. Henry Tizard notice that there appeared to be rather a lot for such a valuable substance. Ern later confessed the tube contained a mixture of table salt and sand.

The weather remained good until Cape Town and rough thereafter. Three days before docking in Australia, the ship's wireless picked up the news that one of the greatest extravaganzas the world has ever known had opened in Europe with a cast of millions, mostly with walk-on, limp-off parts. The name was to change with time, being known progressively as the war, the Great War and the First World War. Confusion reigned on board but when the ship docked in Adelaide the British Association resolved to acquiesce with any changes requested by the Australian Prime Minister who asked for none except a curtailment of some of the more elaborate social functions. Sir Ernest and Lady Rutherford contributed £10 to Australia's Patriotic Fund.

Three overnight trains bore the visitors to Melbourne. They arrived cold and stiff to be greeted by fleets of cars to whisk them to their private billets. The *Melbourne Argus* reporter described the scene and the scientists.

> *The different varieties of the man of science make rather an interesting study. Some of the visitors are spruce, well groomed types of Englishmen,*

who seem to bear the mark "professional man" written all over them. Others, again, conform more nearly to the scientist of fiction, with his detached, absent-minded manner, his wide rimmed spectacles, his strange paraphernalia, and his untidy brown paper parcels. But it mattered not what particular type was represented, the first eager questions were not of science but of war.····

The visitors regrouped that afternoon at Melbourne University. A display of boomerang throwing attracted many. Before long

··· the spirit of research had been roused in the visitors, and in a little while much of the genius of the English-speaking world was in danger of annihilation. Elderly gentlemen who had lost the slimness of youth twisted themselves into strange attitudes of projection, and trotted cheerfully after the bits of stick that refused to return. At first lack of experience made their efforts innocuous but the menace increased with practice, and some of their colleagues had to skip with unwanted activity to avoid bruised shins ····.

Vice-Regal, Mayoral and state receptions followed. Melbourne University conferred honorary degrees on several of the distinguished visitors. Ern received a D.Sc. and a particularly warm reception as an antipodean. But first he had to endure a recitation of his various degrees and awards and praise upon the work which had made his name so famous. As the Argus reported:

··· several of the visitors seemed extremely uncomfortable as they stood facing the audience while their praises were being sung in so embarrassing a fashion, and without exception they all looked exceedingly relieved when the strain was over. ···

During the weekend Ern and over 100 members of the British Association toured the gold mining area of Bendigo. They were feted at every possible occasion including at an oversubscribed conversazione in the Town Hall on the Saturday night during which Ern gave a lecturette on 'Radium'. He pointed out to the audience that radium was nearly two hundred thousand times more expensive than gold, that Australia had begun mining radium within the last year at Radium Hill, near Broken Hill, with an annual production of about a gramme of radium and he *··· handed around several glass tubes in order to illustrate his remarks.* [Did these contain salt and sand? They wouldn't have contained radium.]

He also mentioned the applications of radium in hospitals and pointed out the large amounts of energy stored in radium.

> ⋯ *the amount of energy was somewhere about three million times as great as they could obtain from any chemical explosive, such as gunpowder, etc. They had thus the possibility of obtaining this very much larger amount of energy than they had now. This substance could go on exploding for months at a time. The lecturer pointed out the enormous possibilities of this substance in time of war. ⋯*

This is how the *Bendigo Advertiser* reported Ern's talk during the early days of a major war. The reporter never made a linkage to the current knowledge stated earlier in Ern's talk whereby it would take 2000 years, the half-life of radium, to extract half of this available energy.

With the start of a new week the overseas guests returned to Melbourne for the main meetings of the conference.

When the news came through that the New Zealand portion of the Science Congress had been abandoned because of the war, Ern was fighting a battle of his own. A newspaper reported from the common man's viewpoint of science:

> ⋯ *The physics section and the chemical sections held a joint discussion – and a very technical discussion it was – upon 'The Structure of Atoms and Molecules'. This was opened by Sir E Rutherford, the expert on radium, and contributed to by Professor Armstrong, Professor Hicks, Professor Pope, and Professor Masson. During the afternoon, Professor Hicks and others read physical papers of extreme erudition upon several subjects.*

Ern espoused the nuclear model of the atom based on sound experimentation. Others were not completely convinced, a not surprising reaction in a field being revolutionized so quickly. The placement of the electrons around the nucleus still formed a stumbling block.

Part of the answer lay uncovered in the recent work of Ern's young colleague, Harry Moseley, who was present to reiterate his own brilliant discovery. The frequency of X-rays emitted by an element was related in a simple way to N, an integer which increased by one unit in passing from element to element along the periodic table of elements – the table that governed all of chemistry. Moseley had shown that what is important is not the mass of the atom but this atomic number, later to be recognised as the number of electrons around the atom. Gaps in his sequence showed there were four elements yet to be discovered between aluminium and gold.

The stability of the electron orbit in the Rutherford/Bohr atom caused concern. An electron travelling in a circular orbit would have constant speed but, because its direction of travel changed continuously to form the circular orbit, it perforce had acceleration. One of the cornerstones of electromagnetism stated that an accelerating electrical charge radiates energy. (For example, this happens in a radio aerial. The electrons oscillating back and forth along the aerial wire radiate the radio wave). Hence atoms with orbiting electrons should not be stable because the electrons should radiate energy and hence spiral into the nucleus. Clearly though, atoms were stable because Earth had been around for thousands of millions of years. Ern, the initiator of the concept of the nuclear atom, remained adamant in his final summing up.

> ⋯ *The difficulty of stability is common to all theories of the atom; but what it points to is that there is something wrong with the theory of electromagnetic radiation – not of the atom.*

Discussion about the atom continued on the train to Sydney. In his usual breezy way Ern stated, according to E S Grew's 1937 reminiscence, that ⋯ *we should spend the next twenty years not in splitting the atom, but the electron.* In Sydney the specialist sections reconvened. Ern spoke on the origin and nature of gamma-rays from radium. As a Melbourne reporter had stated about the mathematics and physics section meetings ⋯ *Their papers were of less human interest.* ⋯ *They may be mentioned and then forgotten by all but the specialist.* But one of the features of the British Association was its endeavours to bring science to the public. At each conference they held Evening Discourses and a public lecture, which until 1911 had been called the 'Lecture to the Operative Classes'. Ern had been selected for one of the former, by tradition a formal dress affair.

> *Seldom has the Lyceum Theatre contained such a large audience as that which assembled last evening to hear Sir Ernest Rutherford lecture on "Atoms and Electrons". The lecturer in the space of 20 years has risen from a humble but clever New Zealand university student to a foremost position in the study of radio activity.*

The retiring President of the BA, Sir Oliver Lodge, took the chair introducing Ern as:

> ⋯ *one of those men to whom they owed many discoveries and to whom they were going to owe more. (Applause.) He had struck fertile ground, and it was certain to yield him a rich harvest.*

Another reporter recorded Ern's lecturing style:

> *Though a great scientist, Professor Rutherford is hardly an ideal lecturer, at any rate to a popular audience. He is fond of using specialized terms that convey nothing to the majority of his hearers, while he frequently*

drops his voice as though soliloquising in front of the screen. Nevertheless,
he told a marvellous tale.

As part of that tale Ern stated:

> *There is an enormous amount of work to be done. It is quite possible*
> *that if a BA meeting is to be held here a hundred years hence, a suitable*
> *subject for a lecture may be the structure of the nucleus of the atom.*

Part of Sydney's formal proceedings were disrupted when the Chancellor of
Sydney University dropped dead, causing the abandonment of their honorary
degree ceremony.

The Gentlemen of Science

The three-week-old war dominated the news. The German army had
overrun Belgium, Australia was mobilizing and New Zealand troops were
invading German occupied Samoa, the first allied occupation of German
territory of the War. The three ships which had brought the scientists to Australia
had been requisitioned as troop carriers. Rather than risk being stranded twenty-
six of the overseas delegation had dashed back to Adelaide where a ship was
about to depart for England. Ern led the much diminished advance party over
to New Zealand. The remaining 200 scientists travelled on to Brisbane to
complete the conference before returning to England on a mail steamer, via
the Suez Canal. They narrowly missed encountering the German cruiser *Emden*
and during the stopover at Bombay most of the Lascar crew deserted. Harry
Moseley learned semaphore on board and on arriving back in England joined
the army as a signals officer.

But what of the German members of the British Association? A Melbourne
reporter had diplomatically noted:

> *There are several foreign gentlemen accompanying the association,*
> *and they still remain as honoured members of it – for science preserves*
> *universal neutrality -. ···*

The Germans had attended the Governor General's reception, and at Melbourne
University's Honorary Degree ceremony Professor Johannes Walther, the
distinguished German geologist, had received a reception above all others:

> *A perfect storm of applause greeted him as he came forward to take*
> *his degree, and it was renewed when Professor Masson referred to him*
> *as a "worthy son of the great nation which has done so much to add to*

*the sum of human knowledge." Truly science knows not distinction
between belligerent and belligerent!*

The *Sydney Morning Herald* continued the theme in an editorial devoted to the
B.A.:

··· *But we shall remember that it is the scientists alone who can have
turned the dream of the brotherhood of men into a reality. Their work
will remain when the war is over, and they will be ready to unite again
the best minds of every nation in the same distinguished service.*

Two popular lectures were given in Brisbane. After the one on Wireless
Telegraphy, Sir Oliver Lodge, the chairman and an early researcher in the field,
paid tribute to Hertz and other German pioneers of wireless telegraphy. *"That
we should be in conflict with a nation that produced such men is an abominable
wickedness."*

The BA lent money to the German scientists who could not draw on their
own banks because of the war. However scientific immunity carries only so
much weight. Sir Oliver Lodge believed at least one German, an elderly
geographer from Munich and reputedly a friend of the Kaiser's, was effectively
spying by drawing the Australian harbours the group passed through.

On return to England the Germans were interned.

Visit to New Zealand 1914

May Rutherford had planned for this visit for years, with Ern's family and
her family but in particular with her youngest brother Charlie Newton. Now,
however, as a doctor and Captain in charge of forty men, Charlie was off to
war. May and Eileen advanced their plans to reach New Zealand before he left.
Arriving in Wellington, May received a telegram from Charlie in Christchurch
saying that he was on his way north so she waited there for him. They had
barely an hour together before Charlie left for camp. Ten days later he sailed
from New Zealand to play his part in the war to end all wars. May and Eileen
went on to Christchurch to stay with her mother, Mary Newton, and to await
Ern's arrival.

H G Wells' latest futuristic novel *The World Set Free*, predated the war. It
was written in 1913, published in 1914 and dedicated to Frederick Soddy's
book *Interpretation of Radium*. The novel postulated the invention of atomic
powered engines which had gold as the end product of the decay chain. As a
consequence energy replaced devalued gold as the basis of currency. As the

atomic engines displaced unskilled workers mass unemployment led to civil strife. When the Central European powers suddenly attacked the Slav Confederacy, France and England went to the help of the Slavs. This brutal war of the imagination and the future reached a climax when atom bombs were dropped on all major cities. These bombs were delivered by aeroplane, initiated chemically and, after the initial catastrophic explosion, continued reacting for years thereby maintaining a molten crater as the bomb slowly melted its way deeper into the Earth. H G Wells then wrote the world to its senses by unifying it into a republic in which monarchs and atomic bombs were banned.

When Ern and the advance party of scientists arrived in Auckland on the 31st of August he was interviewed by a *New Zealand Herald* reporter who had read *The World Set Free*. (So, presumably, had the earlier representative of the *Bendigo Advertiser*.) The reporter probed Ern about the likelihood of the construction of an atomic bomb.

> ⋯ *The suggestion of Mr Wells must be considered as a dream of the future, for up to the present there was not the slightest evidence obtained that they would be able to influence in any way the rate of transformation of the radioactive bodies.*

However, he did venture that if one could produce one pound of radium emanation (radon gas):

> ⋯ *this emanation would emit energy at a rate corresponding to 10,000 horse-power but it would diminish with time. With a sufficient amount of this material it would not appear altogether impossible to construct a machine corresponding to that which projected the heat ray described in Wells' 'War of the Worlds'.*

The Mayor of Auckland gave a civic reception during which Ern, in replying to the welcoming speech, stated:

> ⋯*I should not be regarded as a visitor to this country, because it was here that I spent the first twenty-three years of my life. I am a New Zealander first and a Britisher next.*

That night Ern caught the express train south, branching off to Waverley and brother Jim.

Three days after this reunion Ern travelled on to Wellington for his first formal engagement, a public lecture on 'The Transformation of Matter and the Structure of Atoms'. The audience half-filled the Town Hall, one proud member being Jacob Reynolds, Ern's old school teacher at Havelock. A fifteen minute civic reception preceded the meeting.

> *The Mayor, in welcoming the scientists, said that first and foremost among them they had a gentleman who was a New Zealander by birth, by education, by instinct, and by everything that was good and proper. He referred to Sir Ernest Rutherford. (Applause and cheers.)*

In his talk Ern described the structure of the atom and the nature of radioactivity: *Altogether there had been discovered some thirty new unstable elements associated with radium in Sir Ernest Rutherford's laboratory by his students or by himself. (Applause).*

Everyone present knew of radium, the new words of science entering common language the way they still do today, in this case through newspaper advertisements such as one for RADIUM brand boot polish.

Ern demonstrated the electrical detection of individual alpha particles using apparatus set up by Thomas Laby, the Professor of Physics at Victoria College, Wellington. Ern emphasised that this demonstration of counting the atoms had only been performed twice before, once in America and once in England. The critical piece of equipment, the string galvanometer, had been invented by Thomas Laby for the Cambridge Instrument Company. [When Victoria College had established a Physics Chair in 1909, Thomas Laby had been given the position. Ern had been one of the selectors. May had reported to Martha Rutherford at the time about Ern's own students. *None of the men here are in I am glad to say, as I dont think they are up to much.*] Ern concluded his talk with

> ⋯ *The structure of the atom is not fully understood, but when it is so, we will understand the properties of everything upon this Earth. (Applause.)*

Duty done, Ern was rejoined by May and Eileen for a return north to continue the reunion with his parents and siblings. The entourage travelled across the width of the North Island, visiting the geothermal areas at Rotorua and Wairakei, stopping off to see George, Ethel, Florrie, Eva and Ellen (Nell).

James and Martha, now 76 and 72-years-old respectively, still lived at Pungarehu where James ran the flax mill. The *Wanganui Chronicle* of the time reported that prospects for the New Zealand flaxmiller were not very bright and most mills were stopped. The Rutherfords' maid, Margaret Schuler, a Swiss girl who spoke no English when she started working for the Rutherfords four years earlier at age 18, recalled James as a very thoughtful man. He had taken pity on her and purchased a long handled scrubbing brush after seeing her scrub the verandah on her knees.

Ern's brothers and sisters had scattered widely. George, married with five surviving children, still ran the flax mill at Raglan, further north on the west coast near Hamilton. His son Colin had died the previous year.

Ellen's husband, Fred Chapman, farmed at Frasertown near Wairoa on the east coast north of Napier. They had six children at the time. Two sons, Fred and Cecil, hazily recall Ern's 1914 visit: of Ern showing them all the Nobel medal, going along when they were fencing way out the back of the farm, always laughing, leaving Martha, who passed it on to Nell, a spinthariscope (a radium, fluorescent screen and magnifying-glass device for showing particles ejected from decaying atoms.) According to Fred this was tossed out when Nell died but was found years later using a Geiger counter.

Alice had tragically died four years earlier, just 15 months after the birth of her third child George Ernest Elliott, the only Rutherford of his generation to be called Ernest by the family (the other two used their other name). Young Ernie was raised by James and Martha. As Martha said "*When you have raised 12 children another one is neither here nor there*".

Jim and Ern had always been close so Ern had chosen Jim's house as his base for this visit home to New Zealand. Another factor influencing this choice was that Ern was not allowed to smoke in his parents' house.

Jim had six children. Thirteen-year-old Eileen enjoyed meeting up with her New Zealand cousins and they her. She could enjoy such country pursuits as fishing for fresh water crayfish in the creek. Her 9-year-old cousin Jim had a quiet pony for riding to school. He invited Eileen to hop up behind bareback which she did, and enjoyed it until the horse threw both. Another of Jim's recollections was of his uncle giving him a half crown coin on departure.

Florance (Flo or Floss) had been married for three years to Henry Streiff who worked at clearing a bush farm for Arthur Rutherford.

Ethel had married Henry Sergel, one of her father's workmen. Their courtship illustrated the difficulties of the flax mill owner who had several attractive daughters and many single male workers. The girls had been forbidden to talk to the workers so whenever Martha or James inquired as to her whereabouts after Ethel had slipped away to see Henry, her sisters would cover for her by saying she was talking to Tom. As James had no worker called Tom he assumed all was well. For years afterwards Henry Sergel was known as Tom to many of the Rutherford family. At the time of Ern's visit Henry and Ethel farmed near Hamilton.

Eve by then had three children and her husband Leonard Bell farmed at Pohangina, near Palmerston North. On arrival there Ern walked up the path to find two little girls playing marbles, his niece Audrey and her friend from next door. He stooped and kissed them both saying *"I don't know which is my niece but I will treat them both alike."*

Arthur Rutherford, married with two children and the third on the way, was breaking in a bush farm north of Hamilton.

Wherever Ern went the papers were full of war news. New Zealand troops had already occupied German Samoa and the Expeditionary Force to serve overseas was in training. Ern and other readers of the newspapers learned of the high morale of the men undergoing selection through the example of his cousin, Corporal William Rutherford of the Canterbury Mounted Rifles. A contractor from Timaru, 32-year-old William had previously served with the 7th New Zealand Contingent during the Boer War. At his medical examination he was found to be

> ⋯ *literally painted with bullet marks.* ⋯ *He was as keen as mustard to get into the firing line again, and it afforded the examiners considerable satisfaction to be able to pass him. One of the doctors started to count the bullet marks on Rutherford's body, but there were so many of them that he gave up the task.*

William's enlistment record reports bullet marks on the right upper front and back, front left thigh, back left calf and bullet scars on his front right thigh. [He gained more at Gallipoli, died of his wounds on the 13th of July 1915 and is recorded on the Timaru War Memorial and the Lone Pine Cemetery, Turkey.]

On the 13th of October 1914 Ern arrived in Christchurch, to a civic reception and newspaper interviews. He believed in Officer Training Corps at Universities, recommended that examinations in New Zealand Universities be set by staff, encouraged all University departments to carry out original work and stated that the greatest discoveries regarding radioactivity would be made in the field of medicine.

He titled his public lecture 'The Evolution of the Elements'. [This is the one often wrongly attributed to him in 1891. His grandson, Peter Fowler, used the same title in delivering the 1971 Rutherford Centennial Lecture.] Ern gave a specialist lecture on Röntgen rays at Canterbury College and the Board of Governors asked him to address their monthly meeting. They received the same advice he had given them in 1894 and 1905, that Canterbury College needed a physics laboratory: ··· *Physics was the subject which had seen the most rapid development during the last twenty years, and the application of the discoveries made had great practical and economical value.* ··· (The Chairman had shown Ern their plans for such a building and two days later a deputation from the Board visited the Minister of Education in Wellington to seek a grant to allow construction so Ern's public utterances may have been carefully orchestrated. The Physics Laboratory opened in 1917 and perhaps owed its existence in part to the mana of Ernest Rutherford.)

Ern and his family stayed with Mrs Newton while in Christchurch. From this base Ern and May went on various excursions, for example to the new hydroelectric power-station at Lake Coleridge, while Eileen attended a school run by an old college friend of May's.

Ern, May and Eileen sailed from Auckland on the 1st of December on the S S. *Niagara*. Such a voyage was not without hazard as German raiders were known to be in the area. [On leaving Auckland early in the second world war the S.S. *Niagara* sank when it struck a mine laid by a German raider].

Colleagues at War

Returning to Manchester early in January of 1915, via North America and the U-Boat laced Atlantic ocean, the Rutherfords arrived to a changed world. The Universities were drained of their young men. Most of Ern's researchers had joined branches of the armed services which required technical ability, particularly signals and artillery; the latter because of its range finding and enemy gun location problems. Even Professor Radium, the eccentric inventor who featured in *Puck*, a weekly comic book, went to war with devices such as a large horseshoe magnet on a fishing line with which he caught a German submarine.

Ern disseminated any incoming information as to the well being of his ex-colleagues. A S Russell – wounded by shrapnel, Andrade – in pretty lively sector – *Germans spent 3 shrapnel in trying to get him alone the other day*, Moseley – now in the Dardanelles. Of the Germans, Gustave Rumelin and Heinrich Schmidt had died.

The nonsense of war was shown when the two good friends who had carried out the crucial experiments leading to the nuclear model of the atom, Ernest Marsden and Hans Geiger, found themselves on opposite sides of the same sector of the front line in France. While they were there, word had come through that Marsden had been appointed Professor of Physics at Victoria College in Wellington, New Zealand, so Geiger had written a letter to congratulate him.

Such exchanges between scientists on opposing sides were not uncommon. The letters went via mutual friends (such as Niels Bohr) in neutral countries or via the American Consulate. By such routes Ern corresponded with Hans Geiger in the German army, and Stefan Meyer in Vienna. They described their scientific work, reported who was at the front and who had been killed and talked of those young men who had been unlucky enough to have been in the wrong country at the outbreak of war and consequently interned for the duration. James Chadwick, who in 1913 had gone to the University of Berlin on an Exhibition of 1851 Scholarship, continued his experiments in radioactivity as an internee and the Vienna Academy of Sciences unhesitatingly accepted papers from another British scientist internee.

The Swedish newspaper *Svenska Dagbladet* was intrigued by the question of the effects of the war on future co-operation between the warring and the neutral nations. The newspaper sought views from many distinguished people, including Ern who replied

> ⋯ *It is at the present phase of the war very difficult to state any particular opinion on this as so much depends on the outcome of the war and its course during the later stages. Personally I hold hopes that it will not be difficult to establish personal relations with scientific colleagues soon after the war, but this conclusion could be seriously*

> *modified if some of the warring parties use fighting methods which in*
> *the general opinion of the world can be branded as a relapse into*
> *barbarism.*

This response was published verbatim on the 9th of May 1915, much to the annoyance of Ern who had carefully marked his response as private and confidential. To Svente Arrhenius in Stockholm Ern had confided, on supporting Arrhenius's act in signing a protest against the methods of war employed by Germany, ⋯ *I feel, however, that if the neutral world makes no sign of protest, the Germans will continue more and more to use promiscuous murder of non-combatants as their chief method of warfare.*

The lack of young men nearly halted scientific research at Manchester. This was compounded by other factors. Their skilled glass blower, Otto Baumbach, was German but Ern had obtained permission for him to continue his work. However, Otto would regularly burst into a tirade about what the Germans would do to the English so that in the end he too had to be interned, thus halting a promising line of research for Niels Bohr and Walter Makower when their complicated glassware apparatus caught fire and was destroyed.

Niels Bohr recalled that Ern, just before the Somme counter-offensive, quoted Napoleon on the British: *It is impossible to fight them for they are too stupid to understand when they have lost.* Those merely damaged in the fighting went off to hospital. May Rutherford's war work involved helping produce medical supplies and visiting Canadian and New Zealand (particularly Canterbury) soldiers in hospitals scattered throughout Manchester. Those well enough were taken for drives. She and Ern knew at least a month ahead that the ANZACS (Australian and New Zealand Army Corps) were to invade the Gallipoli Peninsula in Turkey, to try to command the narrow straits to the Black Sea. Probably May's brother, Charlie Newton, a medical officer with the New Zealand troops, had forewarned them. Hence too Ern was well aware of the carnage of war.

He and others worried about the misuse of trained scientists during a war and the promising Harry Moseley in particular who, on track for an F.R.S. and a Nobel Prize, served at Gallipoli as a signals officer for the British 38th Brigade. It had been suggested to Ern that Harry Moseley would be much better employed solving some scientific problem relevant to the war effort than in the fighting arm, although it was appreciated that if he were brought home ⋯ *simply for his own security, he would naturally be very much incensed.*

Ern wrote to that effect to the Director of the National Physical Laboratory and wheels were set in motion but not in time to prevent a meeting of Harry

Moseley's head and a Turkish bullet during the landings at Suvla Bay. This loss, this premature snuffing of a highly promising scientific career, affected Ern more than did any other death caused by the war. In writing Moseley's obituary for the scientific magazine *Nature* he concluded

> ··· *It is a national tragedy that our military organisation at the start was so inelastic as to be unable, with a few exceptions, to utilise the offers of services of our scientific men except as combatants in the firing line. Our regret for the untimely death of Moseley is all the more poignant because we recognise that his services would have been far more useful to his country in one of the numerous fields of scientific inquiry rendered necessary by the war than by the exposure to the chances of a Turkish bullet.*

The Gallipoli invasion was a costly disaster. The ANZACS were landed on the wrong beach and spent eight precarious months on steep hillsides overlooked by the Turks. Charlie Newton, the medical officer in charge of a hospital at Gallipoli, recorded the successful evacuation of all ANZAC troops in his diary which he posted several pages at a time to his sister May in Manchester. On arrival in Egypt via the Greek Islands, Charlie was perturbed to read his diary account in the local papers but a letter from May explained all. She had attended a formal dinner party and been seated between the editor of the *Manchester Guardian* and the Chief Censor. When the conversation had inevitably turned to the Gallipoli campaign she mentioned she had that day received the latest entries from her brother's diary telling of the evacuation. Since the news was topical, the Censor cleared the account for anonymous publication in the *Manchester Guardian* under the headlines THE ASTONISHING ANZAC EVACUATION A NEW ZEALAND OFFICER'S STORY. Amongst the final 20,000 men evacuated over two nights, the only injuries sustained were one wound from a stray bullet and three sprained ankles. Charlie's team pulled out during the second to last night, the 19th of December 1915, leaving behind a fully equipped first aid station for whoever might need it and a record, entitled 'A Turkish Patrol', ready to play on the gramophone.

As he sailed away from Gallipoli he wrote, and the *Manchester Guardian* copied,

> ··· *Few of us will ever see it again. Over 8,000 New Zealand and Australian dead lie buried there, and although the object was never gained, it has been the scene of many deeds of heroism and has made the reputation of the Colonial soldier. Suvla Bay will always be one of*

*the disasters in British history, and when one looks back on August 8
and knows that if the Suvla army had made good we should by this
time have defeated Turkey one feels a terrible disappointment and,
alas! resentment.*

Harry Moseley's wastage, as with William Rutherford and William Bragg's
son and all the others, had been in vain.

The British Admiralty's Board of Invention and Research

Various New Zealand soldiers visited the Rutherfords in Manchester while
on leave from the fighting. May confessed in a letter to New Zealand ⋯ *we
can't ask young men to come to Manchester on their very brief leaves when we are so
quiet and dull a household.* Her cousin, Colin Gordon, serving with the New
Zealand General Hospital, recorded in his diary his impressions gained on
various visits:

> *7 July 1916 ⋯ we played auction. None of them are good. Sir E at the
> close of play at 11 was just about asleep while I was feeling very fit and
> inclined to yarn all night if required.*
> *28 Sept 1917 ⋯ May and Ernest had to go to a dinner for Fisher, the
> Minister of Education but arrived home about 10 PM and so Eileen
> was left to give me supper. She is not pretty, too like May for that but
> has plenty to say. She is going in for architecture at the art school.*

Colin went to France where he was almost immediately injured in a shell
blast. Sent to hospital in Dundee, he received various invitations from people
in the area who had been alerted to his presence by May Rutherford. He accepted
one invitation from a family who owned a jute mill. He confided in his diary:
*… I have now decided to stay a whole week here and not go to Manchester, as it
would be very dull and I dislike the place.*

During his first visit to Manchester, Colin was taken by Ern on a visit to
the Physics Department to see the gigantic coil, which would throw a 13-inch
spark from 170,000 volts, used to power a new X-ray tube. ⋯ *He has been
busy for some months on Govt experimental work connected with submarines which
of course we couldn't see.* ⋯

In May of 1915, within days of the start of the Gallipoli landings, the chief
architect of the disaster, the First Lord of the Admiralty (Winston Churchill),
had been fired and replaced by Arthur Balfour. The brother-in-law of Lord
Rayleigh, he was no stranger to science, being a Fellow of the Royal Society

and known to have occasionally helped Lord Rayleigh record his experiments. The new First Lord of the Admiralty established a Board of Invention and Research (BIR) *"to initiate, investigate, and advise generally upon proposals in respect to the application of science and engineering to naval warfare."* The central committee of the BIR consisted of four people: the Admiral of the Fleet (Lord Fisher), a physicist (Professor J J Thomson), an engineer (Sir Charles Parsons) and a chemist who was a coal expert (Dr Beilby).

Their scientific advisory panel consisted of eleven noted scientists and engineers, of whom all were Fellows of the Royal Society, and included Professors Bragg, Crookes, Rutherford and Strutt (Lord Rayleigh's son). *The Times* published the names of those serving on the panel together with its office address. They were charged with sifting through the enormous number of suggestions to aid the war effort, sent in by all manner of people including serving officers, inventors and lunatics. The panel divided their work into six sections of which Ern served in the second, for which he was secretary, that for

> ... *Submarines, mines, searchlights, wireless telegraphy and general electrical, electro-magnetic, optical and acoustical subjects.*

The submarine presented one of the war's greatest threats to Britain, an island nation dependent on shipping for many of its supplies. A submarine was extremely hard to see when surfaced and nearly undetectable when submerged.

The British Navy maintained an Experimental Station at Hawkcraig on the Firth of Forth where Captain Ryan and his team had developed hydrophones for listening underwater. In calm waters these could detect the sounds from a moving capital ship at ten miles or a submerged submarine at one mile. He had suggested hydrophones be used by a stationary ship to detect the presence of submarines, and be combined with mines which could be electrically fired from the listening station. He had already fitted pairs of hydrophones to submarines (one on each side of the hull) to allow the approximate bearing to another ship to be determined.

Captain Ryan's work was of a short term, practical nature. No accurate measurements were involved in comparing devices and very little science was invoked. (Captain Ryan had never heard of Sir Ernest Rutherford.)

An understanding of the propagation and detection of sound in sea water was needed but little experimental work had been carried out since the first accurate measurement of the speed of sound in a freshwater lake back in 1826. The BIR approached Lord Rayleigh, the foremost acoustical scientist, and Professor Sir Horace Lamb, a mathematician specializing in wave propagation, for assistance on the theoretical side. Ern carried out measurements to determine the relative merits of various devices proposed as underwater sound receivers, using a small water-filled tank in the basement of his laboratory. For this he had the assistance of Harold Gerrard of the electrical engineering department, and Albert Wood who had worked on atomic physics with Ern at Manchester before moving to a position at Liverpool University. In July of 1915, after being released from being rated as indispensable, Albert Wood had approached Ern to sign the papers needed for Albert to join the Royal Flying Corps. Ern suggested that his talents might more usefully be employed in research for the Navy than in learning to fly. In agreeing, Albert Wood initiated a distinguished career in Naval Science that was to span nearly fifty years and two world wars.

The torpedoing of a troopship in the Aegean sea, with the loss of 1,000 lives, brought home to members of the Section II Committee the urgency of their work. In September of 1915, Professor Sir Ernest Rutherford visited Hawkcraig to observe Commander Ryan's work and in particular to listen to the sounds produced by the hydrophone from various types of ships, including a submarine. In his official report of the visit Ern pressed for support for Commander Ryan's work recommending the latter be given the finances to allow for more than the present £1 expenditure on any one experiment, a submarine for tests and the services of two or three physicists. He wrote a fuller, eleven page, 'Report on Methods of Collection of Sound from Water and the Direction of Sound' for the BIR, dated September 30th 1915. It came under the Official Secrets Act.

Before concluding that ⋯ *The majority of the inventions sent to the BIR. dealing with the problem of sound detection were of no practical value.* ⋯ he summarized what was known of the physics of sound propagating in water, previous work of using sound to signal to submarines, the devices suggested by many people for detecting sound and the tests carried out to date on those devices, the methods of determining the direction of sound and the possibility of detecting submarines by reflected sound.

When the magnificent *Titanic* had sunk after striking an iceberg during her maiden voyage in 1912, Lewis Richardson had suggested using echoes of underwater sound waves to detect submerged objects such as icebergs or wrecks. Just prior to the war Reginald Fessenden had used this method to detect a large iceberg two miles away. Ern estimated that with this equipment a submarine, broadside on and in deep water, could be detected at a distance of a quarter of a mile. ⋯ *It appears to me that it would be more practical at such short ranges to detect the submarine by its own characteristic sounds when in motion.* However he did point well into the future of Doppler sonar in reporting that ⋯ *Sir Charles Parsons has suggested that there might be a change of note in the*

SECRET.

This paper is the property of
H.M. Government and is subject to the
provisions of the Official Secrets Act.

BOARD OF INVENTION AND RESEARCH,
Victory House,
Cockspur Street, S.W.

REPORT ON METHODS OF COLLECTION OF SOUND FROM WATER AND THE DETERMINATION OF THE DIRECTION OF SOUND

BY

PROFESSOR SIR ERNEST RUTHERFORD, F.R.S.,
MANCHESTER UNIVERSITY.

September 30th, 1915.

The problem of collection of sound from water has
received very inadequate attention in scientific journals,

---

sound returned by a submarine. ⋯ And he briefly mentioned the work of Professor King of McGill University who, at his own initiative and expense, had commenced experiments to rapidly determine the depth of water using the echo method. All in all, the technology was not then adequate to use sound echoes as a practical method of detecting submarines. Hence Ern recommended that

> ⋯ *it is of great importance that the Committee should arrange promptly for investigations along the following lines:*
>
> *(1) Improvements in the existing methods and apparatus for the detection of submarine sound.*
>
> *(2) A comparison under various conditions on a practical scale of the relative advantages and disadvantages of the different methods of collection of sound.*
>
> *(3) Examination of the best methods of transmitting external sounds in water to observing tanks fixed inside a ship.*

(4) *Methods of reducing sound disturbances due to motion of ship, engines, &c., to a minimum.*

(5) *Effect of motion of a ship on the range of detection of submarines, &c.*

(6) *Practical methods for determining the direction of ships by the sound transmitted through water.*

(7) *Investigation of the nature of vibrations emitted by submarines.*

Once again he emphasised that such work required an experimental ship and station staffed by trained personnel. Hence in November Wood, Gerrard and F W Pye (a mechanic from Liverpool University) went to Hawkcraig. From then on Ern spent most of his time on underwater sound work, carrying out experiments in the tank at Manchester while often spending a few days carrying out trials at Hawkcraig. His health, and in particular his rheumatic knee, regularly suffered accordingly.

Early experiments showed that natural resonances of the hydrophone diaphragms and microphones prevented a reliable frequency analysis of the sounds emitted by a submarine propeller. Sir Richard Paget, an assistant secretary to the BIR and an accomplished musician, suggested the direct approach. Sir Richard and a sailor rowed out in a small boat and, while a submarine circled round, Sir Richard ⋯ *leaned over the side of the boat, with a sailor sitting on his legs, put his head under the water, came up, tapped his head and ran up the scale to the required note, which the sailor duly wrote down.* (Sir Richard had a skull note of G sharp.)

By January 20th 1916 the work was sufficiently advanced for Ern to write another secret 'Report on Detection of Enemy Submarines by Acoustical Methods'. Echo location was not mentioned at all and methods using light, heat and electromagnetic influence were all quickly discounted:

> ⋯ *Of these, the only method which has shown itself capable of detecting submarines at ranges of more than 100 to 200 feet is that of detection by the sound emitted by a submarine when in motion.*

To determine direction, experiments had been carried out using two distinct methods – a hydrophone on either side of the ship or a single, rotatable, trumpet-like receiver.

Other conclusions were that the most favourable vessel to hunt submarines was another submerged submarine, and that the skills required by the listeners meant they should be recruited from amongst those with a good ear for music, for example piano tuners and blind musicians. (Three of

The Physics Board visits the Royal Navy's Mining School, Portsmouth, 27 June 1921. Three Nobel Prize winners are seated in the middle (Ern, J J Thompson and W H Bragg). Henry Tizard, Ern's deck tennis partner of 1914 and to be a key scientific adviser during the Second World War, is seated right. The visit included a trip by destroyer to the large underwater explosion range.
(pu, A B Wood, courtesy Journal of the Royal Naval Scientific Service)

1925 visit to Nelson. Standing l to r: W Rout, T Field, Professor T Easterfield (his house), H Duncan, Fred Gibbs (Nelson College classmate), Bill Rutherford (nephew). Sitting l to r : Miss B Easterfield, Ern, Mrs Easterfield, Ernest Marsden (Assistant Director of Education). (Davis, 699, Cawthron Institute)

Eileen Rutherford and Ralph Fowler.
(pu, Rutherford Family)

May, Ern, Rosa Oliphant, Niels and Margrethe Bohr, 1930.
(Mark Oliphant, Rutherford Family)

Grandpapa with Peter, his first grandson.
(May Rutherford, Rutherford Family)

Ern arranging his chair for the group photograph 1 Aug 1924, on board ship enroute to the BAAS in Toronto.
(pu, BAAS archives, 448/68 Bodleian Library, OU)

Royal Institution Lecture 1934, the first public demonstration of splitting the atom using a particle accelerator. Mark Oliphant is assisting in front of Ern. May is sitting front left. *(pu, Mark Oliphant)*

*In 1934 the Nelson Fruitgrowers Association presented Lord Rutherford
with the millionth case of apples exported that season. This may be from
another occasion.* (Kingsford collection, Kg 1/4 381, Nelson Provincial Museum)

*Ern and Sir Josiah Stamp watch Patrick Fowler naming engine S5665. Note
the model train under the nameplate, Patrick's souvenir of the occasion.*
(pu, Rutherford Family)

the latter had already been utilized from a list of 86 supplied by the Royal College for the Blind.)

An even more unusual group of recruits were the sealions of Hengler's Circus. Amongst the enormous number of schemes proposed to the BIR to aid the war effort, and passed on to the Section II Committee for investigation, was one that sealions might be trained to hunt submarines instead of fish. The circus trainer carried out some tests on this possibility which Albert Wood reported on but the final evaluation by high-ranking naval officers concluded with the succinct remark ⋯ *It is recommended that these animals should now be allowed to return to their legitimate business.*

Other unusual methods received trials. Little canvas sacks and hammers were issued to picket boats so that the sack could be secured over a periscope as it rose out of the water. The baffled U-boat commander was then expected to raise his auxiliary periscope whereupon both would be smashed with the hammer. One citizen patented a towed device which, by looking like a submarine and by periodically releasing food, was to train seagulls to congregate above all submarines. In the zanier realm not tested was a proposal to effervesce submarines to the surface with a fizzy laxative.

The scientific establishment at Hawkcraig grew with the appointment of a resident director of research, Professor W H Bragg F.R.S., who had shared the 1915 Nobel Prize with his son for their work on the diffraction of X-rays by crystals.

The scientists at the research station published regular but secret reports on their tests. That covering March 1916 included:- *Relative Efficiency of Hervey-Gardner and Sir E Rutherford's Diaphragms with Trinity House Bell as Sounder* ⋯ *Another form of direction finder, also designed by Sir E Rutherford, has been tested* ⋯ *A towing model designed by Sir E Rutherford was tested.*

The continual association of his name with the directional hydrophone he had developed embarrassed Ern who, after one report, wrote to Bragg ⋯ *I am sorry that the matter has been raised at all as I am not looking for any personal credit but am only too delighted to have developed a definite instrument.* By August 1916 Bragg could report to Ern ⋯ *apparatus to be attached to your diaphragms on board the battleships.*

On the 2nd of August 1916 the Patent Office received, from Bragg and Rutherford, application number 10,887/16 entitled 'Improvements in Apparatus for Detecting the Direction of Sound in Water'. [This is Ern's only patent application. It was accepted in 1919 as number 125,446.]

Relations between the scientists at Hawkcraig and Captain Ryan became increasingly strained. Ern commiserated with Bragg ⋯ *I have long come to the*

AMENDED SPECIFICATION.

Reprinted as amended in accordance with the decision of the Law Officer, dated the
30th day of July, 1920.

PATENT SPECIFICATION

Application Date: Aug. 2, 1916.   No. 10,887 / 16.

Complete Left: Mar. 1, 1917.

Complete Accepted : Apr. 24, 1919.

125,446

PROVISIONAL SPECIFICATION.

Improvements in Apparatus for Detecting the Direction of Sound in Water.

We, WILLIAM HENRY BRAGG, M.A., D.Sc., F.R.S., Resident Director of Research, Hawkcraig Experimental Station, Aberdour, Fife, and Sir
5 ERNEST RUTHERFORD, M.A., D.Sc., F.R.S., Professor, 17, Wilmslow Road, Withington, Manchester, do hereby declare the nature of this invention to be as follows:—

10 This invention relates to improvements in apparatus for detecting the direction of sound in water.

It has already been shown by Morris and Sykes that the direction of the source
15 of a sound in water may be found by the use of a single plate in water, suspended from and pivotted to a heavier mass—the relative movements of the plate and mass being recorded by a point contact micro-
20 phone (Patent No. 15,320/15).

It has also been shown by the same inventors that the direction of sound in water may be found by the use of similar diaphragms, braced together and sup-
25 ported within a massive ring, as described in Patent No. 6700/16.

We have found that satisfactory results may be obtained by the use of a single diaphragm, clamped within a massive
30 ring and having the microphone enclosed within a cylindrical chamber attached to

or forming part of the diaphragm, and placed at its centre. One terminal of the microphone is preferably earthed to the ring, the other may be led from the micro- 35 phone chamber into the iron tube herein-after described by means of any suitable form of water-tight joint, either on the microphone chamber, or preferably at the end of a thin metal tube forming an 40 extension of the microphone chamber, and extending beyond the edge of the diaphragm.

This use of a single diaphragm with directly attached microphone has the 45 advantage of simplicity and of requiring the minimum of adjustment.

The ring—which is preferably stream-lined in cross section—is connected to a long iron tube by a suspension of stout 50 rubber strip or tubing, so as to avoid the transmission of sounds from the tube to the microphone.

When the apparatus is intended for use on board ship, the tube is preferably 55 hung on gymbals in which it is free to revolve by means of a leather to metal bearing.

Dated the 18th day of July, 1916.

W. H. BRAGG,   60
E. RUTHERFORD.

[*Price 1/-*]

conclusion the Navy is the closest "trade union" in the world. Sir Richard Paget sent Bragg a letter which had made him ⋯ *feel as if we were playing in Gilbert and Sullivan opera instead of trying to win a war.*

Once the directional hydrophones were in mass production it was thought best if the scientists shifted to where they could be in close touch with men using the device to attempt to locate submarines. Parkestone Quay at Harwich, the home port of the destroyers and submarines deployed in the North Sea, became an Admiralty Experimental Station from the start of 1917.

The British scientists liaised closely with their French counterparts. Professor le Duc de Broglie, the man whose name will always be associated with the waves assigned to matter, had visited Hawkcraig on three occasions during 1916, the same year that Paul Langevin had produced 100 kHz sound vibrations in water by electrically stressing mica.

When word was also brought to England that Paul Langevin had also been experimenting with generating high frequency sound waves using the piezo-electric effect in quartz crystals, Ern initiated British research into the sound echo method of detecting submarines and carried out relevant experiments in his water tank. Albert Wood later recalled Professor Sir Ernest Rutherford hopefully, if not very optimistically, scratching small pieces of quartz crystals connected to a telephone headpiece as early as 1915. By November of 1916 Ern could report to Bragg:

> ⋯ *We have now pretty well cleaned up a study of diaphragms.* ⋯ *The quartz piezo-electrique works like a charm.* ⋯ *gives a sound that anyone could hear at once in a moderately quiet room. It is astonishing how sensitive the ear is, for it is able to detect a movement of the molecules of about 1/1000th of a diameter of a molecule.*

(When William Bragg became the Scientific Advisor to the Admiralty in 1917 Arthur Eve succeeded him as Director of the Admiralty Experimental Station at Harwich. When Eve and others advocated the view that Ern had originated the method of utilizing the piezo-electric method for detecting submarines whereas Paul Langevin claimed priority, Ern had stated *"If Langevin says the idea was his, then the idea was Langevin's."*)

Dr Robert Boyle of Canada, who had worked with Ern at Manchester on radium emanation, was appointed to lead the sound echo team at the Research Station. The work was top secret and quartz was not to be mentioned. Robert Boyle and the others referred to 'Anti-Submarine Division -ics' (the 'ics' meaning 'pertaining to' as in words such as physics, statics, electronics) thus giving birth to the acronym 'ASDIC'. [This method of detecting submarines only became feasible following the availability of good French electronic valves to amplify the weak signals produced by the hydrophone. The system had advanced beyond the experimental stage and was being developed to be fitted to ships when the war ended.]

Transferring Knowledge to the Americans

The United States of America belatedly entered the war on the Allies' side in April of 1917. Within a month a joint Franco-British Commission was organized to acquaint the Americans with all discoveries and developments in anti-submarine work in order to prevent overlap and waste of effort. The British delegation consisted of Ern and a naval officer. On May 13th he made additions to his will leaving his medals to his wife to hand over ultimately to Eileen, his radium standard to Manchester University and his books to the Physics Department library. He detailed where his financial papers and life insurance policies, etc., were placed, recommended his estate should have one trustee in New Zealand if his wife decided to live there and named a temporary guardian for Eileen until Charlie Newton, her guardian but then on active service, could make definite arrangements, although Ern did specify Eileen should remain in England for her education.

With his personal affairs in order, Ern travelled to Paris to join Commander Bridge and the five members of the French delegation. There he addressed the French Ministry of Inventions on submarine matters, observed various experiments concerned with the French effort in that field and caught up with old friends, a taxi load of whom turned up to take him to lunch on his first full day in Paris. They included the physical chemist, Jean Perrin, an officer in the Engineers, a member of the French Board of Invention and Research and later to receive the 1926 Nobel Prize for physics; Marie Curie, the only holder of two Nobel Prizes but now expending her war effort in the radiology field; Paul Langevin, an old friend from Cambridge days and soon to make practical the echo method of detecting submarines; and Andre Debierne, the discoverer of the radioactive element actinium.

Ern had telegraphed news of his safe arrival in Paris to May but wrote to her that she would not hear from him for ten days or so as he was going to a secret destination. On safe arrival in America he started a steady stream of letters which kept her fully informed throughout his month's visit. Continually complaining of the heat and the difficulty in keeping cool, he told her of meeting senior government officials (such as the Secretary of War), of receiving an honorary degree from Yale and of visiting submarine establishments, Thomas

Edison's lab (⋯ *the old man* ⋯ *was as enthusiastic as a school boy over his ideas* ⋯), radio installations, McGill University, the Bureau of Standards, civil-war sites and the music hall. ⋯ *My constitution stands well the strain of so many lunches and dinners.* The main object of the visit, knowledge transfer, took place in many meetings. The Americans took up the British system of submarine detection, essentially two tubes used as a pair of rotatable underwater ears, and by August their improved version was being fitted on all anti-submarine vessels. The French system, which used a faceted blister on a ship to focus sound, was not directionally sensitive and was not taken up.

Ern expressed to May his satisfaction with the visit.

> ⋯ *I think we shall do good work here and I am very glad I decided to come over.* ⋯ *I think the mission is regarded as the best informed one that has come to USA. We have certainly had a fine series of meetings and told all we know.*

Ern's counterpart, the chairman of the Anti-Submarine Committee of the National Research Council, was Robert Millikan who was to be awarded the 1923 Nobel Prize in physics for using an oil-drop method to measure the charge on the electron.

The knowledge transfer covered many facets of underwater sound, ship noise, and devices for detecting sound and its direction. Ern reported to the BIR that the exchange was of great value even if one-sided. American work was a year to eighteen months behind that of England and France even though, prior to the joint conferences, many Americans were of the opinion they were already ahead.

The Franco-British mission helped in another way. Earlier American efforts in submarine detection had been hampered by the exclusion of academic physicists from the development, partly because Thomas Edison, a practical man, was the main advisor and partly because their presence would complicate the patent situation. Within a week of the arrival of the Allied mission the navy was being advised, in a report entitled 'Recommendations of the National Research Council as to the Organization of Research for the Detection of Submarines', to establish another experimental station at its New London submarine base and to bring in *ten of the* ⋯ *most competent* ⋯ *scientists in the country* to develop the Allied detection devices. In support, Ern wrote a four page 'Memorandum on the Utilization of the Services of Scientific Men During the Period of the War' which was passed up to the Secretary for War. Ern opened with:

> *The experience of France and England in the present war has demonstrated the importance of proper organization and utilization of the services of trained scientific men of these countries on war problems and the serious danger of loss of efficiency here unless some selective system can be put into operation immediately with a view to the employment of such men in the most useful spheres. At the outset of the war, both in France and England, there was no proper organization to deal with the selection of men for special scientific work. ··· Moreover, through the lack of suitable discrimination, men whose services would have been invaluable in the numerous scientific avenues since opened by the war, have been lost in the trenches. This may be well illustrated by the case of Moseley, one of the most brilliant scientific men of his generation, who was killed in active service at the Dardenelles. ···*

The memorandum had no significant effect as it went against the concept of the supposedly classless society of America. Class exemption for graduates could be seen as favouring the rich.

Ern returned to England with a goat, the mascot of some American marines, sleeping under his berth. Shortly afterwards the Admiralty's Board of Invention and Research received his report and its committees went out of existence, their work taken over by the scientists employed by the Admiralty's various research establishments. Ern and others were then appointed to the Government's new Committee for Scientific and Industrial Research. He served on the local (Lancaster) Anti-Submarine Committee and travelled to Paris for the Allied congress on the echo method of detecting submarines held just weeks before the war ended.

However, the hectic war work of Professor Sir Ernest Rutherford had slackened with the demise of the BIR committees in 1917. From then on he had more time for other avenues of endeavour.

The World's First Successful Alchemist

Niels Bohr reported to Ern that the Germans and neutrals continued scientific research into X-ray diffraction and spectra. Ern could only lament ··· *It is a great pity that the work in England on this subject has stopped so completely. The neutrals and Germans seem now to be collaring that field rapidly. ··· It is a pity that it is so difficult for us now to devote our attention to the pure science problems.*

Ern had proposed his nuclear model of the atom to explain the scattering of alpha particles by thin foils. Such experiments indicated that for the heavier elements the electric charge on the tiny nucleus was half the atomic mass number times the magnitude of the charge on an electron. Because of the importance of the very lightest elements, Ern extended the work in 1913 by examining the scattering of alpha particles in gases, and showed that hydrogen had a nuclear charge equal in magnitude to that of an electron, and that the helium nucleus had twice this charge. In such experiments it was anticipated that, using the laws of conservation of momentum, a direct collision between an alpha particle (mass unit 4) and a hydrogen nucleus (mass unit 1) would produce a high speed hydrogen nucleus whose range in a gas was four times that of the impacting alpha particle.

As a consequence Ern had asked Ernest Marsden to play marbles with nuclei. This he did with great success and readily observed the long-range particles.

Late in 1914 Ernest Marsden had been appointed Professor of Physics at Victoria College in Wellington, New Zealand. (Now Victoria University of Wellington). Ern, once again a selector for the position, had obtained money from the Royal Society to supply the previous Professor, T H Laby, with radium. Laby planned to take this with him to his new position in Melbourne so Ern had written once more to the Royal Society. After praising Marsden's abilities and work he stated:

> I do not know whether there is any special fund available for the case of Marsden; but I personally think it would be a very desirable thing to help out a Colonial University like Wellington, which is in a chronic state of poverty.

Ernest Marsden had left England in January of 1915 with his work incomplete. In Wellington he had no strong source of radium immediately available to allow a continuation of the project, so he wrote up the last of his unfinished work in which he reported long range particles occurring in small numbers even when no hydrogen appeared to be present. He tentatively concluded: ⋯ *Thus there seems a strong suspicion that H particles are emitted from the radioactive atoms themselves,* ⋯. Not only the lack of facilities in the Colonial University prevented Ernest Marsden from extending this work to its fruitful conclusion. In 1916 he joined the New Zealand Army as a signals officer and returned to France where he served with distinction, winning the Military Cross and twice being mentioned in dispatches.

Hence, late in 1917, Ern picked up this loose end himself. He studied the generation of long range particles (hydrogen nuclei) by bombarding gases with alpha particles. The particles were detected by the flash of light they produced on impact with the fluorescent (zinc sulphide) screen and the flashes were observed through a microscope. Two people were needed to take measurements. As all the young men were away at the war, Ern's long suffering assistant, William Kay, helped.

The observer, usually Mr Kay, first sat in a darkened room for half an hour to adapt his eyes. Whenever the bright lights were turned on to allow the experimenter to adjust the apparatus the observer had to retire to an attached dark chamber. Because of eye fatigue, counting was limited to alternate minutes for one hour per day and a few times per week.

By December of 1917 Ern could write to Niels Bohr that

> ⋯ I am also trying to break up the atom by this method. ⋯ Regard this as private. ⋯

He had found that hydrogen nuclei were ejected at high speed when alpha particles collided with nitrogen nuclei but not with oxygen nuclei.

This is the experiment for which Ernest Rutherford is most well known. He had split the atom. No longer was the stable atom an indivisible entity, as had been assumed since atoms were postulated by the ancient Greeks. By a strange quirk of fate the element discovered in 1772 by Daniel Rutherford had been split by another Rutherford.

Furthermore, in changing nitrogen atoms into oxygen atoms, Ernest Rutherford had become the world's first successful alchemist. Although alchemy is one of the older branches of chemistry, scientists had long concluded that all alchemists, those attempting to change one element (usually cheap) into another (usually gold), were charlatans.

James Price, a Fellow of the Royal Society, had been the last practising alchemist. He claimed he could turn mercury into gold and silver. In 1783 three Fellows of the Society investigated Price who, on it being discovered that his crucible had a false bottom, drank prussic acid and fell down dead before them. Hence any claimant for atomic disintegration had to be very careful and thorough in his evidence. Ern spent the remainder of his time at Manchester amassing that evidence.

Years later, Dr Karl Compton recalled of making arrangements for a French device for locating submarines to be demonstrated to a group of British and American experts. Ern sent a message to the effect that his attendance would be delayed through the necessity of completing certain laboratory experiments in which he thought he had split the nucleus. ⋯ If this is true its ultimate importance is far greater than that of war.

The Aftermath of War

When the war finally ended in November of 1918 the pieces were picked up again. When the Admiralty disbanded the Lancashire Anti-Submarine Committee Ern implored the Admiralty to continue scientific work. He wrote:

> *War in general and Naval War in particular tends to become more and more scientific in character, and success or defeat may largely depend on the knowledge of utilisation of a single important device. We therefore consider it of first importance that our Navy, through its scientific establishments, should keep in direct touch with scientific development throughout the world and should be in a position to apply without delay this knowledge to naval requirements.*

He continued with some defence related work as did May who continued her involvement in medical supplies. One of her maids had died during the terrible June flu epidemic. May had been lucky in having been confined to bed for only a week. This terrible scourge killed 25 million people world-wide, a casualty total many times higher than that produced during four years of trench warfare.

Ernest Marsden survived the war and returned to Manchester to help Ern with his experiments before returning to New Zealand. An American, Leonard Loeb, had also stopped off at Manchester to work with Professor Rutherford. During the war he had worked with the French on spark plugs for aero engines, sound direction location and a machine-gun mount to follow the direction of the sound locator. Being tall, good looking and from an academic family, he was quickly matched to 18-year-old Eileen by May, whom Leonard regarded as formidable.

Ern hoped to get Niels Bohr as Professor of Mathematical Physics at Manchester but Bohr, who had just obtained the money to build an experimental laboratory in Copenhagen, regretfully turned him down as he had pledged to develop physical science in his homeland. In return Niels Bohr invited Ernest Rutherford to come and stay with him during the laboratory's opening festivities.

On a sadder note, contact was slowly made again with German physicists. Hans Geiger had been called up on the second day of mobilization and fought in major battles but had survived although he had been hospitalized with rheumatism. On hearing from Stefan Meyer of the dreadful conditions in Vienna following the war, Ern sent him scientific journals and repaid an old debt. Always grateful to the Austrian Academy of Science for the loan of the strong radium source, following Ramsay's purloining of the one given for their joint use, Ern initiated a payment of £270 for the source. This act of friendship to an impoverished institute was contrary to the normal confiscation of the property of a defeated adversary.

With the restructuring after the war came another shift for Ernest Rutherford, this time to head the Cavendish Laboratory in Cambridge. William Kay cut off Ern's strong badgering, with ⋯ *my wife doesn't want me to go.*

During his first lecture to the first year students Ern always admonished them that they were no longer at school:

> *You've come here to be told how to reason out things for yourselves, and if you then find you don't get through the subject, read in the library – go and teach yourself.*

To mark his departure from Manchester in the spring of 1919 some 300 first-year students, medical students and all, clubbed together and presented Professor Sir Ernest Rutherford with a gold stop-watch.

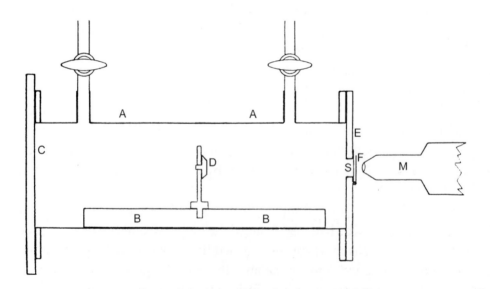

Splitting the atom. Alpha particles from source D disintegrated nitrogen atoms which emitted protons that caused flashes on the scintillation screen F.

Chapter 16

BROADENING RESEARCH

Experiment without imagination, or imagination without recourse to experiment, can accomplish little, but, for effective progress, a happy blend of these two powers is necessary. The unknown appears as a dense mist before the eyes of men. In penetrating this obscurity we cannot invoke the aid of supermen, but much depends on the combined efforts of a number of adequately trained ordinary men of scientific imagination. Each in his own special field of inquiry is enabled by the scientific method to penetrate a short distance, and his work reacts upon and influences the whole body of other workers.

Ernest Rutherford
BA Presidential Address 1923

Home Life

Eileen Rutherford, accompanied by her mother, had travelled to Cambridge to sit the entrance exam for Newnham College. During a leisurely stroll along the 'Backs', the meadows behind the colleges, they found Newnham Cottage, a derelict house in an overgrown garden on Queen's Road. They broke in. Every corner of the old house and garden charmed them, so when the Rutherfords shifted to Cambridge, May went straight to that house. It was still green and empty, as if it had been waiting for her. It was, she later recalled, like coming home.

Ern leased the house from Caius College and commissioned a builder to rebuild and redecorate it. No sooner had he done so than a builder's strike erupted. This lasted for five months so the Rutherfords were not able to move in until December of 1919, and even then they had a further month of sharing the house with the workmen. The large house had two storeys and space for a servant or two. [Today Newnham Cottage has the protection of being a listed building].

At home May ruled. Ern could smoke in his study only and no alcohol was allowed in the house. Dinner guests often met elsewhere beforehand for pre-dinner sherry. May had a great love of gardening and bringing the grounds to order became her major hobby. It also provided Ern with spasmodic exercise in cutting down, then cutting up, unwanted trees. Many a young man took the other end of the cross-cut saw to share virtuous exercise and intimate moments with him. Eventually the overgrown garden was transformed into a delightful haven of tranquility. Large shade trees sprung from manicured lawns bordered by colourful plantings. Ern regularly spent a pleasant morning reading the newspaper in this refuge which also became an extension of the house when entertaining guests.

Eileen Rutherford had her mother's build, short and full-figured. Though bubbly, full of life and attractive to many men, her health was never the best partly because of a tubercular spot on one lung. Eileen spent the three years 1920–22 at Newnham College, having not completed the entrance exam because of poor health and eyesight, where she studied unsuccessfully for the Moral Science Tripos in Logic and Philosophy. As the daughter of a rich professor she led a good life, spending the autumn of 1919 with a French family, and the spring of 1920 holidaying in Sicily and Italy with her mother.

Eileen was twenty years old when, in December of 1921, she married Ralph (pronounced the old French way as Rayf) Fowler in Trinity College Chapel. She was the first of the Rutherford and Newton grandchildren to marry.

Ralph was in her father's image – tall, solid, jovial and moustached. He was a member of Ern's regular golf foursome, a Fellow of Trinity College and an excellent mathematical physicist because he was a master at summing up all the experimental evidence before proceeding to a sound conclusion. Ralph, who was twelve years older than Eileen, had been badly wounded at Gallipoli and had lost half a lung.

Rarely have two men been so well matched as father-in-law and son-in-law. They had similar personalities and interests. Occasionally their combined uproarious laughter at a raconteur's tale switched off all conversation in Trinity's large dining hall. Ralph owned a motorcycle and sidecar but Ern taught him to drive the car so that holiday driving could be shared.

Eileen and Ralph Fowler were to produce four Rutherford grandchildren, Peter Howard, Elizabeth Rutherford, Eliot Patrick and Ruth Eileen.

Academic Life

Newnham Cottage was a pleasant walk across the backs and river from Trinity College, Ern's old college, which elected him a Fellow. He regularly dined there but now at the raised high table which looked down at the bepanelled hall, the portraits of past notables, the long rows of undergraduates and the servants in evening dress. Here Ern could enjoy a drink with his meal, a leisurely port and a smoke afterwards and good conversation throughout with a broad spectrum of academics.

Centuries of tradition were encompassed in that all-male society typified by the Oxbridge Colleges. A proposal to admit women to the same privileges as men at Cambridge drew fierce opposition from traditionalists. J J Thomson had opened his lectures to women students in 1885 and in 1897 had voted with the small minority in favour of granting titular degrees. Now he didn't think women should become full members of Cambridge University but should have their own university. And he wrote a letter to *The Times* to say so. Ern had always been raised with women in lectures and laboratories so in response he and the Professor of Chemistry wrote a letter to the editor of *The Times* (printed 8 Dec 1920) in support of the proposed change. ⋯ *we welcome the presence of women in our laboratories* ⋯ . In conclusion they stated

> ⋯ *Our friends among the opposition seem to forget that every broadening of the University interests – the abolition of the disabilities of Nonconformists and of the restrictions concerning the marriage of College Fellows, the provision of teaching and research facilities in science – has been the starting point for rapid extensions in the usefulness of the University.*
>
> *We write these few lines in the hope of inducing some, so dazzled by the glories of Cambridge that they foresee no future grander than the past, to reflect that there is a great world outside for whose needs we have to cater, and to join with the supporters of Report A in their determination to minister to those needs in even greater measure than before. We cannot afford to retain the women seen but not recognized*

> *in this University nor to leave them at the mercy of another university*
> *which is not yet planned.*

The traditionalists partly won. Woman teachers could sit on Faculty Boards and become Professors but could not be given degrees in the full sense.

Ern's suggestions for reform were not limited to academia and Britain. In January of 1920, at age 48, responding to a request from the President of the New Zealand Institute to approve the list of recently elected Fellows, including himself, he stated

> *··· I hope, when once the fellowship gets going properly, that they will*
> *appoint readily young people who have done good work and not make*
> *it a preserve of the aged and unfit like ourselves.*

As he moved into the mainstream of academic life in Britain many positions came his way. While at Manchester he had, each year, given the Commissioners for the Exhibition of 1851 a written opinion of the reports of two or three of their scholarship holders. In 1921 Ern was elected a Commissioner and went on the Board of Management from 1924. This organization had opened the world to him. He served it well for the rest of his life. During a move to curtail the scholarships, he halted the discussion with *"If it had not been for these scholarships, I would not have been."* [The Commissioners for the Exhibition of 1851 finally ceased their overseas Research Scholarships from 1989. Their Postgraduate Research Fellowships continue for British Universities with approximately one half of the awards being made to overseas candidates.]

The Cavendish Laboratory

Ern's return to Cambridge was facilitated by J J Thomson's resignation as the Cavendish Professor of Physics. JJ, at 62 years old, had elected to concentrate on being the Master of Trinity College. JJ wished to retain some space, staff, facilities and students at the Cavendish so that he could continue research work. To ensure their respective roles were clearly understood Ern sat down with him and they went over a draft agreement which both, after various alterations, deletions and additions, signed. There was no doubt that Ern was boss, the Director of the Cavendish Laboratory.

A A Robb recorded the initial impact on the laboratory by its new broom, Professor Sir Ernest Rutherford F.R.S., in a tribute sung lustily, to the popular tune 'I Love a Lassie', at the laboratory's annual dinner.

INDUCED ACTIVITY

We've a professor,
A jolly smart professor,
Who's director of the lab. in Free School Lane.
He's quite an acquisition
To the cause of erudition,
As I hope very briefly to explain'
When first he did arrive here
He made everything alive here'
For, said he, "The place will never do at all;
I'll make it nice and tidy,
And I'll hire a Cambridge lidy
Just to sweep down the cobwebs from the wall."

Chorus:

He's the successor
Of his great predecessor,
And their wondrous deeds can never be ignored:
Since they're birds of a feather,
We link them both together,
J.J. and Rutherford.

Said he, "I wonder
How in the name of thunder,
All this rubbish has accumulated here,
Since Maxwell and since Rayleigh
It has been a-gathering daily,
That's a thing that is manifest and clear."
And so he spoke to Lincoln,
And, said he, "I have been thinkin'
That the lab. is not as neat as it might be;
You understand my meaning,
That it needs a darned good cleaning,
As I think Mr. Lincoln you'll agree."

Chorus: *He's the successor, etc.*

Such is the story
Of how the laboratory
Came to look again so tidy and so bright;
The Prof. was so elated
When he saw it renovated
He at once started whistling with delight.
So great was the temptation
To begin investigation
That he started his researches there and then,
And what he's been achieving
Would be almost past believing
If he weren't quite a marvel among men!

   Chorus: *He's the successor, etc.*

What's in an atom,
The innermost substratum?
That's the problem he is working at to-day.
He lately did discover
How to shoot them down like plover,
And the poor little things can't get away.
He uses as munitions
On his hunting expeditions
Alpha particles which out of Radium spring.
It's really most surprising,
And it needed some devising,
How to shoot down an atom on the wing.

   Chorus: *He's the successor, etc.*

Those young men whose education had been curtailed by the war flocked back to the universities. Even those still serving had the time to have their education broadened and a group of about fifty young naval officers were taught elementary physics at the Cavendish. As a result the Cavendish was over-crowded and in need of extensions.

The Nucleus

Whenever appropriate, Ern praised and promoted the work of the late Harry Moseley so that Moseley was not forgotten. His native common sense saw him respond quite regularly to dubious claims, for example the one from America that nuclear disintegration had been achieved by discharging a capacitor through a very fine tungsten wire thereby raising temperatures momentarily to some 30,000 degrees Celsius. Ern pointed out that at this temperature the electrons had energies corresponding to a fall in electrical potential of only 6 volts whereas disintegration was not observed in X-ray tubes in which the electrons had been accelerated through 100,000 volts.

Ern spent his first decade at Cambridge using alpha particles to probe the structure of the nucleus, thus building on his Manchester work. Initially he used light target atoms because a given alpha particle approached much closer to such nuclei than they did to the more highly charged nuclei of the heavier atoms, such as gold.

Overall he was to conclude that the alpha particles available to him could reach the nucleus of a light element; that the diameter of a light nucleus was about 10^{-14} m (cf. the diameter of an atom is about 10^{-10} m), that the inverse square law (the force between two electrically charged objects is proportional to the inverse square of the distance between them), when applied to approaching nuclei, held down to such distances but for alpha particles it failed at about this distance [for smaller particles such as electrons it is currently known to hold down to 10^{-17} m]; that the charge on the nucleus was identified with the atomic number; that neutrons may exist in the nucleus; and that isotopes of odd atomic number emitted a proton whose energy could exceed that of the incident alpha particle (i.e. a nuclear reaction had taken place).

Though inspired by one man these were the results of the efforts of a large team. Around thirty people were working in the laboratory at any one time. Ern had inherited several useful colleagues. C T R Wilson had been at the Cavendish studying the formation of clouds when Ern had been a research student there and had, in 1911, developed the Wilson Cloud Chamber, a device for making the passage of an alpha or beta particle visible as a condensation trail. Ern had attempted similar experiments in 1906 but failed to produce trails because his apparatus was contaminated with radium. Wilson shared the 1927 Nobel Prize in physics.

Within a few months of Ern's arrival, Frederick Aston, who had been beavering away for years, finally developed the mass spectrometer in which atoms were fired into a magnetic field which separated them according to their mass and charge. With this he showed that, for example, chlorine consisted of two species of atoms (isotopes) of mass 35 and 37 times that of hydrogen and they existed in natural proportions of about 2 to 1 thus explaining the apparent average mass of an atom of chlorine of 35.5 times that of hydrogen. Such fractional atomic masses had long been a puzzle. [We now know that atoms of a given chemical element have the same number of protons – hydrogen nuclei – in the nucleus but the different isotopes of an element have different numbers of neutrons in the nucleus.] Aston was also to determine the isotopes of lead, and their proportions in minerals, thus advancing the techniques for dating minerals. Aston received the Nobel Prize in chemistry in 1922.

George Crowe, a laboratory assistant, became Ern's personal assistant, a fruitful association that continued for the rest of Ern's life. George Crowe set up apparatus and assisted 'the Prof' with his experiments. In a moment of exasperation following some foolish behaviour of a research student Ern exclaimed to Mark Oliphant *"if the laboratory contained 30 Crowes, instead of 30 research students, a great deal more research would be done."* George Crowe also supervised the large radium source and prepared the daughter radioisotopes from it. As part of the radiation safety procedures he had regular blood tests. Regrettably he disobeyed the rules by not wearing gloves when working with the sources. By 1926 the tips of his fingers had become cracked, horny and insensitive. He was withdrawn from preparing radioactive sources but the damage had been done. Many skin grafts were made and a finger amputated. [George Crowe retired from the Cavendish in 1959, sadly unheralded.]

Ern brought in an assistant, James Chadwick, who also was a superb experimentalist. He had carried out research in Ruhleben internment camp throughout the war, by making or scrounging all of his apparatus. Radioactive toothpaste, popular in Germany at the time, contained traces of thorium. Chadwick oversaw the day-to-day supervision of the laboratory and the research students.

Other men came by similarly diverse routes. Charles Ellis, a young engineering officer in the British army, had had the misfortune to be visiting Germany when war was declared. He had been taught physics in the internment camp by James Chadwick. Patrick Blackett, a young naval officer, arrived at Cambridge as an officer undergraduate, was captivated by experimental physics and left the navy. He was to receive the 1948 Nobel Prize in physics for his work on cosmic rays.

Others came from foreign lands. Three came from India. T Shimizu from Japan photographed alpha particle tracks in a cloud chamber in the hope of capturing a nitrogen disintegration on film. Arthur Compton from America carried out one of Ern's proposed experiments which had been halted by the war. He showed that the rate of decay was uninfluenced by gravity by spinning a radioactive source so that it was subject to an acceleration of 20,000 times that of gravity. Arthur Compton was awarded the Nobel Prize in 1927 for the Compton effect – a gamma ray loses energy, and therefore increases in wavelength, on being scattered by an electron. His wife's recollections of Cambridge just after the First World War were of lack of accommodation; and men at every corner with arms and legs missing.

For some years after the war the Cavendish was overcrowded. In 1924 Jack Hinton of Otago University applied to spend a year there. Ern replied

> ··· *I have been turning away a number of people who wish to work in the Laboratory, but I am prepared to put myself out to take in a New Zealander like yourself, who has not had much opportunity to get in touch with advanced work.*

Peter Kapitza

The most colourful and the most clever of all the young men attracted to Ernest Rutherford after the war was the Russian engineer, Peter Kapitza. He had lost his father, wife and both children in the epidemics following the Russian revolution and civil war. He came to Britain in 1921 to purchase scientific and technical equipment for the Russian Academy of Sciences. Impressed by Ern and the Cavendish, he asked if he could return to work there for a few months. Ern was discouraging as the laboratory was overcrowded and it would be difficult to accommodate another. Kapitza surprised Ern by asking him what accuracy he aimed for in his experiments. On receiving the reply of about 3%, Kapitza pointed out that one more added to the thirty researchers at the Cavendish would come within the experimental uncertainty. Ern accepted Peter Kapitza into the lab, beginning yet another profitable association which was to last over a decade. Peter Kapitza was to be awarded the 1978 Nobel Prize in physics for his basic inventions and discoveries in low-temperature physics.

On the day Peter Kapitza began work Ern laid down an edict – he would not allow communist propaganda in the lab. Within a year Kapitza presented Ern with a reprint of his first paper. He had inscribed on it

> *The author presenting this paper with his most kind regards, would be very happy if this work will convince Prof. E Rutherford in two things.*
>
> *1. That the α-particle has no energy after the end of his range.*

> *2. That the author came to the Cavendish Laboratory for scientifical work and not for communistical propaganda.*

Ern refused to accept this reprint but did take another, uninscribed, one.

Peter Kapitza's regular letters home to Russia yield yet another picture of Ern from the viewpoint of a younger colleague who was from a different background.

> ··· *Last Sunday he invited me for tea, and I had an opportunity to observe him in his own home. He is very pleasant and unpretentious* ··· *Generally speaking, however, he is a fierce character. When he is displeased – look out. He will not mince words, no sir. But what an amazing noddle! He has a distinctly unique mind. His instinct and intuition are colossal. I could never imagine anything like it before I have been attending his lectures and talks. He expresses himself very clearly. He is an absolutely exceptional physicist and a most original human being.*

Ern expected work and results from his students.

> ··· *You should see him giving someone a dressing down! Here are a few samples: "When on earth will you get some results?"; "How long are you going to waste your time?"; "I want your results and more results, and not your empty talk", etc.* ··· *Chadwick is head over heels in love, and Crocodile is grumbling that he is not doing much work.*

Peter Kapitza was initially rather terrified of Professor Sir Ernest Rutherford so gave him the most frightening nickname he could think of – *crocodile*. Late in life Anna Kapitza, his second wife, stated that none of the other more fanciful suggestions that Peter Kapitza encouraged as to the origin of the nickname was true which is a pity because the version he told to Peter Ritchie-Calder deserves to be.

> ··· *In Russia the crocodile is the symbol for the father of the family and is also regarded with awe and admiration because it has a stiff neck and cannot turn back. It just goes straight forward with gaping jaws – like science, like Rutherford.*

Another version, popular in the Cavendish, was that the nickname was derived from the crocodile in *Peter Pan*. The alarm clock it swallowed gave warning of the approach of this fearsome apparition – like Rutherford it could be heard before it was seen. Peter Kapitza wrote home to his mother:

*··· I am a little afraid of him. I work almost next door to his office. This
is bad since I have to be very careful with my smoking: if he could catch
you with a pipe in your mouth you're in trouble. But thank God he has
a heavy tread and I can recognize his footsteps a long way off.*

The riotous Cavendish Dinner enhanced Peter Kapitza's education. Near the
end everyone stood on their chairs, crossed arms and sang Auld Lang Syne. ···
*It was very funny to see such world famous luminaries as J J Thomson and Rutherford
standing on their chairs and singing at the top of their voices.*

Within a year of starting Kapitza suggested using a pulsed electromagnet
to produce the very high magnetic fields required to deflect alpha-particles by
significant angles ··· *The Crocodile is keen on my idea and thinks we shall succeed.
He has the devil of a nose for experiment and if he thinks that something will come of
it that is a very good omen.*

Peter Kapitza completed these experiments within a further year and then
diverged into developing even higher magnetic fields in which to study the
optical and electrical properties of materials. Ern supported Peter Kapitza
wholeheartedly ··· *the one thing which eases my work is the Crocodile's kindness
which bears comparison only with that of a father.* He obtained a very large grant
of £8000 from the Department of Scientific and Industrial Research (DSIR) to
enable Peter Kapitza to have built a large dynamo which could be short circuited
through a magnet designed to withstand the tremendous magnetic forces
generated by the resulting enormous, but short lived, currents. The age of the
large machine had arrived.

Radio Research

It is often claimed that Ern was a one-eyed scientist who never saw beyond
radioactivity and nuclear physics. Yet his reported comments often praised
other fields of science. In particular he had a special regard for radio science.

After the war Edward Appleton worked at the Cavendish attempting to
detect single alpha particles by the magnetic effect they produced when going
through a coil. But his real interest was in radio, stimulated by his experiences
during the war which had shown him how little was known about the creation
of radio-waves and their propagation. Besides, were he to specialize in nuclear
physics he would always trail in the wake of the master.

So he approached the master. Ern listened to his plans, encouraged him to
go off on his own and supported his work. The variable nature of received
radio signals had long puzzled people. [Today, we are usually not aware of this

variability because the receivers have automatic gain control in order to produce a constant output.] Marconi had surprised everyone with his early experiments which showed that radio waves could be received around the Earth's surface at distances greater than line-of-sight. To explain this observation an electrically conducting layer in the atmosphere, the Heaviside-Lodge layer, was postulated to exist thereby reflecting the radio waves around the curvature of the Earth. But did it really exist?

Edward Appleton, assisted by Miles Barnett from Dunedin, New Zealand, arranged an experiment. The supervisor of the Bournemouth radio station broadcast especially for them after close down on the night of the 11th of December 1924. He slowly varied the wavelength of the emission. Appleton and Barnett, situated at Oxford because Cambridge did not have a transmitter a suitable distance away, recorded a signal that waxed and waned showing that their received signal was the interference of two waves – one travelling directly to them and the other coming by another, reflected, path. They had shown that the ionosphere existed. From their record, and the rate at which the wavelength of the transmission had been varied, they determined that the ionosphere was at a height of about 100 kilometres above the Earth.

Ern was delighted and described the discovery at the annual Cavendish dinner two nights later. In their publication Appleton and Barnett expressed ⋯ *gratitude to Prof. Sir Ernest Rutherford for providing facilities for these experiments and for many helpful suggestions* ⋯ . When Appleton moved to Kings College, London, and was given a radio research laboratory it was Ern who formally opened it for him. Miles Barnett later returned to New Zealand and became the Director of the Meteorological Service. In 1947 Appleton received the Nobel Prize in physics for his work on the ionosphere.

Jack Ratcliffe took his degree at Cambridge in 1924. His lecturers in electricity and magnetism had been Edward Appleton and Professor Rutherford. The former had so impressed on him the wide range of physics connected with electromagnetic waves that he resolved to do research in this field and told Professor Rutherford, the Director of Research, so. Said Ern:

"Splendid. I want more things going on in this lab than radioactivity."
Jack Ratcliffe's wife was a north country lass who had had no prior contact with university people. During her first social visit to the Rutherfords' house she sat, rather petrified, on the sofa beside the Professor. Ern turned to her, stretched out his braces to show them to full effect and said:

"Here, look at these. I've just bought them. Do you like them?"

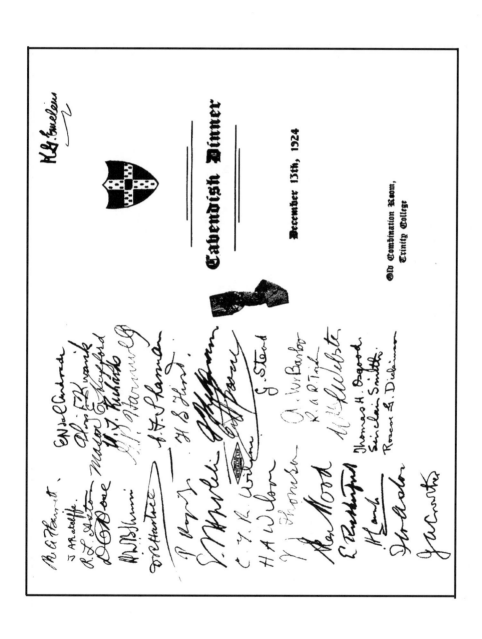

Menu

Huîtres

Tortue claire

Turbot bouilli, sauce Homard

Filet de Bœuf Godard

Dindonneau rôti et Jambon d'York

Céleri au Jus
Pommes Duchesse

Coupe Jacques

Champignons au Parmesan

Dessert

Café

Toasts

To Propose	To Respond
"The King"	
The Chairman	

"The Cavendish Laboratory"

Prof. J. A. Crowther	Prof. Sir E. Rutherford

"Our Guests"

The Chairman	Prof. Sir J. J. Thomson
	Prof. H. Lamb
	Prof. H. A. Wilson

Late in 1921 Percy Burbidge, the newish professor of physics at Auckland University College, wrote to Ern about various matters including his recent preliminary work on measuring the strength of radio signals. Ern arranged for the Radio Research Board of the Department of Scientific and Industrial Research to loan Professor Burbidge apparatus for the accurate measurement of the strength of radio signals.

In 1936 Ern wrote to authorities requesting they financially support the radio work of the New Zealander, Fred White, an ex-student of his, who was going to Canterbury University College as Professor of Physics. The Prime Minister of New Zealand cabled £200 to Fred. [During the second world war radio operators were trained, and radar sets built, in Canterbury. Fred White was seconded to Australia for war work and never returned. He rose to be chairman of the Commonwealth Scientific and Industrial Research Organisation (CSIRO).]

Ernest Rutherford had significant influence in the appointment of physics staff to the four colleges of the University of New Zealand. By the time of the Second World War, two of the colleges specialized in radiophysics showing that Ernest Rutherford was certainly not biased solely towards research in atomic physics.

In 1923 Ern served as President of the British Association for the Advancement of Science, culminating in their annual meeting at Liverpool. By tradition, a President's pennant was created incorporating the nautical background of the city and underneath

RUTHERFORD

LIVERPOOL

1923

To the left of RUTHERFORD were four stars representing the southern cross of New Zealand and to the right the maple leaf of Canada. Younger members created a special coat of arms for Ern. Under RUTHERFORD LIVERPOOL they depicted an arm and axe splitting an atom to the motto ATOM VIRUMQUE

The BA had last met in Liverpool in 1896 which coincidently had been the first BA meeting Ern had attended. Back then he had described his pioneer experiments in using his magnetic detector to register wireless waves over a distance of half a mile from the transmitter. Now the BBC broadcast his Presidential address nationwide through six wireless stations hundreds of miles apart. Sir Ernest Rutherford spoke for an hour and a half and the BBC was overwhelmed with congratulations. These exceeded criticisms by a ratio of 55 to 1, causing that august body to alter its rule of never broadcasting speeches of more than twelve minutes in length. Five years later Ern was invited to join the BBC's new Panel of Advisers who were charged with finding people to deliver National Lectures.

Death-Rays

Death-ray stories were endemic, for example as in H G Wells' novel of 1898 'The War of the Worlds', and they expanded ahead of the growth of radio science. In 1921 reports reached the British War Office that the Germans had produced powerful electromagnetic waves capable of killing men and detonating explosives. Ern, and other scientists connected with defence committees, decided the proposals were unworthy of further consideration. But death-ray stories continued. In 1924 Mr H Grindell Matthews constructed what he claimed to be a death ray and offered it for sale to various governments for a very large sum. Once more Ern was asked to comment. The version of his response, as told by his family in New Zealand and so basically true but probably highly embellished, was that he reported to the King that he could make one equally as harmless for nothing.

In 1925 a reporter asked Ern about recent predictions for the wireless distribution of power. Ern, whose first research was almost certainly stimulated by such hopes, replied: *"Well, no one has yet transmitted power by wireless."* On the startling prophesies occasionally made in respect to the development of scientific discoveries he stated:

> ⋯ *This is a time when there is great general interest in science and there are often sensational paragraphs in the press dealing with possibilities of the future. In many cases these suggestions required to be read with scepticism. It is easy to prophesy in a few minutes what might take 50 years of concentrated investigation to prove or disprove. It is inevitable in a generation that has seen the rapid advance of wireless and broadcasting that there should be a tendency to believe that everything is possible and this gives the opportunity for the sensational*

type of writer to go far ahead of the facts. The public should be on its guard against accepting much that is written about the great achievements of the future.

[Death-ray advocates thought in pictures rather than numbers. After death-ray stories again came out of Nazi Germany in the early 1930s the Air Ministry's Director of Research, in 1935, asked radio scientists if an intense beam of radio waves could incapacitate an enemy aircraft or its crew. They calculated that, even under idealized circumstances, to raise the temperature of a human body to fever level within ten minutes at a distance of 600 metres would require a radio beam many thousands of times more powerful than could then be generated. Hence a radio death-ray was not feasible. The enquiry did however get them thinking of Appleton's experiments as a basis for detecting aeroplanes. Radar, perhaps more than any other device, saved Britain from invasion during the second world war.]

New Zealand was to have its own death-ray proponent in Victor Penny who, in 1935, set up his machine in Auckland and exploded a box of matches from a distance. After being assaulted and injured by, he claimed, agents of a foreign power, the Government placed him under army protection on Somes Island in Wellington harbour and supplied him with anything he needed to build a death-ray. He never delivered.

JUNE 4, 1924.]   PUNCH, OR THE LONDON CHARIVARI.   617

THE DEATH-RAY IN ANTIQUITY.
A KING AND HIS WAR COUNCIL TESTING THE EFFICACY OF THE EVIL EYE AS A LETHAL WEAPON.

Grindell Matthews testing his 'Death Ray' in England. (Underwood, Weekly Press, 18 Dec 1924, courtesy Canterbury Public Library)

Chapter 17

TRIUMPHAL TOUR OF HOME

New Zealand 1925

New Zealand has a great variety of scenery and this is a very great asset which will probably become of ever increasing importance in the future. For this reason every care should be taken to make reservations and keep them protected wherever it is possible.

Ernest Rutherford

Civic Reception, Christchurch, 1925

Extension Lectures in Australia – 1925

Each year the Overseas Lectures Committee of the University of Melbourne arranged to import one speaker. They decided that the 1925 distinguished visitor should be a scientist, either Sir William Bragg or Sir Ernest Rutherford both of whom had flowered in the antipodes. Discrete enquiries elucidated that Sir William would not be available but Sir Ernest would be if officially invited and if the terms offered were acceptable. Failing him, Dr Aston would probably be willing and suitable.

All Australian universities were invited to participate and finally the Extension Board of Sydney University acted for all. The formal offer covered ninteen lectures in Perth, Adelaide, Melbourne, Sydney, Brisbane and Hobart covering six weeks for a fee of £500. ··· *Increased fee if New Zealand cooperates.* Ern cabled back ··· *Appreciate invitation* ··· *impossible programme too heavy* ···.

He settled on three and a half weeks in Melbourne, Sydney, Adelaide and Brisbane for a fee of £350. New Zealand offered £200 for two lectures at each of its four colleges.

Sir Ernest and Lady Rutherford arrived in Adelaide by steamer on the 3rd of September 1925. The crew then went on strike for two months. The Lord Mayor threw a civic reception for Ern and May at which one speaker, Sir Douglas Mawson F.R.S., the geologist and renowned Antarctic explorer, stated:

> No one was more distinguished in the realm of science today than Sir Ernest Rutherford. In fact, he doubted if there ever had been anyone more notable – he was so fundamental, so thorough and complete that his works would stand for all time. Geologists had gained enormously by the studies of radioactivity which were the outcome of Sir Ernest Rutherford's works. More than any other, they had afforded an opportunity of placing time and figures upon geological research. He had put geological chronology on a very fine basis. (Applause)!

May took the train to Sydney, hoping to get an early ship to New Zealand while Ern stayed on to complete his two lectures. At the first, on 'The Structure of Atoms', he enthused about undirected research. Of how the discovery of X-rays led to the two Braggs, Adelaide men, determining the architecture of crystals which in turn had yielded many advances in metallurgy and chemistry. He continued:

> Though the electro-magnetic theory of light was only 25 years old, its outcome had been the use of wireless communication and the invention of powerful oscillators and valves of previously unheard-of strength. Now it was possible to communicate with the whole world with currents of low power. That had resulted from the development of fundamental principles discovered by men working merely for the advance of knowledge, and without an idea of the commercial value of their discoveries. It was their duty to foster any talent which might be in their midst, with the intention of keeping it concentrated on fundamental problems. The university should be their home, and it was the duty of the State to see that the university was adequately supported so that any talent could show itself. That was more particularly the case in a young country than an older one, because in the former a young man might have few opportunities for advancement in science.

The train took him to Melbourne and three more lectures. The first two warranted reports on the ladies page of *The Australian*, an illustrated weekly, mainly concerned with a description of the guests' dress. The Governor of Victoria attended the second lecture when the aisles were full and some could not get in.

The Melbourne University Association laid on a lunch for the distinguished guest. Ern told them of Cambridge and the Cavendish. Forty research students was his limit. He did not take Americans as they were well catered for in their own country but he endeavoured to find room for students from the British Dominions. Ern also had lunch with Jack Erskine, his fellow researcher during the early days at Canterbury College and now on the way to making a frugal fortune on the stock exchange.

Among those meeting the overnight train to Sydney were scientific dignitaries and a reporter from the *Sydney Morning Herald*.

> *In appearance Sir Ernest Rutherford does not suggest the conventional idea of the man of science. Tall and powerfully built, he looks younger than his years (he is 54). A few words, spoken in his deep, earnest voice and a glance from his keen, blue eyes, disclose the charm of his personality, while a quarter-hour interview gives some slight revelation of the splendour of his intellect.*

Following half a column of Ern describing his work on the structure of the atom, the reporter got down to the nitty-gritty.

> *"Can the result of your investigations in this direction be given practical application to every-day problems?"*
>
> *"Without exception the general experience of science has been that any increase in our knowledge of pure physics affects the whole outlook of science, and is also inevitably followed by practical applications."*

At the Royal Society reception Ern continued this theme. How J J Thomson's discovery of the electron led to O W Richardson's invention of thermionic valve which opened the way to modern radio broadcasting. Radioactivity allowed the earth to be dated and spectroscopy yielded the composition of stars.

> *··· so the study of electrons and protons and atoms, though they sounded such abstruse subjects to the average mind, were really essential subjects in the study of mother earth and the forces of heat and energy, and, therefore, of every-day importance to the ordinary individual.*

Following lectures in full-to-overflowing halls in Sydney and Brisbane, Ern proceeded to the event that had lured him back to the Antipodes – a visit home to see his ageing parents.

Visit to New Zealand – 1925

New Zealand was forewarned of the impending visit of Professor Sir Ernest Rutherford F.R.S., O.M. by a personal appreciation which was written for the newspapers by Professor Florance of Victoria College in Wellington.

> *Honours and distinctions have been showered upon him, but he remains modest and unassuming. It is the greatest charm of this genial man that he can be nothing but himself. He realises the importance of being Ernest.*

The Auckland Star dispatched a reporter and a photographer to meet the ship.

> *With an easy flow of language, never faltering for a word, Sir Ernest comes straight to the point when asked a question. A big man physically – the most stalwart of the hundred or so gathered on the deck – he possesses a voice clear and resonant. He is quiet and unassuming and the expressive play of his hands imparts an animation to his talk that is wholly agreeable.*

During the six-week tour, much of it a whirlwind of public lectures and receptions that would do justice to a Royal Tour, Ern was seldom out of the news. He pronounced on agriculture (praising the soil surveys carried out by the Cawthron Institute in Nelson he concluded:

> *I hope that by the time I visit New Zealand again the whole of the country will be surveyed from this point of view)*

and on the environment

> *··· I understand that the government already has made many reservations, even at a late hour, in some of the more scenic parts of New Zealand. This, in my opinion is an exceedingly wise step. I hope that no trespass will be made on these reservations in the future. New Zealand has a great variety of scenery and this is a very great asset which will probably become of ever increasing importance in the future. For this reason every care should be taken to make reservations and keep them protected wherever it is possible.*

Even his lighthearted comments made the news.

> *If you take my advice the more physics you know the less engineering you need.*

Relaxing at the beach.
(Rutherford Family)

The bas-relief portrait in the Mond Laboratory, which caused such a fuss.
(Rutherford Family)

Bay de Renzie and Ern, 1929.
(Rutherford Family)

Ern and Ralph helping ensure the grand-children had a summer holiday with friends in 1931, following their mother's death. (Rutherford Family)

Cavendish Laboratory group photograph 1936. Note the crocodile on the wall of the Mond Laboratory.
(*Cavendish Lab photo, Jack Allen = me*)

Ern opening the Research Laboratory of the Institute of Automotive Engineers, Brentford, 18th march 1936. (pu, Rutherford Family)

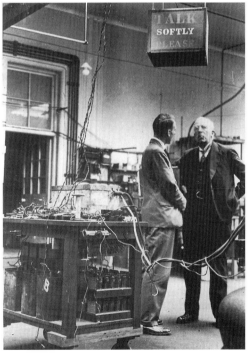

Ern telling Jack Ratcliffe he had the money for the radio atmospheric research station. The sign attempted to prevent Ern's booming voice upsetting vibration-prone amplifiers. An earlier sign was more blunt but didn't last long.
(C Wynn-Williams, Cavendish Laboratory)

Final resting place of the friends who discovered the electron and the atomic nucleus. Westminster Abbey, East end of the nave. The Newton, Darwin, Faraday and Maxwell memorials are nearby. The Flagstones are now almost worn out. (Courtesy of the Dean and Chapter of Westminster Abbey.)

Clay model for a bust of Ernest Rutherford c. 1941. The money to have it cast in bronze never eventuated so the clay was recycled.
(William Trewthewey (1892-1956), Trethewey Family)

His scientific caution showed in his response to two questions asked by a reporter. On the claim that mercury had been turned into gold in an electrical discharge he stated that other investigators had repeated the experiment with thoroughly purified mercury and found no gold ⋯ *During the next few years, no doubt, further experiments of that nature would be heard of, but results obtained in that way must be accepted with great caution.* [cf. the claims of cold fusion of 1990.] On the claim that recent measurements had shown the speed of light to depend on the direction of its travel and therefore the theory of relativity was radically wrong, Ern stated

> ⋯ *If those results could be substantiated, it was probably that Einstein's ideas and the theory of relativity would require to be modified somewhat; but the experiment was a very difficult one, and the effects observed were excessively small. For those reasons, it was not easy to be sure that all possible sources of error had been excluded. ⋯ the theory of relativity was so generally accepted now that the experiments must be verified by other observers before too much weight was attached to the results.*

Radium was still an in-word. The newspapers advertised Radium brand antiseptic floor polish and the Old Priest Bath at Rotorua had been renamed, through common usage following a determination of the radioactivity of various springs, the Radium Bath, the name by which it is still known today. [On an earlier visit Ern had commented that ⋯ *it seemed to him that proof was lacking that the beneficial effect of (mineral) waters was due to radium.*]

In promoting research as a quest for knowledge he talked of his own work in trying to determine the structure of the atomic nucleus, and did himself uncharacteristically speculate on one matter.

> ⋯ *The reason why this problem is so important is that the atom is the source of immense energy. Although the weights of the parts of the atoms are so small, yet they are so near together that the electrical forces and pressures exercised on each other are of the order of thousands of tons; so that enormous stores of energy are locked up inside the atom; and if we discover the nature of the atom it may be possible at some future date to utilise these forces.*

Everywhere he went he praised teachers, both past and present. Between 5,000 and 10,000 pupils had passed through the hands of his contemporary, Frank Milner, the Headmaster of Waitaki Boys High School. He even admonished Canterbury College for its poor treatment of Professor Bickerton, whom it had fired in 1902 and to whom it continued to refuse to grant Professor-Emeritus status ⋯ *He had lectured in an interesting way, although his methods were somewhat erratic, and he made the students very enthusiastic.*

As to Ern's early life, the newspaper reports promised more than they delivered. The subheading *Boyhood Days Recalled* was used on the strength of ⋯ *he readily harked back to his boyhood days when the practical affairs of his father's farm kept him well employed.* Account after account had a snippet seemingly designed solely to tantalize but frustrate future biographers.

> ⋯ *Sir Ernest went over some of the happy old days he had spent at the college.* ⋯ *In a speech punctuated with humour he referred to his early days at the State schools at Foxhill and Havelock, at Nelson College and Canterbury University College.* ⋯ *referred to his early days in New Zealand.* ⋯ *The present headmaster was in the same class at College, and between them they recalled many amusing reminiscences.* ⋯ *here followed a little story – "not for publication" – at the expense of the present Principal* ⋯ *(at Nelson College) he could quite well recall many of his experiences, both pleasant and unpleasant* ⋯ .

But none of these accounts actually recorded the reminiscences. A listing of the colour, style and material of the frocks worn at one reception occupied as much newspaper space as the sum total of all the reminiscences about his early days in New Zealand.

Scientific friends, including Ernest Marsden who as a young man had produced the first measurements on Ern's path to elucidating the structure of the atom but who had turned from research to become Assistant Director of Education in New Zealand, had greeted Ern when his ship arrived in Auckland on Monday the 28th of September 1925. Family members, George, Florrie and Arthur greeted him later at his hotel. The following three days were hectic but typical. On Tuesday forty Nelson College old boys assembled to greet him and to form, under Ern's patronage, an Auckland branch of the Nelson College Old Boys' Association.

On Wednesday he gave an informal talk, on the work of the Cavendish Laboratory, to 100 people at the university. That evening 800 people attended a conversazione thrown in his honour by the university, the Auckland Institute, the Medical Association and the Society of Civil Engineers. Palms, bamboo, arum lilies and the university orchestra decorated Scots Hall for the occasion. The song 'Induced Activity' formed part of the musical programme. Said Ern during his speech,

> *"I have always been very proud of the fact that I am a New Zealander"*

On Thursday the Mayor held a civic reception at which he read a letter from the Returned Soldiers Association expressing their deep appreciation of Lady Rutherford's kindnesses to the New Zealand soldiers in the Manchester Hospital during the war. The President of Auckland University College condemned those who criticized expenditure on higher education because the benefactors inevitably migrated to countries where there were greater opportunities for development and reward. ⋯ *New Zealand should be very proud to give such a son as Sir Ernest Rutherford to Britain. (Applause).* In support, Ern stated it mattered little what country graduates went to ⋯ *as long as they did honour to the Dominion from which they came.*

That evening Ern gave a public lecture entitled 'The Structure of Atoms'. Throughout he endeavoured to give people a mental picture of relative sizes and numbers. Based on the population of the earth

> ⋯ *If 100,000,000 people counted at the rate of 100 a minute it would take about 1,000 years for them to count the atoms in gas occupying a space the size of the end of my thumb.* ⋯ *If a pea in the middle of the Hall might represent the nucleus* ⋯ *then the electrons would be as far away as the walls.*

He also told them of his reaction when Ernest Marsden had reported that, when alpha particles bombarded a sheet of gold, some alpha particles rebounded. *The result was comparable to the imagined return of a great shell which had been fired at a sheet of paper.*

The public lecture was so popular that 1,500 people crowded into the hall, of whom some 500 stood in the aisles throughout. A further 500 were outside and unable to get in, leading to moves to sue the university for obstructing the traffic.

On Friday Ern, George and Florrie took the train to Hamilton where he met nine nephews and nieces, ⋯ [a] *very fine looking crowd of young people* ⋯ he recorded in the account of the trip which he wrote for his family in New Zealand and Britain.

After an overnight stop at Waitomo, where he visited the glow worm caves, he was driven to New Plymouth. May arrived the same day from Christchurch. Ern's parents had retired to a large house adjacent to Pukekura Park. [Number 40 Fillis Street is the only house with a Rutherford association which is left standing in New Zealand.] Both parents were well and cheerful and delighted to see their son. James was tall and slim with a well-trimmed, white beard. Approaching 87, he had the bearing of a fine, distinguished-looking, old gentleman. Martha, three weeks short of her 83rd birthday, had the bearing of a little matriarch but was less active than James. Both sat proudly erect for the photographer preparing a supplementary page on Ern's visit for the *Taranaki Herald*. As for their son, the paper stated

> ⋯ *His career is peculiarly one which may inspire boys today to seek the heights of achievement which may be attained from small beginnings by those who have vision and energy and the capacity to take infinite pains.*

With such thoughts in mind Ern, accompanied by his wife and parents, addressed the boys, girls and guests of the New Plymouth High School. By way of introduction the headmaster, a Nelson College Old Boy, told the pupils he had a vivid memory of seeing Rutherford's name on a school desk and a piece of scientific apparatus. [Did this initiate a bout of initial carving at New Plymouth High School?] Ern opened by mentioning that during his very first day at school, at age five, he had been punished for some misdemeanor. He related his career, praised his parents, gave sound advice on the importance of concentration and sympathised with the pupils as to how

> ⋯ *the whole social structure of mankind, of our world, was undergoing comparatively rapid alterations* ⋯ *It had been said that the modern age (e.g. with motorcar, wireless broadcasting, etc.) was a pleasure-loving age, and when they looked back they did realise that their forefathers lived a simple life compared with that of today.*

For the next three weeks Ern and May visited and received members of his family at Pungarehu, Hamilton and Te Aroha. He was sufficiently taken by one of his young nieces, Alice Chapman, that he offered to take her back to England to give her a good education, another generous offer declined.

With each visit the stories accumulated which evolved into family folklore illustrating the different natures of Ern and May. While staying with Ern's parents, May, who was used to servants, placed her and Ern's shoes outside their bedroom door. James, who had no servants, cleaned them himself.

While dining with Arthur's family Ern praised the service coach driver's knowledge of the countryside. May put down her knife and fork, drew herself to full height and said:

> *"Ernest, he was just a common cabbie."*
>
> *"Yes", said Ernest, "but he was a thorough gentleman Arthur."*

Early one morning Jim's wife Jeannie and her children were in their kitchen. Jeannie had stoked the range which heated a small cylinder of water, enough for one bath, and cooked scones. The children were preparing to go to school. May flounced in.

> *"The water for our baths has run out.*
>
> *Are those scones? Ern doesn't eat scones."*

May flounced out.

Jeannie and the children were flabbergasted. A few moments later Ern entered the kitchen, a bath robe covering his ample stomach.

> *"Who says Ern doesn't eat scones?"*

He sat down and polished off a dozen, all hot and dripping with butter. (Probably May was trying to get him to diet. As he wrote to his sister Nellie ⋯ *May and I are both well and both a bit stouter. I find that I have too little time for exercise on my travels to work it off, especially as I am living on the fat of the land.*)

May insisted that the children should address her as Lady Mary and not as auntie May. So in the main the Rutherford family had little regard for their sister-in-law/aunty May.

On the other hand the children loved their Uncle Ern. Jim's daughter Nan, then seven years old, recalls Ern as kindly, warm, simple, bluff, hearty and enthusiastic. After one walk across the farm he sat on the back porch steps and told the children corny jokes about knees.

If a kid hurts a knee where do they go for a new one?
The butchers. Because that's where they sell kidneys.

If an adult hurts a knee where do they go for a new one?
To Africa, where negroes.

This was the same person who showed them the eerie green glow of radium and told them of the crank letters he had received from around the world pleading with him not to split the atom as the world would fall apart. In April of 1924 Ern had given a talk which may have sparked the relevant *Punch* cartoon the following October.

MYSTERIES OF THE ATOM.

THE DISINTEGRATION OF AN ELEMENT.

Sir Ernest Rutherford delivered a discourse on " The Nucleus of the Atom " at the Royal Institution last night. The research of the last 20 years, he said, had led to the conclusion that the atom was an electrical structure held together by electrical forces. The structure of all atoms was similar,

The Times 5 April 1924

All too soon it was time for the next stage of the formal part of his visit. The Government had granted Sir Ernest and Lady Rutherford a free pass on the Railways, which may explain Ern's glowing tribute after arriving in Wellington ⋯ *Lady Rutherford and I have just travelled down by the Limited, and we can say that we have never had a more comfortable night's rest and journey.*

That afternoon, Monday the 26th of October, Ern talked to seventy students at Victoria College during which he stated that ⋯ *his reason for being so interested in the atom was that he considered it to be the building stone of the universe.* That evening Victoria College accorded him a reception. The library glittered with evening dress, orders and medals. In response to the Governor-General's words of welcome Ern ⋯ *spoke in humerous vein of the 'running of a laboratory' and also of his special interest in the New Zealand students, and his pleasure in welcoming them whenever they came his way.*

The following morning he and May attended a civic reception. He commented favourably on the University of New Zealand:

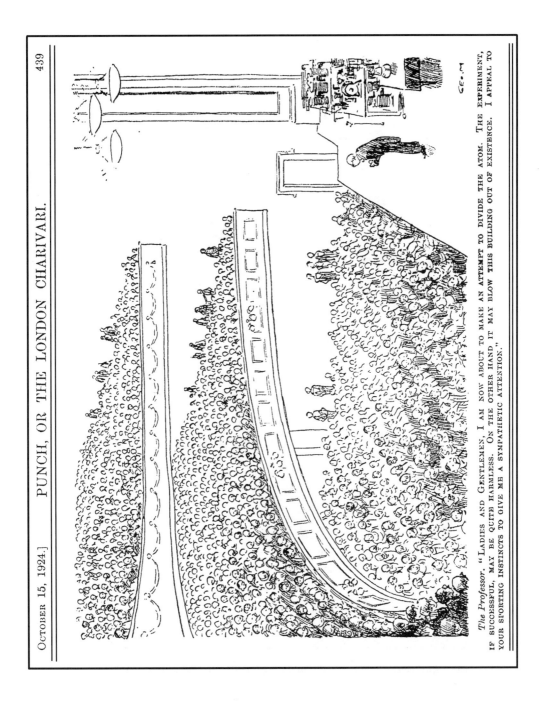

The Professor. "LADIES AND GENTLEMEN, I AM NOW ABOUT TO MAKE AN ATTEMPT TO DIVIDE THE ATOM. THE EXPERIMENT, IF SUCCESSFUL, MAY BE QUITE HARMLESS. ON THE OTHER HAND IT MAY BLOW THIS BUILDING OUT OF EXISTENCE. I APPEAL TO YOUR SPORTING INSTINCTS TO GIVE ME A SYMPATHETIC ATTENTION."

Sir Ernest Rutherford lecturing on the atom, Town Hall, Wellington, 1925.
(H Richardson, ATL)

··· though as the country was very young there were naturally many defects. ··· It is very important that every opportunity should be given to (University) teachers to go to other centres of the world to keep abreast with the world's knowledge. ··· Even practical research directed to the solution of a specific problem must work upon the basis provided by pure science!

That afternoon Lady Rutherford attended an afternoon tea in her honour (to which she *··· wore a frock of dark brown repp trimmed with pale amber and a brown hat with a plume at one side.*) In the evening Ern gave his public address on the atom to a large audience in the Town Hall. Mrs Florance, writing for the *New Zealand Free Lance*, reported that the picture from the moving film on Brownian motion was marred by a nasty dark splodge.

> *In a voice of increasing firmness he demanded that the operator correct the fault. It was a nervous and sickening moment for all when the operator replied that the condenser (lens) had cracked and that nothing could be done, as there was a long distance to be traversed before another condenser could be procured. ··· In a voice of commanding authority he commanded the operator to go and get another condenser, and having seen his order obeyed he became once more the pleasant and charming lecturer, and with an easy smile said that he would do the best he could with some other part of the lecture till the slides could be shown.*

The over-powerful projector cracked many of his slides. (There was no trouble with the projector in Christchurch. As Ern later recorded *··· I think Farr had threatened the lanternist with pain of death if anything went wrong.*)

Ern spent a hectic two and a half days in Wellington. As a reporter wrote: *Yet the man whom New Zealand and the whole world delights to honour went around everywhere radiating cheer and good humour, and looking as fit as the captain of the invincible All Blacks!* (New Zealand's rugby team had just completed a most successful tour of Britain.)

Wellington, the capital of New Zealand, had provided contact with the Government which, following a proposal from the Canterbury Industrial Association, had asked a special committee to consider the needs of manufacturers for industrial research. Ern had been involved with the British Department of Scientific and Industrial Research from its inception in 1915 and since arriving back in New Zealand he had often commented favourably on the service which science could and did render to agriculture, industry and medicine. Not surprisingly the Government asked Sir Ernest Rutherford to comment on the report. Ern advised New Zealand to make scientific research one of the chief objects of national policy.

An editorial writer for the *Evening Post* commented that Ern's remarks on

> ... *the value of pure science should be carefully noted by educationalists, politicians and others who have it in their power to assist research.* ··· *(Politicians) are prone to expect at least twenty shillings in the pound for the funds they grant for research, or better still, twenty pounds in the pound. Ultimately this dividend is paid handsomely, but it is rarely to be had immediately.* ··· *Even practical research directed to the solution of a specific problem must work upon the basis provided by pure science.*

Wherever he went, Ern praised the work of the Cawthron Institute in Nelson.

> *It appears to me that any further assistance given by the State to this important work could well be by the encouragement of the researches of such institutions, with the preponderating value of agricultural and pastoral products.*

> *It seems clear that it is the duty of New Zealand scientists to devote special attention to these subjects. It is in reality one of the first claims of the country on the Government to see that every support should be given to investigators that may benefit the farmers and enable them not only to maintain New Zealand's position as a producing country of the world, but also to improve it, especially in view of what is being done in other producing countries to encourage the producer to work along scientifically correct lines and in the suppression of insect enemies.*

The outcome was that New Zealand established a Department of Scientific and Industrial Research under Ernest Marsden in 1926. [The DSIR served New Zealand well until disbanded in 1992 when separate Crown Research Institutes were established.]

The South Island leg of the tour became a triumphal progression. As the Wellington to Picton ferry steamed sedately up Queen Charlotte Sound on the 28th of October great cheers erupted from passing launches carrying school children on their annual picnic. Ern was entering his home territory.

The Government supplied the latest Cadillac and a driver for Sir Ernest Rutherford and Dr Marsden. Local dignitaries greeted Ern at Picton and at Blenheim but full honours were reserved for the overnight stop at Havelock where strings of flags fluttered across the street. They proceeded directly to the civic reception at the Public Library where the speechmakers included the supervisor of Ern's Marlborough Scholarship's exams forty years earlier. Ern stayed that night with Jessie Brownlee, the one person in Havelock with whom the Rutherford family had kept in close touch. They chatted till midnight about their families and the old days.

The following morning at 8 a.m. Ern visited his old school where he planted a tree ($\cdots$ *being expected to remove about a hundred weight of earth in so doing*), addressed the pupils and gave them a holiday. He had the mana to so do at each school he visited except at Waitaki Boys' High where the Governor-General pre-empted Ern by a couple of hours. His mana may have been lowered in the eyes of those Havelock children who read, in the Blenheim newspaper, the reminiscences of one of Ern's school mates who recalled Ern's nickname as 'Windy'.

At the civic reception in Nelson, at noon the same day, the Mayor was resplendent in the new Mayoral robes and gold chain of office. A self-made man, he committed just one faux pas in an otherwise faultless civic reception. In not getting his tongue around the way the British pronounced laboratory as Labra-tory, he announced:

> " *Ladies and gentlemen today this little boy from our district has risen to be head of the biggest lavatory in the world where the mysteries of nature are found out.*"

After lunch Ern motored out to Foxhill, Spring Grove and Brightwater so that he could look over the land of his childhood, meet relatives and old friends and be greeted by present residents and school children. He found that the house he had been born in had been pulled down and in its place was a chicken run.

Bill Rutherford, Jim's son, was head boy at Nelson College. He too was taken for the drive during which Ern asked Bill *"Well William! do you know any funny low stories?"* Bill told a few, none of which appealed to Ern so he told Bill a few of his own. [Bill could not, or would not, recall the stories for me.] Bill, whose nickname at Nelson College was 'the professor', received financial support from his famous uncle. [Bill's formal education ceased a year later at Canterbury College when he discovered girls, alcohol and horse racing.]

Ern addressed the Nelson College Old Boys, the pupils at the Boys and Girls Colleges and gave a public lecture on 'Matter and Electricity' ($\cdots$ *hundreds were turned away*.)

The pattern of Auckland, Wellington and Nelson was repeated in Christchurch and Dunedin. As the car carrying Ern and May to Christchurch's civic reception crossed the Worcester Street bridge it was besieged by seventy Canterbury College students in gown, who tied a long rope to the car and dragged it to the Municipal Chambers. They paused in Cathedral Square to render several hakas ⋯ *led by a big fellow with a voice of extraordinary range, they gave Sir Ernest a rousing reception in Maori. This was followed by three rousing cheers.*

In Dunedin the students performed the haka in the lecture room causing Ern to record ⋯ *the authorities were afraid that the building would collapse for it was not built for this kind of demonstration.*

May wrote from Christchurch to Ern's sister Floss, ⋯ *Life has been a wild rush down here. Ern was feted everywhere, it was like a Royal Progress.*

The guest list for Christchurch's conversazione of welcome held at the Art Gallery, covered forty column centimetres while for his popular lecture on 'The Building of an Atom' the Caledonian Hall had been booked out a day ahead (reserved seats cost two shillings and sixpence) and many scores were turned away. (Unreserved seats were to cost one shilling and sixpence.) The Radio Society of Christchurch planned to broadcast this popular lecture to the nation. Ern had surely prejudged the influence on radio in producing a pleasure seeking society in New Zealand as this station 3AC transmitted on Tuesdays and Fridays only and then only between 6.45 – 7.15 p.m. 'bedtime stories by Cousin Stella' and again from 8-10 p.m. when the 3AC orchestra played in concert. The following night 3AC again broadcast live, this time the Christchurch results of the General Election.

Schoolboy nephews were regularly taken backstage to meet their illustrious uncle who performed the rich uncle's duty by presenting each with a £5 note. At least from them Ern received candour. After one public talk Ern asked his 10-year-old nephew Brian Strieff what he thought of the lecture.

Brian: *"I did not understand a dashed word."*

Ern laughed and slapped Brian on the shoulder.

"Thank goodness someone is honest anyway."

In Christchurch Ern and May had stayed with her brother Charlie Newton (Ern was godfather to Elizabeth Newton, his most recent niece). While May stayed on to continue her daily visits to her ageing mother, Ern had a swift trip back to New Plymouth for a last visit to his parents where the Press Association announced that Ern had been nominated to be President of the Royal Society.

All too soon it was time to return to England.

Reunited in Wellington, Ern and May said farewell to the Marsdens and boarded their ship which was then delayed daily for four days because of the long-running seamen's dispute. Luckily, it finally left just before they would otherwise have had to activate alternative plans. Unluckily, the ship arrived in Sydney too late for them to connect with their next steamer as it was scheduled to leave Melbourne before the overnight train was due. However, the shipping company delayed the sailing by two hours so that the Rutherfords could make the connection. Fame has its rewards.

The sea voyage back to England was broken by an excursion in Ceylon [now Sri Lanka] and an archaeological week in Egypt where their Christmas dinner consisted of sandwiches eaten on a train. Arriving back in Cambridge on the 2nd of January 1926, Ern concluded one of his two accounts of the voyage with:

> ⋯ *As a result of my travels and the way that I was fed in Australia and New Zealand, I believe that I have gained a pound or two in weight if not in dignity during my travels, otherwise I think there is little change except that I feel fit to tackle work with vigour again.*

Chapter 18

DEATH AND GLORY

I was very uncertain whether to accept; for a title of this sort is of little use to people like ourselves with no social ambitions. I was pressed by Lord Parmoor ⋯ that I ought to accept on general grounds as a recognition of the importance of science to the nation. I understand that no serious expenses are involved. Of course I do not intend to make any difference in our mode of life.

Ern, on being raised to a Peerage,
Letter to May in New Zealand, 19th Dec 1930

Honours

During the 1920s Ern lectured to packed halls in at least eight countries and the decade was peppered with honours for him. He was elected a foreign member of the Royal Dutch Academy of Sciences in 1920 and Professor at the Royal Institution in 1921. In 1922 the Royal Society awarded him its Copley Medal. In 1923 he served as President of the British Association for the Advancement of Science. In 1924 the Franklin Institute of Philadelphia presented him with the Franklin Medal.

In the New Year's Honours List for 1925 he became a Member of the Order of Merit, civil division, an honour restricted to twenty-four living Britons. This prestigious award had been initiated by King Edward VII, an admirer of Prussia's Pour le Mérite. The Order of Merit was the unfettered and personal gift of the Sovereign to *such persons, being subjects of Our Crown, as may have rendered meritorious service in Our Navy and Our Army or towards the advancement of Art, Literature and Science.* The red and blue badge made a colourful sight which men wore on riband around the neck. The insignia for the military badge is crossed swords, that for the civil badge a laurel wreath.

In 1926 Ern formally started his five year term as President of the Royal Society, an event marked in New Plymouth when friends and prominent citizens entertained James and Martha Rutherford to afternoon tea. In 1927 Hans Geiger named his son Ernst Arthur Rowland in memory of happy days at Manchester. In 1928 Ern received the Royal Society of Arts' Albert Medal and was elected an Honorary Fellow of the Royal College of Physicians. In 1929 Russian students elected Ern as the honorary president of the Physics Club ··· *because you proved that atoms have balls.* (It took the Russian, George Gamow, to explain to Ern that in Russian the word for the atomic nucleus had the same derivation as cannonball and the students had picked the wrong meaning from their Russian-English dictionary. *After Rutherford had stopped roaring with laughter, which brought half the laboratory to his door, he called his secretary and dictated a very nice letter to the students' club, thanking them for the honour.*)

George Gamow was an outstanding physicist, a superb popularizer of science, a keen motor cyclist and a practical joker of the first order. Once, when jointly publishing a paper with his student Ralph Alpher, Gamow added, unbeknown, Hans Bethe's name to the list of authors. The pronunciation of Bethe is Bayta. The result was a paper in the Physical Review, the most prestigious of all physics journals, which proclaimed authorage by Alpher, Bethe and Gamow. (α, β and γ.)

George Gamow, who had worked with Niels Bohr in Copenhagen before joining Ern at the Cavendish, set one notable incident in verse.

> ··· *that handsome, hearty British lord*
> *We knew as Ernest Rutherford.*
> *New Zealand farmer's son by birth,*
> *He never lost the touch of earth;*
> *His booming voice and jolly roar*
> *Could penetrate the thickest door,*
> *But if to anger he inclined*
> *You should have heard him speak his mind*
> *In living language of the land*
> *That anyone could understand!*
> *One day George Gamow, as his guest*

By Rutherford was so addressed
At tea in honour of Niels Bohr
(Of whom you may have heard before).
The men talked golf, and cricket too;
The ladies gushed, as ladies do,
About a blouse, a sash, a shawl –
And Bohr grew weary of it all.
"Gamow," he said, "I see below
Your motorcycle. You will show
Me how it works? Come on, let's run!
This party isn't any fun."

So to the motorcycle Bohr,
With Gamow running after, tore.
Gamow explained the this and that
And Bohr, who on the saddle sat,
Took off to skim along the Backs,
A threat to humans, beasts and hacks,
But though he started full and strong
He didn't sit it out for long,
No less than fifty yards ahead
He killed the engine dead
And turning wildly as he slowed
Stopped traffic up and down Queen's Road.

While Gamow, rushing to the fore,
Was doing what he could for Bohr
Who should like Jove himself appear
But Rutherford. In Gamow's ear
He thundered: "Gamow! If once more
You give that buggy to Niels Bohr
To snarl up traffic with, or wreck,
I swear I'll break your bloody neck!"

BA Meeting – South Africa – 1929

Three ships carried members of the British Association for the Advancement of Science to their joint meeting with the South African Association. Sir Ernest Rutherford OM travelled out on the newly repainted S.S. *Nestor*, together with his daughter and son-in-law, Eileen and Ralph Fowler.

May Rutherford had gone on a motoring tour of the Tyrol so Ern wrote a running commentary for her. He knew the Captain from the voyage to Australia in 1925.

> ··· *The passengers are on the whole largely middle aged or ancient like myself* ···. *A little rowdiness at night in the smoke room and the usual man who takes a little too much* ··· . *Our party at table is quite a lively one. Ralph's laughter easily beats the best.* ··· *Eileen is in good form and enjoying herself, and behaving to my eyes in an exemplary manner* ···.

Activities organized to relieve the monotony of a long ocean voyage included a fancy dress parade.

> *Aston at our table came dressed as a Malay and looked cool and attractive. Eileen went as a milkmaid* ··· . *I got into my red gown to give a little colour to our table* ··· *and a mock trial* ··· *in which I was judge* ··· . *It went off very well and there was a good deal of fun with the jury and witnesses.*

Two of the zoologists spent most of the time on the bow watching the sea. Others needed more strenuous exercise to neutralize the effects of regular and large meals. Deck tennis turned out not to be the genteel pastime expected. Lady Sherrington received a black eye and on another occasion during high seas ··· *our game was ended by throwing the quoit overboard.*

Ern usually played four sets of deck tennis each day with Mrs Ruth Egerton as his partner. Ern survived two rounds of the singles and the mixed doubles competition. Ralph had developed into a good player. Though knocked out of the singles by the eventual winner, he and his partner won the mixed doubles in *one of the best exhibitions on the boat.* The match had been played on a rough and windy day in front of *a large audience of tennis fans in overcoats as occasional spray was coming over.*

In one intriguing entry Ern recorded ··· *was cinematographed by Morris of Oxford.* The ship arrived in Capetown on the 19th of July 1929. There followed a whirlwind round of social engagements, tours and scientific lectures during which Ern received an honorary degree, gave a specialist lecture on 'The Origin of Actinium' and an evening discourse on 'The Structure of the Atom.'

After a day's stop-over at the Kimberley diamond mines the meetings resumed at Johannesburg after which Ern, Ralph and Eileen spent five weeks touring in Natal and Zululand. They visited a game reserve park where the highlight was stalking to within twenty metres of a rare white rhino and calf in order to photograph the pair. Eileen reported to her mother ⋯ *You cant think how much Daddy enjoyed himself, he was the life and soul of the party.*

During this tour Ern visited the tsetse fly research station in Zululand and opened the physics laboratory in Grahamstown before looping back to Capetown to catch their ship to England on the 15th of September 1929.

In holding the British Association meeting in South Africa the scientists of the British Empire had once again been brought into contact with each other and the finest of them all had been refreshed, ready for a new decade.

1930

Mary Newton, May Rutherford's mother, was now aged seventy-nine and failing. May planned a visit home to encompass the northern autumn and winter of 1930-31. There was no chance of Ern getting away again so soon. Amongst other ties, his presidency of the Royal Society ran till the end of 1930. All previous visits to New Zealand for which Ern had been able to join her had had to include the break in his academic year, the northern summer and hence the southern winter. As he stated with envy ⋯ *We were always in NZ on our trips at the wrong time except to appreciate what a cold, wet and windy place NZ can be.*

May left the running of the house, and Ern, in Eileen (Bay) de Renzie's hands, reporting to Martha Rutherford that Bay *is affectionate to both* (of us) *and full of spirits – good for us both having her in the house.* Bay was a cousin of May's. Her mother worked as a nurse in London. [Late in 1934 Ern was to write a new will in which he left £100 to Phyllis de Renzie.] Bay came to live with the Rutherfords in 1926 after serious illness. Blue-eyed Bay was in her thirties and so was a lot younger than the Rutherfords. She helped Ern and May considerably for some ten years and was treated as a daughter. Bay lived it up with the aid of friends and May Rutherford's little car. She seemed to be seeking a man and several research students, all many years her junior, recalled being propositioned by her. [In March of 1936 Bay de Renzie was to leave the Rutherfords giving neither notice nor reason. She just vanished. May was very hurt and all she reported to New Zealand was that ⋯ *Since early last summer she has been messing about with some man, motoring out in the evenings to dine and dance at Country Hotels.* Bay used May's little car. When May complained to Mark Oliphant about the large sums being spent on having it regularly serviced he made discreet enquiries. It was the local mechanic Bay was seeing and with whom she ran off.]

One complication to May's departure was that Eileen Fowler was expecting her fourth child in December. Eileen was seldom in good health. The birth of her third child had been particularly difficult and she had been warned to have no more. But she loved having babies even though each pregnancy was difficult. She was to spend nearly eight months of her fourth pregnancy in bed. May, when confirming details of her trip to Martha Rutherford, had written ⋯ *I am sorry to be away when her baby arrives in December but am not at all worried about her. Eileen looks very peaky and we think she shouldn't have thought of having a 4th but she was keen to.*

Bay persuaded May to engage a couple as butler and cook-housekeeper. Having a man fussing about the house and waiting at all meals including breakfast irritated Ern, making him feel that he was never alone. These arrangements did not survive May's return.

Ern gave May a travelling clock for her journey and drove her to Southampton to catch the boat to New Zealand. May and Ern regularly exchanged news by letter. She gave the family news and he reported his activities. She would not be surprised at the pace of his social engagements. Take the month of December 1930 as an example. It opened with a Royal Society Dinner to mark the end of Ern's Presidency. The Prince of Wales and the Prime Minister were the chief guests. Ern sat between the Swedish Ambassador, whom he knew well, and the Prince of Wales, who, in his speech, stated that *Rutherford had altered our whole conception of the nature of the material universe.* The New Zealand Prime Minister came to tea and the Marsdens visited for three days.

Sat 6th Founders Feast at King's College.

Sun 7th Major and Mrs de Renzie came to tea. Eileen still in bed.

Mon 8th Imperial College annual dinner, guest of Henry Tizard.

Tue 9th To Brighton. Eileen wrote to her mother *Ralph, Dad, de Navarro and Southwell go off for three days golf together and will have a riotous time I expect.* This foursome regularly went off for a short golfing holiday following the Oxford-Cambridge rugby match.

Fri 12th Dinner with the Prince of Wales at St James Palace. Ern described this as a pleasant, informal affair. The Prince had a short chat with all 19 guests and Ern signed the visitors' book.

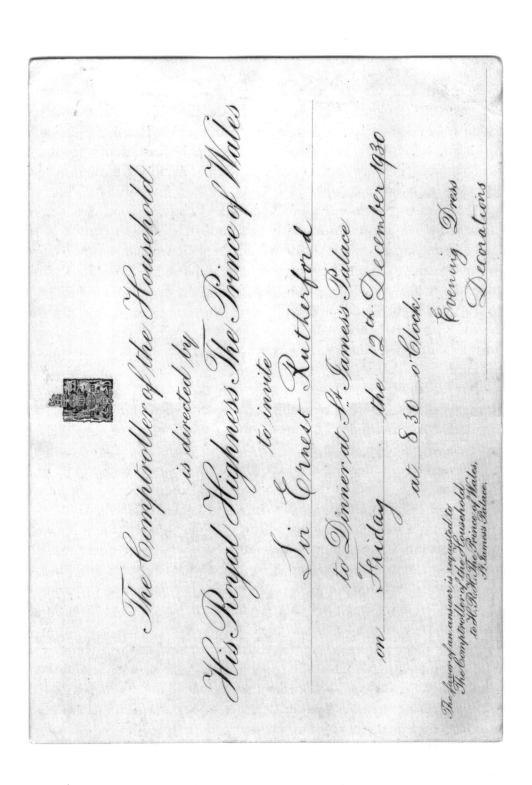

The Comptroller of the Household

is directed by

His Royal Highness The Prince of Wales

to invite

Sir Ernest Rutherford

to Dinner at St. James's Palace

on _____ Friday _____ the 12th December 1930

at _____ 8 30 _____ o'Clock.

Evening Dress

Decorations

The favor of an answer is requested to
The Comptroller of the Household
to H.R.H. The Prince of Wales.
St. James's Palace.

Sat 13th Cavendish Dinner. Ern, in replying to the toast 'The Laboratory' *expressed the hope that the Cavendish would always make its own line of research and not run after any and every discovery made in other laboratories.*

Sun 14th Eileen's fourth child born easily. They named her Ruth Eileen. Her first name recognised Ruth Egerton, the daughter of Lord Parmoor, who, together with her husband, had been on the British Association trip to South Africa with Eileen and Ralph. [A recent guess that the name Ruth was chosen as a contraction of Rutherford is not correct.] Ern telegraphed the news to May *"Eileen baby daughter and us all well".*

The birth had been an easy one and Eileen had two good days before catching a severe gastric flu which spread through the Fowler household to Liddy, then Ralph, then Nurse Racle, then her replacement. Only Anne Brown, the Truby King trained nurse who had been employed to look after Patrick and the new baby, escaped the minor epidemic.

Sat 20th To the Prime Minister.

Tue 23rd of December 1930 Dinner at Trinity. At 7.25 p.m., as Ern was dressing for dinner, Nurse Racle arrived with the dreadful news that Eileen had died.

Ern got out the car and, with Bay, drove to the Fowlers' home, Cromwell House. While Eileen's state of health had caused anxiety there had been no reason to expect any sudden failure. She had died in the prime of her life, at age twenty-nine, of an embolism.

The next day Ern telegraphed May. *Eileen died suddenly but peacefully Wed (sic) evening. Embolism. Baby well. Phyllida taking full charge Cromwell House, all well, no need change your programme write mother* (signed) *Rutherford.*

Ern sent the telegram via May's brother, Charlie Newton, who was a well known doctor in Christchurch. As May was staying with her mother and as all the old relatives were due at Charlie's for dinner that Christmas eve, Charlie resolved not to tell May until later. When May, her mother and two aunts arrived, all were wearing black. May commented *"All in black. We might be mourning."* They were, after Charlie broke the news.

Eileen's older children, Peter (7), Elizabeth (Liddy) (5) and Patrick (3) were not immediately told of their mother's death so as not to spoil their Christmas. When Peter was told his mother was too ill to be present he asked *"Is she ever going to get better?"* Bay de Renzie, the cook and the butler arranged a tree and Christmas dinner for the children.

The Rutherfords had a more sombre Christmas day. May wrote to Martha Rutherford to break the news while Ern wrote to May with all the details ⋯ *It is a sad ending to Eileen's adventure but it may be called in a sense a happy end for*

I was always afraid of her becoming an invalid. If her lung trouble had flashed out again, it would have been a bad complication in any case. May agreed. Her letter ⋯ *Cant help feeling that poor Eileen has been saved a life of invalidism* ⋯ crossed Ern's.

Ralph Fowler wrote to his mother-in-law and described Eileen's last hours and days.

> *I am thankful for our South African trip not merely because Eileen enjoyed it and was happy and well there, but also because she and her father then first really got to know and appreciate each other. He is far happier now realizing something of what manner a person his daughter was than he could ever have been without it.*

Eileen was buried under a Cypress tree in the churchyard at Ashmore, near the Fowlers' holiday home. Her death had taken the gloss off the glad tidings that Ern was bottling up.

Ernest, Lord Rutherford of Nelson

As the New Year of 1931 entered its second day in Christchurch, Mrs Newton awoke as usual before the rest of her household and fetched the morning newspaper. One headline stated that her son-in-law had been raised to the Peerage. She woke May at 7 a.m. with the news. May immediately arose and had her morning bath, during which her brother Charlie burst in to congratulate her. Then the telegrams started arriving, the first from the Governor-General Lord Bledisloe, and ⋯ *the second from dear old Farr.* (The Professor of Physics at Canterbury College.)

May Rutherford wrote to her mother-in-law in New Plymouth. ⋯ *Isn't it splendid that Ernest has been awarded this new honour and is now Lord Rutherford. I had thought he was already at the top of the tree but there was evidently one more twig.* ⋯ *I wish it carried a prize with it but it will only mean a good big fee out of Ern's pocket.*

Soberly May sat down and wrote to Ern about the issues raised by the honour.

> ⋯ *I hope it is only a lifetime peerage and that it does not descend to Peter, it would only be a drawback without money.* [Ern was to reply ⋯ *Of course the title ends with me – otherwise it would have not been politic to accept.* ⋯ It was an hereditary title but he had no male heir to inherit it.] *I expect there will be a good big fee to pay – this has been a heavy year indeed. Well dearest there can be no one who deserved*

it more, or will put on less airs for getting it. We are wondering very much what territorial adjunct you will take. It ought to be something NZ but the pity is that Canterbury or Christchurch would both look English to most people. Havelock where you got your first educational start seems the most appropriate and sounds well too. Lord Rutherford of Havelock. ⋯

Ernest Marsden, the Secretary of the Department of Scientific and Industrial Research in New Zealand and Ern's collaborator on the structure of the atom, read of Ern's elevation while on a visit to New York. In reply to his letter of congratulations Ern was to state it is ⋯ *certainly a strange transformation, but, following my usual radioactive custom, I shall retain the family name.* ⋯ Some did change names, for example the Strutts became Lord Rayleigh.

Another Rutherford had been raised to the peerage earlier and although that line was extinct it was still necessary for Ern to choose a territorial adjunct. He had already selected this before receiving his wife's advice:- Nelson, in honour of ⋯ *my birthplace and home of my grandfather.*

Eileen had died before learning of this latest honour. Ern, in quietly telling Ralph a few days beforehand, had judged Eileen too ill to be told. May Rutherford had no forewarning because no announcement was allowed until the official list was published on New Year's day. A telegram to New Zealand beforehand would have been too public a method of communication and mail took about six weeks between Britain and New Zealand. He had written to her on the 19th of December, presumably by which time he knew for certain his name had gone before the King, stating:

> <u>Private</u> *Before you get this you will have heard the news that my name has been put forward to the King for the conferment on me "of the dignity of a Baronetcy of the United Kingdom". This means a Peerage and membership of the House of Lords. – so I suppose if it goes through I shall be styled Lord Rutherford but there will be no change in your title. I am not sure whether Eileen would have the right to call herself the Honourable Eileen Fowler. It has been rather a worrying business, for I was very uncertain whether to accept; for a title of this sort is of little use to people like ourselves with no social ambitions. I was pressed by Lord Parmoor – through whose department it goes – that I ought to accept on general grounds as a recognition of the importance of science to the nation. I understand that no serious expenses are involved. Of course I do not intend to make any difference in our mode of life. So after a good deal of consideration, I decided to accept for it is difficult to*

refuse after you have already accepted a lower title. Of course, I ought to recognise that it is in a sense a personal tribute to my work as well as to the importance of science to the state.

Considerable pressure had been exerted on him to accept to ensure that science was represented in the House of Lords. Later he wrote to May ⋯ *I understand that my friends and colleagues were in general very pleased at this recognition of the importance of science to the state. As you know this type of honour is personally not very attractive but we live in a practical and not ideal world.* His friends at the Athenaeum generally agreed that ⋯ *it would have been bad for science if I had not accepted.* To his mother he had simply cabled:

Now Lord Rutherford. More your honour than mine.

To escape to a quieter life, Ern and Bay de Renzie spent a fortnight at Celyn (pronounced Kaylin), the Rutherfords' country cottage in Wales, where Ern spent the first week replying to messages of condolence concerning Eileen's death and the second to messages of congratulations concerning the peerage. Mark Oliphant joined them for a week.

Grief and elation could not get in the way of science. By the 11th of February Ern could report to May ⋯ *My work makes very good progress – opened up some interesting questions which Ellis and I are working at together.*

Resplendent in second hand Peer's robes, Baron Rutherford of Nelson, of Cambridge in the County of Cambridge, was formally introduced into the House of Lords on the 4th of February 1931. *The house met at a quarter before four of the clock. The Lord Chancellor on the Woolsack.* Ern was guided by his two sponsors Lords Rayleigh and Crawford, both of whom were old friends of his.

> ⋯ *It is an amusing ceremony to the onlookers but requires rehearsal for the participants. We are preceded by various functionaries, including the Garter King of Arms dressed uncommonly like the Knave of Diamonds, and there is much bowing to the Lord Chancellor at various points in our progress.* ⋯ The elaborate ceremony amused Ern ⋯ *I then advanced and half kneeling presented a request for letters patent and shook hands. Then the clerk read out the oath which I repeated. Finally we went to the back benches and bowed solemnly 3 times to the Lord Chancellor – sitting down between each – doffing the cocked hat which is only used on such occasions.*

Various elements of his life and researches were worked into his coat of arms. A kiwi surmounted the crest. A Maori warrior and Hermes Trismegistus, the patron saint of knowledge and of alchemy, supported the shield which was quartered by two overlapping curves approximating the exponential decay of radioactive elements and the growth of their daughter products. The motto – *primordia quaerere rerum* was taken from Lucretius' 'On the Nature of the Universe' – To seek the first principles of things.

Because of Ern's peerage the Governor-General of New Zealand called on Martha Rutherford.

> Said Lord Bledisloe, *"You must be very proud of your illustrious son."*
>
> Said Martha, *"No more than I am of the rest of my sons."*

Ern's elevation to the peerage had not overshadowed his scientific work. When his milkman reported to the depot that there must have been a great explosion at the Rutherford house it transpired that Ern's servant had stated to the milkman that he ought to be very honoured to be supplying milk to the man who had split the atom.

Ernest, Lord Rutherford of Nelson was to speak only twice in the House of Lords and both times he spoke as the Chairman of the Advisory Council of the Department of Scientific and Industrial Research (DSIR). With the increasing use of fuel oils Britain had become a net importer of energy after a century as a net exporter of energy. The coal mining industry was therefore in a state of disaster. Lord Sanderson suggested to the House of Lords that if oil could be produced from coal both problems would be alleviated. Lord Rutherford, in his maiden speech to the House on May the 20th 1931, raised the spectre that

> ⋯ *if our supplies of oil were at any time suddenly cut short, the greater part of our transport services, our aircraft, our naval vessels, and the larger vessels of the mercantile marine would be very soon immobilised.*

He gave the technical background for the debate and reviewed the relevant research being carried out by various sections of the DSIR. There were two methods of producing oil from coal: the coking process used for iron works and town gas supplies whereby coal was heated in the absence of oxygen, and the more efficient but expensive hydrogenation process whereby coal was heated at high temperatures and pressures while in contact with hydrogen and catalysts. Neither were economic in comparison with the prevailing low price of imported fuel oil which had only to be pumped out of the ground.

The coking process would give a useful ⋯ *smokeless fuel and some oil, but the advance* ⋯ *depends not upon science but upon how far the nation is prepared to pay for a purer atmosphere.* Similarly the development of the hydrogenation method depended *on how far the nation is prepared to pay for the independence of its oil supplies from other countries.*

Ern's speech made the newspapers in New Zealand where Ernest Marsden was vitally concerned with similar issues. Like the rest of the world, New Zealand was in the depths of a bitter depression and wool was at its lowest price for a century. With imported oil being a large drain on a shattered economy, the rise of the American dollar and the introduction of a sixpence per gallon tax on petrol, obtaining oil from coal certainly seemed worth a second look. So Marsden sought Ern's help in having New Zealand's best coal chemist seconded to England for a year to study new developments.

Lord Rutherford's only other speech in the House of Lords occurred on the 9th of May 1933, in support of the second reading of the Rubber Industry Bill. The Rubber Research Association, one of many cooperative industrial research associations, had been set up after the war to support the rubber industry. Financial support had initially been supplied equally by the industry, on a voluntary basis, and by the Government, from the £1,000,000 it initially allocated annually in support of industrial research. Not all rubber manufacturers contributed and after the Government contribution ceased the majority of the Rubber Research Association staff had been dismissed. The Bill aimed to fund the Association's work for five years, entirely from compulsory payments by rubber manufacturers, in proportion to the amount of raw rubber delivered to each. The sum required amounted to about one forty-fifth of a penny per pound of rubber.

The majority of manufacturers, and certainly all the large ones, supported the move, but compulsory contributions to research were a new concept opposed by Conservative members. Lord Urwin moved the second reading of the Bill. Lord Gainford, who had been the Minister responsible for ensuring that the Government had financed industrial research after the war, spoke against the principle of compulsory contributions from industry. ··· *If you want to get the best results from research work you want those who contribute to it to be supporters of research and believers in it.*

Lord Rutherford, about whom Lord Urwin was to say ··· *the noble Lord ··· who intervenes all too rarely in our debates ···*, then spoke at length.

> ··· *Since the war there has been a growing recognition of the importance of research in industry.* ··· *The point before us today may seem a small one, but viewed from the wider aspects it is a question of great importance for the future, and in a sense it is a test of the attitude of the representatives of this country in their relation to research and industry. As a man of science I have had opportunity of seeing, and have seen, the remarkable effects of the application of science to the improvement and development of industry. I am convinced that research is one of the*

most potent weapons for combating the evils of waste and inefficiency in industrial production, and I hope that this House in passing this Bill will show unmistakably its belief in the application of scientific methods and scientific knowledge, as an important aid in keeping this country in the forefront of progress.

The Family

After their mother's death, the Fowler children were raised by Phyllida Cook. The Cooks and the Fowlers had known each other since 1922 or 1923. They all got on well and had even been on holidays together. The Cooks' second daughter developed tuberculosis of the spine and was finally transferred to a tuberculosis hospital. At the same time Eileen, then with three children, had developed a tubercular spot on her lung. Both households needed reorganization so Ralph Fowler and Derek Cook suggested the two households should amalgamate at the Fowlers but under Phyllida's care. The arrangement worked well and Eileen had recovered but sadly the Cooks' second daughter died. The dual household had served its purpose so the Cooks returned to their own house.

When Eileen died Ralph had commitments in France and America but he had no relatives who could help with the family. His only sister was with their mother. Derek and Phyllida Cook therefore offered to return to the Fowlers' house for six months, a situation so mutually beneficial that it continued until Ralph's death. The Fowler household swelled to three adults, seven children and four servants (a cook, a housemaid, a nursemaid and a Truby King nurse for Ruth.)

Peter Fowler was sent off a term early to his planned preparatory school in Oxford, which he did not like. Young Liddy mothered the even younger Pat. Nearly every morning on their way to infant school the pair called in to 'surprise' their grandfather. They were lively youngsters and expected to be invited to a meal at his house at least once a week.

Death was not new to Ern. His father had died in 1928 at the grand age of 89 after suffering for many years from arthritis and five years from chronic heart trouble (fibro-myocarditis). James Rutherford had a reputation as a hard-working, fair, honest man of integrity whose word was his bond. A New Plymouth postman recalls him more simply as the dignified, slim, white-haired old gentleman waiting at the gate for mail from his son in England.

Following a poetry competition sponsored by an Auckland firm, the Kaitaia newspaper published the winning entry.

ODE ON THE PASSING OF A SCOTTISH PIONEER

This fine old man; I see him now;
With merry, loving eyes,
That were but mirrors of a soul
So patient, kind and wise.

His upright figure seemed to those
Who knew him best, the frame
That matched a mind that never stooped
To petty deeds of shame.

His life was like an open book
His faith was good to see.
Methinks one word expressed his life,
And that word – "Charity".

In youth he trod no rosy path;
For comforts were but few.
And all the hardships he endured;
That early settlers knew.

But, like his native heath that blooms
When wild the tempests blow,
Those early years had given strength
To smile thro' weal or woe.

New Zealand's sons will ne'er forget
That brave and hardy band,
Whom Death is claiming, one by one;
The heroes of our land.

The entry had been written by the editor's cousin-in-law, Evelyn Bell, about her father, James Rutherford. [Most reminiscences of Ernest Rutherford are from people who worked with him in the 1930s, after James Rutherford's death, so most make no reference to Ern's father.]

May Rutherford's 1930–31 visit to New Zealand coincided with one of New Zealand's worst natural disasters, the violent earthquake of the 3rd of February 1931, which killed 256 people and levelled the cities of Napier and Hastings. ··· *I should think the nerves of women and children will take years to recover.* None of the Rutherford family farming in that general area were harmed.

May would also report general news to Ern concerning her plant and seed gathering trips, her diet (she had lost 7 pounds in 3 weeks and with the aid of special corsets now had a beautiful figure ··· *I'll have to reorganize your diet when I get home!*), mutual friends (··· *Had tea with old Prof Brown recently, looking splendid. Viola* [his daughter] *looks worn out – the obvious corollary. Selfish old brute*) and the effect of the Great Depression on her own family (Gordon hadn't the faintest chance of getting a job and Charlie's business was very slack as no one called in a doctor unless they had to).

May Rutherford's visit also allowed her to see first-hand, and comment on, Ernest's family as the Great Depression took bitter hold of the world. Flax-milling had died. George Rutherford was in great financial difficulties, his wife was temporarily paralysed by strokes and an upcoming wedding was expected to just about break him. Jim was hard on his wife Jeannie and their children. When Jeannie came into a little money she and the children left him. May did not blame her at all. Jim had gone bankrupt in 1926 owing many hundreds of pounds to unsecured creditors, among whom were his father, two of his brothers-in-law and Ern. Yet still, as May reported ··· *Jim goes on running up bills all the time.* ··· *There is not the slightest use in giving Jim money now.* ··· *Later on if he can't earn owing to unemployment he may have to be helped by regular remittances through a trustee. It is no use giving him more than enough to live on by the week.*

Ern's sisters who had married farmers were also in dire financial circumstances, so much so that Flo had to take son Brian away from high school. Arthur seemed to be the one bright spot in the Rutherford family.

The family matriarch, Martha Rutherford, was not in good health. She could garden but could not walk a hundred metres. In New Plymouth May stayed with Jeannie Rutherford, Jim's estranged wife, who regularly sat with Martha. Although James Rutherford had willed £100 to each of his children, the bulk of his estate had been left to George and Jim only, a fact which enraged May on behalf of the girls. Martha had money, yet it was May who paid her expenses through her own lawyer in Christchurch. May regularly complained to Ern. ··· *If only she would deal out a hundred each now when they are all so hard pressed that they are having to withdraw children from schools!* She could not resist comparing Martha Rutherford with her own mother who ··· *gives every sixpence she can spare from her bare necessities to help the needy ones.*

May had returned home to New Zealand none too soon. When Mrs Newton died in 1933 Ern wrote to Charlie Newton to recall that

> ⋯ *I remember her very well 40 years ago when she was full of energy and enthusiasm and cheerful under all her difficulties at that time. She had a fine unselfish character and her interest in people was a great asset to her all her life. She and I always got along happily together and the mother-in-law complex was never present.*

Ern cabled his mother on her 90th birthday, expressing the hope that she would reach 100. To a *Taranaki Herald* reporter, Martha had talked of how she always practised thrift, her scorn for *the tiny families of today* ⋯ *to which* ⋯ *many modern evils can be traced* ⋯, her belief ⋯ *that hard work is the sovereign remedy for many evils of today* ⋯ and how she had

> ⋯ *always been a great believer in education, but while she considers that it is the duty of every parent to give the children the best education available, she is doubtful on the question of modern education. To her mind it appears as if the people were playing with education, and she considers that there are too many subjects,* ⋯.

On her 91st birthday the *Evening Post* of Wellington interviewed her, commenting that in Lord Rutherford's *fortnightly letters to his mother, carefully preserved, every step in his scientific discoveries can be followed. There is sufficient material in these documents for an intimate biographical study of the great man.*

Martha Rutherford died in 1935, aged 92, and was buried in James' grave in New Plymouth's Te Henui cemetery, near where her mother had first settled. Her grandson Jim still recalls the sound of the blowlamp used to seal the lead-lined coffin she had insisted on. As a pallbearer he also recalls its weight as they struggled it up the cemetery hill.

His mother's death upset Ern. In replying to J J Thomson's note of condolence Ern stated ⋯ *She was a woman of unusual strength of character – intelligence and all the family – particularly myself owe much to her.* Mark Oliphant recounted how Ern normally dozed when sitting in an easy chair but if awake he would always be busy with reading or some other activity. However, for a period following his mother's death he would sometimes *sit staring into the distance, immobile and in deep reverie.*

Martha Rutherford had been a natural hoarder. Her house was full of material such as bundles of newspapers and the *New Zealand Free Lance.* It took several days to clean out her house with two daughters sorting the material, one nephew carting it outside and another, Ernest Elliot, stoking the bonfire.

As a consequence Ernest Elliot gained one of the world's best collections of Rutherford photographs because he kept saying *"We cannot burn that"*. May's letters (plus a few of Ern's) to Martha, spanning forty-five years of family history, went back to May and are still extant. The daughters destroyed James' love letters to Martha as they regarded them as private. Jim took possession of Ern's letters to Martha which spanned not only family history but four decades of scientific development and personalities: British, Canadian, New Zealand, world and nuclear. Jim allowed excerpts of many of these letters to be published as a series in the *Taranaki Herald* until Ern requested him to halt.

Jim had been living with Martha. As her house was to be sold, Jim pitched a tent on the empty section next door and lived there for six months. All his worldly possessions were in the tent and Ern's letters, bundled up in pink ribbon, were in a flour-sack under his bed. Ernest Elliot remembers well the day Jim told him and his wife that Ern's letters had disappeared. They have never surfaced and are assumed to have been dumped when a firm of New Plymouth solicitors shifted offices.

Professor Radium's experiments often resulted in explosions.
(Puck 25/8/1906 p12, British Library)

Professor Radium off to war to catch submarines.
(Puck 7/8/1915 p25, British Library)

Lampshade made from two of Rutherford's degree parchments. (Duncan Shaw-Brown, University of Canterbury)

The Armorial Bearings of
ERNEST, LORD RUTHERFORD of NELSON,
of Cambridge co. Cambridge, Member of the Order of Merit,
Fellow and President of the Royal Society,
Recipient of the Nobel Chemistry Prize (1908),
born at Brightwater, near Nelson, New Zealand 30 August 1871, etcetera
as Recorded in Her Majesty's College of Arms

Conrad Swan
5. V. 82   York
York Herald of Arms

Rutherford Coat of Arms, 1931. (Conrad Swan, Rutherford Family)

LMS Railway engine, model presented to Patrick Fowler, 1935.
(*Rutherford Family*)

Chapter 19

BIRTH OF THE ATOM SMASHERS

If we knew more about the nucleus we'd find it was a much simpler thing than we suppose ⋯ we must look for simplicity in the system first ⋯ I am always a believer in simplicity, being a simple person myself.

Ernest Rutherford,
Göttingen, 14 December 1931

The Neutron at Last

During his 1920 Bakerian lecture to the Royal Society Ern had predicted the existence of the neutron, a particle having the same mass as the proton but with zero electrical charge. In essence a proton and an electron fused together. He expected neutrons to occur in small numbers in the electric discharge of hydrogen where large numbers of protons and electrons were in close proximity and immediately had a student search for them to no avail.

In 1919 James Chadwick, one of Ern's students at Manchester who had recently returned from war-time internment in Germany, took the remaining year of his Exhibition of 1851 Scholarship at Cambridge. Shortly after the Bakerian lecture Ern invited Chadwick to join him in follow-up experiments connected with the artificial disintegration of nitrogen. As they waited for their eyes to adapt to the darkness needed for scintillation counting, Ern regularly expounded to Chadwick on the problems of the structure of the nucleus and how the neutron was needed to account for complex nuclei. Over the ensuing years one or other or both looked out for the neutron in any experiment they carried out, some of which were designed specifically with the neutron in mind.

Ern had stated the basic properties expected of the neutron during his Bakerian lecture including ⋯ *Its external field would be practically zero, except very close to the nucleus, and in consequence it should be able to move freely through matter.* James Chadwick and a research student missed discovering the neutron in June of 1931 because he expected the neutron to leave a track in their cloud chamber. Chadwick was later to chastise himself. *I ought to have arrived sooner. I had failed to think deeply enough about the properties of the neutron especially about those properties which would most clearly furnish evidence of its existence.* The student went off to oblivion.

They were not the only ones to miss the discovery. Marie Curie's daughter, Irene, and son-in-law, Professor Joliot, who had not read Ern's Bakerian lecture because such lectures seldom contained anything novel which had not been published elsewhere, reported a puzzling observation. The unknown radiation produced when alpha-particles were fired at a target of beryllium could eject protons from matter containing hydrogen. James Chadwick quickly repeated the experiment, showed that the emitted 'radiation' had to be a neutral particle, and, on the 17th of February 1932, sent to the editor of the science magazine, *Nature*, a letter entitled 'Possible existence of a neutron'.

The Birth of High Energy Physics

Ernest Rutherford had summed up all of the work on naturally occurring radioactivity, which he had carried out at McGill and Manchester, as ⋯ *We can watch the explosions of these atoms, but are powerless to influence them.* During his last year at Manchester his experiments, whereby nitrogen atoms bombarded with fast alpha-particles became oxygen atoms, showed that such nuclear explosions could at least be induced artificially. Because the nucleus of an atom was so small, only about one in every million alpha-particles fired at a target hit a nucleus. Even with the strongest available sources of alpha-particles, the rate of induced nuclear disintegration was extremely small.

Ern had appreciated that gas discharge tubes produced far higher bombardment rates than those available from radium sources. A current of one thousandth of an ampere corresponds to over 1000 million million particle impacts per second. A similar rate of alpha-particle emissions would require

100 kg of radium, an impossible amount when compared to the one gramme of radium which constituted the Cavendish's powerful source.

To produce an ion of similar energy to that of an alpha-particle the ion would have to be accelerated through a potential difference of a few million volts. Such voltages, on a routine basis, were beyond the then state of high voltage engineering, although several companies were manufacturing the high voltage sources which produced the several hundred thousand volts required by powerful X-ray units.

There were strong links between the Cavendish Laboratory and the Metropolitan-Vickers company in Manchester because the Director of the company's Research Laboratory had worked on anti-submarine work during the war. John Cockcroft, who took up a College apprenticeship at Metropolitan-Vickers after obtaining a masters degree in electrical engineering at Manchester, decided to go to Cambridge to sit the Mathematical Tripos. He then continued on to a PhD at the Cavendish. Throughout he was partially supported by the company in return for keeping in touch with it. Much of Cockcroft's work was in helping with electrical problems connected with Peter Kapitza's plans to develop a high magnetic field facility at the Cavendish. By 1926 the facility was working so Cockcroft was available for other projects.

Thomas Allibone (known as Bones to his friends) worked jointly between Sheffield University and the Research Laboratory of the Metropolitan-Vickers Company. He had always wanted to go to Cambridge so in 1926 submitted to Professor Rutherford a proposal, based on a Tesla coil, to accelerate charged particles in a vacuum tube and to see if they could induce artificial disintegrations. Summoned to an interview, he was taken by Ern to the largest and highest room in the Cavendish and asked:

"How many volts could you generate in here?"

Allibone. *"At least 500 kV but not much more".*

Some weeks later he was accepted and started work to build a suitable machine. Ern had suggested he work with electrons because he believed positive ions had no chance of entering the nucleus unless they could be accelerated to rival the alpha-particles emitted, from radium, with energies of over four million electron volts.

The following year a new research student, Ernest Walton from Dublin, was assigned space in the laboratory occupied by Cockcroft and Allibone and allowed to develop his betatron ideas for the task of accelerating electrons in circular orbits.

In his 1927 Presidential Speech to the Royal Society, Ern had dwelt on the recent work in England and America to produce high voltages for general scientific purposes and stated

> ··· It has long been my ambition to have available for study a copious supply of atoms and electrons which have an individual energy far transcending that of the alpha- and beta-particles from radioactive bodies. I am hopeful that I may yet have my wish fulfilled, but it is obvious that many experimental difficulties will have to be surmounted before this can be realised, even on a laboratory scale.

Help was at hand from a completely unexpected source, which is the usual way in which science advances. In one long unexplained curiosity of radioactive decay, first formulated at Manchester in 1911 as the Geiger-Nuttal law, the energy of an alpha-particle emitted from a disintegrating nucleus was clearly related to the half-life of the parent atom. Strangely, although the energies of alpha-particles emitted from radioactive nuclei ranged roughly from 4 to 8 million electron volts, a variation by only a factor of two, the lifetimes of radioactive nuclei range from about ten thousand million years down to less than a millionth of a second, a range covering 24 orders of magnitude.

In 1928 George Gamow used the new quantum theory to show that radioactive decay was a tunnelling process. Because of its wavelike properties an alpha-particle in the nucleus could quantum-mechanically tunnel through the narrow but otherwise impossibly high barrier around a nucleus rather than the classical way in which the escaping alpha-particle had to have energy sufficient to surmount the barrier. Thus higher energy alpha-particles had a much greater chance of tunnelling than lower energy alpha-particles and hence their parent nuclei decayed more quickly.

In December of 1928 George Gamow sent a manuscript of a subsequent paper, also in German, to the Cavendish. In it he described a theory of artificial disintegration in which the inverse quantum mechanical concept might also hold. Relatively low energy alpha-particles should tunnel through the potential barrier into the nucleus of a light atom thus inducing disintegration of the nucleus. This paper was discussed in the laboratory's physics colloquium at the end of January, following which Cockcroft, Allibone and Walton returned to their room and the other two watched as Cockcroft substituted numbers into the Gamow formula to show that an observable rate of disintegrations should occur for a microampere of protons accelerated to 300,000 volts.

Rutherford gave his approval for the construction of a suitable proton accelerator and Cockcroft started assembling the apparatus. For technical reasons Cockcroft decided not to use Allibone's Tesla coil. Metropolitan-Vickers designed a high voltage transformer small enough to fit into the room. (Later it went into commercial production for the X-ray market.) One of the company's research staff provided his newly developed oil diffusion pumps to evacuate the apparatus and low vapour-pressure plasticine to seal vacuum leaks. Ernest Walton stopped his own work, which had been unsuccessful because of technical problems, in order to help Cockcroft. Allibone was committed to completing his PhD on accelerating electrons so could not join the project although he designed and patented the high voltage rectifiers needed. In 1930 he returned to Metropolitan-Vickers as Director of their Research Laboratory.

The strong linkage between the Cavendish and Metropolitan-Vickers showed when Sir Ernest Rutherford opened the one million volt extension to the company's High Voltage Laboratory on the 28th of February 1930 before an audience which included four present, and three future, holders of the Nobel Prize. In his speech Ern stated

> ··· *I must point out, however, that the ordinary university laboratory with its exiguous finance cannot hope to erect a cathedral-like structure such as we see today to house the high potential installation. What we require is an apparatus to give us a potential of the order of 10 million volts which can be safely accommodated in a reasonably-sized room and operated by a few kilowatts of power. We require, too, an exhausted tube capable of withstanding this voltage and I recommend this interesting problem to the attention of my technical friends.*

[Was this just an exhortation for industry to expand through research or did Ern not have complete faith in George Gamow?]

Ingenuity saw glass tubes from petrol pumps and steel bicycle tube incorporated into the machine thus maintaining the string and sealing wax reputation of the Cavendish. The apparatus first worked at 280 kV in 1930 but in mid-1931, when the pair should have been bombarding targets, the Physical Chemistry Department reclaimed their room. Cockcroft and Walton shifted the apparatus to another room which had an even higher ceiling. Cockcroft had developed a voltage doubling circuit, which the company patented for him, so he took the opportunity of the shift to double the accelerating voltage to 600 kV. [Did he too not have full faith in Gamow's prediction?]

For many months Cockcroft and Walton worked up their apparatus: painstakingly searching for vacuum leaks, running up the voltage, correcting electrical faults, trying to get many facets of a complicated apparatus working at the same time and, whenever this happened, studying the range in air of the accelerated protons. Wasted months passed. Though they had told the world in two scientific papers, the first in August of 1930, how their apparatus worked and what they planned to do with it, Cockcroft and Walton appeared unconcerned about competition. Ern was. Besides, the 28th of April 1932 was fast approaching and on that evening he was due to lead a discussion at the Royal Society on the topic of 'The Structure of the Atomic Nuclei'.

Vivian Bowden, who worked in the room next door, later recalled

> ⋯ *Rutherford came into the lab one day. First of all he hung a wet coat on a live terminal and gave himself an electric shock which didn't improve his temper. Then he sat down and lit his pipe – he always smoked very dry tobacco, so when he lit it, it went off like a volcano with a great big cloud of smoke, flames and piles of ash. Then he summoned Cockcroft and Walton and asked them what they were doing. He told them to stop messing about and wasting their time and get on and do what he'd told them to do months ago, and arrange that these protons be put to good use.*

Suitably chastised, they turned from developing the machine to using it. On Wednesday the 13th of April 1932, while John Cockcroft was lecturing, Ernest Walton operated the accelerator alone, bombarding a target of lithium. Leaving the control table, and crouching low to avoid danger from the high voltages present, he entered the observer's tiny hut at the base of the apparatus. Through the microscope he observed the wonderful sight of many bright flashes of light on the fluorescent screen. Cockcroft confirmed the observation. After a few tests they notified Ern and squeezed him into the little hut. He confirmed that the flashes were indeed due to alpha-particles, after all

> "⋯ *I ought to know one when I see it for I was present at the birth of the alpha-particle and have been observing them ever since.*"

For the first time ever, a nuclear reaction had been induced by completely artificial means. A hydrogen nucleus accelerated to high speed had been combined with a lithium nucleus to form an unstable nucleus which immediately decayed into two helium nuclei.

Ern swore the laboratory to secrecy for a week, during which they had a new field all to themselves, and on the 16th of April, a mere three days after the initial observation, Cockcroft and Walton sent a note to *Nature*. Public adulation and cartoons followed. In America, Ernest Lawrence telegraphed several members of his research group who were skiing in the mountains :

> *Cockcroft and Walton have just disintegrated light elements with accelerated protons. Come right back, let's get with it.*

During his opening speech at the Royal Society's discussion meeting on 'The Structure of the Atomic Nuclei' Ern described Cockcroft and Walton's work and then called out, while looking round the room, "*Cockcroft and Walton must be here somewhere. Stand up you boys and let them see what you look like!*" At the same meeting Chadwick reported on the first observation of the neutron. As Ern said, it never rains but it pours.

Ern was now convinced of the soundness of Gamow's quantum-mechanical tunnelling theory of radioactivity. While Cockcroft and Walton struggled towards ever higher voltages, Ern urgently ordered a portable, off-the-shelf, 100 kV transformer from Metropolitan-Vickers. The resultant little 200 kV accelerator, developed principally by Mark Oliphant, could induce disintegration rates at least a thousand times that of Cockcroft and Walton's apparatus.

For their respective works, Chadwick received the 1935 Nobel Prize in Physics and Cockcroft and Walton shared the 1951 prize. It is a measure of Ernest Rutherford that his name was on neither of the papers announcing these discoveries.

Discoveries Missed

Ern and the Cavendish Laboratory didn't corner the market in nuclear discoveries. Sometimes they missed quite important ones. After all, there was world-wide competition for fame. The Cavendish missed the discovery of the positively charged electron (positron), the first of the anti-matter particles.

Paul Dirac, who obtained his PhD at Cambridge, combined relativity and the new quantum theory and in 1928 predicted that a positively charged counterpart of the electron should exist. For this he received the 1933 Nobel Prize.

Gerald Tarrant's PhD research at the Cavendish Laboratory involved the absorption and scattering of high energy gamma-rays during which he observed two emitted gamma-rays of energy half a million and one million electron-volts. [Using $E = mc^2$, the mass of an electron or positron corresponded to an energy of half-a-million electron-volts. A gamma-ray of one million electron-volts incoming to an atomic nucleus can vanish in creating an electron-positron pair. When a positron meets an electron they vanish, creating a gamma-ray of energy one million electron-volts.] Gerald reminisced that he asked another (reluctant) student, who had a cloud chamber inside a magnetic field, to look for the positron. Alexander reported no effect. In 1932 Carl Anderson at CalTech in America discovered the positron by placing a lead sheet inside a cloud chamber inside a high magnetic field and exposed it to the high energy gamma-rays in cosmic rays. Chadwick immediately borrowed Alexander's apparatus and observed positrons. Gerald Tarrant took a job as a schoolteacher whilst Carl Anderson received the 1936 Nobel Prize.

The Cavendish Laboratory also missed discovering artificially-induced radioactivity whereby a particle fired into a nucleus combined with it to make a new nucleus which was unstable and therefore radioactive. Ern wrote a letter to the discoverers, Marie Curie's daughter and son-in-law, Irene and Frederic Joliot, which they treasured for the rest of their lives.

Cavendish Laboratory
Cambridge
January 29th, 1934

My dear Colleagues

I was delighted to see an account of your experiments in producing a radioactive body by exposure to α rays. I congratulate you both on a fine piece of work which I am sure will ultimately prove of much importance.

I am personally very much interested in your results as I have long thought that some such an effect should be observed under the right conditions. In the past I have tried a number of experiments using a sensitive electroscope to detect such effects but without any success. We also tried the effect of protons last year on the heavy elements but with negative results.

With best wishes to you both for the further success of your investigations.

Yours sincerely
Rutherford

We shall try to see whether similar effects appear in proton and diplon bombardment

Wife. "BUT, DARLING, WHATEVER IS IT? HAVE YOU WON THE CROSSWORD PRIZE?"

Scientist (old sport). "BETTER THAN THAT. GOOD OLD LIGHT BLUES! THEY'VE SPLIT ANOTHER ATOM!"

[With Mr. Punch's compliments to Mr. FEATHER, of Trinity College, Cambridge, who has disintegrated the oxygen nucleus for the first time.]

Ten scientists immediately, but unsuccessfully, nominated Frederic Joliot and/or Irene Joliot-Curie for the 1934 Nobel Prize in Physics. In 1935 the emphasis switched to Chemistry, partly because Ern and the big names of physics had nominated James Chadwick for the Physics Prize, which he was to be awarded. Ern and two others nominated Frederic and Irene for the Chemistry Prize. Late that year he could delightedly telegraph to the pair.

> *WARMEST CONGRATULATIONS ON WELL DESERVED HONOUR OF NOBEL PRIZE FROM MYSELF AND MEMBERS CAVENDISH LABORATORY AM DELIGHTED TO SEE MY HOPES HAVE BEEN REALISED = RUTHERFORD*

Ern was also scooped by Enrico Fermi, whose 1934 discovery of neutron induced radioactivity utilised Ern's earlier prediction that it was easier to use uncharged neutrons to penetrate nuclei. Fermi was awarded the 1938 Nobel Prize. This discovery, more than any other, set the path to Armageddon.

Life Outside the Laboratory

When May Rutherford returned from New Zealand in 1931 she arranged for her granddaughter Liddy to have a weekly piano lesson immediately after lunch at Newnham Cottage. Liddy recalls how her grandfather always seemed to be in his study, usually smoking, and would always offer her one of his cough lozenges with the admonition *"Don't tell Granny."* After lunch Grandpapa, at the head of the table, would light his pipe, taking twenty or so matches to do so, and cough. Granny would then say, *"Ern, must you!"* This ritual happened every lunch time.

Regularly on Sunday afternoons during term, the Rutherfords entertained small groups from the laboratory to afternoon tea. Such events were rather formal and not necessarily looked forward to by the newer research students. Formal invitations were issued, promptness of arrival was expected (to the mortification of one young couple who had forgotten to alter their clocks to summer time), shop talk was forbidden (unless Ern and a student could get out of May's hearing range), no chance was given to out-stay the visit (at the appointed time May led a tour of the garden which finished at the gate) and Lady Rutherford expected a polite note of thanks afterwards. Afternoon tea was served by May who sat on a low chair before a rather small table, pouring tea from a large, solid silver teapot of which she was very proud. Ern sat at the opposite end of the group, all of whom balanced teacup and biscuits or cucumber sandwiches on their knees. Ern, with his loud voice, dominated proceedings. Regularly, his cup would be passed back along the table and eventually he would proclaim "*I haven't had my second cup yet dear. Where is it?*" Equally regularly May would respond rather haughtily "*Dr Yates* (or Mr Fremlin or whoever) *has not finished his first yet. You will wait*" causing the junior person to near scald himself as he gulped down his hot tea.

Ern's main exercise comprised a round of golf on Sunday mornings with a regular group. These outings were generally noisy, jovial affairs. After Ern struck a particularly good shot down the fairway Frederick Mann recalled him as bursting into a song – which Ern called 'The Spinster's Anthem'

> *Give me a man, give me a man,*
>
> *Give me a mansion in the sky!*

One foursome, all of whom were Fellows of the Royal Society, once interrupted their game to search the rough for a skylark's nest which they had found the week before. One-upmanship regularly arose. An opposing player contemplated a shot for which prudence dictated a shortish one to avoid a bunker before the hole. Ern's booming question, "*Now, Brother Bill! Are you a man or a mouse?*", ensured an over-vigorous miss-hit into the bunker.

During one outing a caddy gave Ern advice on how to improve his game. Beamed the caddy, after Ern struck his next shot well, "*With my brains and your brawn we would go far!*"

On one occasion Ern and Ralph Fowler, playing together in a foursome, were well placed a stroke ahead. Ralph's careful preparation and practice swings for the crucial putt seemed interminable. Just before the putter struck in earnest Ern shouted in exasperation "*Get on, get on, correct to 1 in a 1000*" causing Ralph to smote their ball a wild blow. It knocked their opponent's ball into the hole and ricocheted into the nearest bunker. An observer recalled:

> ··· *Fowler walked away in furious silence to the next tee, leaving the Great Man standing motionless and miserable, until with drooping shoulders and head down he walked slowly after his son-in-law, saying sadly* "*It's going to be a long time before I live this down!*

As the most well-known member of the Rutherford/Thompson/Newton family, Ern had many little family duties to attend to whenever a family member required the support of a big name in England. He supported Cecil Thompson's attempt to join the Royal Air Force (unsuccessful because of colour blindness) and introduced his nephew Alan Rutherford (Jim's son) to the Anglo-Persian Oil Company. [Alan had been a well-manager at Taranaki Oil fields. During the Second World War he helped to drill the first oil-producing well in England, at Ettering. Alan is listed amongst the Americans on the memorial there.] As the only family member in England, Ern gave away Audrey Bell, a niece, when she married Hubert Watson in London. Photographers captured Ern and May flanking Hubert and Audrey in a series of photographs which all showed Audrey's train blown high in the gusty winds, culminating in a final photograph of Hubert climbing the iron rails to untangle it.

Ernest Rutherford was not a good lecturer. His forte was research and he could inspire interested people when telling them about his own work. Phrases such as ··· *Allow me, if you will* ··· drew the audience into his world. May Rutherford would castigate her husband "*Must you stand there so long saying er, er?*" He often um'ed and er'ed and paused while struggling for a word. So much so that there was a saying at the Cavendish "*To er is Ernest.*"

During the latter half of his life his world fame, new discoveries and impressive demonstrations all carried him through public lectures. His 1934 Friday Evening Discourse to the Royal Institution serves as a good example. He elected to talk on the Transmutation of Elements. George Crowe spent the preceding few weeks in preparing the diagrams and equipment needed while Mark Oliphant duplicated his accelerator for demonstrating the deuteron-deuteron reaction. On the day in question Oliphant and Crowe drove to London and frantically set up the equipment with the help of the Royal Institution's own lecture assistant. As they did so, Ern and the Director of the Royal Institution, his old friend Sir William Bragg, reminisced that they had first met in Adelaide when Ern passed through on his way to England back in 1895. The Friday Evening Discourses oozed tradition. A white-tie audience of London professors, moneyed people, influential people and society people filled the tiered seats which semicircled the lecturer's platform. Such events were social occasions for members of the Royal Institution, of whom Mark Oliphant estimated that perhaps 9/10ths did not understand what was being discussed.

The Director, who lived on site, gave a small dinner-party beforehand for himself, the lecturer and perhaps two others, after which the lecturer was nominally locked into a room. (This tradition had started after one nervous lecturer had run away prior to his talk). At the appointed time the lecture assistant fetched the speaker. They walked into the lecture theatre and stood together. As the clock finished striking the hour Lord Rutherford commenced his talk.

The audience was treated to the first public demonstration of the transmutation of an atom by artificial means. Deuterium bombarded by deuterium became helium of atomic mass 3, a reaction first induced in the laboratory only weeks previously. The ion source glowed, a high voltage transformer crackled and then, as the voltage was increased, a loud speaker came to life broadcasting the clicks of the amplified particle detectors and counters. Because everything had worked it had not been necessary to invoke plan B whereby the small radioactive source surreptitiously carried by George Crowe would have operated the counters at the appropriate moment.

Following tradition the lecture stopped, and the applause started, as the clock commenced striking the hour. The lecturer immediately walked out to the social function which followed, joined by those in the audience who had not departed for home or nightclubs.

Having no false dignity and no vanity himself, Ernest Rutherford could not abide pomposity. If, after dinner at Trinity College, some Fellows behaved pretentiously he would call out *"Anyone for the Marx Brothers?"*, or whatever comedy was on at the local movie theatre, and off they would go. Henry Tizard recalled Ern reporting to him:

> *"I've just been seeing so-and-so" – mentioning a man well-known in public life!*
>
> *Pause – puff on pipe – then*
>
> *"Nothing much to him is there?" And the fact is there wasn't.*

Another Rutherford put down involved

> *"like the Euclidian Point, he has position without magnitude."*

Ern always dined at Trinity College on Sunday evenings, the most popular night of the week. One night, as the Vice-Master, a Reverend Doctor who was leading the procession into the Hall in the absence of the Master, reached the top of the stairs he rounded on the quiet old Professor of Arabic immediately behind him and rebuked him for some triviality – long, vigorously and intemperately. Ern, as next in line, was a close observer. He recalled that after grace the Vice-Master turned to him and said

> *"Rutherford, I rather gathered from the expression on your face that you don't altogether approve of what I said to Nicholson? And I said, bringing my clenched fist down hard on the table, 'By thunder! Parry if you ever talk to me like that, I'll knock you base over apex down those stairs!' "*

During brief walks from his holiday cottage he regularly chatted to the local dairy farmer about the merits and demerits of different milking schemes. One favourite call was to a retired engineer who generated his own electric power which he stored in batteries.

May Rutherford would talk to anyone about gardening but her inherent carefulness about money and her abrupt manner alienated many people. She had great difficulty retaining servants, especially cooks. "*They say I nag. I never nag. But nothing's right.*" Dick Southwell, one of Ern's golfing mates, was one of the few Fellows at Trinity who felt sorry for May. His wife, Isobella, did not like May whom she regarded as rude to most people. When the Southwells transferred to Oxford the Rutherfords would stay overnight with them whenever motoring to Wales for their holidays. The Southwells' cook would always prepare sandwiches at night for the next stage of the Rutherfords' journey. Inevitably, in the morning May would demand impolitely "*We will need some sandwiches.*" On their being produced she would unwrap them and usually proclaim "*Sardines – don't like sardines – get me something else.*"

May nagged Ern about his smoking, his weight and his drinking. Because of her background she remained violently teetotal all her life. As a principal guest he would usually be segregated from his wife at most dinners but not out of earshot of the occasional "*Ern, you've had enough*" as the dinner became boisterous. The Rutherfords' own parties were not always anticipated with unalloyed pleasure by the junior researchers since they invariably *included charades and ridiculous games like 'sniff'*.

Both Rutherfords were basically shy. In public he hid behind boisterousness and she abruptness.

Chapter 20

ELDER STATESMAN OF SCIENCE

Cambridge 1930–1937

Rutherford ··· exploded with wrath at Hitler's treatment of scientific colleagues whom he knew intimately and valued. ··· He did everything and more to make our going ahead possible. With Rutherford as our President-to-be, going ahead was easy.

Sir William Beveridge,
on forming the Academic Assistance Council, 1933

Public Duties

With age and status came public duties. Ern served as President of the Royal Society (1925–30) and of the Institute of Physics (1931–33). These organizations, and many others, required Ern's regular attendance in London. In 1917, by invitation, he had joined the Athenaeum Club in Pall Mall, a mere bottle of port's throw from the Royal Society. This served as his London home and through it he met men of great distinction from fields other than science and university.

As the foremost New Zealander in Britain, Lord Rutherford featured in New Zealand events. Such as the celebration marking the inauguration of New Zealand Day, in 1933, when four hundred guests, including the Prince of Wales, dined at the Savoy Hotel. (The menu/toast list incorporated a copy of the Treaty of Waitangi.)

That same year Ern and Willie Marris, his old mate from Canterbury College and now Sir William Marris, were the principal speakers at the second annual UK dinner for graduates of the University of New Zealand. The University had not forgotten Ern. It had awarded him the first of its new honorary D.Sc.'s bringing the total number of degrees awarded to him by that University to five (B.A., M.A., B.Sc., D.Sc. and D.Sc.(honorary)), which must be close to a world record.

Some exposure was behind the scenes. After the Institution of Electrical Engineers awarded their 1930 Faraday Medal to Ern, the Institution filmed him for posterity. He sat at a desk in front of a microphone and woodenly read a resume of his lifetime of researches. (This is one of only three movie films of Ern known to exist.)

In December of 1931 Ern and Ralph Fowler went to Göttingen in Germany where, during the celebrations to mark the bicentennial of the founding of the Royal Society of Göttingen by the British King George II, Ern was awarded an honorary Doctorate. He gave a talk on his work. The hall, which seated 400 people, was filled 15 minutes before time and some 300 later arrivals were reluctantly turned away. Professor Pohl recorded Ern's informal talk on 9 small acetate discs so we have an audio record, punctuated by the German custom of an audience showing applause by stamping their feet. During his introduction Ern apologised

> ··· *for speaking to you in English, but I have the excuse that I was born on the other end of the world, in New Zealand, and have not had the time ahh since my arrival in Europe ahh to learn your language. But, I think if you had heard me speak German, you would be grateful that I am addressing you in English.*

Ern covered the fine details of the current knowledge of gamma-rays emitted by nuclei. He emphasised that this was the route to understanding the structure of the tiny nucleus, stating

> ··· *I ahh I ahh have the opinion for a long time, thats a personal conviction, that if we knew more about the nucleus we'd find it was a much simpler thing ahh than we suppose. That ahh these fundamental things I think have got to be fairly simple but it's the non-fundamental things that are very complex usually. So ahh we are hopeful we must look for simplicity in the system first and if the simplicity we can't find it well we got to look at something more complex. I am always a believer in simplicity, being a simple person myself.*

After the talk the chairman asked if he would take discussion.

> *Well err, err, err, the question is whether your – whether your err – whether your dinner is more important than the discussion.*

During the discussion Ern commented

> *··· I've no doubt our mathematical friends can define something that they know what they mean even if I don't.*

Nearly forgotten early researches were recalled when he presented the Marchese Marconi with the Institution of Civil Engineers' Kelvin Medal for 1932. Ern made mention of his own work in developing a simple magnetic detector of wireless waves in 1896.

An error of judgment by one New Year's Eve speaker brought forth calls for Parliament to exercise control over the British Broadcasting Corporation (BBC). Ern's name headed the list of twenty-nine signatories (which also included Willie Marris) who wrote to the editor of *The Times* to put the case for freedom of the BBC:

> *Impartiality should be preserved not by the censorship even of strongly controversial statements, but giving an equal opportunity for the expression of the opposite point of view.*

After Ern had completed his term on the BBC's Panel of Advisers he was asked to give another National Lecture which he did in 1933 speaking for forty-five minutes on the 'Transmutation of the Atom'. One speaker failed to adapt to the medium of radio so the Director of Talks wrote an internal memo recommending that BBC experts give advice to future speakers, holding up Ern as the model who,

> *··· on a difficult subject, succeeded, I think, in interesting a very wide circle of listeners ··· proved the virtue of liaison with the Corporation by being quite unusually friendly and open to suggestion.*

From its formation in 1934 Ern served on, and took an active part in, the BBC's General Advisory Council.

Ern's reasonableness in taking advice is also illustrated by his encounter with a young journalist Peter Ritchie-Calder. While interviewing Ern on the latest breakthrough in science Ritchie-Calder could not follow his description and scientific jargon so asked Ern if he would explain it in simple language. Ern took umbrage, whereupon Ritchie-Calder tossed his shorthand notebook over to the great man and asked:

> *"Can you read that?".*

"No of course not," replied an irritated Ern.

"Nor can my readers," said the young reporter. *"I have a duty to translate that shorthand into language they can understand – and I suggest, Sir, that if your discovery affects the life of a single human being you have a similar duty to me."*

Ern took the point. Later he sent Ritchie-Calder an advance copy of a talk he had prepared for a distinguished scientific audience and asked if he had made his message clear enough. During the talk Ern departed from the text to admonish scientists.

"If you can't explain to the charwoman scrubbing your laboratory floor what you are doing, you don't <u>know</u> what you are doing"

Ern maintained a nationwide and worldwide circle of friends. When Ernest Marsden wrote to him in 1935, enquiring if radioactivity could be used to date the age of the last Moa from bones and/or egg shell, he could pass the enquiry to an expert in the field of geological dating. [Moa, New Zealand's gigantic flightless bird, had survived into Maori times, less than 500 years ago. The time interval was too short for geological dating methods so the problem lay waiting for another twenty years, until radio-carbon dating was perfected.] As a great man of science himself, Ern was asked to review the English edition of Philipp Lenard's book *Great Men of Science : A History of Scientific Progress* for the science magazine *Nature*. The book covered only those scientists who were dead or no longer active. In warmly recommending the book Ern stated that

··· *Among scientific men, the degree of interest in the history of their subject varies curiously with age. As a rule, the young investigator has little interest in the origins of the scientific conceptions with which he works; it is only later when he has gained some personal experience of the ways in which new knowledge is secured, and the way in which the new developments are linked with the past, that he begins to take an interest in the history of his science and the achievements and personalities of the great pioneers.*

Punch, 16 Sep. 1936.

BRAIN-WAVES AT BLACKPOOL

"NOW, BOYS, TALKING ABOUT FIGURES, WHAT DO YOU SAY TO ELECTING A BEAUTY-KING?"

In 1936 the British Association for the Advancement of Science met at Blackpool. Use the Punch cartoon for a 'Spot-the-Ern' Competition.

Peter Kapitza

Ern had arranged for a laboratory, the Royal Society Mond Laboratory, to be built in the courtyard of the Cavendish, for Peter Kapitza's work on high magnetic fields and very low temperatures.

In thanks Kapitza commissioned Eric Gill, one of the best of the modern sculptors, to produce a crocodile in the brickwork near the entrance and a bas-relief portrait of Ern for the entrance hall. May Rutherford hated the portrait. ··· *It is ghastly, like an Assyrian.* Others, infected by the Hitler anti-Jew stunt, thought the nose Jewish. The BBC made a fuss of it as did a member of Parliament. Conservative people asked that it be removed. Even Cambridge University's Buildings Syndicate called a special meeting to consider the outcry.

Ern, though he disliked the nose, tactfully stated that he knew nothing about art and suggested that Kapitza write to their mutual friend Niels Bohr for judgment as Bohr took a great interest in modern art. Bohr pronounced strongly for retention and was rewarded with an artist's copy for himself. (This he inlaid over the fireplace of his office.)

That was not the only fuss initiated by the opening of the Mond Laboratory. Stanley Baldwin, the Prime Minister, officiated as the Chancellor of the University. He had asked Ern for a few relevant notes and used these verbatim. Thus when he was reported as stating ··· *In order to try out the possibilities of these new methods of generating such intense fields* ··· readers of *The Times* stared in horror at the use of the words 'try out' by the Chancellor of Cambridge University. They deluged the Editor with letters decrying the Americanization of the English language. Ern took perverse glee in writing to Mr Baldwin to ask how he liked being 'whipping-boy'.

Less than two years after the magnificent Mond Laboratory was opened, Peter Kapitza returned to Russia for the summer of 1934. This he had done almost annually since 1929 as a consultant for Russian science but now he was told he could not leave and must stay to promote science and technology in Russia.

Kapitza was devastated. So too was Ern though he did write to the secretary of the DSIR.

> ··· *I think I told you Kapitza in one of his expansive moods in Russia told the Soviet engineers that he himself would be able to alter the whole face of electrical engineering in his lifetime.* ··· *This seems to be a very probable explanation of their action and is due to our friend's love of the limelight.*

Very diplomatically Ern appealed to the Russian Ambassador and requested

Paul Langevin in France and Niels Bohr in Denmark to do likewise to theirs. The Prime Minister was approached to raise the matter at high diplomatic levels. All this had been done privately so that no loss of face would occur if the Russians were to back down but eventually, seven months after Kapitza's detention, the story was sensationally splashed through the newspapers.

Ern and the President of the Royal Society wrote a letter to *The Times* appealing for Kapitza to be allowed to return for at least a while to complete the work he had started. Hope ceased when finally the Russian Ambassador publicly defended the Soviet action and concluded:

> *Cambridge would no doubt like to have all the world's greatest scientists in its laboratories, in much the same way as the Soviet Union would like to have Lord Rutherford and others of your great physicists in her laboratories.*

The intrigue, the endless repetitive questions from a stream of reporters, the final realization that Kapitza could not return and his own inability to overturn the situation depressed Ern. One night, after a subdued dinner at Trinity College, Ern invited Frederick Mann to join him for coffee in the parlour. Frederick Mann recorded in his little book *Lord Rutherford on the Golf Course* how Ern slowly filled his pipe and then began reminiscing. He invited a small group of junior Fellows to join the group. As he tired he talked of his earlier days in New Zealand, brightening somewhat as he retold the story of the cow's tail at Foxhill. After dismissing the audience with a weary remark about it being late he sat again with Frederick Mann exclaiming

> ⋯ *I had to talk!* ⋯ *and I had to talk about something else.* ⋯ *What I want is a chance to forget the whole business for a while.*

All had to accept the Kapitza situation. The Russians built the Institute for Physical Problems for Kapitza and Ern arranged to sell the Russians all, or duplicates, of Kapitza's equipment at the Mond Laboratory, an act of great generosity which severely disrupted the work of many Cavendish people for many months. Kapitza was extremely grateful to Ern. In one gesture he produced for his books a book plate which incorporated a crocodile.

Railway Research

The London, Midland and Scottish (LMS) Railway claimed to be the largest commercial undertaking in the world because of its 222,920 employees, 8000 locomotives, 24,000 passenger coaches, 270,000 freight wagons, 20,000 road vehicles, 45 steamers, 31 hotels and 537 miles of canal. To support this vast enterprise the LMS constructed a research laboratory at Derby designed to carry out research into the mountains of materials used by the organization. The company invited Lord Rutherford to open the laboratory in his capacity as Chairman of the Science Advisory Council of the Department of Scientific and Industrial Research.

On the 10th of December 1935 the official party, which included LMS officials, directors of six of the seven Research Associations to which the LMS belonged, prominent industrialists, and distinguished scientists such as Sir William Bragg and Sir James Jeans, assembled at St Pancras Station in London. None were as excited as young Patrick Fowler who had a special role to play. Eight-and-a-half-year-old Patrick was taken on a special tour of the train by Sir Josiah Stamp, the LMS chairman. In pride of place at the head of the procession the brand-spanking-new locomotive, No 5665 the first of its subclass of Jubilee 5XP locomotives, gleamed in the weak winter light. So too did the white-painted coal in its tender.

At the appointed time a beaming Patrick was lifted onto the side of the engine where, before the distinguished guests, the photographers and Derek Cook's unhearing 16mm movie camera, he loudly called out "*I name this engine 'Lord Rutherford of Nelson'*" and drew aside the purple curtain to unveil the locomotive's brass name plate – LORD RUTHERFORD OF NELSON. Also revealed was a magnificent clockwork model of the locomotive, the LMS's gift to Patrick. Lady Rutherford had been invited to name the train but being shy had declined. The honour had then fallen on Patrick as the younger, and hence most photogenic, grandson.

As the train clacked out of London Sir Josiah Stamp switched on the loudspeaker system to say a few words of welcome. On arrival at Derby the train shunted into a siding alongside the laboratory and the official speeches emerged from the loudspeakers as the guests ate lunch in the carriages.

Sir Josiah Stamp described Ern as

> ⋯ *the master of the experimental method. The more we are in contact with him and his work the more we felt it impossible for this age even to realise let alone to pay, the debt it owed to him for his past contributions to modern knowledge.*

In declaring the laboratory open Ern likened the railway system to the skeletal, arterial and nervous system of the country with the Research Laboratory as the heart, pumping in fresh blood.

> ⋯ *As a firm believer in the power of science, and of the scientific method in its application to industry, I am convinced there is hardly a single*

*unit, whether of machinery, or layout, or even of organisation, that
cannot be improved for its purpose by the application of patient scientific
research. ··· To take another example, if you can persuade such a
locomotive as you have been good enough to name after me, to do its
duty with a saving of 1-lb of coal per mile, or still better, if you prolong
its working life between overhauls by 10 per cent, the result should be
applicable to all your 8000 locomotives, leading to a substantial
economic improvement.*

To further mark the occasion a suitably inscribed ink-stand was presented to
Lord Rutherford after which the guests toured the laboratory.

In naming engine No 5665, the LMS had intruded into a long list of famous
British seafarers, No 5664 being named NELSON. After the round trip to Derby
the LORD RUTHERFORD OF NELSON chuffed off into obscurity, being finally
taken out of service, and presumably broken up, late in 1962. [Patrick, a train
buff in his youth, highly treasures his model.]

The Academic Assistance Council

Adolf Hitler came to power in Germany in January of 1933. As he
consolidated his position his violations of human rights escalated. Opponents
of his regime, non-Aryans and other 'unworthys' were fired from their jobs.
These events caused great concern world wide.

Chaim Weizmann, having set up the Hebrew University in Jerusalem, wrote
to influential friends in England suggesting that fund-raising be carried out in
order to allow the Hebrew University to take in some of the most eminent
displaced academics. He requested that Lord Rutherford preside. Meanwhile,
Leo Szilard, a Hungarian-born physicist who had been displaced from his job
in Germany, contacted the young Englishwoman Esther (Tess) Simpson, who
worked for the International Student Service in Vienna. He wished for an
introduction to the secretary to propose to him the idea of a University in
Switzerland for displaced scientists. Nothing came of this approach so Leo
Szilard looked up the guest book at his hotel, saw the name of Sir William
Beveridge, the Director of the London School of Economics, and so met him.
Sir William had read the non-Aryan regulations while on the train to Vienna
where, a few days later, he read the first list of dismissals from Universities.

On returning to London Sir William Beveridge wrote to Lord Rutherford
saying he was coming to Cambridge, was concerned with the problem of
German professors, and would like to talk to him. They met on Sunday the

7th of May 1933. That weekend the embryonic Academic Assistance Council was formed. Sir William endeavoured to persuade Ern to become President, which he at first refused to do citing pressure of work. Lady Rutherford strongly supported Ern's refusal. At a second meeting both were won over: Lady Rutherford by the long friendship between the Rutherfords and Sir William's cousin's wife, whom he wisely took to that second meeting, and Lord Rutherford by his personal knowledge of friends displaced. He served with distinction in that position for the rest of his life. Sir William Beveridge recalled that second meeting.

> *As we talked, he exploded with wrath at Hitler's treatment of scientific colleagues whom he knew intimately and valued. He would have been miserable not to be with us if we went ahead. He did everything and more to make our going ahead possible. With Rutherford as our President-to-be, going ahead was easy.*

Initially Rutherford proceeded quietly behind the scenes. As W H Bragg had cautioned him:

> *My one anxiety is whether or no we really can help. It is possible I suppose to do more harm than good by angering the people in power in Germany. It is a matter of balancing possibilities of good against those of evil. I think myself that we ought to try and help but that we ought to do it in such a way that as far as possible we give no offence.*

Also to be avoided was anger in Britain where high unemployment, a rising Fascist movement and the prospect of young British academics being blocked from positions and advancements, all led to a fear of an influx of continentals displaced from their jobs in Germany. (Doctors, who generally have one of the strongest trade-unions, managed, in 1936, to bar refugee doctors from setting up in practice in Great Britain.) For all his efforts in helping displaced academics Ern received regular abusive mail from people in England, graduates included.

The Royal Society gave office accommodation and in a press release of May 24th, signed by Lord Rutherford and forty other notable academics, the Academic Assistance Council was publicly launched.

> *⋯ We should like to regard any funds entrusted to us as available for University teachers and investigators of whatever country who, on grounds of religion, political opinion or race, are unable to carry on their work in their own country. ⋯ Our action implies no unfriendly feelings to the people of any country; it implies no judgment on forms of government or on any political issue between countries. Our only aims are the relief of suffering and the defence of learning and science.*

The trade unions endeavoured to assist their counterparts. Four groups, the Academic Assistance Council, the International Student Service, the Society of Friends (Germany Committee) and the Refugee Professionals Committee, banded together to raise the funds to support professional people – the Refugee Assistance Fund. The public launch took place before an audience of 10,000 people at the Albert Hall on the 3rd of October 1933. Lord Rutherford chaired the meeting which featured Albert Einstein as principal speaker.

Albert Einstein's name was well known to the general public as the developer of the theory of relativity. Hence he was the most visible of the displaced scientists even though his joint position in America meant he had an assured future there. He and Ern were poles apart – Einstein the lone theorist in an esoteric field and Ern the gregarious experimentalist in a matter-of-fact field. Ern fused Einstein's equivalence of mass and energy with Aston's accurate measurements of the masses of ions to calculate the energy difference before and after a nuclear reaction. Ern's 1920 view of Albert Einstein's work is preserved by Henry Dale who later recalled a discussion concerning prominent press coverage of observations, taken during an eclipse, which agreed with Einstein's General Theory of Relativity. Finally Ern stated:

> "Well, I don't believe there are more than six people in the whole world who really understand what that Einstein theory means." And when I meekly enquired who might be the other five, he looked at me quizzically for a moment, and then, with a gust of laughter – "Good Lord! Dale," he exclaimed, "you don't suppose that I understand it do you?"

[Some years later A S Eddington, the Cambridge astrophysicist, on being asked "Is it true that you and one other man are the only people in England who understand relativity?" hesitated rather a long time. When the questioner prompted him not to be modest he replied "No it's not that; I was trying to think who the other man was."]

Ern, in responding to the toast 'Science' at the annual banquet of the Royal Academy of Arts in 1932 had stated

> ⋯ The theory of relativity by Einstein, quite apart from any question of its validity (laughter), could not but be regarded as a magnificent work of art.

Ever conscious of politics, the Council had insisted that Germany was not to be referred to by name during the meeting. To this end Ern wrote to Einstein requesting to see the manuscript of his speech. Hence, during his twenty minute talk, Einstein would say "It cannot be my task to act as judge of the conduct of a nation which for many years has considered me as her own ⋯ "

In opening the meeting Ern had emphasised the neutrality of the Fund.

> *It is in such a spirit that the four societies which have combined to*
> *make this appeal have worked and intend to work. Their sole concern*
> *is to relieve suffering, and regardless of creed, race, or political opinion,*
> *to save these students and academic and professional workers who are*
> *now dependent for their lives on the charity of humanity.*

This emphasis that the Council was not campaigning *against* Germany but *for* all displaced academics culminated in Lord Rutherford introducing the phrase 'A Defence of Free Learning' and the Council changing its name in 1936 to the Society for the Protection of Science and Learning, the name under which it continues its good works today.

Tess Simpson was appointed secretary to the Academic Assistance Council in July of 1933. [She had asked Leo Szilard that if a job came up to let her know as it was just the sort of job she wanted; one working on behalf of people she respected.] She held the position with decorum and distinction, retiring in 1978 and later being awarded an O.B.E. and an LLD. Tess recalls Lord Rutherford as a very gentle, considerate person whom she liked a lot.

> *I saw him only rarely, on which occasion he would dictate letters to me.*
> *I was impressed then that so great a man should be so diffident; he*
> *seemed almost nervous when he dictated his letters.*

The work for the Academic Assistance Council significantly increased Ern's work load, many elements of which were, however, pleasurable. Max Born, the theoretical physicist who was to receive the Nobel Prize in 1954, remembered with affection the Rutherford's kindliness towards displaced academics. When forced to leave Germany Max Born obtained a temporary position at the Cavendish Laboratory but Trixi, the family dog, went into quarantine for six months, in kennels some miles from Cambridge. During a tea party at the Rutherfords, the Borns mentioned their dog and their sadness at not knowing how she was faring. The Rutherfords said:

> *"But why don't you go and visit her? We shall take you there in our*
> *car." And indeed a few days later they came, drove us to the kennels*
> *and told us not to hurry: they had taken books along and would read*
> *comfortably until we had assured ourselves about Trixi's well-being*
> *in prison.*

Although Max Born disliked the First World War political and military activities of a fellow refugee, the chemist Professor Fritz Haber, he took pity on Haber as a broken man deprived of his position and political influence. Born invited the Rutherfords to meet Haber at a small tea party at his home. Ern ⋯ *declined violently; did not wish to have any contact with the man who had invented chemical warfare with the help of poison gas.*

On the first anniversary of the formation of the Academic Assistance Council Ern wrote an article for *The Times* entitled 'The Wandering Scholars'. He defined them as ⋯ *those scholars and scientists of any nationality who on grounds of religion, race or political opinion are prevented from continuing their work in their own country.* In particular he concerned himself with

> ⋯ *the expulsion from academic positions in Germany of persons possessing pacifist or internationalist convictions or lacking that strangest of qualifications for the life of scholarship, 'Aryan' genealogies.*

Mostly it was a plea for money to continue the work, a plea he repeated two months later in a letter to the Editor.

The Case of Kurt Kreielsheimer

Within eight months of Hitler coming to power 50,000 people had been displaced from their jobs in Germany. For the academic community it marked one of the greatest migrations (or exodus) of academics the world has seen, and it accelerated the rise to pre-eminence of American physics for the second half of the 20th century. The register of displaced scientists has produced fifteen Nobel Laureates and seventy Fellows of the Royal Society.

Individuals get lost in these large numbers but the experience of Kurt Kreielsheimer, a German Jew, is perhaps typical. After completing his doctorate at Darmstadt Kurt went to the Heinrich Hertz Institute in Berlin. Several countries were to participate in the International Polar Year of 1932-3 and Kurt was appointed leader of the German Polar Year Expedition in Tromso, Norway. Its mission was to study the influence of the Aurora Borealis on the propagation of wireless waves. They arrived in December of 1932 and Kurt worked in close collaboration with Edward Appleton, the leader of the British Expedition and who had pioneered many radio propagation studies while at Cambridge under Ernest Rutherford.

Because of difficulties with organizing finance and equipment the German Expedition had started some six months behind the others and late in winter. Kurt therefore recommended that the expedition continue until March of 1934 in order to collect data over a complete winter period. This was agreed.

In June of 1933 Kurt wrote to his director as to his fate and received reassurance. By November of 1933 he learned the true situation from displaced friends. Non-Aryans were being dismissed from their positions. Under the new Aryan Laws only one percent of workers in Universities and Research Laboratories were allowed to be non-Aryan. As all radio research had been transferred to the Ministry of Propaganda under Herr Goebbels, Kurt's future did not look rosy. Several scientific periodicals refused contributions from non-Aryans and there was no possibility of work for him in academia or in industry.

So on the 3rd of January 1934 Kurt Kreielsheimer wrote to the Academic Assistance Council seeking a new position. They asked if he would go to New Zealand where the Jewish community had offered to sponsor a radio scientist at Auckland University College.

In March of 1934 Kurt returned to Germany to report before a special commission of radio scientists on the expedition and to recommend its future continuation. The continuation was agreed to but Kurt was bluntly told that he could no longer be considered a worthy representative of German science abroad and was to be dismissed on the 1st of October 1934. He had been given six months to write up the Arctic work and three weeks in Norway to introduce his successor to the work. Kurt applied for, and was granted, three weeks leave to visit his brother and sister in Germany. Instead he headed straight for the Belgian frontier and London. His surname in his passport had not been underlined (underlining was the mark of a non-Aryan) so there was no problem at the German border.

On arrival at Victoria railway station Kurt rang the only person he knew in London, Edward Appleton of Kings College, who invited him to visit immediately. Professor Appleton commented on the coincidence of Kurt's letter and the offer from Auckland, raised his arm and stated: *"To me it is a wink from above! Do you want to go to New Zealand ?"*

Kurt left his credentials to be forwarded to Professor Burbidge for consideration while he himself returned to Norway to discuss the continuation of the expedition with his newly appointed successor. A few weeks later he was notified that he had been accepted for the position in Auckland. Kurt left Norway once more, this time ostensibly to return to Germany but in fact in May of 1934 he went directly to England en route for New Zealand.

During the second world war Kurt Kreielsheimer worked for the Auckland Technical Development Branch of the Department of Scientific and Industrial Research on radio based projects such as converting the military ZC1 radio set for frequency modulation (FM) operation. He retired in 1968 as Professor of Radio Physics at the University of Auckland.

Kurt later recalled his few days in London while in transit to New Zealand.

Amongst various meetings of different people that were arranged for me the most memorable one was with Lord Rutherford, the President of the Council, at the rooms of the Royal Society. I might be forgiven when I confess that I approached the meeting of this famous man with a certain amount of trepidation. Though I dimly recalled that Rutherford started his scientific work with some interests in the detection of wireless waves, his fame was based on his investigations in the field of radioactivity of which I knew very little. However, when I was admitted to his presence a warm handshake and welcome soon put me at ease. Our conversation was very one-sided. The tenor of his words were: "You want to go to New Zealand – I certainly envy you." There was no mention of Physics or his work nor were there any questions about my own activities. For two solid hours I was treated to a discourse about New Zealand, its people, the scenic beauties both of the North and South Island and the University life and agricultural and scientific activities. I was impressed by the simplicity and straight-forward treatment that I received which gave me more of the impression of a farmer rooted in the love of people and country rather than that of a world famous scientist who at no time tried to impress his visitor. His collar with the corners turned down reminded me of the kind my father used to wear. To end the very interesting and informative meeting he took a Royal Society label out of a rack on his desk and [with a blunt pencil] wrote on it two introductions, the first one to Dr E Marsden, Secretary National Research Council, Wellington and the second one to Prof D L H Florance, Victoria College, Wellington, Professor of Physics, with his signature Rutherford in the bottom left-hand corner. Unfortunately, I did not realize that the label was a gummed parcel sticker. I placed this valuable piece of paper in the back of my passport for safe keeping in my hip pocket and did not realize that the heat of my body caused the label to become permanently glued to the back-cover of my passport [where it remains to this day]. After expressing my thanks, Rutherford wished me Good Luck, and I left the meeting with the definite feeling that this great man who had just farewelled me was very home-sick.

Chapter 21

SUNDOWN

I learned a great deal from Rutherford – not physics but how to do physics.

Peter Kapitza (Russian) to Niels Bohr (Dane)

7 November 1937

Working with Rutherford

Ernest Rutherford was an explorer. He pushed boldly into the unknown leaving others to follow and produce the detailed maps. On complaining to James Chadwick about the progress of two particular students, Ern stated that in his day they would have got on faster. Chadwick's reply, *"It is all very well you complaining about their measurements. They are measuring to ½%. You never measured anything to better than 5%"* caused Ern to laugh.

Mark Oliphant has a vivid recollection of Ern's impatience to obtain results. After one very fruitful day Mark Oliphant and George Crowe decided to postpone developing the photographic strip record of the particle detector until the following morning, when both they and the developer would be fresh. The Professor came in just as they were leaving and insisted they develop the record at once.

"I can't understand it", he thundered. "Here you have exciting results and you are too damned lazy to look at them tonight". We did our best, but the developer was almost exhausted, and the fixing bath yellowed

with use. The result was a messy record which even Rutherford could not interpret. In the end, he went off, muttering to himself that he did not know why he was blessed with such a group of incompetent colleagues. After dinner that night he telephoned me at home: "Er! Er! Is that you Oliphant ? I'm er, er, sorry to have been so bad tempered tonight. Would you call in to see me at Newnham Cottage as you go to the Laboratory in the morning?" Next day he was even more contrite. "Mary says I've ruined my suit. Did you manage to salvage the record?" He drove us mercilessly, but we loved him for it.

Max Born later recalled one dinner party which Ern gave at Trinity for a group of about twenty men.

When the port was circulating some people discussed the question of whether they were satisfied with their profession or would have preferred another one. Rutherford became quite angry and suggested that everybody should declare what he would have preferred to be and why. I had to start and said that I did not think I should be good at anything else but mathematical physics. But many of the others declared they were dissatisfied and would have preferred another profession, art, music, literature, army or navy, even business. When the circle closed with Rutherford he hit the table with his fist and shouted: "I shall be damned if I ever thought of being anything but what I am"

When John Blewett arrived in Cambridge in 1936, on a one year Fellowship from the Royal Society of Canada, he presented an overly ambitious programme of research to Ern who stated:

"In just a year you aren't really going to accomplish anything important. Your real purpose here is to meet our scientists and to learn how we work. A year ago we had an American here who worked much too hard. One morning we came in and found him sitting under a table talking to himself. So don't set unreasonable goals for your short stay here."

To everyone in the lab Ern was *the Professor* except to G F C Searle, the supervisor of the undergraduate laboratories, who called him Professor Radium after an endearing character who appeared in *Puck*, a comic weekly, from 1904 to 1916. Professor Radium's inventions were legion, with most ending in explosions.

To his colleagues Ern often appeared to work from intuition. While

A SELECTION OF THE 34 MEDALS AWARDED TO
ERNEST RUTHERFORD

Franklin Medal of the Franklin Institute, 1924 (gold 63mm).

Order of Merit (civil), 1925.

Wilhelm Exner Medal of the Austrian Trade Unions, 1936 (bronze 75mm).
(Duncan Shaw-Brown, University of Canterbury)

Rutherford Birthplace, Brightwater, Nelson. (Baz Colley, Network Tasman Energy)

New Zealand $100 banknote, 1992 (John Campbell)

Periodic table (c. 1996) on mug signed by the discoverer of rutherfordium (Rf element 104).
(John Campbell)

RUTHERFORD POSTAL STAMPS

Sweden 1968

New Zealand 1971

Canada 1971

Russia 1971

(Merilyn Hooper)

impacting deuterium targets with accelerated deuterium nuclei, Mark Oliphant and he discovered a puzzling particle which, while doubly charged like the helium nucleus, had a much shorter range in air than any known alpha-particle. After a long day of measurements and puzzling over the nature of the particle they went home. At 3 a.m. Oliphant's phone rang. It was the Professor.

> *"Oliphant. I'm sorry Oliphant to disturb you at this time of the morning but I think I know what those little particles are."*
>
> *"What are they Sir ?"*
>
> *"They're helium particles of mass 3."*
>
> *"How could you possibly say that ? What reasons can you have for that conclusion?"*
>
> *"Reasons! Reasons! Oliphant. I feel it in my water."*

Next day they set to work and once again showed that Ern's intuition was right.

The Cavendish Laboratory represented a large operation. At 11 a.m. each morning the Assistant Directors of Research reported to Ern to tell him any news of interest and to discuss research in progress. The smooth running of the Cavendish Laboratory depended on the Assistant Directors and Ern got on well with each of them, not surprisingly, as he had selected each one himself.

Ern had told Mark Oliphant that he intended to retire at 70 in 1941. Oliphant could not envisage working at the Cavendish under any other Professor. Besides, like others before him, he wanted a show of his own so he took a chair at Birmingham. On mentioning that he was tempted to go to Birmingham, he observed a very angry Rutherford even though it had been Ern who had sent Birmingham's Dean of Science to talk to him in the first place.

> *He grew red in the face and shouted that he was fated to be surrounded by ungrateful colleagues, and much else, ending : "Go and be damned to you!" I had never before been on the receiving end of one of Rutherford's choleric outbursts, though I had heard of them, so left his room greatly upset and worried. Shortly afterwards, he came to my room where I was sitting in despair, and asked hesitantly, could I spare time to talk with him. His apology for his reception of my news was complete, reinforcing my distress at having upset him. He went on to discuss how the work upon which I was engaged could be continued, and what he could do to help me if I did move to Birmingham. In the end, it was agreed that I should accept the appointment, provided that*

I could take it up in September, 1937. Rutherford proposed me for election to the Royal Society and it must have been through his influence that I was elected that year.

The academic staff looked after their own areas. The major research thrust was of course in Ern's own field of nuclear physics but he supported and encouraged those in other fields:– Kapitza who developed and used extremely high magnetic fields and extremely low temperatures; Appleton, the pioneer in radio studies of the earth's upper atmosphere; C T R Wilson, who continued the work he started in 1895 on cloud formation thus giving rise to the Wilson Cloud Chamber, a superb device for showing the tracks of ionizing radiations; and J J Thomson, still pottering on in retirement by studying plasmas. All were, or were to be, Nobel prize winners.

No laboratory in the world was more productive in producing major discoveries. And few operated so frugally. Fred Lincoln, the chief assistant and keeper of the stores, took the sharp end of Ern's oft quoted statement:

"··· We don't have much money therefore we must think."

Apparatus, nuts, bolts and even pieces of wood were endlessly recycled. Whenever a student needed a piece of metal Mr Lincoln would unlock the cabinet housing the off-cuts and cut off exactly what was needed. The students soon learned how to take the back off this cabinet. By necessity Mr Lincoln had to be parsimonious. The research students parodied this trait by constructing the Lincoln machine which issued a 'metre' of rubber hose by drawing out three-quarters of a metre from a roll then stretching it to a metre before cutting it off.

Philip Moon, a research student requiring liquid air to cool the materials used in his slow neutron work, came up against the Laboratory's economy when Professor Rutherford finally stated to him ··· *"Mr Moon, the time has come Mr Moon to decide whether the results you are getting are worth the liquid air you are using."*

Whenever May Rutherford went on her regular diets she placed Ern on short rations too. At such times he became moody and irascible and word quickly spread throughout the laboratory. Staff and students vanished as they heard his booming voice approaching. Vivian Bowden once climbed a ladder to keep out of his way. As soon as Ern was back to normal rations his sunny nature returned.

His booming voice regularly caused havoc in the laboratory. The aluminium foil front of the counting chamber and the amplifiers were very sensitive to vibration so Vivian Bowden made up an illuminated sign, which could be turned on whenever the counters were being used, to request 'TALK SOFTLY PLEASE'. A moment when Ern was stationary under the sign, telling Jack Ratcliffe that he had got the grant needed to build a small field station for his radio studies of the upper atmosphere, was too tempting for Wynn-Williams who preserved the moment and sign in a photograph. (An earlier sign by Jack Constable, which bluntly stated 'SHUT UP DAMN YOU' had a short life when it was turned on as the booming Professor walked into the room.)

Ern's booming voice was famous. Around 1927 he had participated in the first radio conversation to America. A friend, when told his broadcast from Cambridge was clearly heard in Harvard across the Atlantic, remarked "*Why use radio?*"

An oral exam comprised the final hurdle for each research student. For two or so hours the candidate would answer questions posed by the Professor and another member of staff. Vivian Bowden, the first student co-examined by Mark Oliphant, recognized that his examiner appeared to be as nervous as himself. Mark Oliphant asked his first question.

> Bowden "*I'm afraid I don't know*".
>
> Rutherford "*What's more to the point, Oliphant, neither would you if you hadn't looked it up ten minutes ago. Let's have the next question.*"

As an old hand Ern knew all the tricks of oral exams. Back in 1925 he had floored George Emeleus with a question about Michelson's stellar interferometer after looking up the topic himself the night before.

Ern liked to ensure that the students had a feel for the order of magnitude of 'common' quantities, so he asked Vivian Bowden to work out, in his head, the velocity of an electron accelerated through one volt. A favourite question, usually saved to conclude the examination of a soon-to-be-married man, harked back to his Canterbury College days. *What is the inductance of a wedding ring?*

Most reminiscences by people who had been students under Ernest Rutherford were gathered at various celebrations of anniversaries so are by people who held him in very high regard. Overlooked are those few who rather quietly say that they preferred Chadwick or Cockcroft because Rutherford was too domineering and had far too much power in selecting physics professors in Britain, New Zealand and Australia. A few thought his comments sometimes verged on bad taste, for example when he commented "*It's a pity JJ does not wash more isn't it?*" Leighton Yates is one of the honest ones to whom Ern's robust sense of humour appeared crude. He was rather shocked to hear part of Oliphant's accelerator, the vertical tube which had a knob on top, referred to as Oliphant's penis. Ern's earthy sense of humour did offend some students from limited backgrounds but others enjoyed a private joke with him.

Philip Dee, an expert on the interpretation of photographs of tracks left by ionizing particles in a Wilson Cloud Chamber, often had to correct the Professor's sometimes wild interpretation of stray tracks. Finally an amused Ern told Philip Dee that ··· *it reminded him of a man who went to the police because he said a neighbour used to "pee" his daughter's name on the wall!*

Policeman. *"How do you know it is your neighbour who does this?"*

Man. *"Because I recognized the handwriting!"*

From then on whenever Philip Dee interpreted a cloud chamber photograph to Ern or a group, Ern would state *"Ah, you recognize the handwriting eh Dee?"* and roar with laughter at their private joke.

Punctually at 6 p.m. Fred Lincoln, the laboratory assistant, would tour the laboratories announcing to all that it was time, gentlemen, to close. One evening he encountered Percy Burbidge, a New Zealand student, who was turning the handle of a vacuum pump.

Burbidge *"Can I play any tune for you, Mr Lincoln?"*

Lincoln *"Yes, 'Ome sweet 'Ome, if you dont mind, Mr Burbidge."*

Ern's statement prevailed. *"If one hadn't accomplished what one wished to by six o'clock, it was unlikely that one would do so thereafter. It would be better to go home and think about what one had done today and what one was going to do tomorrow. "*

The Professor regularly toured the laboratory chatting with the research students, but less frequently as other responsibilities and public duties escalated. On these visits the students would present their results and the Professor, perched on a stool, would discuss the implications and future work, as likely as not taking a blunt stub of a pencil from his waistcoat pocket to illustrate his discussion on a handy piece of scrap paper. On Ern's 60th birthday, some months after he had been raised to the peerage, Peter Kapitza had presented Ern with a propelling pencil ··· *"it is unworthy of your hand to touch any more such wooden pencils."*

Many students long treasured those quiet moments with the Professor. Ern treated them as collaborators and equals, not as junior helpers.

'Below stairs', where the English class system still prevailed, was another story. Each morning as the Professor entered the Cavendish Laboratory through the archway off Free School Lane, the porter would doff his hat, say "Good morning Sir" and remain hatless until the Professor had passed.

Thanks to the technical skill of Wynn-Williams, the Cavendish boasted a network of telephones. Whenever Fred Lincoln or Mr Hayles removed his cap after answering the phone anyone watching knew that the Professor was on the other end.

At the bottom of the hierarchy were the 'boys' who joined the laboratory after leaving school at age fourteen. They spring-cleaned, fetched and carried, ran messages, etc., while receiving some training in workshop skills. They worked 9-6 on weekdays and 9-1 Saturdays, being paid at 1 p.m. on Saturday.

Ron Pryor joined the Cavendish as a boy in January of 1937. Seven months later he received a formal letter.

> *Cavendish Laboratory*
> *Cambridge*
> *20 Aug 1937*
>
> *Dear Pryor,*
> *I have to inform you that your engagement as lab. boy in the Cavendish Laboratory, assuming your work is satisfactory, will last until you are 19 years of age. In the ordinary course of events you will be expected to find work elsewhere on attaining this age.*
>
> *Yours faithfully,*
> *E V Appleton.*

In actual fact, Ron Pryor retired from the Cavendish fifty years later.

Cavendish Laboratory Workshops 1937

Fred Lincoln imposed many strict rules on the boys, some of which just asked to be broken. An openable window looking down Free School Lane from the workshop to the baker's shop ensured that the rule of no eating in the workshop was not religiously obeyed. All boys were called Tommy and were forbidden, by Fred Lincoln, to talk to the senior academic staff. One day as Ron polished the brass on the fire hoses, Ern passed by.

> The Professor *"Hello Tommy. How are you getting on?"*
>
> Ron *"I'm alright thank you very much Sir."*
>
> The Professor *"How do you like working here?"*
>
> Ron *"It's alright Sir"*
>
> The Professor *"Good – good. Carry on."*

Fred Lincoln had overhead the conversation. After the Professor was out of earshot, he called Ron over.

> Lincoln *"I want you. I've told you before not to talk to the senior academic staff. If it happens again you'll have to have your cards.*

October 1937

The Indian Science Congress Association invited members of the British Association for the Advancement of Science to hold a joint meeting with them in Calcutta, starting on January the 2nd of 1938, to mark the Silver Jubilee of the Congress. The Indians had invited Lord Rutherford to be President of the joint meeting. As a great believer in the British Commonwealth of Nations, he happily agreed and looked forward to November 26th when he and May were due to board the ship for India.

The Rutherfords spent their summer holiday of September 1937 at Chantry Cottage which they had had built on a corner of a large dairy farm (appropriately named 'New Zealand') on the Wiltshire Downs. While May gardened, Ern drafted his Presidential speech for the Indian Congress. He focussed on one of natures most fascinating mysteries – the origin of life on Earth and the forces that give rise to it, a topic about which he had first heard speculation from Professor Bickerton at Canterbury College. Now however nuclear reactions could account for the tremendous energy output of the Sun and it was known that ultraviolet light was highly favourable to the growth of living substances and that X-rays had been used to produce mutations and to create new varieties of plants and insects.

It is thus possible that at one period in its evolution from a hot chip of the sun to a cool planet the types of radiant energy emanating on the earth's surface provided just the proper conditions for the emergence of the earliest primordial forms of living matter ··· the original treasure of radiant energy, inherited from the sun-mother, spent in riotous living.

But that Autumn he could not escape scot free from physical exercise and he helped May with some of the heavier work in the garden. For some years he had suffered from a partial hernia near the navel which had caused no great trouble apart from the truss, which he had to wear, getting in the way whenever he was chopping or sawing wood. His occasional exertions at Chantry Cottage may have aggravated the hernia as he often felt quite seedy after returning to Cambridge. Several people noticed that he was not well. Ron Pryor, while polishing the seats at the top of the Maxwell Lecture Theatre (this was accomplished by tying rags to his backside and sliding along the seats) overheard a chance meeting of Rutherford and Appleton outside the lecture room door.

Appleton *"Hello, how are you ?"*

Rutherford *"I've not been well but feel better now.*

But the discomfort persisted. Expert attention was needed, to wit the local pork butcher. Mr Waller had a little room at the back of his Victoria Street butcher shop from which he practiced a second occupation as a masseur and manipulator. Many people swore by him. He had fixed Ern's knee and regularly massaged Ern's shoulders and neck.

Mr Waller took one look at Ern, stated it wasn't his department and that a doctor was needed. That night Ern vomited. Very early the next morning, Friday the 15th of October 1937, the family doctor was called for. Dr Nourse correctly diagnosed a strangulated hernia, an intestinal obstruction whereby the gut is partially closed where it protrudes between abdominal muscles. Because his patient was <u>Lord</u> Rutherford, protocol dictated that a second opinion be sought from Ryle, the Regius Professor of Medicine.

With the diagnosis confirmed, and with an operation therefore needed, Ern was admitted immediately to the Evelyn Nursing Home, a private hospital with full operating facilities. Because he was <u>Lord</u> Rutherford, protocol of the day required that a titled surgeon operate rather than the other equally competent surgeons available at the Evelyn. So Professor Ryle phoned to London, to Sir Thomas Dunhill, who was not only a Harley Street man and a good surgeon but also a friend of his. Sir Thomas arrived by train that night and operated immediately.

The next day May telegraphed the news to the family in New Zealand. She sent it to Jim's son Alan in New Plymouth, as he worked in town whereas the others were in country areas. *Ernest operated on for strangulated hernia operation successful doing nicely.*

But the gut never worked again. Two days later Sir Thomas Dunhill was once more called up to Cambridge. After examining Ern he decided it was no use to operate again and nothing could be done. That night May and Dr Nourse moved into rooms adjacent to Ern's. Throughout his hospitalization May had sat with Ern. They had renewed the deep affection and love of their youth and he spoke to her with tenderness and concern for her future. He also thought of New Zealand, very suddenly telling her that he wished to leave £100 to Nelson College.

Whenever he dozed she knitted and wrote letters, for example to Mark Oliphant and one home to New Zealand, to Ernest's sister Florence, to let the family know what was happening.

Evelyn Nursing Home
Cambridge [Tues] *Oct 19* [1937]

Dear Floss,

I cabled the other day to Allan as I thought being in town he could easily deal with notifying you all. By the time you get this you will know all one way or the other though both doctors have warned me this morning that he is growing weaker. Everything possible has been done for him, we have a good Dr, Nourse and Ryle the Regius Professor of Medicine consulting all the time. He got Sir Thomas Dunhill down from London to operate, such a charming man too. He was the surgeon who operated on Princess Mary for thyroid. Ernest has for some years had a slight weakness of the abdominal wall at the navel. On Wed of last week he was perfectly well on Wed. On Thursday he felt a bit mouldy with flatulence from indigestion. He took caster oil, later was sick and then in the night so I called in doctor about 7.30 a.m. After examination when he feared obstruction he called in Ryle and they both decided he must go into nursing home. They then rang up Sir T. Dunhill and he arrived about 6.30 and at 8 they operated. They found it was strangulated hernia, but no gangrene though it would have in a few hours. He bore it well and all Sat things seemed hopeful and I sent the cable. On Sunday however he began to vomit, which was very exhausting and showed that the bowel was not working properly, paralysed. To stop the vomiting they put in a tube, emptied stomach washed it out, and fixed the tube in so that it would siphon all the time to remove fluids collecting and also they fed him through it and by the rectum and all sorts of stimulating injections. He is a splendid patient and his nurses are splendid, 2 specials and lots of others who come in all the time to assist. This went on all Sunday. On Monday they rang up the surgeon and he came up again to see if it would be any use to operate again. They again consulted for nearly 1/2 hour and then he came to me and said it would be too dangerous to give an anaesthetic with the state of his bronchial tubes and also the shock and further disturbance of the intestine. He is being given intravenous saline injection all the time and this is what keeps him alive. He drops out a surprisingly keen remark now and then. I could hardly bear it last night when he began to say he was sorry he was impatient sometimes, but he had really always depended on my decision of mind etc. He has enormous numbers of friends who love him they all knew he never worked in any way for himself, always for others and he has helped all kinds of people. The doctor is here now and I hear him wondering whether it would be any use to wash out again – he has just talked to me and says he is downhill a little since 8 a.m. Ernest has just told the matron that he feels a good deal better poor darling. His patience is wonderful with all these horrible tubes hanging from his mouth and his arm and he feels the heat of being well covered up and yet they dare not risk any chill.

This letter was never finished. Sixty-six year old Ernest, Lord Rutherford of Nelson died that evening.

Sir Ernest Rutherford gestorben

Nach einer Operation starb in Cambridge im Alter von 66 Jahren der bekannte englische Wissenschaftler Lord Rutherford.

Rutherford, der am 30. August 1871 in Nelson (Neuseeland) geboren war, hat im Cavendish Laboratorium (1895—98) unter Sir J. J. Thomson seine Untersuchungen über die Radioaktivität begonnen.

Aftermath

Mark Oliphant and John Cockcroft were in Bologna, Italy, attending the celebrations to mark the bicentennial of the birth of Luigi Galvani, when Philip Dee's early morning telegram reached them. They immediately told Niels Bohr who, with faltering voice and tears in his eyes, informed the meeting of the dreadful news. Bohr's impromptu eulogy, in which he spoke from the heart about

> ⋯ *the debt which science owed so great a man whom he was privileged to call both his master and his friend,* ⋯ was one of the most moving experiences of Mark Oliphant's life.

Oliphant, Cockcroft and Bohr left immediately for England where Oliphant accompanied Philip Dee who wished to see Rutherford one more time.

> ⋯ *We went to the mortuary where the body lay, pale and still.* ⋯ *we agreed that all that made Rutherford for us had gone and only a shell remained. I was greatly distressed by this experience.*

The death of Lord Rutherford made headlines around the world and many fine tributes were paid. Jack Egerton, the Professor of Physical Chemistry at Oxford wrote to Ralph Fowler:

> ⋯ *One could not help but come to love the great man besides admiring him. He was the living expression of England's greatness more than in anyone one has ever met.*

Peter Kapitza, restricted to Russia, wrote to Niels Bohr in Copenhagen.

> ⋯ *All these years I lived with the hope that I shall see him again and now this hope is gone.* ⋯ *I loved Rutherford* ⋯ *I learned a great deal from Rutherford – not physics but how to do physics.*

The Royal Society arranged for a last great honour to be accorded Lord Rutherford of Nelson. His ashes were to be interred in Westminister Abbey. Hundreds of invitations were sent out from the Cavendish. To save postage, Fred Lincoln dispatched the 'boys' out into the pouring rain to deliver those whose recipients lived in Cambridge. At the Abbey May was supported by Phyllida Cook and Niels Bohr. (A frantic search all over London had finally located a top hat big enough to fit his very large head.) The family was represented only by May, Ralph, the grandchildren and a niece, who had stepped off the boat to England to be greeted by the newspaper hoardings 'Greatest British Scientist Dead'.

Ten honoured men walked beside the coffin as pall bearers. The Presidents of the Royal Society and British Association (positions Ernest had held), the Secretary of the Department of Scientific and Industrial Research (Ernest was Chairman of its Advisory Council), the Presidents of the Royal College of Physicians and the Institution of Electrical Engineers (Ernest was an Honorary Fellow of both), the High Commissioner for New Zealand, the Vice-Chancellors of the English Universities he had worked at (Cambridge, Manchester), and representatives of Trinity College and McGill University. The King, the Prime Minister and the Lord Chancellor all sent representatives as did scores of organizations, the breadth of which mirrored his career, his esteem, his influence, his fame, his humanity – in short his Mana.

Wreaths from all parts of the world formed a continuous mass of colour in the cloisters. One of the most beautiful consisted of New Zealand flowers and foliage inscribed simply

"In memory of school and university days, from F.M."

Another, from a friend and previous Governor-General of New Zealand, Viscount Bledisloe, summed up all:

"In affectionate memory of New Zealand's greatest son."

After the service in the sanctuary, ten purple-cassocked vergers carried the coffin to the diamond shaped, purple-surrounded grave in front of Newton's memorial and near those of Faraday, Darwin, Maxwell, Kelvin and other immortals of science. From a small trapdoor in the end of the coffin, the urn containing Ernest Rutherford's ashes was taken out and to the committal words

– – – earth to earth, ashes to ashes, dust to dust – – –

it was lowered into the ground.

The boy who had been christened in a cob church in rural New Zealand had come a long way.

EPILOGUE

Rutherford was ever the happy warrior – happy in his work, happy in its outcome and happy in its human contact.

Sir James Jeans' eulogy,
Indian Science Congress, 1937

Ernest Rutherford died of fame. His was a needless death. Both Bay de Renzie and Derek Cook had had hernia operations with no complications. The eight hours delay while a titled Harley Street man was contacted and transported to Cambridge meant the difference between life and death to an acute abdominal case. Had he not been <u>Lord</u> Rutherford, the local Cambridge surgeons would have been asked to operate on him forthwith and he may have lived to a ripe old age, like his parents before him, to survive into a period when the world was in need of his wisdom.

Lord Bowden attributed Ernest Rutherford's greatness to his inherent simplicity. Thinking back to his own time as a physics student in Cambridge he recalled

> ··· *There were some very distinguished theoretical physicists in the Cavendish in my time, and I often heard them talking. I always thought that these men were extraordinarily brilliant; I could understand only part of what they were saying and I could never imagine that I could contribute to their ideas in any way at all. But after I heard Rutherford explaining something I thought 'That is perfectly simple and perfectly obvious; why on earth didn't I think of it myself?'*

The secret seemed to be that Ern based all his conclusions on sound experimental investigations whereas too many did not. Claims of cold fusion in 1989 were reminiscent of similar claims from the 1920's when Fritz Paneth claimed to have produced helium by passing an electrical current through hydrogen-laden palladium metal, Sir William Ramsay claimed to have made argon by electrically bombarding sulphur, Japanese and German chemists claimed to have turned mercury into gold and a Swedish engineer attempted to patent cold fusion as a way of making helium. Ern had stopped all such nonsense by remarking that invariably the appearance of an element as an impurity had been mistaken for its creation. His wisdom would not have gone astray in 1989.

Jack Ratcliffe defined the perfect professor as one who

> Ran the lab and led the researches in it,
>
> Exerted an important influence for physics in the university and
>
> Exerted an important influence for science in *the country at large.*

Ernest Rutherford did all three, superbly and as few others have.

Later Nobel Prizes

Curiously, one of the greatest physicists of all time never received a Nobel Prize in physics. Why? He had at least two other revolutionary discoveries which completely altered our view of nature, either of which would have made him a worthy candidate. Strangely he was nominated from Britain only once, when J J Thomson nominated him too late for consideration in 1908, though that was carried over to 1909 and not surprisingly rejected as too soon after Ern's award of the Chemistry Prize in 1908.

Although he had determined the nuclear structure of the atom in 1911 and had artificially induced the transformation of an atom in 1918, he was next nominated in 1922 by Theodor Svedberg, the Swedish chemist who was himself to win the 1926 Chemistry Prize. The examining committee agreed that:

> *Notwithstanding the importance of Rutherford's recent research, the committee nevertheless finds that the question of an award should be deferred until greater experience has been gained about these remarkable phenomena.*

That same year Ern had, for the second time, nominated the eventual recipient, Niels Bohr,

> *··· for his notable original contribution to our knowledge on the constitution of atoms and the origin of spectra.*

For 1923 Theodor Svedberg again nominated Ern but the prize went to the American Robert Millikan for measuring the charge on the electron. The committee were of the opinion that there was a far greater leap forward from Rutherford's model of the atom to that of Bohr's (who incidentally only had his leap because he worked with Ern at the right time) than there was from Thomson's model to Rutherford's. Hence

> ⋯ *The committee does not find this series of research by Rutherford to have the great significance required to be worthy of a Nobel Prize.*

That work was clearly physics. His more recent work on breaking up the nucleus (splitting the atom) by firing alpha particles at light nuclei required far more discussion. Svante Arrhenius, the winner of the 1903 Prize in chemistry and Ern's champion in 1908, wrote the report for the committee. They had little sympathy for awarding the same person with two Nobel prizes and felt Ern's lack of nominations from Britain supported this view. The committee didn't agree with the proposer's suggestion that Marie Curie's double prize (a quarter of the 1903 physics prize for combined research into the radiation phenomena discovered by Henri Becquerel and the whole 1911 chemistry prize for the discovery of radium and polonium) was a precedent. As Ern had received a whole Nobel prize in 1908, for work which a joint meeting of the Physics and Chemistry Committees had decided should be considered under chemistry (even though Svante Arrhenius had spoken against this classification at the time), the 1923 committee had to rule him out on formal grounds. Furthermore,

> ⋯ *It is understood that Sir Ernest's merits are so great and generally acknowledged that his standing outside Sweden would not markedly increase by the award of a new Nobel Prize, nor would it markedly increase his possibilities for research, as these already are as great as possible after he received the most prestigious research position in the field of physics in the British Commonwealth.*

Fame had helped scupper that year's nomination.

For 1924, the American David Gordan of Stanford University nominated Ern for splitting the atom. The physics committee mentioned the extensive research in progress in this field and once again concluded ... *that the question of Rutherford's award should be delayed until greater experience has been gained of these remarkable phenomena.* No physics prize was awarded that year. (Ern had co-nominated C T R Wilson.)

Ern was next nominated in 1931 by the German, Johannes Stark. The physics committee's recommendation was ⋯ *that this research is so closely related to the work for which he received the Nobel Prize in Chemistry that the award of another Nobel prize is not warranted.*

Ern's final string of nominations came from Johannes Stark for 1932, 1933, 1935, 1936 and 1937. All were unsuccessful and what makes them interesting is that Stark, the winner for 1919 for his work in splitting spectral lines with an electric field, was a supporter of Hitler and his policies while from 1933 onwards Ern worked to help the scientists displaced by these policies.

Nobel Prizes cannot be awarded posthumously so that was the end of the matter. Ern had a little more success when nominating others. Of his 12 nominations of physics candidates, some of which were repeats, 4 received the Nobel Prize (Niels Bohr, C T R Wilson, Chandrasekhara Raman and James Chadwick). In Chemistry he failed with the Chemistry Professor at Manchester (twice) and Frederick Soddy (twice) before he was successful with Soddy and Marie Curie's son-in-law and daughter (jointly). Altogether some nine Nobel Prizemen spent their formative years in Ern's laboratories.

The Cavendish Lab

Following Ern's death the Cavendish research students cancelled their annual dinner for 1937 as inappropriate.

When he died so too did nuclear research at the Cavendish. At the Annual Dinner of 1930 Ern had ⋯ *expressed the hope that the Cavendish would always make its own line of research and not run after any and every discovery made in other laboratories.* He had planned to retire at age 70. With his unexpected death the lab needed a new leader. Initially Edward Appleton, the radio physicist, supervised the laboratory until some months later when a new Director, Lawrence Bragg, was finally appointed. He had shared the 1915 Nobel prize in physics with his father for their pioneering work using X-ray diffraction to study crystalline materials, a corner-stone of mineral identification and geological research today.

When the Cavendish Laboratory reassembled after the war a plaintive song at the 1945 Cavendish Dinner marked this transition to new directions. The author's instructions stated – *to be sung seriously and mournfully*.

> *We're three little lambs who have lost their way*
> *Baa Baa Baa*
> *We're three little black sheep who have gone astray*
> *Baa Baa Baa*

Nuclear physicists all of us three
Ousted by crystallography
God have mercy on such as we
Baa Baa Baa

Ern was just a memory. Or a ghost. Another song, the *Professor's Song*, set to the tune of *John Brown's Body* had as its 4th verse

Rutherford was always ten years forward of the rest
He began disintegrating with his never failing zest
And he wanders round the Abbey in a scintillating vest.

The heady days when the Cavendish had led the world in nuclear physics, were over.

His Family

Ern's death shattered May Rutherford. Without him she was a lost soul. She shifted into a small flat in Cambridge. An elderly neighbour, whose hobby was making lampshades out of parchments, was given Ern's degree parchments with the statement that the young grandchildren were not interested. After the war a young Kiwi physicist visiting a friend's landlady noticed that he was sitting under a lampshade made from two of these parchments. On being told their story he asked if he could have the parchments for return to New Zealand and they are now in the University of Canterbury archives, all 32 of them including six made up into three lampshades. [One lampshade, in poor condition, has since been conserved and left dismantled.]

University friends had been Ern's friends and Lady Rutherford's brusque manner had alienated many. After the war she returned to New Zealand, to her hometown of Christchurch. After walking the Cashmere Hills she selected a steep but large section at 116 Dyers Pass Rd, planted it and in 1950 commissioned a new house. She was on the site every day from 8am to enforce her instructions that only quality workmanship and British materials were to be used. In so doing she drove the builder to distraction and, it is reputed, to bankruptcy.

Disregarding Ern's earlier will, she gave Ern's medals, all 34 and probably the finest collection in the world of scientific medals awarded to one person, to the University of Canterbury.

She had her brother and many cousins in Christchurch and made good friends in gardening circles. Through Professor Farr, students from the

Canterbury College science club occasionally gave her assistance with her large garden but regretably none appeared to be sufficiently interested in history to ask her about Ern's early days at Canterbury College.

However she had little time to enjoy her new house and garden. On the 20th of January 1954 Mary (May) Rutherford died of a cerebral thombosis at age 77. She was cremated and her ashes placed on the graves of her father and mother in Linwood Cemetery, near the corner of Ruru and McGregors roads. Her memorial plaque was broken by 1980 and had vanished by 1990.

Ern's son-in-law, Ralph Fowler, died shortly after the second world war. With their mother, father and grandfather all dead, and with their maternal grandmother returning to New Zealand, the grandchildren looked on Phyllida Cook as their mother. She had raised them and they have a very deep affection for her. After a very active life she died in 1993 at age 95.

What became of the grandchildren?

Peter Fowler had two years at Bristol University prior to joining the Royal Air Force in 1942. He served as a radar officer in England, then Europe and eventually India specializing in trouble shooting, anti-jamming and later in navigational aids. In 1944, on his own initiative, he located a German jamming transmitter being used to disrupt the navigation system used by British bombers, which the Royal Air Force promtly bombed out of existence. Returning to Bristol after the war he completed a first class physics degree. He remained at Bristol throughout his working life and had a distinguished research career in cosmic ray research and in particle physics. The Royal Society elected him a Fellow in 1965, a Research Professor in 1964 and awarded him its Hughes Medal in 1974. After retiring in 1988 he was as busy as ever applying neutrons to study problems of relevance to industry, for example in airport baggage surveillance and investigating the interior temperature distribution of components in working jet engines. Peter and his wife Rosemary, who also has a physics degree from Bristol, have three daughters of whom two are geophysicists [Mary was awarded the Geological Society's Prestwich Medal for 1996] and one a teacher of music and science. No grandchildren have specialised in physics so physics has finally escaped from the Rutherford genes. Peter's branch of the family tree retain the custom of having Rutherford as the last of each child's firstnames. On the 8th of November 1996, Peter Fowler unexpectedly died in his sleep.

Elizabeth (Liddy) Fowler graduated in Medicine from Cambridge University. Liddy married Henry Taylor, a school master, and raised five girls and one boy, the only great-grandson of Ernest Rutherford. Liddy has undertaken part-time clinical work in the field of psychiatry and accident and emergency.

Patrick Fowler studied electrical engineering at Cambridge with Trinity as his College. He has retired from his longterm position as an instrument engineer at Winfrith nuclear power plant. In order to transport the very weak signals from the ionization chambers used to monitor the neutron flux in reactors he developed and patented superscreen cable which was widely used in transmitting weak signals through regions of very high electrical interference, for example in electrical power stations and factories. He and his wife Kate have three daughters.

Ruth Fowler studied genetics, gaining a Ph.D. from Edinburgh University. After raising five daughters she worked in ovarian physiology as a Senior Research Associate in the Department of Physiology, Cambridge University, until her retirement in 1989. Her husband, Professor Bob Edwards, is renowned for his in-vitro fertilization work which has helped so many, previously childless, couples.

It is interesting that both Peter and Pat spent their working lives involved with neutrons, those hard-to-detect, uncharged, sub-nuclear particles whose existence was first postulated by their grandfather.

Continuing Honours

Ern's international honours continue long after his death. In 1948 the French organised an international *Hommage à Lord Rutherford* whose attendees included six Nobel Prize winners. In the mid-fifties the old Commonwealth countries raised money to endow Rutherford scholarships and Rutherford lectures. Buildings in several countries are named after him, for example McGill University's 'new' physics building. Britain has the Rutherford Laboratory, the new Cavendish has the Rutherford Building, the Institute of Physics has the Rutherford Conference Centre and the London Conference Centre, which has its rooms named after the greats of Britain's recent past, has a Rutherford Room. He has appeared on the stamps of 4 countries, Sweden in 1968, and Canada, Russia and New Zealand in 1971 to mark the centennial of his birth.

Ern is the only New Zealander to have a chemical element named for him. Chemical elements are distinguished by their atomic number (symbol Z), the number of electrons orbiting in the neutral atom or equally well the number of protons (positive charges or hydrogen nuclei) in the nucleus. Our world and galaxies are made up of just 92 chemical elements of which only 81 are truely stable. All those heavier than bismuth (Z = 83) are radioactively decaying away until eventually there will be none left. These, including uranium which at Z = 92 is the heaviest radioactive element existing naturally, do so solely because they, or their parent, are decaying at such a slow rate that there are still significant numbers of these atoms remaining today, some 15 billion years since the elements first formed.

Some decades ago physicists calculated that the arrangement of particles in nuclei of atomic number around 112 should again be stable. But where were these elements? Extensive searches of nature failed to find them. Therefore it was decided to manufacture them for study. The lighter ones had been extracted from nuclear reactors where they were produced by the large neutron fluxes reacting initially with uranium which then decayed by beta emission leaving a nucleus one higher in the chain. Beyond fermium (Z = 100) this was not possible so large particle accelerators were used to smash light nuclei into the heaviest nuclei abundantly produced in the reactors.

To the discoverer went the honour of proposing a name for each new element. Neptunium (Z = 93) and plutonium (Z = 94) were natural successors to uranium. Names such as americium (Z = 95), berkelium (Z = 97) and californium (Z = 98) commemorated the place of discovery. Curium (Z = 96), einsteinium (Z = 99), fermium (Z = 100), mendelevium (Z = 101) and lawrencium (Z = 103) honoured the discoverers' scientific heroes. Nobelium (Z = 102), claimed first, but never substantiated, by an international group working at the Nobel Institute in Stockholm, was named in honour of the man who left his fortune for prizes to promote science.

The heavier the element the harder its manufacture became and the shorter time it survived, until only three laboratories specialised in this work. Berkeley in California, Darmstadt in Germany and Dubna in Russia. And from element 102 on, the controversies started. These were fueled by the Cold War of the time.

In 1964 the Dubna group, led by G N Flerov, claimed to have manufactured one isotope of element 104 by smashing neon nuclei into plutonium. They proposed the name kurchatovium (Ku), in honour of the Soviet nuclear physicist Igor Kurchatov.

Albert Ghiorso and co-workers at the Lawrence Berkeley Laboratory of the University of California spent a year attempting to repeat this work but finally had to conclude that element 104 could not have been manufactured by Dubna. In 1968 the Berkeley team produced element 104 in an entirely different way. They bombarded the world's supply of californium with high speed nuclei of carbon atoms.

In November of 1969, at celebrations marking the centennial of Mendeleev, the father of the periodic table, Al Ghiorso proposed that element 104 be named rutherfordium (Rf) because Ernest Rutherford was one of his heroes.

"We are suggesting that element 104 be called rutherfordium, after Lord Rutherford, the great pioneer of nuclear science. If in the course of further experiments, contrary to our present expectations, we do confirm the earlier findings of the Dubna group of approximately three-tenths of a second spontaneous-fission activity, we will withdraw our suggested name and accept that proposed by the Soviet group, kurchatovium."

This was most fitting as it was Rutherford who had first explained the nature of radioactivity, that one element was decaying into another. Also he had named the alpha particles. Their emission and energy and the half-life of nuclei were unique for identifying new nuclei.

For nearly two decades the world lived with three names for element 104. Each country used its own name, the Oxford Dictionary listed both but politically correct periodic tables used an interim name Unnilquadlium, the latin for one zero four, or Unq for short.

To solve the impass, a Transfermium Working Group, a joint committee of the International Union of Pure and Applied Physics and the International Union of Pure and Applied Chemistry, was set up in 1985 to determine precedence of discovery for all elements beyond fermium. This would allow unique names to be assigned. In 1992 the committee concluded that the two groups should share credit for discovery of the elements 104 and 105. This conclusion was bitterly rejected by the Berkeley group and others.

An August 1994 meeting adopted a new rule that no element could be named after a living person. Since both Albert Einstein and Enrico Fermi had been alive when they had had elements proposed in their honour, this move was a ploy to take the very much alive Glenn Seaborg's name off element 106 so that that element could then be renamed rutherfordium. This left element 104 open to be be 'officially' named dubnium. Confusion reigned. Elements 104 to 109 were to be named but international arguments continued over most of these.

In September of 1997 a final compromise was reached and all phases of naming were passed. 104 rutherfordium (Rf), 105 dubnium (Db), 106 seaborgium (Sg), 107 bohrium (Bh), 108 hassium (Hs) and 109 meitnerium (Mt). The loser was Otto Hahn, whose name was taken off 105 though some groups may not accept this development.

From its position in the periodic table, rutherfordium should have similar chemistry to hafnium. Its longest living isotope has a half-life of about 70 seconds. Only a few thousand atoms of rutherfordium have ever been manufactured and probably no more than 100 of these atoms have ever been chemically isolated using a special cation exchange column. As you read this there will most likely be not one atom of rutherfordium in existence, unless one of the three groups are painstakingly manufacturing it for other experiments.

Fame is but fleeting. However it is too much of a gamble to hold back a favourite name on the chance that stable heavy-nuclei will eventually be manufactured.

How Myths are Created

New Zealand often gives the impression that it does not cherish achievers in fields other than sport. Its neglect of Ernest Rutherford, at least prior to the last decade, is typical. But this is not the whole reason.

When I first realised that this country could give only an erroneous account of its most famous son I started interviewing New Zealanders who remembered him. As a physicist I was staggered by two who stated disdainfully that Rutherford had invented the nuclear bomb. I hadn't previously heard of this myth, let alone realised that it was so wide-spread in New Zealand. Then later I noticed that any TV item on Ern invariably commenced with a nuclear bomb explosion, including one item prior to which I had carefully explained the origins of this myth to the reporter. Old myths are difficult to exorcise.

New Zealand is the only country to lay this myth on Ern. How could it falsely do so? True, Ernest Rutherford had been the first person to appreciate the enormous energy stored in the nucleus of atoms. But he had died believing that there was no way of releasing this energy such that more energy was obtained than was expended in releasing it. He had stated this several times throughout his life and is even listed in books of quotations people wish they hadn't made because they had later been proven wrong. As *Nature* reported him stating to the British Association Meeting of 1933 ··· *One timely word of warning was issued to those who look for sources of power in atomic transmutations – such expectations are the merest moonshine.* Based on the knowledge of his lifetime he was correct. A year later Albert Einstein made the same dogmatic statement.

It is possible that Ern just blindly hoped this would never be done. Mark Oliphant recalled that in 1934 or 1935, while Ern was absent from the laboratory for some weeks, he, Oliphant, thought that it might be possible to obtain net energy gain by modifying the experiment in which they had bombarded deuterium atoms with accelerated deuterium nuclei. The experiment produced no net gain in energy. On Ern's return Mark Oliphant

July 19, 1922.] PUNCH, OR THE LONDON CHARIVARI. 67

Dazed Scientific Investigator (who has been ordered horse exercise for his health). "Where am I? What's happened? Has some silly fool exploded an atom?"

reported on what he had been doing in his absence. Ern was quite angry. ···
*He soon calmed down and we did some arithmetic. This satisfied him that I was not
a fool, but foolish, and he asked me to stick to the search for facts, not fantasies!* ··· In
later life Mark Oliphant, who worked with the large international team which
developed the nuclear bomb during wartime but who was latter opposed to
the use of nuclear weapons, suggested to me that perhaps Ern had hoped that
the energy would never be able to be extracted from the nucleus efficiently.

Ern's political views were personal. The BBC had privately listed him among
a small group labelled *central or unknown.* In the mid-1930's a Cambridge
University branch of the Democratic Front was formed to counter the
communistic cell centred on the crystallographer Bernal. Ern presided over a
branch meeting at which he stated

> ··· *It is a matter of great importance that those who believe in the
> present type of government should not stand idly by, but see if they can
> convince the waverers, or those who require convincing, of the great
> advantage of democratic government, at any rate in this country where
> we have experienced it so long.*
>
> *At present there is a great feeling of tensions, not only throughout
> Europe, but in a sense throughout the world. That feeling of tension
> and war has been a striking mark of the last few years. This arises
> largely from the fear of the growing power of military aeroplanes with
> sudden and devastating attacks on defenceless cities, involving the
> destruction of combatants and non-combatants alike.*
>
> *I am sure that the greatest possible relief from this fear of war would
> arise, if say, tomorrow we could ensure that aeroplane warfare could
> be abolished by consent of all the nations of the world. That would be a
> great epoch in history, but it may not be possible for a long period.* ···
> *There is no question more important for the future than to see whether
> we can get some form of international agreement on the limitation of
> this air weapon which will undoubtedly grow in strength from year
> to year.*

H G Wells had fictionally dropped an atomic bomb by aeroplane in 1913.
Hollywood invented one for the 1917 film 'The Greatest Power' but curiously,
while enamoured with radium and invisible rays, never went back to the nuclear
bomb until the real one was developed one war later.

In 1916, at the height of the First World War, Ern had given a public talk
on the 'Energy of Radium'. After describing the vast energy stored in nuclei
whereby

··· a few hundred-weights of such material would shake, if not rend, the Earth. ··· the Manchester Guardian *reported ··· Fortunately at the present time we had not found out a method of so dealing with these forces, and personally he was very hopeful we should not discover it until man was living at peace with his neighbour.*

The discovery of the neutron in 1932 had initiated a rush of new work. Marie Curie's son-in-law and daughter discovered artificial radioactivity by bombarding elements with alpha particles and Enrico Fermi quickly showed that uncharged neutrons were more efficient. Leo Szilard, an émigré physicist who had fled Berlin, after reading Ern's pronouncement that the expectation of efficient production of nuclear energy was moonshine, filed a British patent (630,726) in 1934 for the use of neutrons to initiate chain reactions of nuclei.

Ernest Rutherford died over a year before what he had feared in the First World War came to pass during the opening gambits of the Second World War. The German physical-chemists Otto Hahn and Fritz Strassmann, after bombarding uranium with neutrons, reported a curiosity in which their uranium appeared to decay leaving behind barium, a nucleus only half the mass of uranium. Otto Hahn had communicated this news to his old collaborator Lise Meitner, who had been smuggled out of Germany by friends after the Nazis annexed Austria and who had been taken in by the Nobel Institute in Stockholm. That Christmas of 1938 she was visited by her nephew Otto Frisch, himself an émigré physicist who had been taken in by Niels Bohr in Copenhagen. Together they explained how a neutron entering a uranium nucleus could cause it to split into two lighter nuclei. The nucleus had been well and truely split. Otto Frisch told Niels Bohr of this just as the latter embarked for a lecture tour of America. There the news spread rapidly and was reported in the newspapers of Jan 29th 1939. Otto Frisch named the process 'fission' after the biological term for cell division.

This raised the spectre of a super-bomb, a million times the energy of a chemical bomb. No-one appeared to believe it feasible. Otto Frisch, in his review of radioactivity and sub-nuclear phenomena covering 1939 for the American Chemical Society stated:

Fortunately, our progressing knowledge of the fission process has tended to dissipate these fears, and there are now a number of strong arguments to the effect that the construction of a super-bomb would be, if not impossible, then at least prohibitively expensive, and that furthermore the bomb would not be so effective as was thought at first.

In early 1941 Ralph Fowler could report from Washington that the common view was that uranium would not form the basis of an explosive. Niels Bohr also held that view. Curiously, with Europe at war, the magazine *Fortnightly* of January 1941 contained a very clear article giving the history of atomic energy and the way to produce power and/or a bomb. It was known that each fissioning uranium atom gave out about four neutrons so a chain reaction was possible. Only the rare isotope U235 was efficient at capturing neutrons so the main technical problem was to separate this from the more common isotope U238. Any physical process such as centrifuging could do this at least partially. So a bomb was quite feasible.

Meanwhile the British had established the Maud Committee to investigate the instigation of a chain reaction in uranium with a view to power production. The committee received its name after a PS in a note, from Niels Bohr to James Chadwick, which the intelligence service had smuggled out of occupied Denmark. Bohr had asked to give greetings to *Maud Ray, Kent*. The intelligence service worked out that Maud Ray was effectively an anagram of radium and wondered what Bohr was trying to tell them. After he was smuggled to Britain in the bomb bay of a Mosquito aircraft (during which he almost died when he didn't hear the pilot's instructions to put on his oxygen mask) all became clear. Maud Ray had been nanny to the Bohr children.

In America the émigré scientists, who had first hand knowledge of the excesses of the Nazi regime, turned to the most well-known of all émigré scientists in America, Albert Einstein. Communicating in their one common language, German, they drafted a letter under Einstein's influential name in which they recommended to the President that America should start work on a nuclear bomb in case Germany was continuing its pioneering work. A costly (some US$2000 million) and vast international effort, to which New Zealand contributed seven scientists, culminated in the production of the world's first atomic bomb under the scientific leadership of Robert Oppenheimer. This was tested succesfully in America.

Occasionally, and only in America, the development of the atom bomb is attributed to Albert Einstein who not only sent the letter but whose famous equation $E = mc^2$ allowed the energy release to be calculated. Although he stated $\cdots$ *I have done no work on the atomic bomb, no work at all* $\cdots$ he, his equation and a mushroom cloud appeared on the cover of *Time* magazine for the 1st of July 1946.

Books on the development of the atomic bomb seldom mention Ern. For example, in Pringle and Spigelman's 1981 book *The Nuclear Barons* Ern rates only two mentions, because of his moonshine statement and because Peter Kapitza once worked with him.

So why does New Zealand, and only New Zealand, incorrectly lay on Ern the responsibility for inventing the nuclear bomb? If one looks at New Zealand newspapers for July and early August of 1945 one reads, as did the people of the time, of the war in Europe being over but of the war against the Japanese continuing as bloody as ever. Pacific Islands were slowly being retaken with great loss of life on both sides. New Zealanders could read of more personal and harrowing accounts, such as the treatment one of their young men, Flight Lieutenant Emeny, had received while a prisoner of war of the Japanese. On the larger scale they read that 3850 tons of bombs and incendiary devices had been dropped on Japanese cities in one day and that a further 12 Japanese cities had been warned that they too would be bombed.

Newspapers regularly reported the build-up of a vast force for the invasion of Japan itself and there were no illusions as to the scale of the anticipated loss of life on both sides. In one attempted breakout in Burma, 10,000 Japanese troops had been killed. Surrender was not part of their warrior code. Defence of their homeland would be even more desperate.

On the 6th of August 1945 the first atom bomb to be used in warfare was dropped on the city of Hiroshima. The Press Association cabled the news around the world. The Americans supplied information on the key people in this project and not to be outdone so too did the British. Not one of these accounts mentioned Ern. Because the pre-war uranium mines in central Europe had been taken over by the Germans, Canada had geologically prospected for uranium. Their Minister of Munitions released a small announcement of Canada's contribution of uranium and 350 scientists in which he made passing mention that ⋯ *Lord Rutherford had conducted his early research at McGill University 35 years ago.*

The New Zealand newspapers picked up this reference. The following day most carried a photograph of the late Lord Rutherford and a comment such as ⋯ *an eminent pioneer in the exploration of the atom* ⋯ and … *some of his students have taken part in the research which led to the production of the bomb.* This box appeared on the same page of the *Nelson Evening Mail* as the major story of the development of the bomb which had a banner headline 'TRIUMPH FOR SCIENCE'. Hence it is no wonder the public received the wrong impression of Ern's contribution.

Good old New Zealand, attaching itself to the coat-tails of fame even as the horrors of the weapon were being proclaimed. For example, an editorial of August 8th in the *Evening Post* entitled 'What has been started?' recalled the story of Faraday who, on being asked what was the value of his electrical experiments, had replied "What use is a baby?" But, the editorial continued,

> *··· Good fairies seem to have watched over the electrical family hitherto. Have they abandoned it now? The new child has a satanic look.*

ALADDIN RUBS THE LAMP

NZ Herald 9 Aug 1945

So while I can appreciate why New Zealand made ever excessive claims on Lord Rutherford's behalf, which Ern would most certainly not have made himself, such claims backfired to make Rutherford a dirty word, at least in some sections of society, in New Zealand for the next five decades. In much the same way nuclear is still today such a dirty word that it should only be uttered by consenting adults in private. When nuclear magnetic resonance (NMR) was brilliantly applied to revolutionise some diagnostic and surgical procedures by imaging the internal soft tissue of the human body, the N word had to go and that is why all major cities now have an expensive MRI – Magnetic Resonance Imaging – machine.

Belated Honours in New Zealand

Ernest Rutherford's rehabilitation in New Zealand started about a decade or so ago and he is now reclaiming his rightful place in our history and our affection.

In 1991 the site of his birth at Brightwater near Nelson was turned from a wasteland, which had been a disgrace to the nation, into The Rutherford Birthplace, a haven of beauty and tranquillity where New Zealanders and visitors can learn of his life and work though fourteen display panels and six sound stations set in an attractive garden setting.

In 1992 the Reserve Bank of New Zealand placed New Zealanders on the country's banknotes for the first time. The Queen remained on the $20 note, the most used banknote. Following public submissions the bank selected Ed Hillary, the co-conquerer of Mt Everest for the $5 note; Kate Sheppard, the leader of the movement which saw New Zealand as the first country in the world to allow women the vote, for the $10 note; Apirana Ngata, the first Maori graduate and later a cabinet member of government, for the $50 note; and, topping the list, Ernest Rutherford for the $100 note. The portrait is that of 1914, just prior to his visit home to New Zealand, and the background includes the Nobel medal and his curves of radioactive growth and decay. One fortuitous curiosity is that the spirograph design around the map of New Zealand is centred on Nelson, the geocentre of New Zealand and the place of his birth. Another is that he knew two of the other three honoured New Zealanders: he was at University with Ngata and his mother-in-law had been Kate Sheppard's assistant.

As this book is going to press it was announced he will appear on one stamp in a series honouring the millennium and New Zealand firsts. And there are preliminary plans proposed to convert the basement room, where he carried out his later researches at Canterbury College, from a national disgrace into the Rutherford Den, another site of international tourism standard. A museum display of international standard will be appropriate for 2002, the centennial of his first great discovery, the transmutation of atoms. [And again in 2011 and/or 2018.]

Shouldn't we forget Rutherford? That was posed to me by a senior scientist in this country shortly before he was awarded a prize for work done three decades earlier and before the money to fund pure research in New Zealand was named the Marsden Fund rather than the Rutherford Fund. No, we must never forget Ernest Rutherford. We should tell our children his story, that of a rural New Zealand child who, with no more advantage than they, rose to world fame. And we should praise his ingenuity, a quality on which greatness, science and countries depend. And besides, he was a nice fellow.

One last farming story. After Ern's death May Rutherford sent Ern's clothes to New Zealand, to his brother Jim who was on hard times. The clothes were too large for Jim who distributed them around the more bulky of Ern's nephews. Which is how one pair of smart, striped trousers, with an ample bottom and carrying the laundry mark 'Lord Rutherford' and which had rubbed shanks with some of the most prominent people in Britain, came to serve out its days protecting the nether regions of a farmer-nephew while he worked around his sheepyards in rural New Zealand.

Ern would have liked that.

ILLUSTRATIONS

Colour

Black and White Photographs

B12   Canterbury College buildings c.1891.

B13   (a) The soaking pond at the Tipoka flaxmill.
(b) Alice Fordham's dance card for 4th Nov 1892.

B14   The Tin Shed, where Ern carried out his first researches in 1893.

B15   Manuscript of Ern's second research work, his first paper.

B16   (a) May Newton 1896.
(b) Jack Erskine.

B17   (a) On a cycling holiday in Lowestoft, Easter, 1896.
(b) Ern in 1896 with Professor John Brown and his daughter Millicent.

B18   Map of Cambridge showing the sites relevant to Ern's wireless signalling.

B19   Cavendish Laboratory, Physics research students, 1898.

B20   (a) Ern at Montreal.
(b) Physics department, McGill c.1899.

B21   (a) Ern and May's wedding, Christchurch, 28 June 1900.
(b) Ern and Hans Geiger at Manchester.

B22   Physicists celebrating the 20th Anniversary of Clark University, 1909.

B23   (a) Going for a drive in the 1910 Wolseley-Siddeley.
(b) The first Solvay Conference, 1911.

B24   (a) Sir Ernest Rutherford in court dress, 1914.
(b) Professors Bragg, Rutherford and Strutt at the BIR.

B25   (a) The Physics Board visits the Royal Navy's Mining School, Portsmouth.
(b) Visit to Nelson, 1925.

B26   (a) Eileen Rutherford and Ralph Fowler.
(b) May, Ern, Rosa Oliphant, Niels and Margrethe Bohr, 1930.
(c) Grandpapa with Peter, his first grandson.
(d) Ern arranging his chair on board ship.

B27   Royal Institution Lecture 1934.

B28   (a) Presentation box of pears.
(b) Naming the LMS engine S5665 the 'Lord Rutherford of Nelson'.

B29   (a) Relaxing at the beach.
(b) The bas-relief portrait that caused all the fuss.
(c) Bay de Renzie and Ern.
(d) Ern and Ralph on holiday with grandchildren and friends 1931.

B30   Cavendish Laboratory group photograph 1936.

B31   (a) Opening the Inst. of Auto Engineers research laboratory.
(b) Talk softly please.

B32   (a) Final resting place in Westminster Abbey.
(b) Clay model for a bust of Ernest Rutherford c.1941.

Diagrams Embedded in Text are listed in
Sources of Information

SOURCES OF INFORMATION

Interviews and Notes on Archival Research

I have filled 10 quarto 120 page record books and three filing cabinet drawers with such notes. These have been willed to the Rutherford Collection at the Alexander Turnbull Library. The master manuscript refers to these notes. The biography also draws extensively on the local newspapers of the day, Rutherford family correspondence and the official and unofficial records of the relevant organisations.

Master Copies

In such a major research sometimes every paragraph, sentence or even phrase requires a reference or further comment. This is too detailed for most users. In this book only the main points will be referenced due to space considerations. A master copy, which also includes material edited out of the printed version, will be hand annotated with full references and comments on the sources of every statement. One year after publication date, thus allowing for the incorporation of any new information which may come to light as a result of the book, I will donate a copy of this master manuscript to public repositories in each country with a Rutherford association. This will make the details more freely accessible to interested people. There will be one condition imposed, that for ten years after the deposition date any person can copy no more than 10 pages per day. After that period copying will be as per the usual custom for the particular archive. During that 10 year period I will invite people seriously interested in Rutherford to purchase their own copy from AAS Publications, PO Box 31-035, Christchurch, New Zealand. Purchasers will be encouraged to donate their copy to any other appropriate public repository.

Repositories of Master Copies

Alexander Turnbull Library of the National Library of New Zealand.
Nelson Provincial Museum.
Cambridge University Library (Manuscripts).
National Library of Scotland.
Center for the History of Science, Royal Swedish Academy of Sciences, Stockholm.
Musée Curie (France).
McGill University Library (Archives).
P L Kapitza Institute for Physical Problems (Moscow).
American Institute of Physics, Niels Bohr Library.
National Library of Australia.

ABBREVIATIONS
including newspapers referred to

AIM	Auckland Institute and Museum
ANZP	Australian and New Zealand Physicist
AR	Adelaide Register
AS	Auckland Star
ATL	Alexander Turnbull Library of the National Library of New Zealand – Te Puna Matauranga o Aotearoa
AWN	Auckland Weekly News
CC	Canterbury College, now University of Canterbury
CPR	Collected Papers of Rutherford. 3 volumes, George Allen and Unwin, 1962-1965.
CPS	Cambridge Physical Society
CUL	Cambridge University Library
CUP	Campbridge University Press
du	date unknown
EP	Evening Post (Wellington)
EF	Erskine family
HL	Hocken Library
JC	John Campbell
LT	Lyttelton Times (Christchurch)
MDT	Marlborough Daily Times
ME	Marlborough Express
MH	Montreal Herald
MP	Marlborough Press
MG	Manchester Guardian
MS	Montreal Star
NA	National Archives
NC	Nelson College
NMNZ	National Museum of New Zealand
NPM	Nelson Provincial Museum
NZG	New Zealand Government Gazette
NZGL	New Zealand Graphic and Ladies Journal (Auckland)
NZH	New Zealand Herald
NZST	New Zealand Science Teacher
NZT	New Zealand Times (Wellington)
OUP	Oxford University Press
PC	Private Collection

PG	Pelorus Guardian
pu	photographer unknown
RC	Rutherford Correspondence. (CUL, bound copies at eg UC.)
RF	Rutherford Family
UC	University of Canterbury
SMH	Sydney Morning Herald
TB	The Bulletin (Sydney)
TC	The Colonist (Nelson)
TD	The Dominion (Wellington)
TH	Taranaki Herald
TP	The Press (Christchurch)
TS	The Star (Christchurch)
TT	The Times (London)
UNZ	University of New Zealand
ud	undated
WP	Weekly Press (ChCh)

REFERENCES
including line drawings etc. embedded in the text

Page

xvi Map of New Zealand. (Tim Nolan)

2   Thompson Family Tree. (JC from British birth etc records.)

3   Rutherford Family Tree. (JC and others from NZ and Scottish birth, christening, death, marriage and parish records, and family records in bibles.)

4   Family background from *Rutherford's Ancestors*, John Campbell, AAS Publications, 1996.

4   School inspector's reports NZG 2 Dec 1861 p92, 15 Aug 1864 p70.

6   Birth Register for Waimea South 1871. (Registrar of Births, Nelson.)

6   The plaid dress was gifted to Canterbury Museum by Lady Rutherford.

9   Map of Spring Grove/Brightwater. (JC and Tim Nolan from land records.)

9   Map of Foxhill. (JC and Tim Nolan from land records.)

10   Records of Foxhill School (now in NPM.)

14   Nelson College Annual Reports. (NC and newspaper reports of prizegiving.)

19   Map of Havelock. (Tim Nolan). Flaxmill, NEM 12 Aug 1884.

24   Havelock School, new building described in MDT 23 Jun 1883.

29   School inspector's report. Supplement in ME 8 Apr 1885.

33   Scholarship results. These were published in the Nelson and Marlborough newspapers eg ME 23 Dec 1885.

34   Letter, Nell Rutherford to Mary Thompson 11 Jan 1886. (RF)

37   In Memoriam cards for Percy, Charles and Herbert Rutherford. (Percy JC donated to NPM, others PC destined for ATL.)

38   Civil Service exams were reported in NZG, eg p1695 23 Dec 1886.

41   Nelson College scholarship, examiner's comments TC 7 Jan 1887.

42   Ern declines job in the Civil Service. ME 4 Oct 1887.

44   Marlborough Scholarship, Laura Matthews, ME 4 Feb 1885.

46   Baneful system of cramming. TC 6 Jan 1880.

46   'The large majority of people.' MP 11 Mar ud.

48   'Porky' Littlejohn. p141-2 Life of Dr W S Littlejohn, A E Pratt, Lothian, 1934.

51   'nibbling around so tasty a carrot.' TC 20 Dec 1887.

53   'Ern had his mother's family's looks.' Ted Jeffries reminiscence.

55   Nelson College report card for Dec 1888. (NC)

59   Map of Taranaki. (Kelvin Day and Tim Nolan.)

63   Ern on Littlejohn, Pratt p175.

67   University of New Zealand Junior National Scholars, 1889. (UNZ Calendar 1890-1 p136).

71   Map of Christchurch. (Tim Nolan.)

72   Some of the information on Canterbury College is from History of Canterbury College, J Hight and A Candy, Whitcombe and Tombs, 1927.

72   Some of the information on Alexander Bickerton is from Scholar Errant, R M Burdon, Pegasus Press, 1956.

75   'Bicky and white cuffs' LT 12 May 1923.

77   Some of the information on John Brown is from the book The Memoirs of John Macmillan Brown, University of Canterbury, 1974.

82   Joynt letter CUL Add 7653 J46.

89   Canterbury College Matriculation Book 1891. (UC)

90   O'Brien's boot factory. NZGL 7 Feb 1891.

93   Article on Apirana Ngata, TP 10 Apr 1891. Also NZ Ill. Mag. p11-12 1900.

102   Archie MacDiarmid's letter home Jan 1892. (MacDiarmid Family.)

109   Alice Fordham's Diploma Day songbook 1892. (Fordham Family)

118   Exam papers were bound with the UNZ calendar.

125   Dialectic Society programme 1893. (PC)

127   George Rutherford diary. (RF now ATL)

133   Rutherford's Timing Device. From the manuscript (Thesis II) submitted for the 1851 Scholarship. (CUL Add 7653/PA2 p5) Note that this manuscript covered his first year of research i.e. 1893 but the work was published as his second paper. (Trans. NZ Inst. xxviii 182-204 1895)

134   Details of Rutherford's timing device. (CUL Add 7653/PA2 p27.)

140   Votes for women. Ashley Hunter in NZGL p249 1893. (Copy neg C3028, AIM)

141   Song by Henderson from CC Diploma Day song book 1896. (Fordham family.)

145   Rutherford's notebook. CUL Add 7653 NB1 p53

146   Ern applies for a teaching job. (CC inwards letter book).

161   Rutherford's magnetometer. From the second manuscript (Thesis I) submitted for the 1851 Scholarship. This covers his second year of research i.e. 1894. (CUA Add 7653/PA1 p17.)

161   Determining the depth of penetration of magnetisation of a needle. (Trans. NZ Inst. XXVII plXLVIII fig 2 1894.)

162   Rapid rate of decay of damped oscillations. (Trans. NZ Inst. XXVII plXLVIII fig 7 1894.)

162   Apparatus to determine the relative size of the second half oscillation with respect to the first. (CUL Add 7653/PA1 p24.)

163   Measuring the speed of electrical waves along a wire. (p26 manuscript of Ern's first paper, Hector Papers, NMNZ)

164   Hertz's dumb-bell vibrator – detector in the generating circuit.(CUA Add 7653/PA1 p33.)

164   Hertz's dumb-bell vibrator – detector in the receiver circuit. (CUA Add 7653/PA1 p34.)

165   Arrangement to measure the difference in currents in two circuits. (CUA Add 7653/PA1 p64.)

167   Canterbury College Science Society – programme for 1894. (PC)

174   Report of the special committee of inquiry into the department of physics and chemistry 1895 p51. (PC)

180   TP editorial 14 Mar 1895.

184   Saunders' letter. ATL MS 1342 Folder 252.

186   UNZ telegram. NA(NZ) UNZ 10/29/8474.

186   Gray letter. 26 Feb 1895. Archives of the Commissioners for the Exhibition of 1851.

190   Rutherford's references from Canterbury College in CUL Add 7653/PA295.

200   Hevesy to Ern 14 Oct 1913. (RC)

214   Rutherford's frequency meter. (CPR p102 – from Phil. Trans. RS A189 pp1-24 1897)

217   Rutherford's receiver of electromagnetic waves. (CPR p87 – from Phil. Trans. RS A189 pp1-24 1897.)

219   Ern and Ball. TII 26 June 1896.

226   Early Topler vacuum pump – manually operated.

227   Hittorf-Crookes tube for studying cathode rays.

230   Two X-ray cartoons. Metal clothes to prevent unauthorised X-ray photographs and uses of X-Rays by customs officials. (From a German book whose title I failed to record.)

231   X-ray cartoon – John Bull and the German Emperor. (Punch 25th Jan 1896 p45.)

233   Cloud cover in Paris Feb-Mar 1896. Nebulosity is the amount of cloud cover in tenths. (From Annales du Bureau Central Meterologique 1896. Courtesy of Larry Badash.)

238   Apparatus for measuring the time of recombination of ions induced by X-ray irradiation. (Phil Mag xliv 426 1897.)

239   Apparatus for measuring the speeds of negative or positive ions induced by X-ray irradiation. (Phil Mag xliv 436 1897.)

240   Apparatus for measuring the speed of negative charges induced by ultraviolet irradiation. (Proc. Cam. Phil. Soc. ix 401-406 1898.)

242   J J Thomson's e/m tube in which he showed that cathode rays were sub-atomic particles (electrons).

244   Rutherford's apparatus in which he determined that uranium emitted two distinct types of radiation which he called alpha and beta. (Phil Mag xlvii 114 1899.)

245   Cambridge Philosophical Society programme for 21st Feb 1898. (CPhilSoc Archives, CUL.)

254   Radon emanation. (Phil. Mag. xlix 5 1900.)

255   Decay of radon emanation. (Phil. Mag. xlix 6 1900.)

269   Wireless telegraphy dangers. (E S Hodgson in Punch 9 Jul 1902 p18.)

274   Rutherford's apparatus for the magnetic deflection of alpha particles. (Radioactivity, E Rutherford, CUP, 1905, p143. Plate detail Phil. Mag. 6v 1903 p183.)

278   Radium decay chain as at 1904. (p450 of Radioactivity, E Rutherford, CUP, 1905.)

279   McNaughton quote from McGill Univ Mag, Apr 1904 p17.

282   Hepburn reminisce, NEM 15 Aug 1945 p4g.

287   Alpha ray electroscope devised by Rutherford. (Practical Measurements in Radioactivity, Makower and Geiger, Longman, 1912.)

297   Mr Butler Burke of the Cavendish Lab believed he had produced life using radium and beef bouillion. (Punch 12 July 1905 p28)

298   MH 12 Sept 1905.

304   I had this lecture slide for years but lost track of the source. Sorry.

305   Nobel Prize. Material pertaining to prizes awarded more than 50 years ago are now open records, Nobel Archives, Centrum för vetenskapshistoria, Kungl. Vetenskapsakademien, (Center for History of Science, Royal Swedish Academy of Sciences), Stockholm. A summary of nominees and nominators is given in The Nobel Population 1901-1937, Elisabeth Crawford et al, 1987, Office for History of Science and Technology, UC Berkeley. Pen sketches of the physics winners are given in *Pioneers of Science*, R Weber, IOP, 1974. Lists and short biograhies of prizewinners are available on the web at www.nobel.se. May Rutherford wrote a 16pp daily record of their trip to Stockholm, various typed copies of which were sent home to relatives. Some of these are now in public archives. A Nobel Museum is being planned for Stockholm.

309   Three countries claim Ern. (The Times 10 Dec 1908, Auckland Star 25 Nov 1908, Montreal Star 16 Jun 1903.)

310   Bickerton interview in NZT 28 Nov 1908.

312   May's letter to her mother. She gave this to Ernest Marsden. ATL MS 1342 folder 251.

313   Alpha Ray song. Post-Prandial Proceedings of the Cavendish Society, Bowes and Bowes, 1926.

315   The Nobel ceremony 1908 woodcuts. (Top Aftonbladet 11 Dec 1908, Bottom Dagens Nyheter 11 Dec 1908.)

319   Reynold's letter. Copy held by Reynold's family.

325   Ramsay and radium. May to Martha undated page, c.1907 (RF)

326   Rutherford-Geiger detector of individual alpha particles. (Proc. Roy. Soc. A81 141-161 1908.)

326   Strip photo-record from a Rutherford-Geiger detector, 25 Jul 1912. (Given to Victoria University of Wellington, Physics Department, by Ernest Marsden.)

330   Ramsay and radium. May to Harriet Pitcher (nee Brooks) 28 Dec 1907. (Pitcher Family)

338   Deflection of 6 Mev alpha particles by a gold nucleus. (Peter Fowler)

353   Crew reminiscences. (John O'Londons Weekly 29 Oct 1937.)

357   Radium brand bootpolish – advert.(Taranaki Herald 1 Jul 1914 5d.)

367   Rutherford's report to the Board of Invention and Research 30 Sept 1915. (CUL Add 8243/1)

370   Bragg-Rutherford Patent 125,446, Patent Office.

378   Apparatus for splitting the atom. (Phil. Mag. xxxvii 543 1919.)

383   Induced activity song. Post-Prandial Proceedings of the Cavendish Society, Bowes and Bowes, 1926.

387   Kapitza. When Kapitza's correspondence was released several books were published. English translations of the letters include Kapitza: Letters to Mother, D and E Lockwood, NRC Canada, 1989, and Kapitza in Cambridge and Moscow, Eds D Shoenberg *et al.*, North Holland, 1990. David Shoenberg

was Kapitza's last Cambridge research student and told me about those days.

393   Rutherford - Liverpool BA unofficial Pennant (photo held by RF)

391   Cavendish Dinner 1924. Edward Appleton and Miles Barnett (NZ) had just confirmed the existence of the ionosphere. (PC destined for ATL)

392   Cavendish Dinner 1924 menu. (PC destined for ATL)

395   Death-ray in antiquity. (Punch 4 June 1924 p617.)

396   Grindell Matthews 'Death Ray', the first photograph. He intended to demonstrate its working in America. (Underwood, Weekly Press (ChCh) 18 Dec 1924, Canterbury Public Library.)

398   'Though the electro-magnetic ··· AR 4 Sept 1925 p11c.

399   Interview with Ern. (SMH 14 Sept 1925 p8)

400   Ern on the environment. AS 28 Sept 1925

401   Radium floor polish. (TD 29 Oct 1925 14a)

404   'the whole social structure' (TH 9 Oct 1925)

406   The Disintegration of an atom, RI Lecture 4 April 1924. (TT 5 April 1924.)

407   Splitting the atom cartoon (lecture in huge theatre). (Punch 15 Oct 1924 p439.)

408   Sir Ernest Rutherford lecturing on the atom at the Town Hall, Wellington, 1925. (H L Richardson, ATL.)

414   Rutherford. Pencil sketch Randolph Schwabe 1928, presented to the Athenaeum Club by the artist in 1938. When I saw it in 1989 it hung in the light luncheon room.

416   Gamow poem from Biography of Physics, George Gamow, Hutchison, 1962, p221-2.

421   Invitation to Dinner with the Prince of Wales 12 Dec 1930, prior to Peerage. (RF)

428   Phyllida Cook was still an impressive lady when I met her. It was easy to see why the Rutherford grandchildren were so attached to her.

431   Martha's 90th birthday interview, TH 29 Oct 1932.

435   A good source of reminiscences about the Cavendish in the early 1930's is Cambridge Physics in the Thirties, John Hendry (Ed), Adam Hilger, 1984.

437   Metropolitan-Vickers HV lab opened 28 Feb 1930.

440   Gerald Tarrant wrote a popular physics book for schools, and lectured at Canterbury University College before moving to a university in Persia (Iran). During the revolution he retired to Nelson, New Zealand.

441   Splitting the atom cartoon (Feather splits oxygen?). (Punch 31 Aug 1932)

443   Frederick Mann, Lord Rutherford on the Golf Course, Trinity College, 1976.

447   A Defence of Free Learning, Wm Beveridge, OUP, 1959

448   Recording of Ern at Göttingen, 14 Dec 1931. When tidying up Ern's papers Mark Oliphant found one of Prof Pohl's acetate discs. The rest were tracked down and sets of modern 74rpm records made by HMV. Disc 3 is usually missing because that had already been manufactured by Telefunken, who then held the copyright. The history of these recordings has recently been gathered by Ronald Smeltzer in the Association for Recorded Sound Archives Collections Journal, XXVIII 174-187 1997.

449   Peter Ritchie-Calder, Letter to the Editor, The Guardian, 14 Feb 1982.

451   BA Blackpool cartoon. (Punch 16 Sep 1936.) I could pick Bragg and Rutherford. Mark Oliphant identified others for me.

457   Ern on relativity, H Dale, Memories of Rutherford, CC, 1949 p17

459   The archives of the Society for the Protection of Science and Learning are in the Bodleian Library, Oxford.

464   Born reminiscences. My Life, Max Born, Taylor and Francis, 1978, p265.

465   Outburst at Oliphant. I am most grateful to Mark Oliphant for being granted permission to draw on his papers, recordings and book Rutherford: Recollections of the Cambridge Days, Elsiever, 1972

469   Cavendish laboratory workshops 1937. He has another showing the forge? area. (Ron Pryor)

473   Death notice. (Münchner Neueste Nachrichten 21 Oct 1937.)

478   Nobel Archives, see reference p305.

484   For more details of element 104. See Rutherfordium - Elementary my Dear Ernest, ANZP, **35**, 12-14 1998 and The Elements Beyond Uranium, Glenn Seaborg and W Loveland, Wiley, 1990.

487   Splitting the atom cartoon (horserider). (Punch 19 Jul 1922)

492   Aladdin rubs the lamp. (NZH 9 Aug 1945)

493   Birthplace. ANZP **32** 109-110 1995

493   Banknote. NZST **71** 21-23 1992

INDEX

E Rutherford

May 5 - 1929

K. Fajans, 5. V. 29.

Meenfodunden 5. Vi 29
W. Marckwald
N. Wieland
A. Einstein,
Max Planck
Bayer.
H. Geiger
L. Meitner
F. Paneth
M. o. Laue.

Complimentary Dinner

to

Professor E. Rutherford, F.R.S.

Windsor Hotel,
Montreal,
7th December, 1904.

New Zealand University.

—

Inaugural Dinner

HELD AT THE

RESTAURANT FRASCATI,

Oxford Street, W.

ON

Saturday, 19th November, 1932.

❧ ❧

Chairman:

LORD RUTHERFORD OF NELSON,

O.M., F.R.S.